MOLECULAR SPECTROSCOPY: MODERN RESEARCH

Contributors

JAMES E. BOGGS

P. R. BUNKER

ALAN CARRINGTON

H. DREIZLER

T. M. DUNN

M. ASHRAF EL-BAYOUMI

KENNETH FOX

P. HOROWITZ

K. KEITH INNES

MARILYN E. JACOX

M. KASHA

A. W. MANTZ

C. WELDON MATHEWS

DOLPHUS E. MILLIGAN

IAN M. MILLS

JACQUES MORET-BAILLY

YONEZO MORINO

DAVID M. RANK

K. NARAHARI RAO

SHUJI SAITO

R. B. SANDERSON

J. I. STEINFELD

RICHARD N. ZARE

MOLECULAR SPECTROSCOPY: MODERN RESEARCH

Edited by

K. NARAHARI RAO

DEPARTMENT OF PHYSICS
THE OHIO STATE UNIVERSITY
COLUMBUS, OHIO

AND

C. WELDON MATHEWS

DEPARTMENT OF CHEMISTRY
THE OHIO STATE UNIVERSITY
COLUMBUS, OHIO

1972

ACADEMIC PRESS   New York and London

CHEMISTRY

ACADEMIC PRESS, INC.
111 Fifth Avenue, New York, New York 10003

United Kingdom Edition published by
ACADEMIC PRESS, INC. (LONDON) LTD.
24/28 Oval Road, London NW1

LIBRARY OF CONGRESS CATALOG CARD NUMBER: 72-77728

PRINTED IN THE UNITED STATES OF AMERICA

CONTENTS

Chapter 4.   ELECTRONIC SPECTRA

4.1   Progress in Electronic Spectroscopy of Polyatomic Molecules
K. Keith Innes

4.2   Rotational Line Strengths: The $O_2{}^+$ b $^4\Sigma_g{}^-$–a $^4\Pi_u$ Band System
Richard N. Zare

4.3   A Chrestomathy of Energy Transfer Research on Iodine   223
J. I. Steinfeld

4.4   Nuclear Hyperfine Structure in the Electronic Spectra of Diatomic Molecules
T. M. Dunn

7.3 Large Plane Gratings for High-Resolution Infrared Spectrographs

K. Narahari Rao

Chapter 8. TABLES OF STANDARD DATA

C. Weldon Mathews and K. Narahari Rao

LIST OF CONTRIBUTORS

Numbers in parentheses indicate the pages on which the authors' contributions begin.

James E. Boggs (49), *Department of Chemistry, The University of Texas, Austin, Texas*

P. R. Bunker (1), *Division of Physics, National Research Council of Canada, Ottawa, Canada*

Alan Carrington (29), *Department of Chemistry, The University of Southampton, Hampshire, England*

H. Dreizler (59), *Institut für Physikalische Chemie, Abt. Chemische Physik, Universität Kiel, Kiel, Germany*

T. M. Dunn (231), *Department of Chemistry, University of Michigan, Ann Arbor, Michigan*

M. Ashraf El-Bayoumi (287), *Department of Biophysics, Michigan State University, East Lansing, Michigan*

Kenneth Fox (79), *Jet Propulsion Laboratory, California Institute of Technology, Pasadena, California and Department of Physics and Astronomy, The University of Tennessee, Knoxville, Tennessee*

P. Horowitz† (287), *Institute of Molecular Biophysics, Florida State University, Tallahassee, Florida*

K. Keith Innes (179), *State University of New York, Binghamton, New York*

Marilyn E. Jacox (259), *National Bureau of Standards, Washington, D.C.*

M. Kasha (287), *Department of Chemistry and Institute of Molecular Biophysics, Florida State University, Tallahassee, Florida*

A. W. Mantz (141), *Air Force Avionics Laboratory, Wright-Patterson Air Force Base, Ohio*

C. Weldon Mathews (353), *Department of Chemistry, The Ohio State University, Columbus, Ohio*

Dolphus E. Milligan (259), *National Bureau of Standards, Washington, D.C.*

Ian M. Mills (115), *Department of Chemistry, University of Reading, Reading, England*

†Present address: Department of Chemistry, Dartmouth College, Hanover, New Hampshire

Jacques Moret-Bailly (327), *Laboratoire de Spectroscopie Moleculaire, Faculté des Sciences de Dijon, Dijon, France*

Yonezo Morino (9), *Sagami Chemical Research Center, Sagamihara, Kanagawa, Japan*

David M. Rank (73), *Department of Physics, University of California, Berkeley, California*

K. Narahari Rao (141, 343, 353), *Department of Physics, The Ohio State University, Columbus, Ohio*

Shuji Saito (9), *Sagami Chemical Research Center, Sagamihara, Kanagawa, Japan*

R. B. Sanderson (297), *Department of Physics, The Ohio State University, Columbus, Ohio*

J. I. Steinfeld (223), *Department of Chemistry, Massachusetts Institute of Technology, Cambridge, Massachusetts*

Richard N. Zare (207), *Department of Chemistry, Columbia University, New York, New York*

PREFACE

This volume was conceived to commemorate the twenty-fifth anniversary of the annual Columbus Symposium on Molecular Structure and Spectroscopy held in September, 1970. It is not a record of that conference, but is rather a testament to the active role molecular spectroscopy plays in contemporary scientific research.

The book is made up of reviews of current advances in several phases of research in molecular spectroscopy, with particular emphasis on the spectroscopic studies of molecular species in the gas phase and in matrices. Representative articles are also included which cover the applications of molecular studies in a wide variety of areas such as biophysics, astrophysical problems, and energy transfer processes. The progress achieved in the technology of high resolution spectroscopy has been described and the techniques and terminology of Lamb-dip spectroscopy have been introduced as examples of fields offering interesting possibilities for the future. A comprehensive bibliography is included for most of the subjects discussed and the volume concludes with tables of standard data listing secondary wavelength standards, fundamental constants, atomic masses, and conversion factors of interest to spectroscopists. We believe that the information appearing in this publication will be of use in the day-to-day work of research laboratories pursuing investigations in molecular spectroscopy.

We are grateful to Professor Harald H. Nielsen for his efforts in starting this series of symposia and conducting several of them. The success of these conferences must be attributed to the participation, year after year, by distinguished scientists who are too numerous to acknowledge individually.

CHAPTER 1

LAMB-DIP SPECTROSCOPY

1.1 Hyperfine Structure in the Electronic Spectrum of I_2

P. R. Bunker

Division of Physics
National Research Council of Canada
Ottawa, Canada

Lamb-dip spectroscopy [1–3] involves the use of a simple trick whereby the effects of Doppler broadening in a spectrum are eliminated and very high resolution is obtained; the resolution is such that, for example, lines with a half-width at half-height of 2 MHz have been measured in the 6328 Å region of the spectrum of iodine [4]. The technique has been used in the microwave [5], infrared [6], and visible [4] regions of the spectrum and will be used in the ultraviolet region when suitable lasers become available.

To understand the technique it is necessary only to have a clear understanding of the concept of "hole burning," which will now be explained with the aid of Fig. 1. The top part of Fig. 1 shows intense, highly monochromatic light with frequency ν_L being passed through an absorption cell containing a gas, and the intensity being measured at the right. We suppose that ν_L is at a higher frequency than the resonant frequency ν_{res} of the gas molecules and that only molecules with a velocity v_a away from the light source absorb. Molecules with velocity v_a are therefore pumped from the ground state into the upper state and since the light is intense there is saturation. Consequently, the population of molecules with velocity v_a in the ground state is depleted and there is a "hole" burnt in the ground-state velocity distribution at the velocity v_a (see the bottom left part of Fig. 1). The width of the hole will be

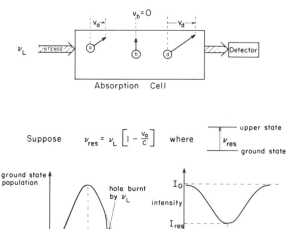

FIG. 1. Hole burning in the ground-state velocity distribution curve.

characteristic of the natural linewidth of the transition at pressures low enough that collisions are unimportant. As ν_L is tuned through ν_{res} the position of the hole will move and the intensity at the detector will be as shown at the bottom right of Fig. 1; the width of this line will be the saturated Doppler width.

To introduce the Lamb dip we first discuss the inverse Lamb dip with the help of Fig. 2. The top part of Fig. 2 is a repeat of the top part of Fig. 1 except that a mirror has been put on the right and the detector moved to the left. This use of a mirror is the trick that allows us to get rid of the Doppler width; it should have been thought of 20 years ago! On its first pass through the gas the light of frequency ν_L pumps molecules with velocity v_a, but on its second pass through (after being reflected by the mirror) the light pumps molecules with velocity $-v_a$. There are thus two holes burnt in the ground-state velocity distribution curve, as shown in the diagram at the bottom left of Fig. 2. The intensity of absorption at frequency ν_L will be twice that obtained with the setup as shown in Fig. 1 since we have now effectively doubled the path length. However, when ν_L is tuned to be ν_{res} we get much less than twice the absorption intensity since on the first pass through molecules with velocity zero are pumped out of the ground state and there are not many left to absorb the light on its second pass through. Therefore there is an increase in the detected light as ν_L is tuned through ν_{res}. This is shown at the bottom right of Fig. 2 and we have a sharp "inverse Lamb dip" at $\nu_L = \nu_{res}$. The width of this "line" is determined only by the lifetimes of the states. This is

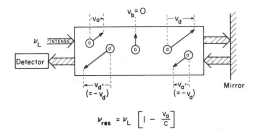

$$\nu_{res} = \nu_L \left[1 - \frac{v_a}{c} \right]$$

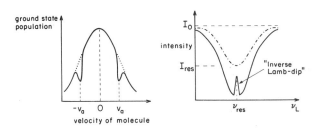

FIG. 2. The appearance of the inverse Lamb dip.

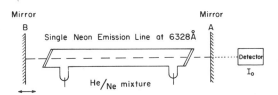

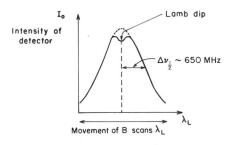

FIG. 3. The appearance of the Lamb dip.

essentially the experimental setup used by Costain [5] in obtaining sharp lines in the microwave region of the spectrum.

We now consider the Lamb dip. The top half of Fig. 3 is a schematic representation of a He/Ne laser which is operating in a single mode that is tuned by moving the mirror B. The discharge maintains a population inversion in the gas in the cell (the gain cell). Suppose mirror B is set such that the cavity mode is off exact resonance with the center of the atomic laser line. In this case only atoms with a certain velocity, v_a say, will be stimulated to emit as the emitted light moves from left to right in the gain cell. On its passage from right to left the laser light will only stimulate atoms with a velocity $-v_a$, and we will get a steady light output at this frequency with holes burnt in the excited-state velocity distribution at velocities v_a and $-v_a$. Tuning the laser through the resonant frequency, the output will trace a Doppler line shape except that there will be a "Lamb dip" at its center. This dip arises because only molecules with zero velocity emit the resonant frequency and have to provide intensity to both the left–right and right–left traveling light beams. Whereas in Fig. 2 holes are burnt in the ground-state velocity distribution curve and we look at absorption intensity, in Fig. 3 holes are burnt in the excited-state velocity distribution curve and we look at emission.

Both the Lamb dip and the inverse Lamb dip are involved in obtaining high-resolution spectra in the visible region of the spectrum. Figure 4 shows the setup schematically. Light is emitted by the gain cell with an intensity

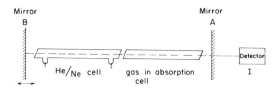

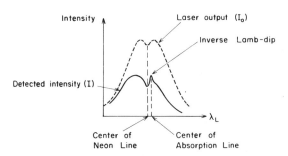

FIG. 4. The technique for obtaining an inverse-Lamb-dip line with a laser.

distribution I_0 as a function of wavelength shown by the dashed line in the bottom half of Fig. 4; this output is obtained by tuning a single cavity mode through the region. When gas is introduced into the absorption cell the output intensity goes down (assuming that the gas has an absorption feature coincident with the laser line) and we see the intensity I with an inverse Lamb dip. The bottom part of Fig. 4 is the same as the bottom right part of Fig. 2 except that I_0 is not a level background. The sharp inverse-Lamb-dip line can be detected and a precise measurement of its position made.

We now discuss briefly the application of this technique to the spectrum of the iodine molecule as published by Hanes and Dahlstrom [4] and as obtained by Hanes, Lapierre, Bunker, and Shotton [7]. In Fig. 5 the potential energy

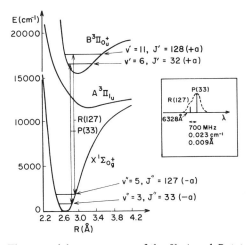

FIG. 5. The potential energy curves of the X, A, and B states of I_2.

curves of the X, A, and B states of iodine are drawn and the two transitions coincident with the 6328 Å He/Ne laser line drawn in. The identification of these lines as being coincident with the laser line is made by standard spectroscopic analysis of the fluorescence. With the resolution afforded by Lamb-dip spectroscopy each of these two rotational lines has been resolved into its nuclear hyperfine structure. In Fig. 6 the structure of the $P(33)$ line is shown. The inverse-Lamb-dip "bumps" are weak because the level of saturation is low and because the lines are very close together and overlap to well within the Doppler width of each. In Fig. 7 three of the hyperfine components (in a derivative plot) of the $P(33)$ line are shown; the separation of components t and u is 22 MHz.

To interpret the observed hyperfine structure it is necessary not only to consider the nuclear electric quadrupole moment interaction, but also the interaction between the nuclear magnetic moment and the rotational magnetic

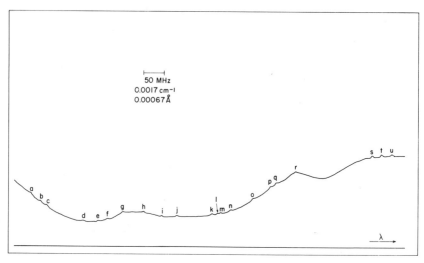

FIG. 6. The 21 nuclear hyperfine structure components in the $P(33)$ line of the 6–3 band.

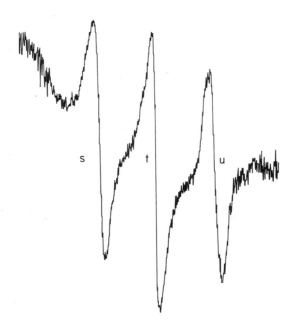

FIG. 7. The three components s, t, and u of the $P(33)$ line.

moment of the molecule (the so-called $I \cdot J$ interaction). From the spectrum we can determine, for each of the two transitions, the change in eQq and c_I, the constants which characterize these two interactions. The results and the comparison between observed and calculated line positions are given in Fig. 8.

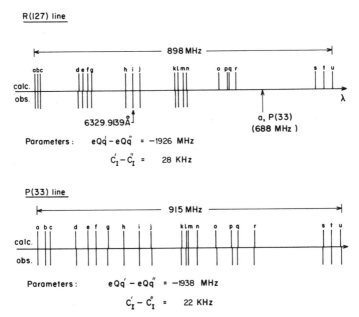

FIG. 8. The comparison between the observed and calculated hyperfine structure for the $R(127)$ and $P(33)$ lines.

References

1. R. A. McFarlane, W. R. Bennett, Jr., and W. E. Lamb, Jr., *Appl. Phys. Lett.* **2**, 189 (1963).
2. W. E. Lamb, Jr., *Phys. Rev. A* **134**, 1429 (1964).
3. P. H. Lee and M. L. Skolnick, *Appl. Phys. Lett.* **10**, 303 (1967).
4. G. R. Hanes and C. E. Dahlstrom, *Appl. Phys. Lett.* **14**, 362 (1969).
5. C. C. Costain, *Can. J. Phys.* **47**, 2431 (1969).
6. R. L. Barger and J. L. Hall, *Phys. Rev. Lett.* **22**, 4 (1969).
7. G. R. Hanes, J. Lapierre, P. R. Bunker, and K. C. Shotton, *J. Mol. Spectrosc.* **39**, 506 (1971).

CHAPTER 2

MICROWAVE SPECTRA

2.1 Microwave Spectroscopy

Yonezo Morino and Shuji Saito

Sagami Chemical Research Center
Sagamihara, Kanagawa, Japan

1. Introduction

The acknowledgment of microwave spectroscopy as an important research field can be dated from the initiation of the Symposium on Molecular Structure and Spectroscopy in 1946. Although Cleeton and Williams [1] reported absorption of microwave energy in the centimeter region by ammonia gas in 1934, microwave spectroscopy started essentially in 1946, with the sudden appearance of a large number of papers on microwave absorption spectra. This burst of microwave research was brought about by the availability of monochromatic, tunable klystron oscillators and the mastery of microwave techniques.

It was a fortunate coincidence that the Symposium on Molecular Structure and Spectroscopy started in the same year. From the very beginning of the first meeting attention has been devoted to the promotion of research in microwave spectroscopy. Nearly every year an invited speaker has been called in to review the progress of this field or of associated theoretical background. Figure 1 illustrates the number of papers read at each Symposium. One may note that an almost constant number of contributed papers on microwave studies were presented in the initial years, with an abrupt increase after 1960, which parallels closely the increase in the total number of papers presented. It is therefore interesting to trace the progress in microwave spectroscopy, bearing in mind how these symposia have reflected the

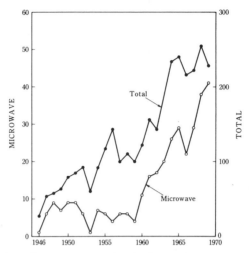

FIG. 1. The number of papers presented at the Symposium on Molecular Structure and Spectroscopy.

developments in this research field over the years. In this review we have adopted the convention of referring to microwave work presented at the annual Symposia on Molecular Structure and Spectroscopy by giving the authors or the work followed by the year of the meeting in parentheses.

Because of the limited space available for this review, references quoted cannot cover all the published papers in the last 25 years. Those quoted are given as indications of the progress of microwave spectroscopy. The early period of microwave spectroscopy is well reviewed and documented in the books on microwave spectroscopy by Gordy et al. [2], Strandberg [3] and Townes and Schawlow [4]. There also exist reviews [5–10] and books [11–15] which treat experimental and theoretical aspects of microwave spectroscopy not discussed at length here. Reference should also be given to a publication in the Landolt–Börnstein Series [16] containing an extensive compilation of molecular constants from microwave spectra and to the National Bureau of Standards tabulations of measured line frequencies and derived molecular constants [17]. A Microwave Gas Spectroscopy Bibliography compiled by Guarnieri and Favero [18] up to and including 1966 is available.

2. Development of Techniques

First of all, we should glance back at the progress in microwave instrumentation and spectroscopic techniques which has taken place during the past 25 years. Two experimental contributions of lasting significance in increasing the sensitivity of microwave spectrometers were made in 1947. Hughes and

Wilson [19] introduced the ingenious Stark-effect-modulation method, which has enabled the detection of microwave spectra with high sensitivity. Gordy and Kessler [20] employed successfully the source-frequency-modulation method, which is of great importance in the millimeter and submillimeter regions, where the Stark-effect-modulation method, due to experimental difficulties, is less advantageous. Continuous improvement in these techniques has made it possible to observe even extremely weak transitions of molecules. The ultimate sensitivity of a Stark-effect spectrometer may now attain $\alpha = 4 \times 10^{-11}$ cm^{-1}. For instance, we can observe the $J = 1 \leftarrow 0$ transition at 11 120 MHz of $^{18}O^{12}C^{34}S$ in a natural abundance of 0.009 % with a signal-to-noise ratio of 25 (using a 1N78 mixer diode as a detector followed by a lock-in amplifier with a bandwidth of 0.02 Hz). The sensitivity can be further improved by employing a phase-stabilized microwave source with a detection amplifier of narrower bandwidth [21–23]. More recently application of a data acquisition system using a digital computer for signal averaging and data reduction has been successfully carried out by Gwinn et al. [24].

The accuracy of frequency measurements with a standard instrument is now ± 0.01 MHz, and the resolution is usually 0.2 MHz. If signal averaging is employed the accuracy of the frequency measurement is enhanced by a factor of 5–10 [24]. The molecular-beam method has further increased the accuracy of frequency measurement to ± 0.1 kHz (resolution is 1 kHz) by a reduction in Doppler broadening, whereas the application of maser techniques can improve the accuracy to ± 0.02 kHz (resolution is 0.35 kHz). The substantial increase in spectrometer sensitivity has resulted in high-resolution studies of complex multiplets caused by nuclear quadrupole [25] interaction or high barrier tunneling [22]. Studies of the Zeeman effect in diamagnetic molecules using a high-resolution spectrometer are discussed in Section 4.

Microwave spectroscopy has been extended to the millimeter- and sub-millimeter-wave regions by Gordy and co-workers (1954, 1965) [26]. The highest transition frequency attained by Jones and Gordy [27] in 1964 was 691 472.60 MHz (~ 23 cm^{-1}) for the $J = 6 \leftarrow 5$ transition of $^{12}C^{16}O$. Recently Helminger et al. [28] have extended these earlier measurements to a wavelength of 0.37 mm employing a Mullard photoconducting indium antimonide detector [29] operated at 1.6°K. So far the highest microwave frequency measured is the $J = 67 \leftarrow 66$ transition of $^{16}O^{12}C^{32}S$ at 813 353.706 MHz. These measurements on OCS combined with Lamp-dip measurements by Winton and Gordy [30] allowed the precision determination of the spectroscopic constants $B_0 = 6081.49255 \pm 0.00012$ MHz and $D_0 = 0.00130192 \pm 0.00000004$ MHz for $^{16}O^{12}C^{32}S$.

Cupp et al. [31] determined spin–spin and spin–rotation coupling constants for H_2S using a millimeter electric resonance spectrometer. The accuracy of their frequency measurement was two parts in 10^{10}; i.e., the frequency of

a transition of H_2S was determined to be 168 762 762 373 $\pm$ 20 Hz. De Lucia and Gordy (1969) [32] extended high-resolution molecular-beam maser spectroscopy into the millimeter and submillimeter regions and applied it to the $J = 1 \rightarrow 0$ and $J = 2 \rightarrow 1$ rotational transitions of HCN and DCN, with significant improvements in the rotational constants for HCN, $B_0 = 44\ 315\ 975.7 \pm 0.4$ kHz and $D_J = 87.24 \pm 0.06$ kHz, and for DCN, $B_0 = 36\ 207\ 462.7 \pm 0.3$ kHz and $D_J = 57.83 \pm 0.04$ kHz.

Another promising achievement is that of Costain (1970) [33] in applying the Lamb-dip method to microwave absorption spectroscopy. He measured the frequency of the $J = 3 \leftarrow 2$ absorption line of OCS at 36 488 812.8 kHz, with a half-width of 1.7 kHz, and resolved ten components of the nuclear quadrupole hyperfine structure with a 6–8 kHz splitting of the $J = 2 \leftarrow 1$ transition of CH_3CN. Winton and Gordy [30] have extended the Lamp-dip measurements into the millimeter region, while Winton and Winnewisser (1970) applied this method to resolve the ground-state splitting in the $^R Q_0$ transitions of the ground vibrational state of H_2S_2.

Cox and Wilson (1963) [34]† carried out double-resonance experiments with conventional Stark-modulated spectrometer and discussed applications of this technique to the identification and confirmation of complex rotational spectra. Unland et al. [35] used this method to acquire a positive confirmation for the assignment of $1_{01} \leftarrow 0_{00}$ and $2_{02} \leftarrow 1_{01}$ transitions in 2-chloropropene. In another type of double-resonance experiment an assignment of a weak transition of O_3 between the rotational levels belonging to different vibrational states ($v_1 = 1$ and $v_3 = 1$) was established by Tanaka and Morino [36]. Extending the above principle, Woods et al. [37] constructed a double-resonance modulated microwave spectrometer which is a powerful tool for assigning complex spectra and convenient in searching for linked transitions. The spectrometer was applied with success in the assignment of the very intense and rich spectrum of fluoral [38]. Oka (1966–1969) [39] has opened a new aspect of microwave double resonance by observing new selection rules for collision-induced transitions in ethylene oxide. In contrast to the static method of Oka, Unland and Flygare [40] measured directly the rotational relaxation time by using a dynamical microwave double-resonance method.

In order to measure microwave spectra of very slightly volatile substances various types of high-temperature spectrometers (1952, 1963, 1966, 1968) [41] operable up to about 1000°C have been developed to measure accurately the spectra of such substances. The structural parameters, such as internuclear distance, vibration–rotation parameters, dipole moment, and mass ratios of various isotopes, have been determined for many inorganic diatomic molecules with remarkable accuracy [15] using these techniques.

† Notice that Yajima and Shimoda reported three level gas maser in HDCO in advance [34a].

3. Molecular Structure

Determination of molecular geometry from microwave spectra has been a major endeavor in this field of research. The structural information concerning bond lengths and bond angles in a particular molecule is contained in the principal moments of inertia, which are inversely proportional to the rotational constants A, B, C derived from the microwave spectrum. The effective bond length derived from B_0 or I_0 for the ground vibrational state is designated r_0 and the associated structure is called the r_0 structure. When the total number of structural parameters to be determined for a particular molecule exceeds the number of rotational constants available, additional information can be supplied from isotopic species. In calculating the r_0 structure the assumption is made that the structure is not altered by isotopic substitution. However, the r_0 structure is actually strongly affected by the zero-point vibrational effects, which differ with the isotope. Costain (1958) [42] has shown that these effects tend to cancel in the evaluation of internuclear distances when Kraitchman's equations [43] for substitution coordinates are used, leading to a more consistent set of structural parameters. The molecular structure derived in this way from various combinations of isotopic information is usually called the r_s structure. Many interesting examples have been given in the papers presented at the various symposia. As an example of the application of this method to large molecules we note the elaborate studies on the structures of pyridine, thiophene, furan, and other ring compounds by Bak and co-workers [44]. Another merit of the r_s structure lies in the fact that the structure obtained is close to the r_e structure. Watson (1969) gave a theoretical justification for the approximate relation $I_s = (I_e + I_0)/2$ noted by Costain.

In order to obtain the r_e structure one must extrapolate the r_0 structure to the equilibrium state. For this purpose the vibration–rotation interaction constants, usually called α, must be determined for all the normal vibrations. This can be done by measuring microwave spectra for the molecules in each of the first excited vibrational states. However, this is a formidable task, because it often happens that at least one normal vibration has a high frequency, and the microwave spectrum in the excited state of that vibration is too weak to be detected, even with our present techniques.

The r_e structure is thus rarely obtained for polyatomic molecules. Examples are O_3, OF_2, SO_2, and SeO_2 studied by Morino and co-workers (1965) [45]. By relying on the assumption that the r_e structure is identical for isotopic species it was possible to use the B_e values of $^{14}NF_3$ and $^{15}NF_3$ to arrive at the r_e structure of NF_3 [46]. The infrared and microwave results used together enabled Lafferty et al. to obtain the r_e structure of ClCN (1964) [47] and Morino and Nakagawa that of OCS [48].

Oka et al. [49,50] and Herschbach and Laurie (1960, 1963) [51] proposed the r_z, structure which represents the average positions of atoms in a given

vibrational state. This structure is convenient for studies of medium-size molecules for which it is not possible to obtain all of the α constants, and for comparisons of microwave and gas electron diffraction data. The r_z structure can be easily calculated when the quadratic force field is known. The four well-defined types of molecular structures r_0, r_s, r_e, and r_z were compared for SO_2 (1965) [45], where the r_z structure in vibrationally excited states indicates distinctly the distortion of the molecule characteristic of each normal vibration.

A few comments must be made about the electric dipole moment, which is an indispensable item of microwave spectroscopic studies of molecules. Since it is difficult to measure the absolute value of the applied electric field in conventional Stark waveguide cells, the dipole moment of a particular molecule is usually determined by reference to a standard molecule, usually OCS, whose dipole moment has been determined by Muenter [52] with the molecular-beam electric-resonance technique to be 0.71521 ± 0.00020 D and more recently by de Leeuw and Dymanus (1969) to be 0.71499 ± 0.00005 D. It should be noted that up until 1968, 0.7124 ± 0.0002 D was used for the dipole moment of OCS [53], which was derived from Stark-effect measurements and which is not in agreement with the above values, so that care must be exercised in the comparison of dipole moments. Dijkerman and Ruitenberg [54] have repeated the Stark-effect measurements in an absorption cavity and their value for the OCS dipole moment is in agreement with the above values refined.

With a spectrometer employing a very high Stark field Muenter and Laurie (1964) [55] observed the $J = 1 \leftarrow 0$ transition of HC≡CD, which is evidence for the existence of a small, permanent electric dipole moment attributable to the difference in the mean positions of the H and D atoms due to the anharmonicity of the stretching vibrations. In this connection it should be noted that Wofsy et al. (1969) [56] determined the electirc dipole moment of CH_3D in two rotational states $J = 1$, $K = 1$ and $J = 2$, $K = 2$ using molecular-beam electric-resonance. The electric dipole moments $\mu(J, K)$ are

$$\mu(1, 1) = 0.005641 \pm 0.000003 \quad \text{D}$$
$$\mu(2, 2) = 0.005679 \pm 0.000003 \quad \text{D}$$

These are the smallest dipole moments ever measured.

4. Nuclear Quadrupole Coupling

Nuclear spin angular momentum couples with rotational angular momentum to produce hyperfine structure in the rotational spectrum. The coupling is realized through the electric interaction between the quadrupole moment of

a nucleus and the electric field gradient at the nucleus. The electric quadrupole coupling constants have been determined for many molecules which contain one or more nuclei with nonzero quadrupole moments [16].

When a molecule involves more than one such nucleus its rotational spectrum is tremendously complicated. Townes *et al.* (1948) [57] analyzed the spectra of cyanogen halides, which contain two quadrupolar nuclei, by using the intermediate coupling theory developed by Bardeen and Townes [58]. Gwinn and co-workers (1961) [59] studied methylene chloride, which has two identical quadrupolar nuclei, and concluded that the principal axis of the quadrupole tensor at the chlorine nucleus coincides with the C–Cl inter-nuclear axis. Wolf *et al.* [60] derived a theory explaining the hyperfine structure in the rotational spectrum of a symmetric-top molecule containing three identical quadrupolar nuclei and applied it to the molecules $CH^{35}Cl_3$ and $CF^{35}Cl_3$ with satisfactory results.

The electric field gradient has its orgin in the electron distribution around the nucleus, so that the quadrupole coupling constants make it possible to obtain information about the bonding of the atom in the molecule. Townes and Dailey (1943, 1950) [61] and Gordy [62] have developed methods to correlate the quadrupole coupling constant with the nature of chemical bonds such as ionic character or the degree of hybridization of bonding involved. The quadrupole coupling constants of molecules studied up to 1967 have been tabulated by Starck [16].

It should be mentioned that Flygare and Weiss (1963, 1964) [63] determined the deuterium nuclear quadrupole coupling constants for several molecules by using high-resolution techniques introduced recently. They discussed the linear relationship first proposed by Salem [64] between the force field of the molecule and the deuterium field gradient.

5. Zeeman Effect in Diamagnetic Molecules

Two types of interactions occur for a diamagnetic molecule in an external magnetic field. The principal interaction is produced by a small magnetic moment which is induced by the coupling of rotational and electronic motion. The perturbation energy for this case is linear in the applied magnetic field. It has been treated by Strandberg and co-workers [65]. The proportionality constant in the interaction energy is the molecular **g** tensor, which has been discussed by several authors [66] to elucidate the effect of electrons on the moments of inertia. Townes *et al.* [67] showed that the sign of the electric dipole moment in a molecule can be obtained when the magnitude and sign of the g values are available for two isotopic species. In addition to this first-order interaction, the magnetic field itself induces a magnetic moment proportional to the field, $\chi \cdot \mathbf{H}$, where χ is the magnetic susceptibility tensor,

and the resulting interaction energy is $-\mathbf{H} \cdot \chi \cdot \mathbf{H}/2$. Recently Hüttner and Flygare [68] and Levy [69] have developed the theory of this quadratic magnetic interaction in detail. They have indicated that when the molecular **g** values and magnetic susceptibility anisotropies are determined by studying the high-field rotational Zeeman effect, fundamental parameters are obtained which describe the electronic charge distribution in the molecule: the molecular quadrupole moments, the diagonal elements of the paramagnetic susceptibility tensor, and the anisotropies in the second moment of the electric charge distribution. If the bulk magnetic susceptibility is known, one can determine the diagonal elements of the diamagnetic and total magnetic susceptibility tensors and in addition individual elements of the second moment of the charge distribution can be evaluated.

Since the **g** value is roughly proportional to the rotational constant, and the magnetic susceptibility tensor indicates the rigidity of electron clouds in a molecule under the influence of the external magnetic field, light molecules have rather large **g** values and small χ values. Thus in the earlier studies of Zeeman effects, where experimentally feasible magnetic field strengths were limited to several thousand gauss, only the **g** values for rather light molecules were obtained without observing the quadratic Zeeman effects [16]. It is clearly desirable to use a highly stable and highly homogeneous strong-field magnet and a microwave spectrometer of high resolution and high sensitivity.

In the last few years Dailey and co-workers [70–72] and Flygare and collaborators [73–75] have extensively studied the high-field rotational Zeeman effect and have determined the molecular quantities described above. The former used an X-band absorption cell of short length placed between the pole faces of a conventional magnet with a high-resolution microwave spectrometer and studied OCS [70], H_2O [71], and SO_2 [72]. Flygare *et al.* [73] used a special magnet with 12×72 or 2×72 in. flat pole faces which produce fields up to 30 kG with a field stability of 0.02% and field homogeneity of about 0.2%. The microwave system they used was phase-stabilized with a frequency stability on the order of one part in 10^8. Among the molecules they have studied are OCS [73], H_2CO (1967) [74], the methyl halides (1964, 1969), [75] and small ring compounds [76]. Recently Hüttner and Morgenstern [77] have successfully studied the high-field rotational Zeeman effect in several rotational transitions of the (010) vibrational state in OCS and HCN. The observed magnetic field splittings can be explained with a first-order treatment, which they found holds for the Zeeman energies of rotation–vibration states of linear polyatomic molecules showing rotational *l*-type doubling. This is the first experimental indication that molecules in a π vibrational state possess intrinsic magnetic moments.

In response to the experimental development of this field, theoretical studies on the high-field rotational Zeeman effect concerning molecules with internal rotation have recently been undertaken [78,79].

6. Internal Rotation and Other Large-Amplitude Motions

Internal rotation of part of a molecule around a single bond is an old but still up-to-date problem in microwave spectroscopy. Lin and Swalen [80] in 1959 and, more recently, Dreizler [81] have reviewed the theory and application of rotational spectroscopy to the problem of internal rotation. Research on the subject can be classified under two main topics: rotational isomerism and potential barriers. The latter has been treated from the time of the Columbus meeting (1951) as a leading subject and the rotation of the CH_3 group was studied preferentially. Tunneling through the barrier hindering internal rotation splits each state with a given torsional excitation, including the ground state, into two sublevels of symmetry A and E in the C_3 point group. The nondegenerate A and degenerate E levels do not combine. The corresponding line intensities depend on the statistical weight resulting from the fact that a rotation of a methyl group is equivalent to the exchange of proton nuclei.

Although the potential barrier restricting the rotation of the methyl group depends on the surroundings of the rotating group in the molecule, the V_3 term in the expansion of the potential barrier has been found to be several kcal mole^{-1} or less. Historically speaking, Kemp and Pitzer in 1936 [82] first estimated the barrier height in ethane to be about 3.15 kcal mole^{-1} from such thermodynamic quantities as entropy and heat capacity. Kistiakowsky et al. [83] revised the value to 2.75 kcal mole^{-1} on the basis of a heat capacity measurement at low temperature. It is an outstanding achievement of microwave spectroscopy that the existence of such a high barrier has been confirmed for the CH_3 torsion and the precise value of the barrier height has been determined for various molecules.

Two approximation methods have been pursued for the calculation of the energy levels: IAM (internal axis method) by Nielsen [84] and Dennison et al. (1954) [85], and PAM (principal axis method) by Wilson et al. [86], Crawford [87], and Herschbach and Swalen (1957) [88]. In the former the axis of the internal rotation is chosen as one of the coordinate axes. This has the advantage of simplifying the expressions for the interaction energies, but it has a disadvantage in that this axis does not coincide with any one of the principal axes of the whole molecule. The PAM has just the opposite characteristics.

With regard to the barrier in molecules with rotating groups having symmetries other than C_{3v}, Quade and others [89, 90] treated the theory for molecules with two asymmetric internal rotors. Meakin et al. (1968) [91] extended the theory to 3-fluoropropene. Recently Günthard and co-workers (1969) [92] developed the theory of hindered rotation with C_{2v}-type internal rotors and succeeded in explaining the variation of the rotational constants and the inertia defects of nitroethylene in the series of excited states of a torsional motion.

As for the higher-fold potential barriers, Tannenbaum *et al.* [93] determined a very small V_6 (6.0 cal mole^{-1}) for CH_3NO_2. Rudolph and co-workers (1965) [94] have obtained similar small values of V_6 for the derivatives of toluene. The two-top problem is reviewed by Dreizler in Chapter 2.4 of this volume.

Microwave studies of rotational isomerism were first carried out by Hirota (1962) [95] for *n*-propyl fluoride CH_3—CH_2—CH_2F and cyanide CH_3—CH_2—CH_2—CN. He confirmed the coexistence of the *trans* form and the *gauche* form, which is obtained by the rotation of the CH_2F group by about 120° from the *trans* position. He also found two rotational isomers for allyl fluoride CH_2=CH—CH_2F, but in this case the isomers identified were the *cis* form and the *skew* form, which is realized by the rotation of CH_2F by about 120° from the *cis* position [96]. Since this work many studies have been carried out where rotational isomers were found to coexist. It is remarkable that the isomers found are always of *trans* and *gauche* forms for the molecules with an internal rotation axis which is a single bond between carbon atoms forming sp^3 bonds, whereas they are of *cis* and *skew* forms (for allyl chloride [97] and cyanide [98], butene-1 [99], and propionyl fluoride [100]), or the *cis* and *trans* forms (for fluoroacetyl fluoride [101], fluoroacetone [102], and acrylic acid [103]), when a double bond is adjacent to the single-bond rotation axis.

Now that comprehensive data on the energy differences and barrier heights between rotational isomers have been accumulated we are in a position to formulate a theory with which we may be able to grasp the underlying principles of the potential function of internal rotation. Semiempirical approaches have been tried by Lowe [104], Flygare *et al.* (1969) [105,6], and Stiefvater and Wilson [100], and the attack from the theoretical computations of electronic energies has been carried out by several researchers. For instance, Pitzer and Lipscomb [106] derived 3 kcal for the barrier in ethane and Holyland [107] obtained a potential function for propane and *n*-butane which reproduced surprisingly well the observed barrier height and energy difference of the rotational isomers.

Hydrogen peroxide (H_2O_2) and hydrogen persulfide (H_2S_2) both possess a *skew* chain or C_2 symmetric structure with internal rotation of the two OH or SH bars relative to each other. For the former molecule Oelfke and Gordy [108] obtained from the analysis of the millimeter-wave spectra an accurate value of $342\ 885.0 \pm 2.0$ MHz for the doublet splitting of the vibrational ground state caused by barrier tunneling. The internal rotation splitting of HSSH in the ground vibrational state is extremely small (1966, 1969, 1970 [109] and has only recently been measured by Winton and Winnewisser (1970) by means of the Lamb-dip method. The observed splitting of 120 kHz gives a splitting of the rotational levels of only 60 kHz. This small splitting is due to tunneling through the relatively high *trans* barrier. The potential barrier can be represented by $V_{trans} = 2373$ cm^{-1} and $V_{cis} = 2550$ cm^{-1}.

Inversion of pyramidal molecules and puckering of four- or five-membered ring compounds are also large-amplitude motions which have been elucidated by microwave spectroscopy. The essential characteristic of both motions is tunneling through a barrier between two stable positions, similar to tunneling between two rotational isomers. NH_3 is a well-known, historically important case of inversion and trimethylene oxide [110] is the first case of puckering motion studied. The combined motions of inversion and internal rotation were studied in detail for methylamine [111].

Another example of internal motion of finite amplitude is the bending motion of quasilinear molecules. Lide and co-workers (1966) [112] studied the effect of the large-amplitude bending motions in CsOH and RbOH on the rotational spectrum. Several excellent attempts to give a theoretical treatment of such molecules have been made, notably by Freed and Lombardi [113], and Hougen et al. (1967, 1968) [114].

7. Vibration–Rotation Interactions

It was fortunate for the development of microwave spectroscopy that the general theory of molecular motion [115–117] had been formulated by Dennison, Nielsen, Wilson, and others before microwave spectroscopy came to the front. The theory of rotation–vibration interactions has been refined to third and fourth orders of approximation by Amat (1955, 1958), Nielsen, and others [118]. Accurate values of the observed microwave frequencies were utilized to their full accuracy in the precise treatment of the phenomena based on the highly detailed theoretical treatment of the vibration–rotation interactions.

A. Centrifugal Distortion

The first problem treated was that of centrifugal distortion. The first-order perturbation due to the centrifugal distortion effects in an asymmetric-top molecule was formulated first by Wilson and Howard in 1936 [119] and by Nielsen [120] and extended by Kivelson and Wilson (1952) [121] with six distortion constants. Watson [122] found, however, a correlation among them, thus reducing the number of independent distortion parameters to five. For planar molecules the number is four, independent of Watson's relation.

Deformation of a molecule by centrifugal forces is balanced by an increase of the potential energy, and the quadratic force field of the molecule may be obtained from analysis of the centrifugal distortion. The first example of this method was SO_2, studied by Kivelson [123]; O_3 was studied by Pierce [124], and many other examples have been given since then [15].

It should be mentioned that complicated effects of higher-order terms must

be eliminated in order to obtain the values of centrifugal constants applicable to the force field consideration. Pierce *et al.* [125] discussed the procedure on OF_2, and Gora (1964, 1965) [126] and Steenbeckeliers [127] on SO_2. Chung and Parker (1965) [128] considered the effect of the P^6 term, based on the higher-order perturbation theory by Goldsmith *et al.* [118].

B. CORIOLIS COUPLING

Coriolis coupling is the most important factor in the vibration–rotation interactions. It produces interactions between two rotational levels in the same or different vibrational states. Classification and nomenclature of the rotational and vibrational resonances in axially symmetric molecules were discussed by Amat and Nielsen [129].

Coriolis interaction produces first the Coriolis doubling, $\pm 2A\zeta lK$, of the degenerate levels of a symmetric-top molecule, though there is no effect of this kind in linear molecules. The twofold degeneracy, $K = l = +1$ and $K = l = -1$, of each component is further removed by the *l*-type doubling, mainly due also to the Coriolis interaction. The *l*-type doubling constants are therefore good sources for obtaining the Coriolis coupling constants for symmetric tops as well as for linear molecules.

The *l*-type doubling in linear molecules was first pointed out by Herzberg [130] and an analytic expression for it was derived by Nielsen [131]. For symmetric-top molecules it was first discussed by Nielsen and later more elaborately by Grenier-Besson [132] and Oka (1965) [133], who pointed out the importance of cubic potential constants in the *l*-type doubling constants.

The *l*-type doubling has been observed in the fine structure of both infrared bands and microwave rotational spectra, but microwave spectra provide a more straightforward means of obtaining the doubling constants through the measurement of direct transitions between the doublet states. Shulman and Townes [134] first observed such transitions in HCN; Maki [135] in 1967 observed direct *l*-type doubling transitions for OCS from $J = 35$–50 and Lafferty [136] for FCN from $J = 20$–38. Maki and Lide (1965) [137] were able to analyze direct *l*-type doublet transitions for HCN and DCN in higher excited vibrational states in addition to the $v_2 = 1$ state. In the case of HCNO Winnewisser and Bodenseh [138] could observe these transitions for both bending modes, v_4 and v_5, of this linear four-atomic molecule as well as for the $v_5 = 3$ vibrational state. From the analysis of millimeter-wave data Winnewisser and Winnewisser (1970) were able to determine the vibrational constants g_{44}, g_{55}, g_{45}, and r_{45} for HCNO.

In a symmetric-top molecule there often happens to be a near-degeneracy between the rotational levels, for instance, between the $K = 0$ level and one component of the $K = 2$ levels for the excited state of a doubly degenerate vibration, thus leading to the so-called *l*-type resonance. Costain (1955,

1962) [139] first observed an example of this as an anomalous feature in the v_6 spectrum of fluoroform, which was explained later by Maes and Amat (1964) [140] and further confirmed experimentally by observing a forbidden transition $J, K = 2, 2 \leftarrow 1, 0$ (1967) [141]. Detailed studies on stronger l-type resonances have also been made for NF_3 [142] and PF_3 [143].

When two vibrational states coupled by the Coriolis interaction come accidentally close in energy, the rotational levels in both states are seriously perturbed. Analysis of the rotational spectrum in such a case is painstaking, but offers an excellent means for obtaining the Coriolis coupling constant. The perturbation of the microwave spectra in the first excited states of v_1 and v_3 of the ozone molecule is a good example of this Coriolis coupling [45]. The quadratic force constants were determined with the help of the Coriolis coupling constant obtained in this way.

The inertial defect $\Delta = I_c - I_a - I_b$ for a planar molecule is also closely related to the Coriolis coupling constants. Its importance in the discussion of the force field was pointed out by Laurie (1960) and formulated in a concrete form by Oka et al. [144]. The use of the Coriolis coupling constants together with the three fundamental vibrational frequencies provided all four of the harmonic force constants for the bent triatomic molecules OF_2, SO_2, and SeO_2 (1965) [145]. The results are in good agreement with those obtained from the centrifugal distortion constants and from the frequency shifts in isotopic species.

C. VIBRATION–ROTATION INTERACTION CONSTANT α

To the second-order perturbation approximation, the constant α is obtained by taking the difference between the rotational constant in the first excited state of a normal vibration and that in the ground state. The constant α has two uses for molecular structure investigations: it is used for the evaluation of the cubic potential constants and for the determination of the equilibrium structure as already stated. Examples of the former application are given for O_3, OF_2, SO_2, and SeO_2 (1965) [145]. Herschbach and Laurie (1960) [146] noted regularities in the cubic constants for bond stretching, which may be expressed by an empirical relation analogous to Badger's rule for quadratic force constants.

D. FERMI RESONANCE

When a Fermi resonance takes place between two vibrational states of the same symmetry, effective rotational constants of the perturbed states are given by a linear combination of the original constants of the unperturbed states and therefore the microwave spectral lines are displaced from the regular positions. Low and Townes [147] clearly demonstrated such anomalous

displacements of the microwave lines for OCS and OCSe in the vibrationally excited state $v_2 = 2$, for which a Fermi resonance with the v_1 state exists. Since the displacement due to a Fermi resonance is proportional to the mixing ratio of the two resonating states, precise analysis of the spectrum leads to determination of the mixing ratio. Morino and Saito (1965) [45] found the mixing ratio of the v_1 and $2v_2$ states of OF_2 to be 32.5%, with the energy difference $v_1 - 2v_2 = 3.65$ cm^{-1}. Lafferty and Lide (1964) [148] found a similar effect between the v_1 and $2v_2$ states of FCN ($\omega_{12} = 35.2$ cm^{-1}).

Fermi resonance is primarily concerned with the vibrational motion of the molecule. It appears very often in infrared vibrational spectra, but the correct mixing ratio is seldom obtained from the analysis of infrared data. This is because the effect of anharmonicity is difficult to eliminate in the vibrational spectrum, while such higher-order corrections are usually small in the microwave spectrum, as was shown for SO_2 by Saito [149].

8. Free Radicals and Unstable Molecules

In 1953 Sanders et al. [150] first observed Λ-type doubling transitions for the OH and OD radicals. It was a very long time before the detection of radicals was reported again. It was generally believed that the detection of free radicals by microwave spectroscopy could hardly be achieved because of their short lifetimes and low concentrations. Recent improvements in microwave techniques, especially in sensitivity, have made it possible to attack this tough problem. Powell and Lide (1964) [151] and Winnewisser et al. [152] detected the rotational spectrum of SO ($X^3\Sigma^-$) independently and simultaneously in 1964. This finding has encouraged researchers to attempt detection of other radicals. The ClO ($^2\Pi_i$) radical was thus detected by Amano et al. (1968) [153], BrO ($^2\Pi_i$) by Powell and Johnson [154], and NS ($^2\Pi_r$) by Amano et al. [155]. The spectrum of SO in the first excited vibrational state was also measured by Amano et al. [156].

Molecules which have an unpaired electron were always found in the $^2\Pi$ state in their ground electronic state, as one might expect. The radicals OH, ClO, and NS are examples of this category. CS was found to be in a $^1\Sigma$ state [157], as is CO, whereas SO has a $^3\Sigma^-$ state as the ground electronic state, exactly analogous to the $^3\Sigma_g^-$ ground state of O_2. Recently, however, Saito [158] found a rotational transition $J = 3 \leftarrow 2$ of SO in the $^1\Delta$ state, about 6350 cm^{-1} above the ground state.

Stimulated by the first detection of the triatomic NCO radical by Carrington with gas-phase EPR, Saito and Amano [159] measured microwave absorption spectra of NCO ($^2\Pi_{3/2}$ and $^2\Pi_{1/2}$) by employing Carrington's process of producing the radical [160].

The investigation of many free radicals by gas-phase EPR has been carried out with great thoroughness by Carrington and co-workers. Carrington (1970)

has summarized their excellent results in another article of this volume. Microwave rotational spectra and electron paramagnetic resonance spectra are complementary tools in the study of free radicals. Rotational constants and dipole moments may be obtained more precisely by microwave rotational spectroscopy, whereas magnetic parameters are obtained by EPR spectroscopy.

A few bent-triatomic unstable molecules should be mentioned. The spectrum of the SiF_2 molecule detected by Curl et al. [161] is so strong that even the spectrum of the molecule in the $v_2 = 1$ state was observed. They also made a centrifugal distortion analysis for SiF_2 to determine the quadratic force constants. CF_2 (1966, 1967) [162] and SF_2 [163] were also detected by the group at the National Bureau of Standards. Kirchhoff (1969) discussed the analysis of the centrifugal distortion effect for both molecules. Two rather stable but paramagnetic molecules ClO_2 (1960–1962) [164] and NO_2 (1957, 1962, 1963) [165] have been extensively studied by Curl and co-workers to clarify various interactions occurring in such simple but paramagnetic molecules.

Several unstable four-atomic molecules have also been observed and found to have interesting spectra. Among them one should mention thioformaldehyde (H_2CS), which has recently been successfully produced and characterized from its gas-phase rotational spectrum [166].

ACKNOWLEDGMENTS

The authors would like to express their sincere thanks to Dr. M. Winnewisser and Dr. B. P. Winnewisser for reading over the manuscript critically and contributing many valuable suggestions.

References

1. C. E. Cleeton and N. H. Williams, *Phys. Rev.* **45**, 234 (1934).
2. W. Gordy, W. V. Smith, and R. F. Trambarulo, "Microwave Spectroscopy." Wiley, New York, 1953. Republication. Dover, New York, 1966.
3. M. W. P. Strandberg, "Microwave Spectroscopy." Methuen, London, 1954.
4. C. H. Townes and A. L. Schawlow, "Microwave Spectroscopy." McGraw-Hill, New York, 1955.
5. D. R. Lide, Jr., *Annu. Rev. Phys. Chem.* **15**, 225 (1964).
6. W. H. Flygare, *Annu. Rev. Phys. Chem.* **18**, 325 (1967).
7. Y. Morino and E. Hirota, *Annu. Rev. Phys. Chem.* **20**, 139 (1969).
8. H. D. Rudolph, *Annu. Rev. Phys. Chem.* **21**, 73 (1970).
9. E. B. Wilson, Jr., *Science* **162**, 59 (1968).
10. J. E. Parkin, *Annu. Rep. Progr. Chem.* **64**, 181 (1967); **65**, 111 (1968).
11. D. J. E. Ingram, "Spectroscopy at Radio and Microwave Frequencies." Butterworth, London, 1955. Second edition. Plenum, New York, 1967.
12. T. M. Sugden and C. N. Kenney, "Microwave Spectroscopy of Gases." Van Nostrand-Reinhold, Princeton, New Jersey, 1965.

13. J. E. Wollrab, "Rotational Spectra and Molecular Structure." Academic Press, New York, 1967.
14. D. H. Martin, ed., "Spectroscopic Techniques for Far Infra-Red, Submillimetre and Millimetre Waves," Chapter 5. North-Holland Publ., Amsterdam, 1967.
15. W. Gordy and R. L. Cook, Microwave molecular spectra. *In* "Chemical Applications of Spectroscopy" (W. West, ed.), Part II, Vol. IX. Wiley (Interscience), New York, 1970.
16. B. Starck, Molecular constants from microwave spectroscopy. *In* Landolt–Börnstein, Numerical data and functional relationships in science and technology, Group II, "Atomic and Molecular Physics," Vol. 4. Springer-Verlag, Berlin and New York, 1967.
17. Microwave spectral tables. *Nat. Bur. Stand. U.S. Monogr.* **70**, Vol. I, Diatomic Molecules (1964), P. F. Wacker, M. Mizushima, J. D. Petersen, and J. R. Ballard; Vol. II, Line strengths of Assymmetric Rotors (1964), P. F. Wacker and M. R. Pratto; Vol. III, Polyatomic Molecules with Internal Rotation (1969), P. F. Wacker, M. S. Cord, D. G. Burkhard, J. D. Petersen, and R. G. Kukol; Vol. IV, Polyatomic Molecules without Internal Rotation (1968), M. S. Cord, J. D. Petersen, M. S. Lojko, and R. H. Hass; Vol. V, Spectral Line Listing (a listing of the spectral lines reported in Vols. I, III, IV) (1968), M. S. Cord, M. S. Lojko, and J. D. Petersen.
18. A. Guarnieri and P. Favero, "Microwave Gas Spectroscopy Bibliography 1954–1967." Inst. Chimico G. Ciamician Univ. di Bologna, Bologna, 1968.
19. R. H. Hughes and E. B. Wilson, Jr., *Phys. Rev.* **71**, 652 (1947).
20. W. Gordy and M. Kessler, *Phys. Rev.* **12**, 644 (1947).
21. R. W. Zimmerer, *Rev. Sci. Instr.* **31**, 106 (1960).
22. H. D. Rudolph, *Z. Angew. Phys.* **13**, 401 (1961).
23. A. Narath and W. D. Gwinn, *Rev. Sci. Instr.* **33**, 79 (1962).
24. W. D. Gwinn, A. C. Luntz, C. H. Sederholm, and R. Millikan, *J. Comput. Phys.* **2**, 439 (1968).
25. W. H. Flygare, A. Narath, and W. D. Gwinn, *J. Chem. Phys.* **36**, 200 (1962).
26. W. Gordy, *Pure Appl. Chem.* **11**, 403 (1965).
27. G. Jones and W. Gordy, *Phys. Rev.* **135**, A295 (1964).
28. P. Helminger, F. C. De Lucia, and W. Gordy, *Phys. Rev. Lett.* **25**, 1397 (1970).
29. E. H. Putley, *Appl. Opt.* **4**, 649 (1965).
30. R. S. Winton and W. Gordy, *Phys. Lett. A* **32**, 219 (1970).
31. R. E. Cupp, R. A. Kemp, and J. J. Gallagher, *Phys. Rev.* **171**, 60 (1968).
32. F. De Lucia and W. Gordy, *Phys. Rev.* **187**, 58 (1969); Millimeter and submillimeter wave molecular beam masers. *Proc. Symp. Submillimeter Waves, Polytech. Inst. of Brooklyn, Brooklyn, New York, March 31, April 1–2, 1970.*
33. C. C. Costain, *Can. J. Phys.* **47**, 2431 (1969).
34. A. P. Cox, G. W. Flynn, and E. B. Wilson, Jr., *J. Chem. Phys.* **42**, 3094 (1965).
34a. T. Yajima and K. Shimoda, *J. Phys. Soc. Jap.* **15**, 2036 (1960).
35. M. L. Unland, V. Weiss, and W. H. Flygare, *Rev. Sci. Instr.* **42**, 2318 (1965).
36. T. Tanaka and Y. Morino, *J. Chem. Phys.* **49**, 2877 (1968).
37. R. C. Woods, A. M. Ronn, and E. B. Wilson, Jr., *J. Chem. Phys.* **37**, 927 (1966).
38. R. C. Woods, *J. Chem. Phys.* **46**, 4789 (1967).
39. T. Oka, *J. Chem. Phys.* **45**, 754 (1966).
40. M. L. Unland and W. H. Flygare, *J. Chem. Phys.* **45**, 2421 (1966).
41. M. L. Stitch, A. Honig, and C. H. Townes, *Rev. Sci. Instr.* **25**, 759 (1954); *Phys. Rev.* **86**, 607A, 813L (1952); P. A. Tate and M. W. P. Strandberg, *Rev. Sci. Instr.* **25**, 956 (1952); *J. Chem. Phys.* **22**, 1380 (1954); T. Törring, *Z. Naturforsch. A* **23**, 777 (1968); D. R. Lide, Jr., *Rev. Sci. Instr.* **35**, 1226 (1964); *J. Chem. Phys.* **42**, 1013 (1965); E.

Pearson and W. Gordy, *Phys. Rev.* **152**, 42 (1966); **177**, 52, 59 (1969); A. N. Murty and R. F. Curl, Jr., *Rev. Sci. Instr.* **39**, 1885 (1968); *J. Mol. Spectrosc.* **30**, 102 (1969).

42. C. C. Costain, *J. Chem. Phys.* **29**, 864 (1958).

43. J. Kraitchman, *Amer. J. Phys.* **21**, 17 (1953).

44. B. Bak, L. Hansen-Nygaard, and J. Rastrup-Andersen, *J. Mol. Spectrosc.* **2**, 361 (1958); B. Bak, D. Christensen, and J. Rastrup-Andersen, *Ibid.* **7**, 58 (1961); B. Bak, D. Christensen, W. B. Dixon, L. Hansen-Nygaard, J. Rastrup-Andersen, and M. Schottlander, *Ibid.* **9**, 124 (1962).

45. O_3, T. Tanaka and Y. Morino, *J. Mol. Spectrosc.* **33**, 538 (1970); OF_2, Y. Morino and S. Saito, *Ibid.* **19**, 435 (1966); SO_2, Y. Morino, Y. Kikuchi, S. Saito, and E. Hirota, *Ibid.* **13**, 95 (1964); SeO_2, H. Takeo, E. Hirota, and Y. Morino, *Ibid.* **34**, 370 (1970).

46. M. Otake, C. Matsumura, and Y. Morino, *J. Mol. Spectrosc.* **28**, 316 (1968).

47. W. J. Lafferty, D. R. Lide, Jr., and R. A. Toth, *J. Chem. Phys.* **43**, 2063 (1965).

48. Y. Morino and T. Nakagawa, *J. Mol. Spectrosc.* **26**, 496 (1968).

49. T. Oka, *J. Phys. Soc. Jap.* **15**, 2274 (1960).

50. Y. Morino, K. Kuchitsu, and T. Oka, *J. Chem. Phys.* **36**, 1108 (1962).

51. D. R. Herschbach and V. W. Laurie, *J. Chem. Phys.* **37**, 1668 (1962); V. W. Laurie and D. R. Herschbach, *Ibid.* **37**, 1687 (1962).

52. J. S. Muenter, *J. Chem. Phys.* **48**, 4544 (1968).

53. S. A. Marshall and J. Weber, *Phys. Rev.* **105**, 1502 (1957).

54. H. A. Dijkerman and G. Ruitenberg, *Chem. Phys. Lett.* **3**, 172 (1969).

55. J. S. Muenter and V. W. Laurie, *J. Amer. Chem. Soc.* **86**, 3901 (1964).

56. S. C. Wofsy, J. S. Muenter, and W. Klemperer, *J. Chem. Phys.* **53**, 4005 (1970).

57. C. H. Townes, A. N. Holden, and F. R. Merritt, *Phys. Rev.* **74**, 1113 (1948).

58. J. Bardeen and C. H. Townes, *Phys. Rev.* **73**, 97 (1948).

59. R. J. Myers and W. D. Gwinn, *J. Chem. Phys.* **20**, 1420 (1952); W. H. Flygare and W. D. Gwinn, *Ibid.* **36**, 787 (1962).

60. A. A. Wolf, Q. Williams, and T. L. Weatherly, *J. Chem. Phys.* **47**, 5101 (1967).

61. C. H. Townes and B. P. Dailey, *J. Chem. Phys.* **17**, 1182 (1949).

62. W. Gordy, *Discuss. Faraday Soc.* **19**, 14 (1955).

63. W. H. Flygare, *J. Chem. Phys.* **41**, 206 (1964); W. H. Flygare and V. W. Weiss, *J. Amer. Chem. Soc.* **87**, 5317 (1965); V. W. Weiss and W. H. Flygare, *J. Chem. Phys.* **45**, 8, 3475 (1966).

64. L. Salem, *J. Chem. Phys.* **38**, 1227 (1963).

65. J. R. Eshbach and M. W. P. Strandberg, *Phys. Rev.* **85**, 24 (1952); B. F. Burke and M. W. P. Strandberg, *Ibid.* **90**, 303 (1953).

66. T. Oka and Y. Morino, *J. Mol. Spectrosc.* **6**, 472 (1961); B. Rosenblum, A. H. Nethercot, and C. H. Townes, *Phys. Rev.* **109**, 400 (1958); H. R. Johnson and M. W. P. Strandberg, *J. Chem. Phys.* **20**, 687 (1952).

67. C. H. Townes, G. C. Dousmanis, R. L. White, and R. F. Schwarz, *Discuss. Faraday Soc.* **19**, 56 (1955).

68. W. Hüttner and W. H. Flygare, *J. Chem. Phys.* **47**, 4137 (1967).

69. D. H. Levy, *J. Chem. Phys.* **48**, 5026 (1968).

70. H. Taft and B. P. Dailey, *J. Chem. Phys.* **48**, 597 (1968).

71. H. Taft and B. P. Dailey, *J. Chem. Phys.* **51**, 1002 (1969).

72. P. K. Bhattacharyya and B. P. Dailey, *J. Chem. Phys.* **51**, 3051 (1969).

73. W. H. Flygare, W. Hüttner, R. H. Shoemaker, and P. D. Foster, *J. Chem. Phys.* **50**, 1714 (1969).

74. W. Hüttner, M. K. Lo, and W. H. Flygare, *J. Chem. Phys.* **48**, 1206 (1968); D. Eisenberg, J. M. Pochan, and W. H. Flygare, *Ibid.* **43**, 4531 (1965); W. H. Flygare, *Ibid.* **42**, 1563 (1965).

75. D. L. Vanderhart and W. H. Flygare, *Mol. Phys.* **18**, 77 (1970); W. Hüttner and W. H. Flygare, *J. Chem. Phys.* **49**, 1912 (1969).
76. R. C. Benson, H. L. Tigelaar, S. L. Rock, and W. H. Flygare, *J. Chem. Phys.* **52**, 5628 (1970); J. H. S. Wang and W. H. Flygare, *Ibid.* **52**, 5636 (1970); R. C. Benson and W. H. Flygare, *Ibid.* **52**, 5291 (1970).
77. W. Hüttner and K. Morgenstern, *Z. Naturforsch. A* **25**, 547 (1970).
78. D. Sutter, A. Guarnieri, and H. Dreizler, *Z. Naturforsch. A* **25**, 222 (1970).
79. D. Sutter and A. Guarnieri, *Z. Naturforsch. A* **25**, 1036 (1970).
80. C. C. Lin and J. D. Swalen, *Rev. Mod. Phys.* **31**, 841 (1959).
81. H. Dreizler, *Fortschr. Chem. Forsch.* **10**, 59 (1968).
82. J. D. Kemp and K. S. Pitzer, *J. Chem. Phys.* **4**, 749 (1936); *J. Amer. Chem. Soc.* **59**, 276 (1937).
83. G. B. Kistiakowsky, J. R. Lacher, and F. Stitt, *J. Chem. Phys.* **7**, 289 (1939).
84. H. H. Nielsen, *Phys. Rev.* **40**, 445 (1932).
85. K. T. Hecht and D. M. Dennison, *J. Chem. Phys.* **26**, 31 (1957); D. G. Burkhard and D. M. Dennison, *Phys. Rev.* **84**, 408 (1951); J. S. Kohler and D. M. Dennison, *Ibid.* **57**, 1006 (1940); E. V. Ivash and D. M. Dennison, *J. Chem. Phys.* **21**, 1804 (1953).
86. E. B. Wilson, Jr., C. C. Lin, and D. R. Lide, Jr., *J. Chem. Phys.* **23**, 136 (1955); E. B. Wilson, Jr., *Chem. Rev.* **27**, 17 (1940).
87. B. L. Crawford, *J. Chem. Phys.* **8**, 273 (1940).
88. D. R. Herschbach, *J. Chem. Phys.* **25**, 358 (1956); **27**, 975, 1420 (1957); J. D. Swalen, *Ibid.* **24**, 1072 (1956); J. D. Swalen and D. R. Herschbach, *Ibid.* **27**. 100 (1957); **29**, 761 (1958).
89. C. R. Quade and C. C. Lin, *J. Chem. Phys.* **38**, 540 (1963).
90. J. V. Knopp and C. R. Quade, *J. Chem. Phys.* **53**, 1 (1970).
91. P. Meakin, D. O. Harris, and E. Hirota, *J. Chem. Phys.* **51**, 3775 (1969).
92. A. Bauder, E. Mathier, R. Meyer, M. Ribeaud, and Hs. H. Günthard, *Mol. Phys.* **15**, 597 (1968).
93. E. Tannenbaum, R. J. Myers, and W. D. Gwinn, *J. Chem. Phys.* **25**, 42 (1956).
94. H. D. Rudolph and H. Seiler, *Z. Naturforsch. A* **20**, 1682 (1965).
95. E. Hirota, *J. Chem. Phys.* **37**, 283, 2918 (1962).
96. E. Hirota, *J. Chem. Phys.* **42**, 2071 (1965).
97. E. Hirota, *J. Mol. Spectrosc.* **35**, 9 (1970).
98. K. V. L. N. Sastry, V. M. Rao, and S. C. Dass, *Can. J. Phys.* **46**, 959 (1968).
99. S. Kondo, E. Hirota, and Y. Morino, *J. Mol. Spectrosc.* **28**, 471 (1968).
100. O. L. Stiefvater and E. B. Wilson, Jr., *J. Chem. Phys.* **50**, 5385 (1969).
101. E. Saegebarth and E. B. Wilson, Jr., *J. Chem. Phys.* **46**, 3088 (1967).
102. E. Saegebarth, *Symp. Gas Phase Mol. Struct., 2nd, Austin Texas, February 1968*, M.4.
103. F. Mönnig, H. Dreizler, and H. D. Rudolph, *Z. Naturforsch. A* **20**, 1323 (1965).
104. J. P. Lowe, *Progr. Phys. Org. Chem.* **6**, 1 (1968); *J. Chem. Phys.* **51**, 832 (1969).
105. S. L. Hsu and W. H. Flygare, *J. Chem. Phys.* **52**, 1053 (1970).
106. R. M. Pitzer and W. N. Lipscomb, *J. Chem. Phys.* **39**, 1995 (1963).
107. J. R. Holyland, *J. Chem. Phys.* **49**, 1908, 2563 (1968).
108. W. C. Oelfke and W. Gordy, *J. Chem. Phys.* **51**, 5336 (1969).
109. G. Winnewisser, M. Winnewisser, and W. Gordy, *J. Chem. Phys.* **49**, 3465 (1968).
110. S. I. Chan, J. Zinn, J. Fernandes, and W. D. Gwinn, *J. Chem. Phys.* **33**, 1643 (1960).
111. K. Shimoda, T. Nishikawa, and T. Itoh, *J. Phys. Soc. Jap.* **9**, 974 (1954); T. Itoh, *Ibid.* **11**, 264 (1956); T. Nishikawa, *Ibid.* **12**, 668 (1957).
112. D. R. Lide, Jr. and R. L. Kuczkowski, *J. Chem. Phys.* **46**, 4768 (1967); C. Matsumura and D. R. Lide, Jr., *Ibid.* **50**, 71 (1969).
113. K. F. Freed and J. R. Lombardi, *J. Chem. Phys.* **45**, 591 (1966).

114. J. T. Hougen, P. R. Bunker, and J. W. C. Johns, *J. Mol. Spectrosc.* **34**, 136 (1970).
115. B. T. Darling and D. M. Dennison, *Phys. Rev.* **57**, 128 (1940).
116. H. H. Nielsen, The Vibration–Rotation Energies of Molecules and their Spectra in the Infrared. *In* " Handbuch der Physik " (S. Flügge, ed.), Vol. 37/1. Springer-Verlag, Berlin and New York, 1959.
117. E. B. Wilson, Jr., J. C. Decius, and P. C. Gross, " Molecular Vibrations." McGraw-Hill, New York, 1955.
118. M. Goldsmith, G. Amat, and H. H. Nielsen, *J. Chem. Phys.* **24**, 1178 (1956); G. Amat, M. Goldsmith, and H. H. Nielsen, *Ibid.* **27**, 838, 845 (1957).
119. E. B. Wilson, Jr. and J. B. Howard, *J. Chem. Phys.* **4**, 260 (1936).
120. H. H. Nielsen, *Rev. Mod. Phys.* **23**, 90 (1951).
121. D. Kivelson and E. B. Wilson, Jr., *J. Chem. Phys.* **20**, 1575 (1952); **21**, 1229 (1953).
122. J. K. G. Watson, *J. Chem. Phys.* **45**, 1360 (1966); **46**, 1935 (1967); **48**, 181, 4517 (1968).
123. D. Kivelson, *J. Chem. Phys.* **22**, 904 (1954).
124. L. Pierce, *J. Chem. Phys.* **24**, 139 (1956).
125. L. Pierce, N. DiCianni, and R. H. Jackson, *J. Chem. Phys.* **38**, 730 (1963).
126. E. K. Gora, S. A. Clough, and F. X. Kneizys, *J. Mol. Spectrosc.* **19**, 7 (1966).
127. G. Steenbeckeliers, *Ann. Soc. Sci. Bruxelles Ser. I,* **82**, 331 (1968).
128. K. T. Chung and P. M. Parker, *J. Chem. Phys.* **43**, 3865, 3869 (1965).
129. G. Amat and H. H. Nielsen, *J. Mol. Spectrosc.* **23**, 359 (1967).
130. G. Herzberg, *Rev. Mod. Phys.* **14**, 219 (1942).
131. H. H. Nielsen, *Phys. Rev.* **75**, 1961 (1949); **77**, 130 (1950).
132. M. L. Grenier-Besson, *J. Phys. Radium* **21**, 555 (1960).
133. T. Oka, *J. Chem. Phys.* **47**, 5410 (1967).
134. R. G. Shulman and C. H. Townes, *Phys. Rev.* **77**, 421 (1950).
135. A. G. Maki, *J. Mol. Spectrosc.* **23**, 110 (1967).
136. W. J. Lafferty, *J. Mol. Spectrosc.* **25**, 359 (1968).
137. A. G. Maki and D. R. Lide, Jr., *J. Chem. Phys.* **47**, 3206 (1967).
138. M. Winnewisser and H. K. Bodenseh, *Z. Naturforsch. A* **22**, 1724 (1967); H. K. Bodenseh and M. Winnewisser, *Ibid.* **24**, 1966, 1973 (1969).
139. C. C. Costain, *J. Mol. Spectrosc.* **9**, 317 (1962).
140. S. Maes and G. Amat, *Can. J. Phys.* **43**, 321 (1965).
141. C. C. Costain, *Can. J. Phys.* **43**, 244 (1965).
142. M. Otake, E. Hirota, and Y. Morino, *J. Mol. Spectrosc.* **28**, 325 (1969).
143. E. Hirota and Y. Morino, *J. Mol. Spectrosc.* **33**, 460 (1970).
144. T. Oka and Y. Morino, *J. Mol. Spectrosc.* **6**, 472 (1961); **8**, 9 (1962); K. Kuchitsu, T. Oka, and Y. Morino, *Ibid.* **15**, 51 (1965).
145. Y. Morino, *Pure Appl. Chem.* **18**, 323 (1969).
146. D. R. Herschbach and V. W. Laurie, *J. Chem. Phys.* **35**, 458 (1961).
147. W. Low and C. H. Townes, *Phys. Rev.* **79**, 224 (1950).
148. W. J. Lafferty and D. R. Lide, Jr., *J. Mol. Spectrosc.* **23**, 94 (1967).
149. S. Saito, *J. Mol. Spectrosc.* **30**, 1 (1969).
150. T. M. Sanders, A. L. Schawlow, G. C. Dousmanis, and C. H. Townes, *Phys. Rev.* **89**, 1158 (1953); G. C. Dousmanis, *Ibid.* **94**, 789A (1954); T. M. Sanders, A. L. Schawlow G. C. Dousmanis, and C. H. Townes, *J. Chem. Phys.* **22**, 245 (1954); G. C. Dousmanis, T. M. Sanders, and C. H. Townes, *Phys. Rev.* **100**, 1735 (1955).
151. F. X. Powell and D. R. Lide, Jr., *J. Chem. Phys.* **41**, 1413 (1964).
152. M. Winnewisser, K. V. L. N. Sastry, R. L. Cook, and W. Gordy, *J. Chem. Phys.* **41**, 1687 (1964).
153. T. Amano, S. Saito, E. Hirota, Y. Morino, D. R. Johnson, and F. X. Powell, *J. Mol. Spectrosc.* **30**, 275 (1969); T. Amano, E. Hirota, and Y. Morino, *Ibid.* **27**, 257 (1968).

154. F. X. Powell and D. R. Johnson, *J. Chem. Phys.* **50**, 4596 (1969).
155. T. Amano, S. Saito, E. Hirota, and Y. Morino, *J. Mol. Spectrosc.* **32**, 97 (1969).
156. T. Amano, E. Hirota, and Y. Morino, *J. Phys. Soc. Jap.* **22**, 399 (1967); **25**, 300 (1968).
157. R. C. Mockler and G. R. Bird, *Phys. Rev.* **98**, 1837 (1955); R. Kewley, K. V. L. N. Sastry, M. Winnewisser, and W. Gordy, *J. Chem. Phys.* **39**, 2856 (1963).
158. S. Saito, *J. Chem. Phys.* **53**, 2544 (1971).
159. S. Saito and T. Amano, *J. Mol. Spectrosc.* **34**, 383 (1970).
160. A. Carrington, A. R. Fabris, B. J. Howard, and N. J. D. Lucas. *Mol. Phys.* **20**, 961 (1971); A. Carrington, A. R. Fabris, and N. J. D. Lucas, *Mol. Phys.* **16**, 195 (1969); *J. Chem. Phys.* **49**, 5545 (1968).
161. V. M. Rao, R. F. Curl, Jr., P. L. Timms, and J. L. Margrave, *J .Chem. Phys.* **43**, 2557 (1965); V. M. Rao and R. F. Curl, Jr., *Ibid.* **45·** 2032 (1966).
162. F. X. Powell and D. R. Lide, Jr., *J. Chem. Phys.* **45**, 1067 (1966).
163. D. R. Johnson and F. X. Powell, *Science* **164**, 950 (1969).
164. R. F. Curl, Jr., J. L. Kinsey, J. G. Baker, J. C. Baird, G. R. Bird, R. F. Heidelberg, T. M. Sugden, D. R. Jenkins, and C. N. Kenney, *Phys. Rev.* **121**, 1119 (1961); R. F. Curl, Jr. and R. F. Heidelberg, *Ibid.* **125**, 1993 (1962); M. G. K. Pillai and R. F. Curl, Jr., *J. Chem. Phys.* **37**, 2921 (1962); R. P. Mariella, Jr. and R. F. Curl, Jr., *Ibid.* **52**, 757 (1970).
165. G. R. Bird, J. C. Baird, A. W. Jache, J. A. Hodgeson, R. F. Curl, Jr., A. C. Kunkle, J. W. Bransford, J. Rastrup-Andersen, and J. Rosenthal, *J. Chem. Phys.* **40**, 3378 (1964); R. M. Lees, R. F. Curl, Jr., and J. G. Baker, *Ibid.* **45**, 2037 (1966).
166. D. R. Johnson and F. X. Powell, *Science* **169**, 679 (1970).

2.2 Rotational Levels of Free Radicals

Alan Carrington

Department of Chemistry
The University of Southampton
Hampshire, England

1. Introduction

Most of our knowledge of the energy levels of free radicals has been obtained from visible and ultraviolet gas-phase spectroscopy. The development of flash photolysis by Norrish and Porter [1] made it possible to produce high concentrations of free radicals in the gas phase and, both in principle and in practice, it is relatively easy to record their absorption or emission spectra in the visible and ultraviolet using well-established photographic techniques. Such studies have been, and will continue to be, the main source of information about the structure and properties of free radicals in both ground and excited electronic states. There is, however, a limit to the information to be gained, imposed by the limits of resolution. The Doppler linewidth at the wavelengths used is considerable (for example, OH at 3000 Å has a Doppler width at room temperature of approximately 3000 MHz), although special techniques for overcoming this limitation are just being developed. The traditional answer to the problem of obtaining higher resolution, however, is to work at lower frequencies, and hence to move into the far-infrared, microwave, and radiofrequency regions of the spectrum.

Why should one seek higher resolution? The reason, of course, is that the smaller the spectral linewidth, the greater the spectral information. Direct information about electronic structure comes from measurements of interactions between electrons and nuclei, and between the molecule (electrons and nuclei) and applied electric and magnetic fields. Such interactions are usually small in magnitude and therefore only revealed by high-resolution spectroscopic studies.

In this chapter I intend to review past and current work on the microwave and radiofrequency spectra of free radicals. I have avoided using the term "microwave spectroscopy" in the title because although such inclusion would be appropriate, some readers might infer that it is my intention to review

studies using a specific technique, rather than the more general area of spectroscopy which is actually of concern. In point of fact, the traditional methods of microwave spectroscopy have been less successful in the study of free radicals than other less commonly exploited techniques. I shall discuss the use of electron resonance, radiofrequency–optical double-resonance spectroscopy, and molecular-beam methods, as well as conventional microwave spectroscopy. Since the work has invariably been carried out on gases at low pressures, where the rotational motion of the molecules is quantized, information about the fine and hyperfine structure of the rotational levels is obtained; hence the title I have chosen.

It is my intention to stretch the meaning of the term "free radicals," but also to restrict my coverage in other ways. Free radicals are of particular spectroscopic interest because of their open-shell electronic structure and the resulting magnetic interactions within the molecule and with external magnetic fields. This interest is shared by molecules in open-shell excited electronic states, which may well have closed-shell ground states, and I shall therefore include discussion of open-shell excited states. However, I restrict discussion to linear molecules (diatomic and triatomic), partly because my own experience is with them, but mainly because very little work on open-shell nonlinear molecules has been reported. This account will be essentially qualitative but I hope the references to original work will satisfy the reader seeking a more detailed account of the theory.

2. Microwave and Electron Resonance Spectra of the OH Radical

The first microwave spectrum of a short-lived free radical to be detected was that of OH by Dousmanis et al. [2] in 1955; this was followed by the observation of the electron resonance spectrum by Radford [3] in 1961. These studies of OH provide excellent examples of the experimental techniques employed and the information to be gained. They also illustrate the relationships between the two types of experiment.

The pure microwave spectrum of OH was detected with a conventional microwave spectrometer, and the absorption cell used by Dousmanis et al. is illustrated in Fig. 1. Water vapor was passed through a radiofrequency discharge, and the products pumped continuously through the microwave cell. Microwave absorption lines due to OH were detected at frequencies ranging from about 7000 MHz to 24 000 MHz, magnetic field modulation at 227 kHz or 100 kHz being employed. The electronic ground state of OH is $^2\Pi_{3/2}$, with the $^2\Pi_{1/2}$ state lying about 140 cm^{-1} above the ground state. The rotational constant of OH is, of course, quite large (18.87 cm^{-1}) so that the rotational levels are widely spaced, as shown in Fig. 2. Hence the spectrum arising from rotational transitions lies in the far-infrared. However, the rapid rotation of the molecule also means that there is strong coupling between the

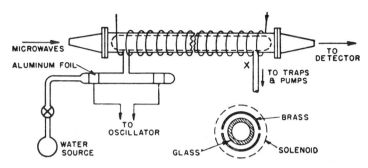

FIG. 1. Absorption cell for the microwave spectrum of OH [2].

rotational and electronic motions of the radical, leading to large Λ-doubling. Transitions between Λ-doublets within a particular rotational level are electric-dipole-allowed, and these were the transitions observed by Dousmanis *et al.* A further complication is that magnetic hyperfine coupling to the proton (which has nuclear spin $I = \frac{1}{2}$) results in a doublet splitting of each level, and the transitions for each rotational level are therefore of the form shown on the right-hand side of Fig. 2. Absorption lines from several rotational levels of ^{16}OH, ^{18}OH, and ^{16}OD in both the $^{2}\Pi_{3/2}$ and $^{2}\Pi_{1/2}$ states were observed; it was therefore possible for a number of Λ-doubling and hyperfine parameters to be determined.

The main feature of what we call " pure " microwave spectroscopy is that the spectrum is obtained by sweeping the microwave frequency. In the electron resonance experiment, however, one works at a fixed microwave frequency and sweeps an external magnetic field. Electron resonance can

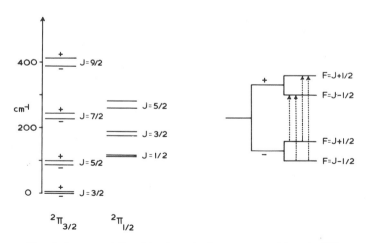

FIG. 2. Lower rotational levels and microwave transitions in OH.

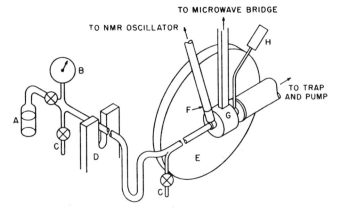

FIG. 3. Gas handling system and spectrometer cavity. A: H_2O or D_2O sample vial; B: Wallace and Tiernan vacuum gauge; C: inlet for admixing foreign gases to vapor stream; D: waveguide discharge resonator; E: pole face of electromagnet; F: nuclear magnetic resonance probe; G: spectrometer microwave cavity (TE_{012}, 3 cm); H: thermocouple vacuum gauge.

therefore only be used to study molecules which interact strongly with an applied magnetic field, that is, molecules with unquenched electronic angular momentum (spin or orbital). Radford's experiments on OH were made at a fixed frequency close to 9000 MHz and the spectrometer cavity system he used is shown in Fig. 3. The OH radicals were again produced by passing water vapor through a discharge, this time operating at a microwave frequency. Figure 4 illustrates the transitions observed for the lowest rotational level ($J = \frac{3}{2}$) of the $^2\Pi_{3/2}$ state. The applied magnetic field removes the $2J + 1$ spatial degeneracy of the total angular momentum $\mathbf{J}$, so that each Λ-doublet is split into four levels, with the very small proton hyperfine splitting further superimposed. The spectrum appears as two groups of lines whose separation depends upon the magnitude of the Λ-doubling. The observed transitions satisfy the selection rule $\Delta M_J = \pm 1$ and because the Zeeman effect is not exactly linear, the three $\Delta M_J = \pm 1$ transitions in each group occur at slightly different magnetic field values; we shall call this the second-order Zeeman splitting. The proton hyperfine coupling produces a further doublet splitting. Radford was able to observe resonance from several rotational levels of both the $^2\Pi_{3/2}$ and $^2\Pi_{1/2}$ states. In a molecule which approximates closely to Hund's case (a), such as NO, the $^2\Pi_{1/2}$ state is essentially diamagnetic and therefore not accessible by electron resonance methods. However, the rapid rotation of OH leads to heavy mixing of the $^2\Pi_{3/2}$ and $^2\Pi_{1/2}$ states (the so-called rotational distortion) and consequently both states can be studied. Radford's measurements confirmed many aspects of the earlier analysis of the pure microwave spectrum, provided g values for the various rotational levels, and also led to a more complete analysis of the hyperfine coupling.

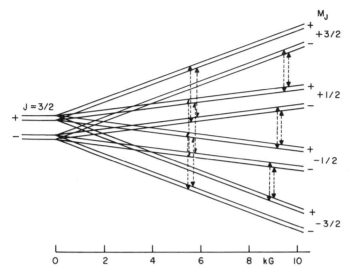

FIG. 4. Electron resonance transitions in the $J = \frac{3}{2}$, $^2\Pi_{3/2}$ level of OH.

In the case of OH the microwave and electron resonance spectra are closely related since they both involve transitions between the Λ-doublet components of a single rotational level. However, we shall see that OH is, in many ways, a special case. Most of the free radicals studied have much smaller rotational constants, so that the Λ-doubling is much smaller. The pure microwave spectrum then arises from transitions between different rotational levels ($\Delta J = \pm 1$), while the electron resonance spectrum is of the same type as that described here for OH, except that the Λ-doubling is small and often unresolved.

Those familiar with electron resonance in condensed phases will recognize many differences between the experiments described here and those on liquids and solids. Perhaps the most important point to note is that the electron resonance transitions studied in OH and nearly all other gas-phase radicals to date are electric-dipole-allowed, whereas in condensed phases the observed transitions are invariably magnetic dipole. We will discuss the reasons for this in due course, but take note of the fact that recognizing this difference is crucial in performing a successful experiment. In the study of condensed phases it is necessary to use a resonant cavity mode which enables one to place the paramagnetic material in the region of maximum microwave magnetic field, and to orient the cavity with the microwave magnetic field perpendicular to the applied static magnetic field. In the gas-phase studies described here the exact opposite conditions must be fulfilled. Nearly all experiments have employed cylindrical cavities operating in TE_{011} modes and Fig. 5 illustrates

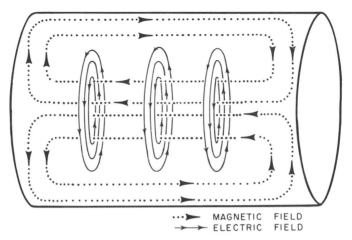

FIG. 5. Microwave electric and magnetic fields in the TE_{011} mode.

the distribution of microwave magnetic and electric fields in the TE_{011} mode. For the observation of electric dipole transitions it is best to orient the cavity with the cylinder axis parallel to the static magnetic field. Moreover, since the microwave electric field is a maximum approximately midway between the center of the cavity and the cylinder walls, this is where the free-radical concentration should also be maximized.

3. Recent Pure Microwave and Electron Resonance Studies

Following his work on the OH radical Radford [4] detected the spectra of the related radicals SH, SeH, and TeH. The spectra were detected by passing water vapor through a discharge and adding a second gas, H_2S, H_2Se, or H_2Te, to the discharge products prior to passage through the cavity. The electron resonance spectra are similar to that of OH, the main difference being the decreased Λ-doubling in the heavier hydrides.

Our own work commenced in 1965 and is essentially a development of that initiated by Radford. We use a continuous flow system in which atoms (O, H, N, F, etc.) generated by passing a primary gas through a microwave discharge are mixed with a secondary gas inside the spectrometer cavity. In our early experiments we employed a conventional TE_{011}-mode cylindrical cavity containing quartz cells and using 100-kHz magnetic field modulation. In more recent work we have used a cavity [5] which is designed to be vacuum-tight, thereby dispensing with the need for quartz inserts. Moreover, the end walls of this cavity, which again operates in the TE_{011} mode, are insulated from the cylinder body and can therefore be used as Stark plates for applied oscillating or static voltages. Electric field modulation at 100 kHz offers a number of advantages over magnetic field modulation, and the Stark splittings

produced by static electric fields make it possible to determine electric dipole moments [6].

In Fig. 6 we show the electron resonance spectra of the radicals ClO,

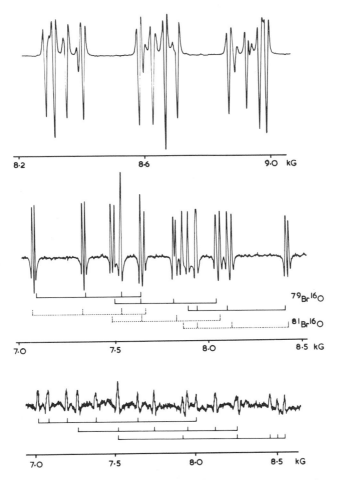

FIG. 6. Electron resonance spectra ($J = \frac{3}{2}$, $^2\Pi_{3/2}$) of ClO, BrO, and IO.

BrO, and IO. ClO was detected [7] simply by passing a Cl_2/O_2 mixture through a microwave discharge and then through the spectrometer cavity; BrO [8] and IO [8] were produced by mixing O atoms with Br_2 and CH_3I, respectively, inside the cavity. All three radicals have $^2\Pi_{3/2}$ ground electronic states and the electron resonance spectra arise from radicals in the lowest rotational level with $J = \frac{3}{2}$. The spectrum of ClO is representative of that obtained

from a number of $^2\Pi_{3/2}$, $J = \frac{3}{2}$ radicals and illustrates the information which can be obtained. The main features are as follows:

(a) The center of the spectrum corresponds to a g value very close to 4/5, the value predicted for Hund's case (a) coupling. The observed value is actually 0.793, the departure from 0.800 being due in the main to rotational mixing of the $^2\Pi_{3/2}$ and $^2\Pi_{1/2}$ fine structure states.

(b) The three groups arise from the three $\Delta M_J = \pm 1$ transitions shown in Fig. 7. As mentioned earlier the groups are separated because the Zeeman

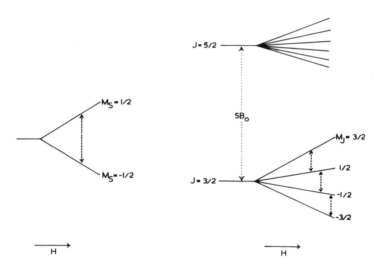

FIG. 7. $\Delta M_J = \pm 1$ transitions in a $J = \frac{3}{2}$ rotational level.

effect is not exactly linear; the magnetic field removes the $2J + 1$ degeneracy of the $J = \frac{3}{2}$ level and also couples $J = \frac{3}{2}$ to the next rotational level, $J = \frac{5}{2}$. Consequently, measurement of the separation between the groups yields the value of the rotational constant B_0.

(c) The quartet splittings in each group arise from magnetic hyperfine coupling to the ^{35}Cl and ^{37}Cl nuclei, each with spin $I = \frac{3}{2}$. The nuclear spin is coupled to the electron spin S via the Fermi contact interaction and the dipolar interaction, and also to the electron orbital motion L. In a good case (a) molecule the magnetic moments due to L and S lie along the internuclear axis; consequently, the spectrum shown in Fig. 6 yields the axial component of the total hyperfine coupling.

(d) The spacings between the hyperfine lines in the center group are essentially equal, but they are clearly unequal in the outer groups. This is due to the electric quadrupole interaction and determination of both the magni-

tude and sign of the ^{35}Cl and ^{37}Cl quadrupole coupling constants is straight-forward.

In contrast to the earlier example of OH, the Λ-doubling in ClO is smaller than the linewidth and therefore unresolved. However, application of a static electric field results in a first-order Stark splitting from which the electric dipole moment can be determined [6, 9].

At first sight the spectra of BrO and IO seem quite different from that of ClO, but they nevertheless possess the same major features. The triplet second-order Zeeman splitting is obscured by the much larger hyperfine and quadrupole splittings, but the analyses shown beneath the spectra show that their construction is similar to that of ClO, and the same molecular constants can be determined.

Most of the diatomic radicals studied by electron resonance have been $^{2}\Pi_{3/2}, J = \frac{3}{2}$ systems and we will say more about them when considering pure microwave studies. However, two other electronic states in diatomic radicals have been detected by electron resonance, namely $^{1}\Delta$ and $^{3}\Sigma$ states. The $^{1}\Delta_{2}$ excited states of O_2 [10], SO [11], and SeO [12], (which all have $^{3}\Sigma$ ground states) have been studied. In the lowest rotational level J is equal to 2 and an external magnetic field interacts with the magnetic moment arising from orbital angular momentum. Hence the ground state is split into five Zeeman components and the electron resonance spectrum consists of four $\Delta M_J = \pm 1$ transitions. As in the case of $^{2}\Pi_{3/2}, J = \frac{3}{2}$ states, the second-order Zeeman splitting of the four lines yields the rotational constant B_0, and application of a static electric field produces a first-order Stark splitting, from which the dipole moment can be deduced.

$^{3}\Sigma$ states present a situation somewhat different from that encountered in $^{2}\Pi$ states, in that there is no first-order spin–orbit coupling. Apart from molecular oxygen, the free radicals SO and SeO with $^{3}\Sigma$ ground states have now been studied by electron resonance and the types of spectra observed are best discussed in terms of the energy level diagrams shown in Fig. 8. Because of strong second-order spin–orbit coupling, SeO corresponds approximately to case (a) coupling and the observed transitions [12] ($\Delta J = 0$, $\Delta M_J = \pm 1$) arise from the $J = 1$ rotational level as indicated on the right-hand side of Fig. 8. Transitions shown with dotted lines are strictly electric-dipole-forbidden, but can be induced by applied electric fields and have been observed. The spin–orbit coupling in SO is much weaker and the radical therefore approximates to case (b) coupling [13]. The spectrum is considerably more complicated and transitions of the types $\Delta J = 0$, $\Delta K = 0$, ± 1, $\Delta M_J = 0$, ± 1 have been observed.

Table I lists all the diatomic radicals which have been studied by microwave or radiofrequency techniques. The pure microwave spectrum [14] of SO was detected at much the same time as the electron resonance spectrum; the microwave spectra of ClO [15], NS [16], BrO [17], and $^{1}\Delta$ SO [18] were

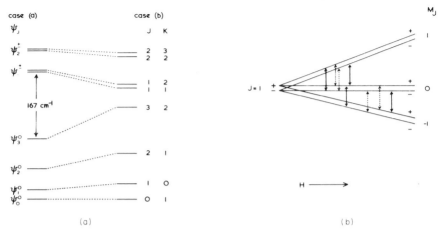

FIG. 8. (a) Lower rotational levels for $^3\Sigma$ states (SeO and SO), and (b) the electron resonance transitions in SeO.

TABLE I

HIGH-RESOLUTION STUDIES OF DIATOMIC MOLECULES IN OPEN-SHELL
ELECTRONIC STATES

Molecule	Electronic states	Spectrum	References
O$_2$	$^3\Sigma$, $^1\Delta$	(a, b)	29, 10
NO	$^2\Pi_{3/2}$, $^2\Pi_{1/2}$	(a, b)	30, 31
OH	$^2\Pi_{3/2}$, $^2\Pi_{1/2}$, A$^2\Sigma^+$	(a, b, d)	2, 3, 32, 25
SH	$^2\Pi_{3/2}$	(b)	4, 6, 9
SeH	$^2\Pi_{3/2}$	(b)	4, 33
TeH	$^2\Pi_{3/2}$	(b)	4
ClO	$^2\Pi_{3/2}$, $^2\Pi_{1/2}$	(b, a)	7, 15
BrO	$^2\Pi_{3/2}$, $^2\Pi_{1/2}$	(b, a)	8, 17
IO	$^2\Pi_{3/2}$	(b)	8
CF	$^2\Pi_{3/2}$	(b)	34
NS	$^2\Pi_{3/2}$, $^2\Pi_{1/2}$	(b, a)	35, 16, 9
SO	$^3\Sigma$, $^1\Delta$	(b, a)	14, 13, 37, 11, 18
SeO	$^3\Sigma$, $^1\Delta$	(b)	12
CO	$^3\Pi$	(c)	23
CS	$^1\Pi$	(d)	24
SF	$^2\Pi_{3/2}$	(b)	36, 9
SeF	$^2\Pi_{3/2}$	(b)	36, 9
CN	A $^2\Pi$, B $^2\Sigma^+$	(d)	26

^{a} Pure microwave.
^{b} Electron resonance.
^{c} Molecular beam.
^{d} Radio frequency/optical double resonance.

observed after the electron resonance studies, and the results obtained from the two methods are complementary. The main advantages to be gained from the pure microwave spectrum are as follows:

(a) The diamagnetic $^2\Pi_{1/2}$ states are accessible as well as the $^2\Pi_{3/2}$ states studied by electron resonance. This enables the hyperfine parameters to be more readily separated.

(b) The complications due to the strong magnetic field (which, for example, destroys **J** as a good quantum number) are absent and consequently the theoretical analysis of the spectra is much simpler.

(c) Frequencies can be measured more accurately than magnetic fields.

On the other hand, more free radicals have been detected by electron resonance, its compensating advantages being: (a) use of a high-Q resonant cavity which is smaller than a nonresonance waveguide cell and consequently easier to fill with short-lived free radicals; and (b) a much simpler "search" problem, in that even a relatively crude theory of the Zeeman effect will usually predict the required magnetic field strengths to within a few hundred gauss.

A recent development [19] has been the detection of the electron resonance spectra of two linear triatomic free radicals, NCO and NCS. These molecules are of particular interest since they have electronically degenerate ground

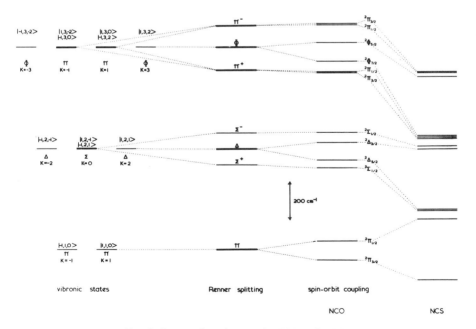

FIG. 9. Lower vibronic states in NCO and NCS.

states ($^2\Pi$), and therefore the coupling of electronic and bending vibrational angular momentum gives rise to the Renner effect. The vibronic (Renner) states can be characterized by the values of three quantum numbers, namely; Λ, the component of $\mathbf{L}$ along the linear axis ($\Lambda = \pm 1$); n, the vibrational quantum number associated with the bending vibration v_2 ($n = v_2 + 1$); and l, the component of vibrational angular momentum along the linear axis ($l = v_2, v_2 - 2, \ldots, -v_2$). A further characterization of the vibronic states is provided by the quantum number K, which is equal to $|\Lambda + l|$; vibronic states are labeled Σ, Π, Δ, Φ, etc. as $K = 0, 1, 2, 3$, etc. The energies of the lower vibronic states have been determined by Dixon [20] from analysis of the

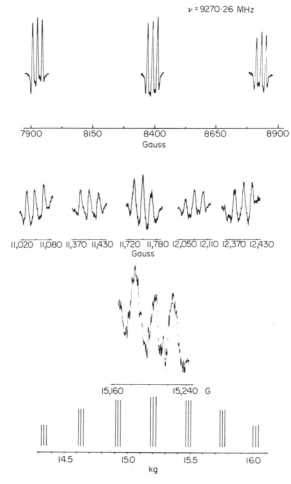

FIG. 10. Electron resonance spectra of NCO in the $J = \frac{3}{2}$, $^2\Pi_{3/2}$; $J = \frac{5}{2}$, $^2\Delta_{5/2}$; and $J = \frac{7}{2}$, $^2\Phi_{7/2}$ vibronic states.

ultraviolet spectrum and an energy level diagram is shown in Fig. 9. Clearly there exists the possibility of studying the electron resonance spectra of NCO in excited vibronic states and at the present time spectra of the ground $^2\Pi_{3/2}$ ($n = 1$) and excited $^2\Delta_{5/2}$ ($n = 2$) and $^2\Phi_{7/2}$ ($n = 3$) states have been described. The spectra are shown in Fig. 10, in each case for the lowest rotational level, with $J = \frac{3}{2}$, $\frac{5}{2}$, and $\frac{7}{2}$, respectively. Subsequently the pure microwave spectra of the $n = 1$ $^2\Pi_{3/2}$ and $^2\Pi_{1/2}$ states have been reported [21].

The most interesting result of the electron resonance studies has been the observation of an anomalous contribution to the Zeeman effect. For good case (a) coupling the first-order g values for the $^2\Pi_{3/2}$, $^2\Delta_{5/2}$, and $^2\Phi_{7/2}$ states are readily calculated to be $\frac{4}{5}$ ($= 0.800$), $\frac{4}{7}$ (0.571), and $\frac{4}{9}$ (0.444). The experimental values are close to these values (0.791, 0.564, and 0.436, respectively), but after taking account of all the higher-order corrections which are well-understood from the studies of diatomic species, there remains an anomalous contribution to the g value. This contribution is found to be essentially linear in the vibrational quantum number n, and a detailed theoretical investigation [19] indicates that the g-value anomaly actually represents a partial quenching of the orbital angular momentum due to vibrational mixing of excited electronic states with the ground state. The theory also shows that the g-value anomaly is closely related to the Renner coupling constant ε. If present searches for the spectra of other excited vibronic states are successful, particularly the $n = 2$, $^2\Sigma$ and $n = 3$, $^2\Pi$ states, it should be possible to unravel many as yet poorly understood aspects of the Renner coupling. Observation of the pure microwave spectra of excited vibronic states of NCO would also be of great interest.

4. Molecular-Beam and RF/Optical Double-Resonance Methods

The molecular-beam magnetic resonance method of studying atoms is so important that it is surprising that, to the author's knowledge, no studies of short-lived, open-shell ground-state molecular species have yet been reported. We are at present constructing apparatus in an attempt to detect free radicals in their ground states, and we will consider the possible merits of such experiments later. However, successful experiments on open-shell excited states have been carried out and although they are few in number as yet, their potential importance is considerable.

The first successful experiment was that of Lichten [22], who studied a metastable excited electronic state of H_2, the $c(1\sigma_g, 1\pi_u)$ $^3\Pi_u$ state, which lies approximately 12 eV above the ground state. Lichten's apparatus is illustrated in Fig. 11; a beam of H_2 molecules emerges from the source and some are excited to the $^3\Pi$ state by electron bombardment. The figure shows a typical molecular trajectory, the molecule first passing through an inhomogeneous dipole magnetic field (A), which deflects it as shown if it is in a

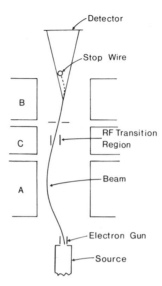

FIG. 11. Molecular-beam apparatus used in the study of $H_2(^3\Pi)$ [22].

particular desired quantum state. A second dipole field B is then arranged so that the molecule follows the dotted trajectory to reach a stop wire, which prevents it from passing onward to the detector. However, between the A and B magnets is located a third magnet C which is homogeneous and in which radiofrequency or microwave transitions can be induced by passing the beam through a coil or cavity. If a transition occurs, the quantum state of the molecule changes and the conditions of the B magnet, which previously refocused the molecule on to the stop wire, now cause it to miss the stop wire and reach the detector. The detector used by Lichten was a nickel secondary electron emission detector with an electrometer amplifier. Hence the radiofrequency spectrum is obtained by plotting the electrometer current as a function of the radio frequency for various fixed values of the magnetic C field. Lichten actually studied the fine structure transitions $J = 2 \leftrightarrow J = 3$ and $J = 2 \leftrightarrow J = 1$ in the $N = 2$ rotational level of para-hydrogen at frequencies between 5000 and 6000 MHz, and made measurements of the Zeeman effect. Thus the type of spectroscopy he performed is very similar to that described in Section 3, but the techniques are quite different. Klemperer and Freund [23] have carried out similar molecular-beam investigations of CO in its excited a $^3\Pi$ state, the main differences being that they used electric deflecting fields and a homogeneous electric C field.

Electron resonance or pure microwave studies of excited metastable states suffer from the fact that at the pressures used, the excited-state lifetimes are determined by collision frequencies; molecular-beam studies simply require

that the radiative lifetime be longer than the flight time in the beam chamber. In principle, molecular-beam methods should be suitable for studying free radicals in their ground states, the main problem to be overcome being that of beam intensity. Metastable excited electronic states are particularly suitable candidates for molecular-beam studies because they can be detected with high efficiency using surface ionization detectors. However, for ground-state molecules it is usually necessary to use mass spectrometric detection, which is two or three orders of magnitude less efficient. It remains to be seen if this handicap can be overcome, but an encouraging feature is that the sensitivity is independent of whether the transitions detected are magnetic- or electric-dipole-allowed. Since one is not attempting to measure directly the absorption of electromagnetic radiation in a beam experiment, the only requirement is to have sufficient radiofrequency or microwave power available to approach saturation.

An exciting recent development has been the study of radiofrequency–optical double resonance. An excellent example which illustrates the important features is the study of CS by Silvers et al. [24]. The energy level diagram shown in Fig 12 is somewhat oversimplified but will serve to explain the principles. CS in the $J = 7$ rotational level of its $^1\Sigma$ ground state is excited to one of the Λ-doublet components of the $J = 8$ rotational level of the $^1\Pi$ excited

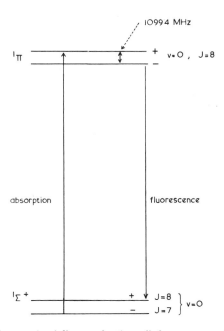

FIG. 12. Simplified energy level diagram for the radiofrequency–optical double-resonance study of CS ($^1\Pi$).

electronic state. Excitation is accomplished by means of an atomic manganese emission line which has the correct wavelength. Fluorescence back to the $J = 8$ rotational level is parity-forbidden, but if the Λ-doublet transition is pumped (the required pumping frequency being 1099.4 MHz), fluorescence to the $J = 8$ level from the $(-)$-parity Λ-doublet component is allowed. Hence the experimental procedure is to monitor the fluorescence intensity while sweeping the radio frequency until resonance occurs. In practice more than one ground-state rotational level is involved, and whether resonance results in an increase or decrease in fluorescence intensity depends upon the finer details of the experiment. The principles should be clear from Fig. 12, and the experimental arrangement used by Silvers *et al.* is illustrated in Fig. 13.

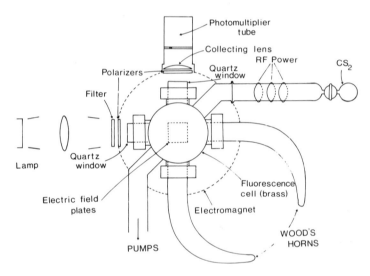

FIG. 13. Fluorescence cell used in the study of CS ($^1\Pi$) [24].

It should be noted that the $^1\Pi$-state lifetime is only 2×10^{-7} sec. Nevertheless, it is possible to make high-resolution measurements of Zeeman and Stark effects in the $^1\Pi$ state. Very similar experiments have been carried out by German and Zare [25], who have studied hyperfine transitions in the excited A $^2\Sigma^+$ state of OH. They use a fixed frequency in the range 1–8 MHz and tune pairs of levels to resonance by sweeping a magnetic field.

These double-resonance experiments have an interesting precursor in the work of Evenson *et al.* [26] on the CN radical. The reaction of N atoms with CH_2Cl_2 produces CN almost exclusively in the excited A $^2\Pi$ state, the ground state being X $^2\Sigma^+$. It happens that the $v = 10$ levels of the A $^2\Pi_{3/2}$ state are very close to the $v = 0$ levels of a second excited state, the B $^2\Sigma^+$ state. Transitions between the two states can be induced by pumping at a microwave

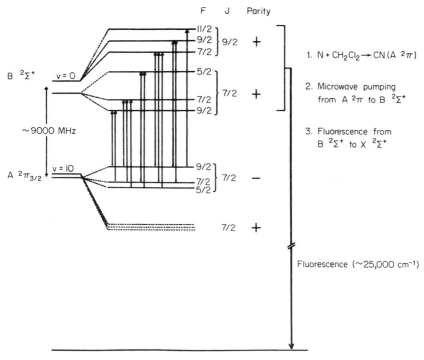

FIG. 14. Energy level diagram illustrating the microwave–optical double-resonance stud of CN [26].

frequency, and monitored by observation of the B $^2\Sigma^+ \rightarrow$ X $^2\Sigma^+$ fluorescence. The transitions studied are illustrated in Fig. 14 and the "microwave spectrum" is shown in Fig. 15. The spectrum, of course, provides information about the rotational levels of both excited electronic states. A natural question to ask is whether this type of experiment can be performed on other radicals. One of the authors concerned has been heard to state publicly that "this is a very general experiment that can be performed on just one molecule!." The six years which have elapsed since the work was described have certainly not contradicted that assessment. On the other hand, there seems little doubt that the experiments on OH and CS using radiofrequency–optical double-resonance are only the first of many.

Finally, we must refer to the recent beautiful and novel work of Jefferts [27] on the radiofrequency spectrum of H_2^+. Molecular hydrogen at a pressure of 5×10^{-9} Torr is subjected to electron impact to form H_2^+ in its (1s σ) ground state. The H_2^+ is in turn irradiated with an intense light beam to form $H_2^+(2p\,\sigma)$, which dissociates into H + H⁺. The ratio of H⁺ to H_2^+(1s σ) concentration is monitored, and observed to change when the H_2^+(1s σ) is subjected to a radiofrequency field which induces proton

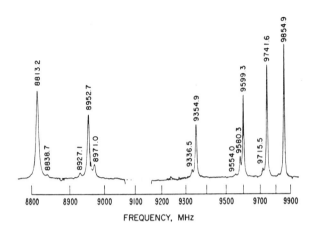

FIG. 15. Microwave–optical double-resonance spectrum of CN [26] at a pressure of 0.5 mm Hg with 0.3-W microwave power. Corrections for drift in the microwave power and frequency are shown by dotted lines. Deviations from dotted line are due to variations in the klystron's power level and frequency caused by manual readjustment of the various instrumental parameters during the frequency scan. The microwave power was accidentally allowed to nearly double at about 9830, causing the signallike blip at that frequency.

hyperfine transitions. Jefferts has recorded hyperfine transitions in the $K = 1$ and $K = 2$ rotational levels of the $v = 4$–8 vibrational levels, using frequencies in the range 4–1300 MHz and obtaining linewidths as small as 200 Hz.

5. Conclusions and Possible Future Developments

The main conclusion of this review is that there is at present no single best method for the high-resolution study of open-shell electronic states. The electron resonance method has been the most successful up to now, but even so, progress has been slow. All our electron resonance experiments have utilized atom–molecule reactions as the source of free radicals, and there is clearly scope for thermochemical and photochemical experiments. Our efforts to build a sensitive, high-temperature ($\sim 1000°C$) cavity have had discouraging results, and we are now attempting to use continuous ultraviolet photolysis as a means of producing detectable concentrations of free radicals.

It is important to note that electron resonance studies have so far been restricted to linear molecules with unquenched orbital angular momentum. The ability to tune appropriate energy levels with an applied magnetic field depends on the presence of large magnetic moments from orbital and spin angular momenta. If there is to be an allowed electric dipole transition between magnetically tunable pairs of levels, the electron spin must necessarily

be quantized in the molecular frame of reference, and this requirement is usually met by the presence of strong spin–orbit coupling. In most nonlinear radicals, however, the orbital angular momentum is almost completely quenched, and the spin is then decoupled from the molecule by relatively small magnetic fields. Under these conditions the electron resonance transitions have magnetic dipole intensity only, and will consequently be rather weak. It is going to be difficult, therefore, to obtain electron resonance spectra from nonlinear radicals, partly because the transitions are only magnetic-dipole-allowed, and partly because of much larger rotational partition functions.

Pure microwave methods suffer from the second limitation, but not the first. If the molecule possesses an electric dipole moment, a pure microwave electric dipole spectrum is, in principle, detectable. The search for the spectrum is often likely to be tedious and requires sustained confidence. Nevertheless, the relative success in recent years should encourage further efforts in this field.

Radiofrequency–optical double-resonance methods look to be particularly promising for the study of excited electronic states. There might be a small doubt over the generality of these methods, since the experiments on CS and OH seem to require that some rather specific conditions be satisfied. The availability of a tunable ultraviolet laser would clearly do much to stimulate double-resonance studies, but even without it, this is a field of much promise.

Molecular-beam methods are also well suited to the study of excited electronic states, but it remains to be seen whether ground-state free radicals can be detected with sufficient sensitivity to enable spectroscopic measurements to be made. Beams of methyl radicals were detected [28] as long ago as 1937, giving the author, at least, some reason for optimism.

Many research groups are at present engaged in studies of the type described in this review; it will be surprising if Table I is not incomplete by the time this chapter is published.

ACKNOWLEDGMENT

I should like to thank Dr. J. M. Brown for many interesting discussions on the topics reviewed in this paper.

References

1. G. Porter, *Proc. Roy. Soc. Ser. A* **200**, 284 (1950).
2. G. C. Dousmanis, T. M. Sanders and C. H. Townes, *Phys. Rev.* **100**, 1735 (1955).
3. H. E. Radford, *Phys. Rev.* **122**, 114 (1961); **126**, 1035 (1962).
4. H. E. Radford, *J. Chem. Phys.* **40**, 2732 (1964).
5. A. Carrington, D. H. Levy, and T. A. Miller, *Rev. Sci. Instr.* **38**, 1183 (1967).
6. A. Carrington, D. H. Levy, and T. A. Miller, *J. Chem. Phys.* **47**, 3801 (1967).
7. A. Carrington, P. N. Dyer, and D. H. Levy, *J. Chem. Phys.* **47**, 1756 (1967).

8. A. Carrington, P. N. Dyer, and D. H. Levy, *J. Chem. Phys.* **52**, 309 (1970).
9. C. R. Byfleet, A. Carrington, and D. K. Russell, *Mol. Phys.*
10. A. M. Falick, B. H. Mahan, and R. J. Myers, *J. Chem. Phys.* **42**, 1837 (1965).
11. A. Carrington, D. H. Levy, and T. A. Miller, *Proc. Roy. Soc. Ser. A* **293**, 108 (1966).
12. A. Carrington, G. N. Currie, D. H. Levy, and T. A. Miller, *Mol. Phys.* **17**, 535 (1969).
13. A. Carrington, D. H. Levy, and T. A. Miller, *Proc. Roy. Soc. Ser. A* **298**, 340 (1967); J. M. Daniels and P. B. Dorain, *J. Chem. Phys.* **45**, 26 (1966).
14. T. Amano, E. Hirota, and Y. Morino, *J. Phys. Soc. Jap.* **22**, 399 (1967); F. X. Powell and D. R. Lide, *J. Chem. Phys.* **41**, 1413 (1964); M. Winnewisser, K. V. L. N. Sastry, R. L. Cook, and W. Gordy, *Ibid.* **41**, 1687 (1964).
15. T. Amano, S. Saito, Y. Morino, D. R. Johnson, and F. X. Powell, *J. Mol. Spectrosc.* **30**, 275 (1969).
16. T. Amano, S. Saito, and E. Hirota, *J. Mol. Spectrosc.* **32**, 97 (1969).
17. F. X. Powell and D. R. Johnson, *J. Chem. Phys.* **50**, 4596 (1969).
18. S. Saito, Private communication
19. A. Carrington, A. R. Fabris, and N. J. D. Lucas, *J. Chem. Phys.* **49**, 5545 (1968); A. Carrington, A. R. Fabris, and N. J. D. Lucas, *Mol. Phys.* **16**, 195 (1969); A. Carrington, A. R. Fabris, B. J. Howard, and N. J. D. Lucas, *Ibid.*
20. R. N. Dixon, *Phil. Trans. Roy. Soc. London Ser. A* **252**, 165 (1960).
21. S. Saito and T. Amano, *J. Mol. Spectrosc.* **34**, 383 (1970).
22. W. Lichten, *Phys. Rev.* **120**, 848 (1960); **126**, 1020 (1962).
23. W. Klemperer and R. S. Freund, *J. Chem. Phys.* **43**, 2422 (1965).
24. S. J. Silvers, T. H. Bergemann, and W. Klemperer, *J. Chem. Phys.* **52**, 4385 (1970).
25. K. German and R. Zare, *Phys. Rev. Lett.* **23**, 1207 (1969).
26. K. Evenson, J. Dunn, and H. Broida, *Phys. Rev. A* **136**, 1566 (1964).
27. K. B. Jefferts, *Phys. Rev. Lett.* **23**, 1476 (1969).
28. R. G. J. Fraser and T. N. Jewitt, *Proc. Roy. Soc. Ser. A* **160**, 563 (1937).
29. M. Tinkham and M. W. P. Strandberg, *Phys. Rev.* **97**, 937, 951 (1955).
30. R. Beringer and J. G. Castle, *Phys. Rev.* **78**, 581 (1950).
31. C. C. Lin and M. Mizushima, *Phys. Rev.* **100**, 1726 (1955).
32. A. Carrington and N. J. D. Lucas, *Proc. Roy. Soc. Ser. A* **314**, 567 (1970).
33. A. Carrington, G. N. Currie, and N. J. D. Lucas, *Proc. Roy. Soc. Ser A* **315**, 355 (1970).
34. A. Carrington and B. J. Howard, *Mol. Phys.* **18**, 225 (1970).
35. A. Carrington, B. J. Howard, D. H. Levy, and J. C. Robertson, *Mol. Phys.* **15**, 187 (1968).
36. A. Carrington, G. N. Currie, T. A. Miller, and D. H. Levy, *J. Chem. Phys.* **50**, 2726 (1969).
37. A. Carrington, D. H. Levy, and T. A. Miller, *Mol. Phys.* **13**, 401 (1967).

2.3 Information on Rotational Energy Transfer from Microwave Line Broadening[†]

James E. Boggs

Department of Chemistry
The University of Texas
Austin, Texas

When one rotating molecule approaches another, its energy states are perturbed by the force fields of the second molecule. Electric, magnetic, and gravitational interactions are possible, but the electric interactions are far more significant than the others. If the interaction is sufficiently strong, rotational energy is transferred during the collision and the quantum states of the molecules after the collision are different than they were initially. Of primary interest is the fact that relatively long-range forces are involved, so that the transfer of rotational energy during molecular collisions serves as a probe of the molecular field out to distances much greater than can be examined by kinetic theory studies of the transfer of translational energy. Aside from its intrinsic interest in gaining a deeper understanding of molecular force fields, the study of rotational energy transfer has practical applications to radar propagation through the atmosphere of the earth and other planets, to aeronomy, to the study of gas-phase kinetics, and to other fields.

Several experimental techniques are available for the study of rotational energy transfer, but they all appear to share the common characteristics of being difficult, indirect, and incompletely understood. Several of these methods are discussed in this volume and the recent, elegant double-resonance experiments by Oka [1] are particularly noteworthy. In this chapter, however, I will restrict my attention to what has now become nearly a classical technique, the broadening of microwave absorption lines.

The width of a rotational absorption line is affected by many factors, including molecular collisions, collisions with the wall, the Doppler effect, natural line broadening, and various types of modulation purposely or accidentally introduced by the spectrometer used. Under appropriate condi-

† This work has been supported in part by The National Science Foundation and in part by The Robert A. Welch Foundation.

tions of observation, the most important of these is the effect of molecular collisions, and it can be separated from the others because it is the only pressure-dependent term. A series of linewidth measurements is made at different pressures, and the slope of the straight line obtained by plotting Δv (the line half-width at the half-power points) against the pressure is taken as the line-broadening parameter, sometimes loosely referred to as the linewidth.

On the theoretical side, the Hamiltonian of an absorbing molecule being disturbed by a collision with another molecule can be written

$$\mathscr{H} = \mathscr{H}^0 + V(t)$$

where $\mathscr{H}^0$ is the Hamiltonian of the isolated molecule and $V(t)$ represents the time-dependent interaction potential. The problem may be approached using a perturbation treatment, as was done by Anderson [2] or by means of the density matrix approach used by Murphy [3]. In either case the translational motion is treated classically and attention has been restricted to bimolecular collisions, the latter being a very good approximation at the low pressures used in the observations. Murphy's treatment is rigorous except for the neglect of higher-order terms in an expansion of the diagonal matrix elements [3, Eq. 31]. The argument is made that these terms are negligible since they are very small unless $V(t)$ is large. If $V(t)$ is large, the transition probability is nearly unity anyway on the basis of the terms that are retained. In a pictorial sense, the approximation considers only direct transitions out of the nth level, ignoring transitions of the type $n \rightarrow m \rightarrow k \rightarrow \cdots$. In particular, it ignores the probability of the molecule making a transition back to the nth level once it has left it and, for this reason, tends to overestimate the transition probability. This approximation is emphasized here since the treatment is otherwise an accurate development of the model on which it is based. Any lack of agreement with observation must be attributed to this approximation, to an inadequate expression for $V(t)$, or as an indication that the original model is inadequate.

A comparison of calculations based on Murphy's theory with those from Anderson's theory is shown in Fig. 1. The probability that a molecule of OCS in the state $J = 1$ will no longer be in that state after collision with an OCS molecule in the state $J = 10$ is plotted against the distance of closest approach of the two molecules. Anderson's theory agrees with the more accurate result at long distances, where $V(t)$ never becomes large, as a perturbation treatment should. As the molecules approach more closely, however, the probability exhibits the disconcerting feature of going to infinity rather than approaching unity. Anderson suggested several methods for rounding off the corner, but the most common approach has been to extend the curve until it reaches the point B and then to assume unit probability for energy transfer between A and B. The difference between the Murphy and

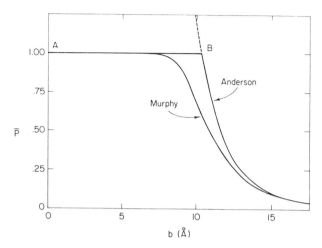

FIG. 1. The probability of an OCS molecule making the transition $J = 1 \rightarrow 2$ as a result of colliding with an OCS molecule in state $J = 10$ as a function of distance of closest approach, calculated according to Anderson and according to Murphy.

the Anderson treatments is considerably greater for some other molecules than it is for OCS. Incidentally, the kinetic theory diameter for OCS is about 4 Å, so the greater range of the forces responsible for rotational energy transfer can be seen, together with some justification for a straight-line, classical treatment of the translational motion.

The effect of any diffuse system of electric charge can be expressed in a multipole expansion and the interaction between such charge systems can be expressed in terms of multipole interactions; dipole–dipole, dipole–quadrupole, quadrupole–induced dipole, etc. The interaction energy $V(t)$, then, may be expressed in such terms, the convenience of the expression depending on how rapidly the series converges. It is customary to include all terms through r^{-6} in the interaction potential and hope that shorter-range terms are insignificant, although there are many calculations in the earlier literature in which significant terms have been omitted.

As indicated, the first step in the theoretical prediction of rotational linewidths involves calculating the probability that a molecule will undergo a transition out of a given rotational state when it passes at some velocity a certain distance from another molecule in a given rotational state. Next, the result is averaged over the Boltzmann distribution of molecular velocities, over all distances of closest approach, and over all rotational states of the collision partner, weighted according to their populations at the chosen temperature. A similar calculation is performed for the final state of the transition and the width of the line can be obtained by adding the two terms.

The objective of experimental measurements of rotational linewidths is to

test theories of energy transfer during molecular collisions. The experiments, unfortunately, represent complicated averages of collisions with molecules in various rotational states and various relative velocities and distances of closest approach rather than individual events. Furthermore, the experiments are not highly accurate, so that most measured linewidths must be viewed with a certain degree of caution. For this reason, rather extensive comparisons between theory and experiment are necessary, since it would be quite possible to have completely fortuitous agreement in a few isolated cases. While agreement between theory and experiment cannot show the correctness of a given model, lack of agreement can demonstrate the inadequacy of the understanding incorporated in the model. It is important, therefore, to test any model for the collision process by actual computation of linewidths for a wide variety of cases.

The only model for the transfer of rotational energy that has been extensively tested by comparison with measured linewidths is that which is incorporated in the developments of Anderson [2] and of Murphy [3]. These two treatments do differ markedly in their approach and in their accuracy (the Anderson result sometimes being 25% larger than either the Murphy result or the experimental measurement [4]), but they are both based on the model of broadening due to collision-induced transitions with a classical treatment of translation. How well, then, does this model predict the results that are observed experimentally?

The most straightforward test comes from the study of symmetric-top molecules, since it can be shown [4] that broadening due to a symmetric top arises almost entirely from dipole–dipole interactions, so that the required molecular parameters are well known. The results which have been published [4] will not be reproduced here, but in general the agreement is within the range of experimental error, perhaps 2–5%. This result is certainly encouraging.

For line broadening in which the incident molecule is linear, other shorter-range forces become important. All of the interaction terms through r^{-6} in the potential can be taken into account without difficulty except for the fact that molecular quadrupole moments, in general, are very poorly known. The procedure used [5] was to adopt an interaction potential including all terms through r^{-6} but using the molecular quadrupole moment as an adjustable parameter in fitting the calculated linewidths. Most of the quadrupole moments obtained in this way appear to be quite reasonable compared with other independent determinations, although the check is only approximate because of the inaccuracies in other methods for determining quadrupole moments. The best comparison is for the $J = 1 \rightarrow 2$ transition of OCS, which has been measured carefully by more independent observers than any other rotational transition. The widths obtained at room temperature agree to about $\pm 2\%$. The quadrupole moment of OCS is also known more accurately than that of most other molecules on the basis of recent Zeeman effect measurements

[6], which appear to be of good quality. If the microwave linewidth is calculated using the Zeeman effect value of the quadrupole moment, the result is about 8 % lower than the average measured width. It is not certain that this is outside the combined uncertainties of the experiments; if it is, it may simply indicate that interactions of shorter range than r^{-6} must be considered. Of course, it might also indicate that the theory is inadequate.

The effect of various terms in the interaction potential can be clearly seen in Figs. 2–4. Figure 2 shows the transition probability for CH_3Cl, a symmetric top, as a function of distance of closest approach. Each curve except

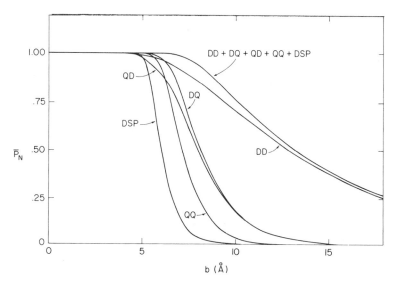

Fig. 2. Plot of the average transition probability per collision against impact parameter for the $J, K = 0, 0$ level of CH_3Cl at 297°K.

the outer one shows the transition probability if only a single term in the interaction potential, as labeled in each case, were operative. The outermost curve shows the combined effect of all of the terms considered simultaneously. As mentioned previously, dipole–dipole interactions are dominant for broadening by symmetric-top molecules and this effect alone accounts for nearly the entire width. Since the quadrupole moment of CH_3Cl is not well known, the possibly unrealistically large value of 8.3 D · Å was used in these calculations so that interactions involving the quadrupole moment may be even less significant than shown.

For the self-broadening of N_2O the situation is quite different, as indicated in Fig. 3. Here the dipole moment is so small that any interaction involving it is negligible and the quadrupole–quadrupole interaction predominates with some small contribution from dispersion. As shown in Fig. 4, OCS presents

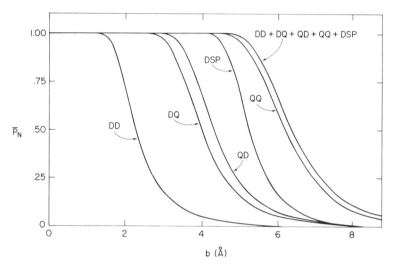

FIG. 3. Plot of the average transition probability per collision against impact parameter for the $J = 0$ level of N_2O at 297°K.

an interesting case in that all of the interaction terms considered are significant, although the dipole–dipole term contributes most. The calculations leading to Fig. 4 used a quadrupole moment for OCS required to fit the calculated linewidth to the average of the linewidths measured by various investigators. If the quadrupole moment obtained by the Zeeman effect measurements were used, all of the quadrupole interactions would be somewhat less significant.

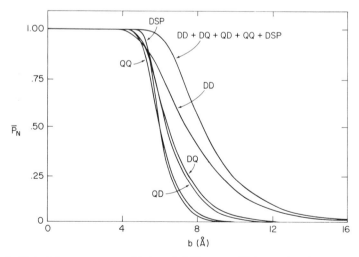

FIG. 4. Plot of the average transition probability per collision against impact parameter for the $J = 1$ level of OCS at 297°K.

Since the dispersion interaction is so important for OCS, it may well be that even steeper interactions should also be considered.

It may be well to point out the misleading character of many of the quadrupole moment determinations existing in the literature based on microwave linewidth measurements. Most of these have made use of the Anderson development of the impact model, which overestimates the linewidth from 5 to 25% for reasons described above. In many cases, significant terms in the interaction potential have been omitted, as for example the dispersion interaction in the case of OCS, which contributes about 8% to the linewidth. Since the quadrupole interactions contribute only about 5% to the OCS linewidth, their effect is completely lost and any value obtained for the quadrupole moment is clearly meaningless. Even if all significant terms in the interaction potential are considered, any determination making use of the Anderson formalism must be considered inaccurate.

There are cases for which interaction terms of power greater than r^{-6} appear to be needed. Since atoms have neither dipole nor quadrupole moments, the only terms through r^{-6} available for the broadening of OCS transitions by inert gases are dipole–induced dipole and dispersion interactions. Even here, however, the calculated results are only about 10% below the measured widths [5]. Similar effects are found for the self-broadening of O_2 and the broadening of O_2 lines by N_2 and inert gases [7]. Although experimental measurements of these parameters exhibit a great deal of scatter, the calculated values appear to be low by 10–50%. With the possible exception of OCS self-broadening, there appears to be no case where the need for shorter-range terms is convincing unless one of the collision partners is an atom or both partners have zero dipole moment.

The calculation of linewidths has also been extended to the general case of asymmetric-top molecules with reasonable success [8]. In some cases the agreement is excellent and one is led to have faith in the adequacy of the theory. In a few cases the calculated and measured values do not agree as well as should be expected, but the nature of linewidth measurements seems to be such that one should not place too great confidence in the results of one experiment. It is discouraging to learn of recent unpublished measurements by two presumably competent investigators using similar techniques on the same line that differ by 50%.

It might next be worthwhile to look at a few cases for which the original theory is clearly inadequate. The direct application of the theory as outlined above to the self-broadening of NH_3 transitions leads to results that average about 15% higher than the experimental values (use of the Anderson formalism leads to still higher values, of course). The difficulty arises from the special energy level pattern of the NH_3 molecule, which has closely spaced pairs of inversion doublet levels widely separated from similar pairs for other rotational levels. This extreme pairing of levels violates the conditions neces-

sary for the validity of the approximation made in the theory that, in effect, neglects transitions of the type $n \to m \to n$. The theory has been modified for this special case [9], although it is still not possible to give a general treatment. The results for NH_3 self-broadening appear to agree with experiment within the somewhat large uncertainty of the data.

The impact theory of rotational energy transfer fails completely when applied to pure rotational transitions that fall in the infrared region of the spectrum. For the $1_{1,0} \to 2_{2,1}$ transition of the H_2O molecule, for example, the predicted width is only 40% of the observed width. This failure is not unexpected, since purely adiabatic collisions in which energy transfer is ignored have been shown [10] to account reasonably well for the width of such lines. Some deviations between theory and experiment noted in the millimeter region of the spectrum have been attributed to this effect [11], but it is not yet clear how high in frequency the impact theory is applicable.

If it is assumed that the impact theory gives an acceptably accurate representation of the energy transfer process responsible for line broadening in the microwave region, one may look to the theory for details of the collisional interaction that have not yet been observed experimentally or that have been observed by other types of experiment. It automatically follows from the development of the theory that collisional energy transfer must follow selection rules which are the same as the electromagnetic selection rules; dipole selection rules if $V(t)$ contains dipole interactions, quadrupole selection rules if there are quadrupole interactions, etc. Since dipole–dipole interactions always predominate if the molecules have any appreciable dipole moment, the dipole selection rules, $\Delta J = \pm 1, 0$, are the most important. The contribution of quadrupole selection rules can be calculated without difficulty, but a problem arises in that it is not yet certain to what extent ignoring higher-order terms, i.e., ignoring collisions of the type $n \to m \to k$, may invalidate the results. If the contribution of such collisions is small compared with the $\Delta J = \pm 2$ transitions obtained directly by quadrupole selection rules, the straightforward calculation may be adequate. The existence of selection rules during molecular collisions has been demonstrated in a more direct way by the experiments of Dr. Oka and others [1].

One may also see to what extent the old idea of "rotational resonance" has meaning. Figure 5 shows a plot of the partial half-width of three levels of formaldehyde as a function of the J quantum number of the colliding molecule. It can be seen that collision partners in rotational states near the observed one are most effective in energy transfer, but that appreciable contributions come from states far removed in energy. The zigzag effect seen in portions of these curves comes from the effect of the nuclear statistical weights.

Looking to the future, more accurate linewidth measurements are badly needed to test theories of energy transfer. The literature contains a large amount of inaccurate data, presumably indicating the ease of succumbing to

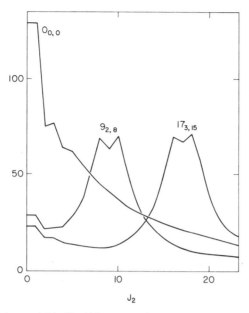

Fig. 5. Plot of the partial half-width, averaged over all values of K_2^- and K_2^+, as a function of J_2 for three levels of H_2CO at $300°K$.

one or more of the many sources of error in the experiment. In view of this, it may be well to do the experiment as simply as possible but to do it very well. The most common technique at present involves the use of double or triple modulation in the spectrometer, presentation of the derivative of the line shape, and measurement of the frequency separation between the inflection points. Perhaps it would be better to observe the line shape directly and digitally fit the line-shape function to the observed curve, using the peak height, width, and possibly the center frequency as adjustable parameters. Aside from considerations of simplicity, this makes use of all of the available data rather than utilizing only two points on the curve. Olson [12] has shown the feasibility of this method and several laboratories are actively developing it. For good results, extreme stability and reproducibility are required in the spectrometer.

One phenomenon that has received little attention is collision-induced shifts in the center frequency of a rotational absorption line. The prediction of such effects comes directly from phase shift effects in the impact theory [3], and such frequency shifts have indeed been observed for NH_3 transitions in a maser [13]. The observed effects are very small and they offer a particularly challenging test to any theory purporting to reflect an understanding of collisional processes, since the frequency shift arises from the difference in terms for the two levels rather than their sum and consequently requires high

accuracy in evaluation. Of particular interest is the fact that the observed effect may be more prominent in distortion of the line shape than it is in the direct shift in the center frequency. If the effect has any appreciable magnitude at all, it would limit the accuracy of linewidth measurements made by the derivative method, which assumes a symmetric line.

The degree of broadening as well as the extent of shift of the center frequency of an energy level depend on the quantum state of the molecule with which it collides. Theory indicates that the combined result is an asymmetric shift of broader lines in one direction, leading to distortion of the line shape. There is no experimental confirmation of this whatsoever; in fact, there is no published observation of a shift in the line center frequency as seen by conventional microwave techniques. The effects should be small, but it is hoped that they can be observed with an ultrastable spectrometer equipped for digital recording of the line shape.

Different theoretical approaches to the interpretation of microwave linewidths based on different models of the molecular interaction problem are possible. In view of the extensive averaging required for comparison with the experimental data and the mediocre quality of much of that data, it is to be hoped that new theoretical approaches will be accompanied by extensive computational work to allow comparison between theory and experiment over a wide range of conditions.

References

1. T. Oka, *Can. J. Phys.* **47**, 2343 (1969); P. W. Daly and T. Oka, *J. Chem. Phys.* **53**, 3272 (1970).
2. P. W. Anderson, *Phys. Rev.* **76**, 647 (1949); C. J. Tsao and B. Curnutte, *J. Quant. Spectrosc. Radiat. Transfer* **2**, 41 (1962).
3. J. S. Murphy and J. E. Boggs, *J. Chem. Phys.* **47**, 691 (1967).
4. J. S. Murphy and J. E. Boggs, *J. Chem. Phys.* **47**, 4152 (1967).
5. J. S. Murphy and J. E. Boggs, *J. Chem. Phys.* **49**, 3333 (1968).
6. W. H. Flygare, W. Hüttner, R. L. Shoemaker, and P. D. Foster, *J. Chem. Phys.* **50**, 1714 (1969); F. H. deLeeuw and A. Dymanus, *Symp. Mol. Struct. Spectrosc., Columbus, Ohio, 1969*, Paper R6. Columbus, Ohio (1969).
7. J. S. Murphy and J. E. Boggs, *J. Chem. Phys.* **54**, 2443 (1971).
8. J. S. Murphy and J. E. Boggs, *J. Chem. Phys.* **51**, 3891 (1969).
9. J. S. Murphy and J. E. Boggs, *J. Chem. Phys.* **50**, 3320 (1969).
10. E. Lindholm, *Ark. Mat. Astron. Fys.* **32**, 17 (1945); H. M. Foley, *Phys. Rev.* **69**, 616 (1946).
11. G. Birnbaum, E. R. Cohen, and J. R. Rusk, *J. Chem. Phys.* **49**, 5150 (1968).
12. D. S. Olson, Ph.D. Dissertation, Univ. of Texas, Austin, Texas, 1970.
13. K. Matsuura, Y. Sugiura, and J. Hatoyama, *J. Phys. Soc. Jap.* **11**, 1301L (1956).

2.4 Rotational Spectra of Molecules with Two Internal Degrees of Freedom

H. Dreizler

Institut für Physikalische Chemie
Abt. Chemische Physik
Universität Kiel
Kiel, Germany

This contribution is limited to a discussion of rotational spectra of free molecules exhibiting two low-energy internal motions. This restriction is made in view of the limited experimental information presently available, and for the sake of relative simplicity in the theoretical analysis. The essential interactions between the two internal motions and the overall rotation will be considered, thus providing a basis for the possible inclusion of more internal motions.

For the analysis of the rotational spectra we introduce a molecular model with five degrees of freedom, three of overall rotation and two of internal motion. This procedure is necessarily an approximation, a fact which should be kept in mind. In doing this it is assumed that there is only a weak coupling to the remaining $(3N - 8)$ internal degrees of freedom, where N is the total number of atoms.

Formally, the more rigorous theoretical approach to the analysis might also be taken. One may start with a general formulation of the molecular problem, comprising all the $3N - 6$ internal plus 3 rotational degrees of freedom [1–3]. This approach is of interest in principle. It cannot, however, be applied to the analysis of a rotational spectrum, since the rotational spectra of molecules in a sufficient number of states of internal motion are not experimentally accessible. The lack of experimental information necessitates simplification of the model down to the level of the approach followed here. Then there is no longer any basic difference in the method used in the two approaches.

There is another practical reason for the choice of this simple model with only two degrees of freedom. A precise numerical treatment requires very large computer storage and a large amount of computing time. Both requirements are reduced by limiting the number of internal degrees of freedom.

In this discussion I shall consider two types of molecules which can be treated in this way:

1. Molecules with two equivalent interacting methyl groups. The two internal motions are hindered internal rotations. The internal rotation barrier is assumed to be low enough to produce a perturbation on the overall rotation which is observable as a splitting of rotational lines.
2. Molecules with one methyl group. The two internal motions are a low-barrier-hindered internal rotation of the methyl group and one low-energy vibration interacting with the internal rotation.

Spectra of the second type of molecule, with one internal rotor, are especially well-suited for the intended investigation, for the internal rotation splitting is an additional source of information. This splitting depends strongly on the height of the barrier to internal rotation and upon the interaction between the torsion and the other internal motion. Details concerning the interaction between the internal motion and the overall rotation will be given below. In the case of a molecule without internal rotation but with two low-energy vibrations, only the frequency position of an absorption line is the source of information.

Recently, Knopp and Quade [4] published a Hamiltonian for molecules with internal rotation of two asymmetric tops. A simplified version of their Hamiltonian includes type 1 by making the tops symmetric. Type 2 is only included in their treatment if a torsion-like vibration is assumed as one of the internal motions.

It should be pointed out that rotation–internal motion interaction must be reflected in the spectra [5–7]. This point may be clarified by using a still simpler model of a one-top molecule. The splitting of internal rotation levels is transferred to rotational levels by rotation–internal rotation interaction. This fact is illustrated in Figs. 1 and 2. Starting with the internal rotation

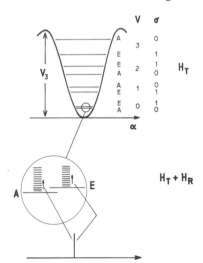

FIG. 1. One-top molecule torsional levels and rotational levels built on torsional sublevels. Rotational transitions are unsplit.

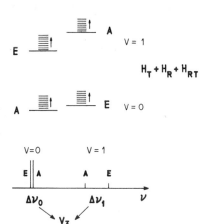

FIG. 2. One-top molecule torsional levels modified by the inclusion of the H_{RT} interaction operator: the effect is to split rotational transitions associated with different torsional substates.

operator H_T and its energy level system, H is stepwise completed by adding H_R and H_{RT}, which means that the effective internal motion state is produced by

$$H = H_T + H_{RT} + H_R \rightarrow H_{R,\,eff}$$

This form of the Hamiltonian can be derived from a classical Hamiltonian of the appropriate molecular model [5–7]. It is then translated into the quantum mechanical Hamiltonian [8, 9].

If the above mentioned four-degree model is extended to the five-degree model, the interaction H_{RT} remains essential, but is modified by the additional degree of freedom. The Hamiltonian [5, 7, 10, 11] for this case may be written symbolically as an extension of the preceding formula by introducing H',

$$H = H' + H_T + H_{RT} + H_R \rightarrow H_{Reff}$$

Taking the specific case of two interacting equivalent methyl groups or symmetric tops, H becomes in detail

$$
\begin{aligned}
H = &\ Fp_1^2 + \tfrac{1}{2}V_3(1 - \cos 3\alpha_1) & & H_{T1}\\
&+ Fp_2^2 + \tfrac{1}{2}V_3(1 - \cos 3\alpha_2) & & H_{T2}\\
&+ F'(p_1 p_2 + p_2 p_1) & & \\
&+ V_{12}\cos 3\alpha_1 \cos 3\alpha_2 & & H_{TT}\\
&+ V'_{12}\sin 3\alpha_1 \sin 3\alpha_2 & & \\
&+ AP_x^2 + BP_y^2 + CP_z^2 & & \\
&+ FP_1^2 + FP_2^2 & & H_R\\
&- 2Fp_1 P_1 - 2Fp_2 P_2 & & \\
&- 2F'(p_1 P_2 + p_2 P_1) & & H_{RT}
\end{aligned}
$$

where $P_i = \sum_g (\lambda_{gi} I_\alpha P_g / I_g)$; P_g is the component of total angular momentum in the molecule-fixed principal inertia axis g; p_i is the angular momentum of top i; A, B, C are the rotational constants of the molecule; F is the reduced rotational constant of either top [5]; F' is a kinetic interaction constant [5, 10]; λ_{gi} is a direction cosine between the internal rotation axis of top i and the principal inertia axis g; I_g is the moment of inertia of the molecule about the g axis; V_3 is the barrier height; and V_{12} and V'_{12} are potential coupling constants. H_{T1} and H_{T2} are Hamiltonians of two isolated, hindered rotors. They are coupled by kinetic (F') and potential (V_{12}, V'_{12}) terms H_{TT}. The usual Hamiltonian $AP_x^2 + BP_y^2 + CP_z^2$ of the molecule with frozen internal degrees of freedom is modified by internal rotation. H_{RT} gives the interaction between overall rotation and internal rotation.

This Hamiltonian has been derived by Herschbach [5] and was applied later to the rotational spectra of the torsional ground state of several molecules.†
Studies of rotational spectra in excited vibrational states are rare [13–17].

In connection with our present aim, special attention should be given to H_{TT}, the interaction operator of the two internal motions. Here the operator consists of a kinetic coupling term $F'(p_1 p_2 + p_2 p_1)$ (where p_1 and p_2 are the momenta of the two internal motions) and a potential coupling term $V_{12} \cos 3\alpha_1 \cos 3\alpha_2 + V'_{12} \sin 3\alpha_1 \sin 3\alpha_2$ (α_1 and α_2 are configuration symmetry the position of the two tops within the molecule). C_{2v} the angles describing of the molecule is assumed in formulating the potential coupling term.

Essential features of the energy level scheme are sketched in Figs. 3 and 4. In order to understand these diagrams, the Hamiltonian matrices of the different parts of the total Hamiltonian should be studied. Starting with $H_{T1} + H_{T2}$, one gets the left column of Fig. 3 just by superposition of the energy level scheme of two independent torsional oscillators. The designation on the left side gives the torsional (internal rotation) states $v_1 v_2$ and the symmetry species of the invariance group $C_{3v}^- \otimes C_{3v}^+$ [7, 8, 18] of the total Hamiltonian. Addition of the interaction operator $V_{12} \cos 3\alpha_1 \cos 3\alpha_2$ mainly causes a shift of the energy levels. The direction of the shift depends on the sign of V_{12}. However, this holds only for the lowest torsional states. In the $v_1 v_2 = 02$ or 20 state, a significant splitting of the levels should occur. In Fig. 3, this is indicated by V_{12}. This splitting results from the removal of a degeneracy by the interaction operator $V_{12} \cos 3\alpha_1 \cos 3\alpha_2$. (The effect in the $v_1 v_2 = 01$, 10; AE, EA substate is rather small).

By including the interaction operators $V'_{12} \sin 3\alpha_1 \sin 3\alpha_2 + F'(p_1 p_2 + p_2 p_1)$, as illustrated in Fig. 4, the internal motion part of H can be completed. Now a degeneracy is destroyed in the $v_1 v_2 = 01$, 10 state. The potential parameters V_{12} and V'_{12} could be determined if a pure torsional energy level scheme

† For a complete list see the work of Starck [12].

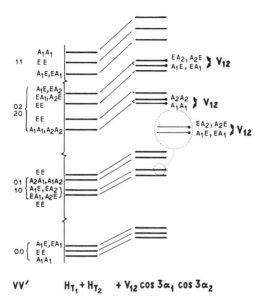

FIG. 3. Two-top molecule: Torsional levels of two uncoupled torsional oscillators and the effect of V_{12} coupling.

of the five lowest states were known. F' depends only on atomic masses and molecular geometry, which is assumed to be known from the ground-state microwave spectrum.

Since we are studying rotational spectra, we rely on the influence of the internal motion on the rotational spectra. The operator H_{RT} plays here the same role as in the simple example illustrated in Figs. 1 and 2. The rotational lines should therefore show a fine structure pattern as indicated in the lower part of Fig. 4. The intensities given by spin statistics are included [18–20], but will not be discussed in detail here.

Thus it may be seen that a determination of V'_{12} with known F' requires lines of at least the $v_1 v_2 = 01$, 10 torsional states, and the determination of V_{12} requires lines of at least $v_1 v_2 = 02$, 20 torsional states.

Until now, only rotational lines of $v_1 v_2 = 00$, 01, 10 torsional levels have been assigned in the spectrum of this type of molecule. Assignment of higher torsional states should be possible in principle but will be difficult in practice, so one is confined to the determination of V'_{12} in addition to the barrier height V_3 until experimental data allow more detailed information to be extracted.

For the analysis of these spectra, Trinkaus [17] has developed a program in which first the torsional part $H_{T1} + H_{T2}$ was diagonalized (matrix with rank 55, $(v_1 + v_2) \leq 9$). After this, the matrix of H was set up in the mixed

basis, $U_{(v_1v_2)\sigma_1\sigma_2}$ $(\alpha_1\alpha_2)\theta(\phi, \delta, \psi)$. The eigenfunctions of the two coupled torsion oscillators are $U_{(v_1v_2)\sigma_1\sigma_2}(\alpha_1\alpha_2)$ and $\theta(\phi, \delta, \psi)$ are the symmetric-top eigenfunctions.

A Van Vleck transformation of second order was applied aiming at a certain level $(v_1 v_2)$, or, if necessary, at a near-degenerate pair of levels $(v_1 v_2, v_2 v_1)$. The resulting effective rotational matrix was then diagonalized.

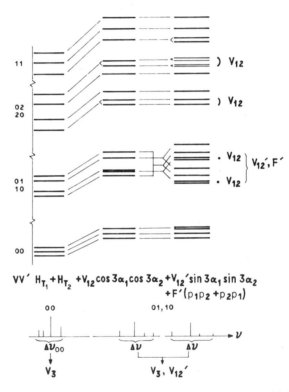

FIG. 4. Two-top molecule: Torsional levels of Fig. 3 modified by additional coupling, and the resulting fine structure pattern.

An optimizing calculation results in numerical values for V_3 and V_{12}'. However, V_{12} is correlated with V_3, as was expected in considering the energy level diagram of the states $v_1v_2 = 00, 01, 10$ (Fig. 3). This correlation cannot be removed even by inclusion of the ground-state splitting of the CH_3—CD_3 isotopic species. The information from the spectra of isotopically substituted molecules was at one time believed to contain additional information [11], but this now seems rather improbable.

Şome examples of barriers determined in this way are as follows:

$(CH_3)_2CH_2$ $V_3 = 3294 \pm 10$ cal mole^{-1}, $V'_{12} = -158 \pm 15$ cal mole^{-1}, $V_{12} = (0)$

$(CH_3)_2SiH_2$ $V_3 = 1646 \pm 3$ cal mole^{-1}, $V'_{12} = -38 \pm 2$ cal mole^{-1}, $V_{12} = (0)$

$(CH_3)_2S$ $V_3 = 2182 \pm 7$ cal mole^{-1}, $V'_{12} = 36 \pm 9$ cal mole^{-1}, $V_{12} = (0)$

It is important to mention that in the above analyses only the splittings within the multiplets of the different torsional states were used. The splittings between the multiplets could not be fitted.

This discrepancy may be the result of an insufficient numerical treatment of the Hamiltonian, which included some approximative procedures such as the Van Vleck perturbation treatment, or it may be the result of an inadequate model and initial Hamiltonian. In an attempt to exclude the first possible source of discrepancy, Legell [21] wrote a program in which the Hamiltonian matrix is set up in a basis of symmetric-top and free internal rotor functions. Here the limitation is only the finite basis set and the inaccuracy of the diagonalizing procedure. Since the final result is not yet available, a comparison cannot be made.

Since it seems that the model with two internal degrees of freedom should be refined in order to completely reproduce the measured spectra, the model of r_e relaxation recently proposed by Günthard [22] for other molecules should be considered. In Günthard's approach, the number of internal degrees of freedom is not increased. Instead, the entire molecular structure is assumed to be a function of the torsional angle. Thereby, the Hamiltonian is changed and new parameters come in. It is not yet decided whether the experimental information is sufficient to determine those parameters.

If one asks for a physical interpretation of the potential coupling constants V_{12} and V'_{12}, the picture of two geared methyl groups is sometimes proposed [23]. With the usual definition of torsional angles, this means $\alpha_1 + \alpha_2 =$ const. If the favored motion is gearing, the potential surface should consist of valleys and ridges parallel to lines $\alpha_1 + \alpha_2 =$ const as sketched in Fig. 5. Such a potential surface can only be specified by V'_{12} and V_{12} terms together. Since the present information is limited to V'_{12}, no more specific discussion of the picture of geared groups can be made.

In the following we consider molecules of the second type. In these molecules there is an interaction between the internal rotation of the methyl group and a vibration of nearly the same energy. This interaction can be observed even in molecules where, in the harmonic oscillator limit of small-amplitude internal motion or torsion, no interaction with the vibration should occur

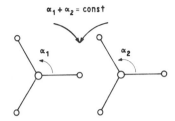

$\alpha_1 + \alpha_2 = \text{const}$

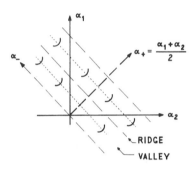

FIG. 5. Two geared methyl groups and potential surface favoring this motion.

because of symmetry considerations. In our laboratory, we have started the investigation of molecules of that type with the aim of checking a fundamental assumption usually made in the internal rotation analysis. This assumption is that internal rotation may be considered separable from all other vibrations. But investigations of the internal rotation fine structure of rotational spectra in vibrationally excited states has shown a difference in the splitting of excited- and ground-state transitions [24]. Under the assumption of a strict separation of internal motion from all other vibrations, these splittings should be equal. For illustration, fine structure patterns [25] of CH_3CH_2CN are given in Fig. 6. In addition, the energy level diagram [26] for the torsional mode and the lowest bending vibrations of CH_3CH_2CN is reproduced in Fig. 7. Rotational spectra of the lowest states were and may be observed. The vibrational levels have the torsional fine structure of the torsion ground state, as indicated symbolically for the $v = 1$ CCN— bending. The arrow indicates interaction of two near-degenerate states, which changes the level splitting. Effects of this type are known from the rotational spectra of a number of molecules:

Propionaldehyde, CH_3CH_2CHO [27]
Dimethyldisulfide, $(CH_3)_2S_2$ [24]
Methylthiocyanate, CH_3SCN [28]
Fluoroacetone, CH_2FCH_3CO [29]
Ethylcyanide, CH_3CH_2CN [25]
Methanesulfenyl chloride, CH_3SCl [30]
Propionylfluoride, CH_2CH_2COF [31]

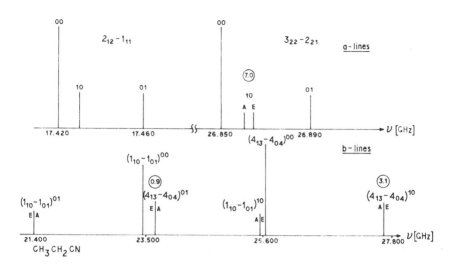

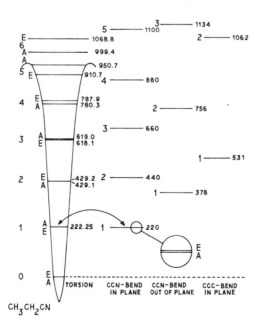

FIG. 6. Typical fine structure patterns of selected transitions of CH_3CH_2CN (J_{K-K+} — J'_{K-K+})$V_t V_v$. Numbers in circles indicate splitting in MHz.

FIG. 7. Low-energy vibrational and torsional levels of CH_3CH_2CN.

For the analysis of this type of rotational spectra, we use a quantum mechanical Hamiltonian which is derived from the classical Hamiltonian of a rotating molecule with only the torsional and one vibrational degree of freedom [28, 32]. Since an Eckhart system is used, direct Coriolis coupling is formally eliminated and included in other terms of the Hamiltonian.

By selecting molecules with the internal rotation axis contained in the symmetry plane and restricting the vibrational motion to an in-plane vibration, the Hamiltonian may be somewhat simplified. Since torsional and vibrational momenta are thus perpendicular, direct kinetic coupling is no longer present. The Hamiltonian formulated under these assumptions [32] may be written as follows:

$$
\begin{aligned}
H = & (A^\circ + A'q + A''q^2)P_a{}^2 \\
& + (B^\circ + B'q + B''q^2)P_b{}^2 \\
& + (C^\circ + C'q + C''q^2)P_c{}^2 \\
& + (D_{ab}^\circ + D_{ab}'q + D_{ab}''q^2)(P_aP_b + P_bP_a) \\
& - 2(Q_a{}^\circ + Q_a'q + Q_a''q^2)p_\alpha P_a \\
& - 2(Q_b{}^\circ + Q_b'q + Q_b''q^2)p_\alpha P_b \\
& + (F^\circ + F'q + F''q^2)p_\alpha{}^2 \\
& + \tfrac{1}{2}V_3(1 - \cos 3\alpha) \\
& + V_c q(1 - \cos 3\alpha) \\
& + \tfrac{1}{2}Mp_q{}^2 + \tfrac{1}{2}(\omega^2/M)q^2 + V_a q^3 \\
& + W'q + W''q^2
\end{aligned}
$$

$H_{\text{rot}} + H_{\text{rot, vib}}$

$H_{\text{rot, tors}} + H_{\text{rot, tors, vib}}$

$H_{\text{tors}} + H_{\text{tors, vib}}$

H_{vib}

where the following notation is used: P_g is the component of angular momentum; p_α is the angular momentum of a top; p_q is the vibrational momentum; A°, A', A'', etc., $Q_g{}^\circ$, $Q_g{}^1$, Q_g'', F°, F^1, F'', M, W', W'' are molecular constants depending on molecular structure, vibrational mode, and atomic masses; V_3, V_c, V_a are potential constants; ω is the vibrational frequency, and q is the vibrational coordinate.

This Hamiltonian consists of three limiting parts

for rotation: $\quad A^\circ P_a{}^2 + B^\circ P_b{}^2 + C^\circ P_c{}^2$

for torsion: $\quad F^\circ p_\alpha{}^2 + \tfrac{1}{2}V_3(1 - \cos 3\alpha)$

for vibration: $\quad \tfrac{1}{2}Mp_q{}^2 + \tfrac{1}{2}(\omega^2/M)q^2$

In addition, there are many interaction operators including only two or all three types of motions. The terms containing W' and W'' are a consequence of the translation from the classical to the quantum mechanical Hamiltonian [8, 9].

For the analysis of the spectra, this Hamiltonian is treated numerically. For checking the numerical procedures and approximations and the programs themselves, a system of programs was written, which allows mutual checks. The detailed procedures are indicated in Fig. 8.

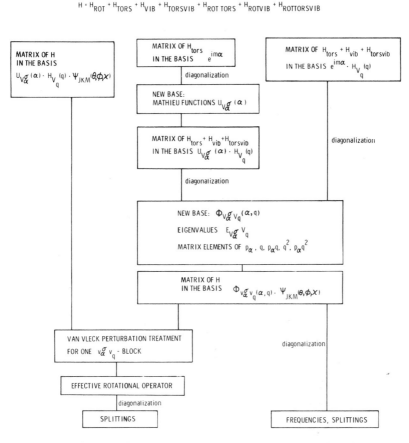

FIG. 8. Block diagram of computer programs for the rotation–torsion–vibration interaction problem.

Computations were made for CH_3SCN starting with the basis functions $U_{v_t\sigma}(\alpha)H_{v_v}(q)\Psi_{JKM}$ as indicated on the left side of Fig. 8. Here the Mathieu function $U_{v_t\sigma}(\alpha)$ is the eigenfunction of the pure internal rotation problem and $H_{v_v}(q)$ is the harmonic oscillator eigenfunction of the "pure" C—S—C bending vibration. The Ψ_{JKM} are the rigid-rotor eigenfunctions of the limiting symmetric top. The results for the $v_t v_v = 00, 01$, and 02 spectra are

given in Fig. 9. These are revised results from the work of Dreizler and Mirri [28]. It should be noticed that the splittings of the 00, 01, and 02 spectra are reproduced within 10% by optimizing only two parameters, the reduced barrier height s and the coupling constant V_c.

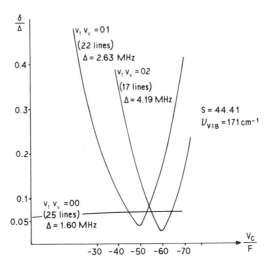

FIG. 9. Fit of absorption line splittings of CH_3SCN for CSC bending excited states; δ is the mean square deviation of calculated and measured splittings; Δ is the mean of measured splittings.

We found that the quality of the fit depends on the structure of the molecule, especially on the inclination of the internal rotation axis of the methyl group with respect to the principal axes. Therefore an r_s structure was determined [33].

The form of the vibrational normal mode also influences the results. However, an admixture of the SCN bending to the CSC bending did not remove the difference of optimal V_c values for 01 and 02 spectra.

It is interesting to note that for CH_3SCN, the $v_t v_v = 00$ spectrum is nearly independent of V_c. That means that the reduced barrier height $s = 4V_3/9F_0$ alone determines the splittings of the ground state.

This result may perhaps indicate that barrier determination from ground-state spectra is the most reliable. It is necessary, however, for the excited-state spectra to include V_c and the $H_{tors, vib, rot}$ kinetic interactions.

For CH_3SCN [34], CH_3CH_2CN [25], and CH_3SCl, an analysis of ground- and excited-state spectra is in progress using the programs shown in the second and third columns of Fig. 8. As the calculations are not yet complete, final results cannot be given. For CH_3CH_2CN and CH_3SCl, different values for A_{eff}, the effective rotational constant A in the ground-state and excited-

state spectra, can roughly be reproduced. The calculations are very sensitive to the frequency difference of torsion and vibration and less sensitive to the vibrational mode assumed for the model.

The conclusions which may at present be drawn from these investigations are as follows. The most reliable determination of the methyl torsion barrier height may be made from ground-state spectra if the splittings are observable with sufficient accuracy. Barrier determinations based on the splittings of excited torsional states must be checked for the possible influence of another vibration.

Acknowledgments

I thank Dr. H. D. Rudolph, Dr. A. Guarnieri, Dr. D. Sutter, Dr. A. Trinkaus, Dipl. Phys. U. Andresen, Dipl. Phys. H. Mäder, and H. Legell for their cooperation, L. Charpentier and C. Martens for assistance in preparing the manuscript, and the Deutsche Forschungsgemeinschaft for research and travel funds.

References

1. B. Kirtmann, *J. Chem. Phys.* **37**, 2516 (1962).
2. C. R. Quade, *J. Chem. Phys.* **44**, 2512 (1966).
3. R. Meyer and H. H. Günthard, *J. Chem. Phys.* **49**, 1510 (1968).
4. J. V. Knopp and C. R. Quade, *J. Chem. Phys.* **53**, 1 (1970).
5. D. R. Herschbach, *J. Chem. Phys.* **31**, 91 (1959).
6. C. C. Lin and J. D. Swalen, *Rev. Mod. Phys.* **31**, 84 (1959).
7. H. Dreizler, *Fortsch. Chem. Forsch.* **10**, 59 (1968).
8. B. Podolsky, *Phys. Rev.* **32**, 812 (1928).
9. E. B. Wilson, Jr., J. C. Decius, and P. C. Cross, "Molecular Vibrations," Chapter 11-3. McGraw-Hill, New York, 1955.
10. J. D. Swalen and C. C. Costain, *J. Chem. Phys.* **31**, 1562 (1959).
11. L. Pierce, *J. Chem. Phys.* **34**, 498 (1961).
12. B. Starck, "Landolt-Börnstein, Neue Serie," II/4. Springer-Verlag, Berlin and New York, 1967 [Suppl. 1971].
13. L. Pierce and M. Hayashi, *J. Chem. Phys.* **35**, 479 (1961).
14. M. Hayashi, Private communication (1964).
15. H. Dreizler and G. Dendl, *Z. Naturforsch. A* **20**, 1431 (1965).
16. E. Hirota, C. Matsumura, and J. Morino, *Bull. Chem. Soc. Jap.* **40**, 1124 (1969).
17. A. Trinkaus, Thesis, Univ. of Freiburg, Freiburg, Germany, 1969.
18. R. J. Myers and E. B. Wilson, Jr., *J. Chem. Phys.* **33**, 186 (1960).
19. H. Dreizler, *Z. Naturforsch. A*, **16**, 1354 (1961).
20. H. Dreizler, *Z. Naturforsch. A*, **16**, 477 (1961).
21. H. Legell, Thesis, Univ. of Kiel, Kiel, Germany, 1971.
22. H. H. Günthard, Invited Paper, Bangor, Maine, July 1970.
23. H. Dreizler and D. Sutter, *Z. Naturforsch.* **24**, 2013 (1969).
24. D. Sutter, Thesis, Univ. of Freiburg, Freiburg, Germany, 1966.
25. H. Mäder, Thesis, Univ. of Kiel, Kiel, Germany, 1971.
26. E. N. Duncan and G. J. Janz, *J. Chem. Phys.* **23**, 434 (1955).
27. S. S. Butcher and E. B. Wilson, Jr., *J. Chem. Phys.* **40**, 1671 (1964).
28. H. Dreizler and A. M. Mirri, *Z. Naturforsch. A* **23**, 1313 (1968)

29. E. Saegebarth and U. C. Krisher, *J. Chem. Phys.* **52**, 3555 (1970).
30. A. Guarnieri, *Z. Naturforsch. A* **25**, 18 (1970).
31. O. L. Stiefvater and E. B. Wilson, Jr., *J. Chem. Phys.* **50**, 5385 (1969).
32. H. Dreizler, *Z. Naturforsch. A* **23**, 1077 (1968).
33. H. Dreizler, H. D. Rudolph, and H. Schleser, *Z. Naturforsch.* **25**, 1643 (1970).
34. U. Andresen, Thesis, Univ. of Kiel, Kiel, Germany, 1972.

2.5 Interstellar Molecules and the Interstellar Medium[†]

David M. Rank

Department of Physics
University of California
Berkeley, California

The matter which lies between the stars in our galaxy has been studied intensively for the last forty years. All of the early work on interstellar gases was performed with high-resolution spectrographs and optical telescopes operating mostly in the visible spectral region. Such optical studies have detected absorption features due to interstellar Na, Ca, K, Ti, and Fe atoms in the spectra of distant stars. CH and CN molecules have also been observed by similar techniques. Much of our galaxy, in particular those regions which contain large amounts of interstellar gas, is often opaque to visible radiation due to light scattering by small "dust grains" and thus is not amenable to study by standard optical techniques with the photographic plate.

A great advance in radiofrequency techniques during the period 1940–1945 made sensitive microwave receivers available to astronomers. In 1945, van de Hulst [1] predicted the existence of the 21-cm hydrogen line, and a few years later Ewen and Purcell [2] detected the 21-cm line in our galaxy. Radio and microwaves are not attenuated by dust clouds in the galaxy, and for the first time astronomers had the opportunity to examine the galaxy as a whole and look into and beyond large dust clouds. In 1963, another fundamental step was taken in the study of the galaxy when Weinreb *et al.* [3] discovered OH molecules by observing their absorption lines at 18 cm against galactic radio sources. Their work marked the beginning of a new field of astronomical research combining microwave spectroscopy and radio astronomy. It is to this subject that I will address myself here.‡ In particular, I will discuss the molecules which have been detected in the galaxy by these techniques, and some of the information which they can give us about conditions in the galaxy.

The transitions in the OH molecule at 18 cm are due to Λ-doubling of its

† Work partially supported by the National Aeronautics and Space Administration Grant NGL–05–003–272.

‡ A more general review of the interstellar medium is presented by Dieter and Goss [4].

ground state. OH absorption or emission at 18 cm is detected in a large number of radio sources in the galaxy, indicating that the OH molecule is widely distributed. The molecules seem to exist in two distinct classes of excitation. In the first class of excitation, the OH molecule has an excitation temperature of a few degrees Kelvin and is observed in absorption against nearly all sources of galactic background radiation. Observations of this type of "normal" OH absorption, as detected by Weinreb et al. [3], can give measures of OH abundances and internal motions of gas clouds as well as information on general galactic rotation and estimates of temperatures within clouds. The second type of OH, which was observed by Weaver et al. [5] in 1965, is anomalous. The OH molecules are undergoing stimulated emission and hence have a nonthermal population distribution, which produces strong emission lines much narrower than spontaneous emission lines coming from the same regions. The exact mechanism for the production of this radiation is not completely understood; however, satisfactory pumping mechanisms for OH population inversion can be obtained by collisional excitation or infrared absorption of radiation. The complex nature of OH spectra indicates that both mechanisms probably play a role in most sources. A large number of excited OH rotational states (up to $J = \frac{7}{2}$) [6] have been observed to date. Many of these also show nonthermal population distributions.

In 1968, NH_3 molecules were discovered in gas clouds near the center of the galaxy [7]. The NH_3 molecules showed emission lines in transitions arising from metastable $J = K$ rotational states. NH_3 has many transitions at about 1.25 cm; hence a great deal can be learned about the gas clouds. In particular, the 1–1, 2–2, 3–3, and 4–4 states have excitation temperatures of 24°K, 65°K, 125°K, and 203°K, respectively. Thus, one can determine temperatures very accurately by comparing line strengths to statistical theory. NH_3 is particularly useful as an interstellar thermometer since all of these lines can be detected by a single radio telescope with essentially the same beam size. Generally, a telescope measures the antenna temperature T_A of an object, which is related to the brightness temperature T_B of an object by $T_A = (\Omega_S/\Omega_A)T_B$ when $\Omega_S/\Omega_A \leq 1$. $T_A = T_B$ when $\Omega_S \geq \Omega_A$, where Ω_A is the solid angle of the antenna pattern and Ω_S is the solid angle of the source as seen from the antenna. If measurements can be made with the same telescope, then T_B for different spectral lines will be simply related to T_A for the lines, and one does not have the complication of source size and geometry. The brightness temperature T_{BJK} of a spectral line from a rotational state specified by the quantum numbers (J, K) can be related to the optical depth of the line T_v and the excitation temperature of the molecule T_{exc}:

$$T_{BJK} = T_{exc}(1 - e^{-T_v}) \tag{1}$$

For $T_\nu \ll 1$, we can expand and integrate Eq. (1),

$$\int T_{BJK}\, dv \approx \int T_{exc} T_\nu\, dv$$

$$= \int T_{exc} L \int \gamma_\nu\, dv$$

where γ_ν is the line strength, which can be determined from theory or laboratory experiments. The result is

$$\int T_{BJK}\, dv = [(8\pi^3/3ck)|\mu_{JK}|^2 v_{JK}^2 g(2J+1)]NL \exp(-W_{JK/kT_{exc}}) \qquad (2)$$

The quantity in brackets is the product of the matrix element, frequency, statistical weight, and other constants of the transition. NL is the column density of the molecules in the line of sight, W_{JK} is the energy of the rotational state, and k is the Boltzmann constant.

Taking the ratio of the brightness temperature for two lines (which, if they have very nearly the same frequency, is just the ratio of their antenna temperatures), NL cancels, and Eq. (2) can be solved for T_{exc}. For the gas cloud near the center of our galaxy, $T_B(22)/T_B(11) = 0.34$, which implies that the temperature there is about 25°K $\pm$ a few °K.

For a spectral line to be observed in emission, there must be sufficiently rapid excitation of the molecules to keep them out of equilibrium with the background 3°K radiation. The radiative lifetime of NH_3 at 1.25 cm is a few million seconds, and the induced transition rate by stimulated emission due to background radiofrequency radiation corresponds to a lifetime of 10^6 sec. Hence, if collisions are exciting the molecules, they must occur more rapidly than 10^{-6} sec.$^{-1}$ This means the gas density in the cloud must be $\geq 10^3$ cm^{-3}. The strength of the NH_3 lines indicates that the NH_3 density is about 10^{-6} of that, or 10^{-3} cm^{-3}. The bulk of the remaining gas is most probably molecular hydrogen.

Another useful property of NH_3 which can be related to temperature studies of interstellar gas is that there are two different spin states for the molecule, which divide the rotational states of the molecule into two independent groups, *ortho* NH_3, where the rotational quantum number K is a multiple of 3, and *para* NH_3, where K is not a multiple of 3. Conversion by collisions from one form of NH_3 to the other requires a time greater than 10^6 years in interstellar gases. Collisions, however, can bring molecules with the same spin state into equilibrium in a time of about 10^7 sec. Thus, the distribution of population in the rotational states of *ortho* NH_3 or *para* NH_3 reflects the present temperature of the gas, while the relative population of *para* NH_3 or *ortho* NH_3 reflects the temperature history of the gas. A demonstration of this effect has been observed [8] in a gas cloud which is in the central region of our galaxy, though not coincident with the true dynamical center. The

present cloud temperature is about 40–50°K and the *ortho*-to-*para* NH_3 ratio indicates that the temperature has changed by about 40–50°K in a complicated fashion during the last few million years. NH_3 promises to be very useful as a probe to measure conditions inside interstellar dust clouds, since it has proved to be rather well behaved and understandable on a simple physical basis. This is not true of OH and many of the more recently discovered molecules in the interstellar medium. Nearly all of them have anomalous excitation which makes the interpretation of their spectra difficult.

Water vapor emission was also discovered [9] by our Berkeley group soon after the detection of NH_3 lines. The water vapor emission line at 1.3 cm comes from the $6_{16} \rightarrow 5_{23}$ in H_2O. These levels are not metastable and, hence, it is somewhat surprising that they are observed in the interstellar medium. In fact, the 6_{16} level can decay by far-infrared emission in about 1 sec, whereas the microwave radiation lifetime of the level is 10^8 sec. Strong line emission from such unstable levels requires a very special excitation process in a tenuous gas cloud. Further observations demonstrated antenna temperatures on the order of a few thousand degrees and linewidths which were considerably narrower than usual thermal or tubulent widths. The water vapor is undergoing stimulated emission or maser action much like that observed in the OH molecule. It would seem that OH and H_2O should be connected by interstellar chemistry and be found in fairly similar regions. In fact, most OH sources of emission also show water vapor emission. The situation is very complicated and as yet no complete and convincing explanation has come forth. Also, as one might guess, there have been no cases of "normal" H_2O absorption from the galaxy because the transition is a very highly excited one. Hence, no column densities have been measured. Recent long-baseline interferometry has determined that the emitting regions are <0.003 seconds of arc for most of the H_2O sources [10]. This means that the radiation is apparently coming from regions a few tens of astronomical units in size.

In 1969, the formaldehyde $1_{11} \rightarrow 1_{10}$ ground-state transition at 6 cm was detected [11] in absorption against a large number of galactic radio sources. Surprisingly, H_2CO absorption lines are also detected in directions which have no galactic continuum radio sources [12]. These anomalous absorption lines appear to be due to a pumping mechanism which tends to keep the H_2CO molecules out of equilibrium with the 3°K isotropic blackbody radiation. This effect is a type of "interstellar refrigerator" which cools the blackbody radiation below its value of 3°K to about 2°K in those directions which have large clouds of H_2CO. The $J = 2$ and $J = 3$ rotational states of H_2CO have also recently been detected [13, 14] and these excited states promise to give us some detailed information about the intensity of the 3°K isotropic radiation.

The list of molecules which are present inside the dark clouds in our galaxy is expanding very rapidly (Table I). Within the last few months CO

TABLE I

LIST OF MOLECULES PRESENT IN DARK CLOUDS OF THE GALAXY
(NUMBER DENSITY GIVEN PER CM^3)

$NH_3 \sim 10^{-3}-10^{-4}$	$H \leq 3 \times 10^{-2}$
H_2O ?	$H_2 > 10^3$
$H_2{}^{12}CO \sim 10^{-4}-10^{-5}$	$CO \sim 10^{-1}-10^{-2}$
$H_2{}^{13}CO \sim 10^{-5}-10^{-6}$	$CN \sim 10^{-4}-10^{-5}$
$HCN \sim 10^{-4}$	$^{16}OH \sim 10^{-5}-10^{-6}$
$HCCCN \sim 10^{-5}$	$^{18}OH \sim 10^{-7}-10^{-8}$
$CH_3OH \sim 10^{-4}(?)$	
$HCOOH \sim 10^{-4}(?)$	

[15], CN [16], HCN [17], HCCCN [18], CH_3OH [19], and HCOOH [20] have been detected by microwave techniques and H_2 [21] has been found by ultraviolet rocket observations. In addition $^{13}C^{16}O$ [22], $^{12}C^{18}O$ [22], $H^{13}CN$ [23], CS [24], SiO [25], CH_3C_2H [26], HNCO [26], OCS [27], CH_3CN [28], NH_2HCO [29] and two unidentified molecules with line frequences around 90 GHz [30, 31], have been detected as of mid-1971. Much has already been learned from the interstellar molecules and they promise to provide a versatile tool for probing the galaxy. The molecules can provide us with interstellar temperatures, mass and radiation densities, isotopic as well as atomic abundances, and a variety of other parameters which will ultimately lead to a detailed and complete picture of the interstellar medium and its chemistry.

References

1. H. C. van de Hulst, *Ned. Tijdschr. Natuurk.* **11**, 201 (1945).
2. H. I. Ewen and E. M. Purcell, Observation of a line in the galactic radio spectrum, *Nature (London)* **168**, 356 (1951).
3. S. Weinreb, A. H. Barrett, M. L. Meeks, and J. C. Henry, Radio observations of OH in the interstellar medium, *Nature (London)* **200**, 829 (1963).
4. N. H. Dieter and W. M. Goss, Recent work in the interstellar medium, *Rev. Mod. Phys.* **138**, No. 2, 256–297 (1966).
5. H. F. Weaver, D. R. Williams, N. H. Dieter, and W. T. Lum, Observations of a strong unidentified microwave line and of emission from the OH molecule. *Nature (London)* **208**, 29 (1965).
6. B. E. Turner, P. Palmer, and B. Zuckerman, Detection of the $^2\Pi_{3/2}$, $J = 7/2$ state of interstellar OH at a wavelength of 2.2 centimeters. *Astrophys. J.* **160**, L125 (1970).
7. A. C. Cheung, D. M. Rank, C. H. Townes, D. D. Thornton, and W. J. Welch, Detection of NH_3 molecules in the interstellar medium by their microwave emission. *Phys. Rev. Lett.* **21**, 1701 (1968).
8. A. C. Cheung, D. M. Rank, C. H. Townes, S. H. Knowles, and W. T. Sullivan, III, Distribution of ammonia density, velocity, and rotational excitation in the region of Sagittarius B_2. *Astrophys. J.* **157**, L13 (1969).

9. A. C. Cheung, D. M. Rank, C. H. Townes, D. D. Thornton, and W. J. Welch, Detection of water in interstellar regions by its microwave radiation. *Nature* (*London*) **221**, 626 (1969).

10. B. F. Burke, D. C. Papa, G. D. Papadopoulous, P. R. Schwartz, S. H. Knowles, W. T. Sullivan, M. L. Meeks, and J. M. Moran, Studies of H_2O sources by means of a very-long-baseline interferometer. *Astrophys. J.* **160**, L63 (1970).

11. L. E. Snyder, D. Buhl, B. Zuckerman, and P. Palmer, Microwave detection of interstellar formaldehyde. *Phys. Rev. Lett.* **22**, 679 (1969).

12. P. Palmer, B. Zuckerman, D. Buhl, and L. E. Snyder, Formaldehyde absorption in dark nebulae. *Astrophys. J.* **156**, L147 (1969).

13. N. J. Evans, II, A. C. Cheung, and R. M. Sloanaker, Microwave absorption of the $2_{12} \rightarrow 2_{11}$ rotational transition in interstellar formaldehyde. *Astrophys. J.* **159**, L9 (1970).

14. W. J. Welch, Private communication (1970).

15. R. W. Wilson, K. B. Jefferts, and A. A. Penzias, Carbon monoxide in the Orion Nebula. *Astrophys. J.* **161**, L43 (1970).

16. K. B. Jefferts, A. A. Penzias, and R. W. Wilson, Observation of the CN radical in the Orion Nebula and W51. *Astrophys. J.* **161**, L87 (1970).

17. D. Buhl and L. E. Snyder, "Radio Emission from HCN," I. A. U. Circ. No. 2251, 1970.

18. B. E. Turner, "Radio Emission from Interstellar Cyanoacetylene," I. A. U. Circ. No. 2268, 1970.

19. J. A. Ball, C. A. Gottlieb, A. E. Lilley, and H. E. Radford, Detection of methyl alcohol in Sagittarius. *Astrophys. J.* **162**, L203 (1970).

20. B. Zuckerman, J. A. Ball, C. A. Gottlieb, and H. E. Radford, "Interstellar Formic Acid," I. A. U. Circ. No. 2286, 1970.

21. G. R. Carruthers, Rocket observations of interstellar molecular hydrogen. *Astrophys. J.* **161**, L81 (1970).

22. A. A. Penzias, K. B. Jefferts, and R. W. Wilson, Interstellar $^{12}C^{16}O$, $^{13}C^{16}O$, and $^{12}C^{18}O$. *Astrophys. J.* **165**, 229 (1971).

23. L. E. Snyder and D. Buhl, Observations of radio emission from interstellar hydrogen cyanide. *Astrophys. J.* **163**, L47 (1971).

24. A. A. Penzias, P. M. Solomon, R. W. Wilson, and K. B. Jefferts, Interstellar carbon monosulfide. *Astrophys. J.* **168**, L53 (1971).

25. R. W. Wilson, A. A. Penzias, K. B. Jefferts, M. Kutner, and P. Thaddeus, Discovery of interstellar silicon monoxide. *Astrophys. J.* **167**, L97 (1971).

26. L. E. Snyder and D. Buhl, Detection of interstellar isocyanic acid, methyacetylene and hydrogen isocyanide. *B. A. A. S.* **3**, 388 (1971).

27. K. B. Jefferts, A. A. Penzias, R. W. Wilson, and P. M. Solomon, Detection of interstellar carbonyl sulfide. *Astrophys. J.* **168**, L111 (1971).

28. P. M. Solomon, K. B. Jefferts, A. A. Penzias, and R. W. Wilson, Detection of millimeter emission lines from interstellar methyl cyanide. *Astrophys. J.* **168**, L107 (1971).

29. R. H. Ruben, G. W. Swenson, Jr., R. C. Benson, H. L. Tigelaar, and W. H. Flygare, Radio detection of interstellar formamide. *Astrophys. J.* To be published.

30. D. Buhl and L. E. Snyder, Unidentified interstellar microwave line. *Nature* **228**, 267 (1970).

31. L. E. Snyder and D. Buhl, *B. A. A. S.* To be published.

CHAPTER 3

INFRARED SPECTRA

3.1 High-Resolution Infrared Spectroscopy of Planetary Atmospheres

Kenneth Fox

Jet Propulsion Laboratory	*and*	*Department of Physics and Astronomy*
California Institute of Technology		*The University of Tennessee*
Pasadena, California		*Knoxville, Tennessee*

Introduction

The infrared region of the electromagnetic spectrum has been a productive working ground for recent advances in our quantitative knowledge of planetary atmospheres, and for several startling discoveries. High-resolution spectroscopic techniques have made many of these developments possible. The techniques are theoretical as well as experimental, in laboratories and at observatories. High resolution facilitates the determination of precise values of spectral line positions and intensities, which makes possible the identification of molecular species and the determination of quantitative properties such as temperature, abundance, and pressure.

This review †‡ will concentrate on rotation–vibration spectra of molecules in the range 0.7–2.5μm, or about 4000–14000 cm^{-1}.§ Examples of various

---

† The literature search for this review was originally completed on 26 June 1970, and then updated to 1 January 1971 in the final revision of the manuscript. Some additions were included in proof on 2 December 1971.

‡ An informative review of the infrared spectra of stars has been made recently by Spinrad and Wing [1].

§ One micron $\equiv 1$ μm $\equiv 10^{-6}$ m $= 10\,000$ Å $= 10^{-4}$ cm; 1 μm corresponds to 10 000 cm^{-1} etc.

molecular species in the atmospheres of the planets will be considered. "High resolution" here will mean spectral resolution of approximately 0.1 cm^{-1} or better.

The outer planets, Jupiter, Saturn, Uranus, and Neptune, will be discussed first. The Jovian atmosphere will be considered in detail. It is simple in some respects, complex in others, and intriguing in any event. Then the inner planets, Venus, Mars, Mercury, and Earth will be taken up. Recent developments concerning Venus and Mars will be emphasized. A separate section will be devoted to needed future laboratory and theoretical research. Finally, some consideration will be given to the potential importance of high-resolution infrared spectroscopy in air pollution and other meteorological studies of the Earth's atmosphere.

Table I summarizes some data for molecules in planetary atmospheres to be discussed in this article. There are striking differences among the atmospheric compositions of the outer and inner planets. The Earth's atmosphere appears to be unique in that it consists mainly of molecular nitrogen and oxygen. Table II indicates some of the isotopic variants and other minor molecular constituents which have been, or might be, sought for in planetary atmospheres by means of spectroscopic techniques.

The important questions of how the different atmospheres evolved and how living matter developed will not be discussed here. These aspects have very recently been considered by Rasool [1a].

The Outer Planets

JUPITER

The largest planet in the solar system has an atmosphere whose composition, structure, and dynamics are complicated. Much of our present knowledge and understanding of it was summarized at the Third Arizona Conference on Planetary Atmospheres† held in Tucson during the spring of 1969. Owen has recently presented an excellent general review of the atmosphere of Jupiter [4]. He discussed spectroscopic observations and emphasized that careful study could reveal "essential clues to the origin and evolution of the solar system, and perhaps of life as well." Teifel has written a monograph devoted to the atmosphere of Jupiter [4a]; he has also done a short review of principal results of optical investigations of the structure and chemical composition of the atmospheres of the outer planets [4b].

The only molecules known to be in the Jovian atmosphere are hydrogen, methane, and ammonia. Helium is presumed to be a major constituent, but it

---

† A general review of the atmospheric compositions of the outer planets was given by McElroy [2]. The conference review was presented by Goody [3].

TABLE I

SOME IDENTIFIED MOLECULES IN PLANETARY ATMOSPHERES

Planet	Molecule	Amount[a] (m-atm)	Recent studies		Original detection	
			Dates	Refs.	Dates	Refs.
Jupiter	H_2	67 000–85 000	(1968 –1969)	[19, 21, 22]	(1960)	[12]
	CH_4	30–100	(1969)	[40, 41, 49]	(1932)	[6]
	NH_3	13	(1970)	[57]	(1932)	[6]
Saturn	H_2	190 000	(1969)	[65]	(1963)	[63]
	CH_4	40–350	(1971)	[65a, 65b]	(1952)	[26]
Uranus	H_2	250 000–480 000	(1971)	[72, 73]	(1949 –1952)	[26, 68, 69]
	CH_4	3 500	(1967)	[74]	(1952)	[26]
Neptune	H_2	250 000–480 000	(1963)	[71]	(1949 –1952)	[26, 68]
	CH_4	6 000	(1967)	[74]	(1952)	[26]
Venus	CO_2	3 300	(1967)	[80]	(1932)	[84]
	CO	0.15	(1968)	[123]	(1963 –1968)	[111, 121 –123]
	HCl	0.002	(1967)	[80]	(1967)	[80]
	HF	0.00002	(1967)	[80]	(1967)	[80]
	H_2O	Variable	(1963 –1968)	[91]	(1963 –1964)	[196, 197]
Mars	CO_2	54–90	(1964 –1971)	[104, 143, 159, 160, 164–166, 169a]	(1947)	[26]
	H_2O	0.01–0.04	(1964 –1970)	[143, 146, 147, 150, 152]	(1963)	[75, 144]
	CO	0.05–0.2	(1969 –1971)	[166, 170, 172a]	(1969)	[170]
Earth[b]	N_2	6 240				
	O_2	1 670				
	H_2O	8–200				
	CO_2	2–3				
	CH_4	0.01–0.02				
	H_2	0.004				
	CO	0.0005–0.008				

[a] The references cited should be consulted for the basis, e.g., reflecting-layer or scattering model, of each "amount" determination.

[b] No attempt has been made here to enumerate the recent studies or original detection of molecules in the terrestrial atmosphere. In addition to the molecules listed, primarily for comparison with those in the atmospheres of other planets, the following are also present as nonvariable or variable constituents [195, 195a, 195b]: CH_2O, H_2S, HNO_3, NH_3, NO, NO_2, N_2O, O_3, and SO_2.

TABLE II

SOME POSSIBLE MINOR MOLECULAR CONSTITUENTS IN
PLANETARY ATMOSPHERES

Planet	Molecule	Upper limit on amount[a] (m-atm)	Refs.
Jupiter	HD	500	[29]
	HCN[f]	0.01–2	[29][b]
	CH$_3$D[f,g]	0.06–20	[29][b]
	SiH$_4$[f]	0.01–20	[29][b]
	CH$_3$NH$_2$	0.0005–3	[29][b]
	C$_2$H$_2$	0.004–3	[29][b]
	C$_2$H$_4$	0.005–2	[29][b]
	C$_2$H$_6$	0.03–2.5	[61][b]
	C$_2$N$_2$[f]	0.02	([b])
	PH$_3$	0.03	([b])
	H$_2$S	3	([b])
	H$_2$O	([c])	—
	^{13}CH$_4$[h]	([c])	—
	GeH$_4$[f]	([c])	—
Saturn	NH$_3$	2.5	[26, 55]
	C$_2$H$_6$	2.5	[61]
	O$_3$	0.001	[26]
	SO$_2$	0.0001	[26]
	C$_2$H$_4$	([c])	—
Uranus	O$_3$	0.001	[26]
	SO$_2$	0.0001	[26]
Venus	O$_2$	0.07–0.26[i]	[134, 136]
	C$_3$O$_2$	0.05–0.10	([d])
	HCN	0.003	[80]
	CH$_4$	0.003	[80]
	CH$_3$Cl	0.003	[80]
	CH$_3$F	0.003	[80]
	C$_2$H$_2$	0.003	[80]
	C$_2$H$_4$	0.03	[26]
	C$_2$H$_6$	0.01	[26]
	N$_2$O	1	[26]
	NH$_3$	0.04	[26]
Mars	O$_2$	0.2–0.7	[134, 143, 173a]
	CH$_2$O	0.003–0.005	([e,j])
	CH$_2$O$_2$	0.007	([j])
	CH$_4$	0.004	([e])
	C$_2$H$_2$	2	([j])
	COS	0.002–0.15	([e,j])
	C$_3$O$_2$	0.02	([j])

TABLE II (*continued*)

Planet	Molecule	Upper limit on amount[a] (m-atm)	Refs.
Mars	NO	0.20	([e])
	NO_2	0.025	([j])
	N_2O	0.0008	([e])
	N_2O_4	0.05	([j])
	NH_3	0.001	([e])
	HCl	0.0011	([j])
	H_2S	3	([j])
	O_3	([c])	—
Mercury	O_2	1	[174]
	CO_2	0.58	[175]
	H_2O	0.04	[174]
	CO	0.10	[176]
	N_2O	0.02	[176]
	NH_3	0.01	[176]
	CH_4	0.003	[176]

[a] The references cited should be consulted for the basis, e.g., reflecting-layer or scattering model, of each " amount " determination.

[b] The lower, or only, as the case may be, upper limit was deduced by F. C. Gillett, F. J. Low, and W. A. Stein, *Astrophys. J.* **157**, 925 (1969) from spectra in the 2.8–14-μm region, with resolving power $\lambda/\Delta\lambda = 50$.

[c] There is no measured upper limit for the amount of this molecule in the planetary atmosphere.

[d] T. Owen, *J. Atmos. Sci.* **25**, 583 (1968).

[e] G. P. Kuiper, *Comm. Lunar Planet. Lab.* **2**, 79 (1964).

[f] A possible identification has been discussed very recently by Münch and Neugebauer [62a].

[g] Beer *et al.* [62c] have now reported an observation of deuterated methane..

[h] Detected recently by Fox and Owen [62d].

[i] A new upper limit is being deduced by J. S. Margolis, R. A. Schorn, and L. D. Gray Young (personal communication, 1971).

[j] The higher, or only, as the case may be, upper limit was produced recently by R. Beer, R. H. Norton, and J. V. Martonchik, *Icarus* **15**, 1 (1971) from spectra in the 2500–3500 cm^{-1} region, with a resolution of 0.58 cm^{-1} (apodized).

has not yet been directly detected. The detection of helium and the determination of the relative abundance of hydrogen to helium have cosmological implications. It is of great importance to determine helium concentrations in different astronomical bodies [5].

H_2

Although the abundance of hydrogen in the Jovian atmosphere is very much larger than that of methane and ammonia, the latter molecules were first identified spectroscopically by Wildt [6] in 1932. Molecular hydrogen has no allowed dipole spectrum, but does have a weak allowed quadrupole spectrum [7–9]. In 1938, Herzberg [7] suggested that a sufficiently large amount of H_2 could be detected by means of its quadrupole rotation–vibration spectrum. Several of these lines were later observed in the laboratory [10, 11], with pressures of 5–10 atm of H_2 and path lengths of up to 5500 m achieved in a 22-m multiple-reflection absorption tube. The observed lines were $S(0)$, $S(1)$, $S(2)$, and $Q(1)$ in the 2–0 and 3–0 bands; these lines were sharp and widely spaced.

Not until 1960 was a detection of H_2 in the Jovian atmosphere reported: Kiess *et al.* [12] observed four lines at wavelengths very close to those in Herzberg's 3–0 laboratory spectrum. Estimates of the H_2 abundance were made possible by subsequent laboratory intensity measurements of Rank *et al.* [13, 14]. They used a 44-m multiple-reflection absorption tube in conjunction with an 8.5-m grating spectrograph to measure line strengths in the 1–0, 2–0, and 3–0 bands. The $S(1)$ line of the 3–0 band at 8150.7Å was the weakest measured under the following conditions: resolving power $\approx 2 \times 10^5$, plate dispersion $= 0.557$Å mm^{-1}, H_2 pressure ≈ 3 atm, and number of reflections ≈ 100. This quadrupole line was observed to be extremely sharp [13]. Saturation was taken into account in a determination of line strengths by the curve-of-growth method.† These results were applied to equivalent widths† determined from the 3–0 band of the Jovian spectrum [17, 18]. In addition, the strength of the $S(1)$ line of the 4–0 band, which was too weak to be observed in the laboratory, was calculated [14] and applied to the line observed in the Jovian spectrum by Spinrad and Trafton[18]. The average hydrogen

---

† It is desirable here to define several terms related to absorption lines, formed either in the laboratory or in an atmosphere: The *equivalent width* of an absorption line is simply the integrated area under the curve of absorption (relative to incident intensity) versus frequency or wavelength, and its units are cm^{-1} or Å, respectively. The *curve of growth* is the curve of equivalent width versus the product of the number of absorbing molecules times the absorption coefficient or line intensity. In the region where the curve of growth is approximately linear, the absorption line is said to be *unsaturated*. The extent of nonlinearity or *saturation* depends on the line shape. For more details, see, for example, the work of Goody [15] or Moroz [16].

abundance was deduced [4] to be on the order of 100 km-atm, a value much greater than any earlier investigation had yielded.

Recently, Owen and Mason evaluated the equivalent widths of the $S(1)$ lines in the 3–0 and 4–0 bands from a series of new observations of Jupiter [19]. The 3–0 $S(1)$ line is reproduced [4] in Fig. 1. Using the laboratory data [14] and the extended calculations of matrix elements [20] for the 4–0 quadrupole transitions, they deduced a H_2 abundance of 85 ± 15 km-atm. In a similar way, independent measurements by Emerson et al. [21] of the $S(1)$ 4–0 lines were analyzed using the work of Rank et al. [14] and Birnbaum and Poll [20], and yielded 75 ± 15 km-atm, neglecting scattering, for the Jovian H_2 abundance.

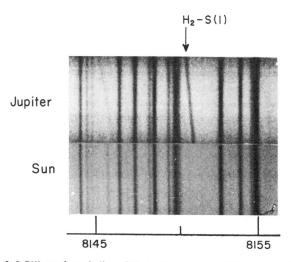

FIG. 1. The 3–0 $S(1)$ quadrupole line of H_2 in the spectrum of Jupiter, originally recorded at 2.5 Å mm^{-1} dispersion at the McDonald Observatory (courtesy of Owen [4]; copyright 1970 by the American Association for the Advancement of Science). Inclination of the Jovian line results from the Doppler effect caused by the planet's rapid rotation.

Fink and Belton (22) have made photoelectric observations of the $S(0)$ and $S(1)$ lines of the 3–0 band and the $S(1)$ line of the 4–0 band. They calculated curves of growth based on line shapes which are *narrowed* as a result of collisions between the absorbing molecules and their neighbors. The latter take up some of the excess momentum from the absorbed photons, and the probability of absorption at line center is thus increased. Collision narrowing was first predicted by Dicke [23], and subsequently observed by Rank and Wiggins in the H_2 quadrupole spectrum [24]. The line-shape theory developed by Galatry [25] for this phenomenon was used by Fink and Belton. They concluded that the interpretation of Jovian absorption lines in the H_2 3–0 and (as yet unobserved) 2–0 and 1–0 bands requires careful consideration of collision

narrowing. The effect on the weak 4–0 $S(1)$ line appears to be negligible for the interpretation of its equivalent width. An abundance of 67 ± 17 km-atm of H_2 at an effective temperature of $145 \pm 20°K$ was found on the basis of a simple reflecting-layer model atmosphere. An analysis of the data on the basis of a very simple scattering atmosphere led to an unsatisfactory result.†

A short summary of some measured H_2 quadrupole rotation–vibration lines is given in Table III. There is a need for further laboratory and theoretical studies on the H_2 quadrupole lines. This work will be discussed in some detail later in this article, where a separate section will be devoted to future research.

TABLE III

SOME MEASURED H_2 QUADRUPOLE ROTATION–VIBRATION LINE POSITIONS

Line	Band			
	1–0ᵃ (cm⁻¹)	2–0ᵃ (cm⁻¹)	3–0ᵃ (cm⁻¹)	4–0ᵇ (Å)
$Q(1)$	4155.243	8075.42	11764.96	—
$S(0)$	4497.830	8406.36	12084.66	6435.03
$S(1)$	4712.895	8604.26	12265.55	6367.80
$S(2)$	4916.990	8785.54	12424.44	—
$S(3)$	5108.399	—	—	—

ᵃ Rank *et al.* [149]; line positions are in vacuum.
ᵇ Giver and Spinrad [64]; line positions are in air.

CH_4

Recent studies of methane absorption provide an excellent example of the importance of high-resolution spectroscopy. Compared to hydrogen, CH_4 is a relatively minor constituent of the Jovian atmosphere. The abundance of CH_4 was first estimated by Kuiper [26] to be 150 m-atm on the basis of comparisons of low-resolution laboratory and Jovian spectra of absorption bands in the 0.6–0.9-μm region.

† The values of abundance, temperature, and pressure deduced from planetary spectra depend on the particular model used for line formation in the atmosphere. These models range from a simple, reflecting cloud layer in the atmosphere to scattering of various degrees of complexity. The dependence of scattering of radiation on its wavelength can lead, for example, to different abundance determinations for a given molecular species in an atmosphere. Details will not be given in this article. A general discussion can be found, for example, in the work of Goody [15], with further specific details in the original references given there. Also, Hunt [25a] has recently reviewed computational techniques for analyzing the transfer of radiation through a model cloudy atmosphere.

Walker and Hayes [27] in 1967 reported equivalent widths of several lines in the Jovian methane band centered at about 1.105 μm (≈ 9050 cm^{-1}). Their observations were made with an S-1 image tube,[†] and represent an early application of this mode of observation to planetary spectroscopy. Owen [29] had previously assigned rotational quantum numbers to many of the lines in this Jovian band on the basis of assignments by Childs [30] for a medium-resolution (~ 0.5 cm^{-1}) laboratory spectrum. This rotation–vibration band was interpreted as the second overtone $3v_3$ of the triply degenerate methane fundamental v_3 at 3020 cm^{-1} [31]. Walker and Hayes tried to deduce a rotational temperature for the portion of the Jovian atmosphere where this band was formed, but only inconclusive results were obtained.

Margolis and Fox [32] obtained laboratory spectra of the $3v_3$ band with resolution of about 0.06 cm^{-1}. Most of the fine structure splitting, due to Coriolis interactions, in the rotational J multiplets was resolved. The R branch of $3v_3$ is shown in Fig. 2. This spectrum has a strikingly regular appearance, with fine structure comparable to that observed in v_3 [33] and $2v_3$ [34] of CH$_4$ and $2v_3$ of CD$_4$ [35]. The patterns of spacing and intensity of fine structure components in the J multiplets have turned out to be useful for the assignment of rotational quantum numbers in rotation–vibration bands of tetrahedral molecules [36, 37]. On the basis of the patterns observed in the high-resolution spectra of $3v_3$, the earlier assignments [27, 29, 30] were confirmed.

Margolis and Fox then began studies [38–41] of the Jovian $3v_3$ equivalent widths to obtain a rotational temperature and an abundance for CH$_4$. The critical point of departure of this work was the inclusion of saturation effects. A Lorentz shape was assumed to be adequate to describe a single unblended absorption line. It was first shown [38] that, for a Lorentz half-width $\gamma = 0.08$ cm^{-1},[‡] the $R(1)$ line in the Jovian spectrum was considerably saturated. The line strengths for the Jovian absorptions were determined by constructing a curve of growth for each J multiplet for a large range of values of γ. By means of the relation between the line strengths and the Boltzmann factor, a rotational temperature was deduced for each value of γ. All the multiplets $R(1)$–$R(7)$ were used in obtaining a least squares fit for the Jovian temperature, but $R(0)$ was excluded because Owen and Woodman [43] had noted that this singlet was badly blended with a telluric line.

To determine the Jovian CH$_4$ abundance, a series of laboratory measurements were made [44]. The line intensity of each of the J multiplets $R(0)$–$R(7)$ was determined by a curve-of-growth method. Equivalent widths were measured at a constant pressure of 500 Torr over paths from 8 to 160 m, sufficient to

---

[†] A review of the use of image tubes in astronomy has been given by Baum [28].

[‡] This value of γ was based on the estimate $0.06 \leq \gamma \leq 0.08$ cm^{-1} from observations of Jovian methane absorptions at 6190 Å by Spinrad and Trafton [18] and Beckman [42].

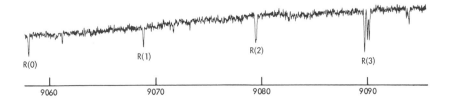

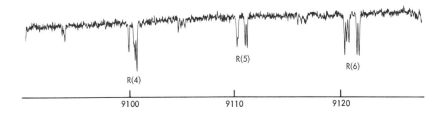

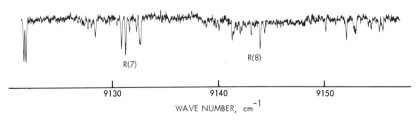

WAVE NUMBER, cm^{-1}

FIG. 2. Laboratory spectrum of CH_4 in the R branch of the $3\nu_3$ band centered at about 9050 cm^{-1}. The absorption path was 64 m, the pressure 75 Torr, and the temperature 294° K [32].

cause saturation of the multiplets. A Voigt profile† was used for the absorption coefficient $k(\nu)$ of *each* line in a J multiplet. The Doppler half-width was calculated to be 0.017 cm^{-1} at 295°K. The Lorentz half-width at 500 Torr was determined to be 0.058 cm^{-1} from direct laboratory measurements on the relatively isolated singlets $R(0)$ and $R(1)$. As in the rotational temperature determination, the line positions and relative intensities to be used in $k(\nu)$ were taken from the high-resolution laboratory spectra [32]. From the Jovian and laboratory line strengths, the product $\eta N_{2\!\!\!\downarrow}$ was then determined for each J multiplet, where $N_{2\!\!\!\downarrow}$ is the abundance of Jovian methane (the subscript $2\!\!\!\downarrow$ conventionally denoting Jupiter) and η is the " air mass " factor, which takes into consideration the actual absorbing path in the planetary atmosphere.

† See, for example, the work of Jeffries [45].

Appropriate partition functions and Boltzmann factors for Jovian and laboratory temperatures were used.

The results for the methane rotational temperature and abundance are summarized in Figs. 3 and 4. The horizontal lines on the right-hand ordinates

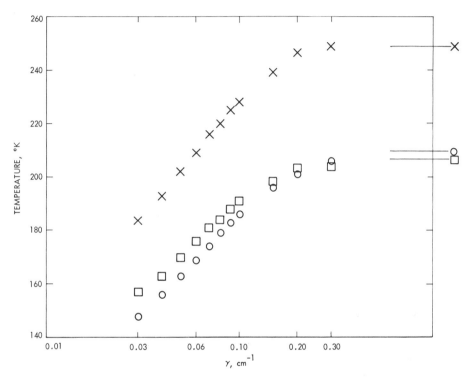

FIG. 3. Variation of the calculated Jovian CH_4 rotational temperature with Lorentz half-width γ; based on an analysis of the $3\nu_3$ band. (O) ECL-396, ($\times$) ECL-405, and (□) trace average refer to two plates of Jupiter and their average reported by Walker and Hayes [27] (see [39–41]).

denote asymptotic values corresponding to no saturation. The studies originally done [39, 40] for $0.03 \leq \gamma \leq 0.10$ cm^{-1} were extended [41] to larger values of γ because of higher-resolution Jovian spectra in the 1.1-μm region obtained by Farmer [46] and Owen [47]. A preliminary study of several unresolved J multiplets in these spectra by a technique described in the appendix to Ref. 41 suggested that γ might be somewhat larger than 0.10 cm^{-1}. However, more recent measurements by Bergstralh [48] indicate that $\gamma \approx 0.07$–0.09 cm^{-1}.

The results of Margolis and Fox suggest that the Jovian methane abundance is probably less than 100 m-atm but greater than 30 m-atm, with a likely

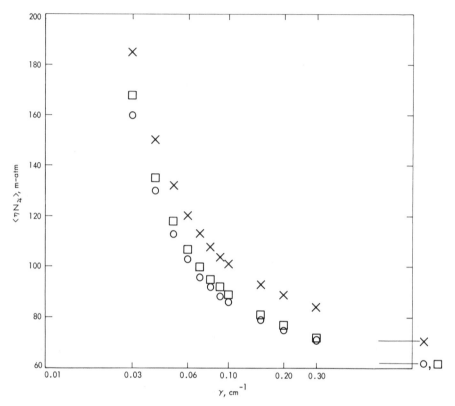

Fig. 4. Variation of the calculated product of Jovian CH$_4$ abundance and air mass factor with Lorentz half-width γ; based on an analysis of the $3\nu_3$ band. (O) ECL-396, ($\times$) ECL-405, and ($\square$) trace average refer to two plates of Jupiter and their average reported by Walker and Hayes [27] (see [39–41]).

value of 40–45 m-atm indicated by the most recent measurement of γ [48]. The range of values of $N_{2\text{l}}$ arises partly from the range of γ; other sources of uncertainty are the value of η, errors in the measured equivalent widths, and neglect of atmospheric scattering. The validity of a reflecting-layer model atmosphere has been examined recently [48a]. Belton [49] has also recognized the importance of saturation in his estimate of the methane rotational temperature and abundance in the Jovian atmosphere. On the basis of Walker and Hayes' data and the strength of $R(2)$ from Margolis' laboratory spectra, Belton obtained $N_{2\text{l}} \approx 30$ m-atm. This result may be about 25% too low [40] because saturation in the blended regions between fine structure components of the multiplets was neglected.

An accurate value for the CH$_4$ abundance, together with that of H$_2$, would provide the C/H ratio. This is relevant to the origin and evolution of the solar

system, since it bears on the mass-dependent fractionation processes which could dominate in the outer planets such as Jupiter.

In the shorter-wavelength regions, higher spectral and spatial resolution become possible. The latter would permit studies of CH_4 absorption in the Great Red Spot, for example. Methane bands at wavelengths shorter than 1 μm have already been observed in the Jovian atmosphere, in the 8500 Å region [12, 50] and below. In fact, the 6190Å methane band was one of the first two (the other was the 6450 Å ammonia band) observed in Jupiter's atmosphere [51]. Also, a CH_4 band at 6800 Å obtained by Kuiper [52] in the laboratory with an effective path of 5.5 km-atm has been identified by Owen [53] in the spectra of Jupiter, Saturn, and Uranus. However, none of these bands can yet be used effectively to understand planetary atmospheres, because of the absence of adequate laboratory and theoretical studies. For example, although the 6190 Å band has been used recently to make inferences regarding the Jovian atmosphere [18, 19, 42] this band has not been analyzed theoretically. Details of the needed studies will be presented in a later section on future research.

NH_3

High-resolution studies of ammonia absorption have been based primarily on the red band at 6450Å [18, 54–57]. From laboratory curves of growth for individual lines in this band, Mason [57], using Jovian spectra taken by Owen at the McDonald and Kitt Peak National Observatories between 1963 and 1968, has recently deduced an abundance of 13 ± 3 m-atm. This may be compared with Kuiper's [26] earlier estimate of 7 m-atm. Laboratory measurements of NH_3 self- and H_2-broadening [14, 56] of lines in the 6450 Å band had been used to derive [56] an upper limit of 2.6 atm for the pressure at the top of the Jovian cloud layer seen in red light. A determination, based on the laboratory studies of Rank et al. [14] and an assumed Jovian temperature of 150°K where the 6450 Å band was formed, of the effective pressure by Mason [57] yielded 2.5 atm. By comparison, Farmer [46] obtained 2.3 ± 0.5 atm from high-resolution spectra of the 1.1-μm CH_4 band. In addition to the omnipresent scattering problem, the nonuniform distribution and the condensation of NH_3 in the Jovian atmosphere make strong inferences difficult.

Three lines in the 5520 Å band [56, 57a] of NH_3 have been discovered by Owen [57b] on spectrograms of Jupiter taken at the McDonald Observatory. As pointed out by Giver et al. [56], these absorptions may give insight into the possible wavelength dependence of the Jovian atmospheric opacity. However, Owen [57b] has stressed that the lack of theoretical knowledge concerning temperature effects on line intensities, and especially energy level studies for the observed transitions, precludes precise comments on any variation of atmospheric transparency with wavelength.

Chemical equilibrium calculations [58, 59], including the most recent work

by Lewis [60], based on assumed distributions of elements, have concluded that H_2, CH_4, NH_3, and He are the only gases likely to be present in detectable amounts in the Jovian upper atmosphere. However, Owen [4] has suggested that, under suitable conditions, H_2O and H_2S may be detectable spectroscopically at high resolution. Using laboratory and planetary spectra in the photographic infrared region, Owen [29, 61] has obtained an *upper limit* on the Jovian abundance of HD (from the 3–0 rotation–vibration allowed dipole band [62]) and CH_3D, SiH_4, HCN, CH_3NH_2, C_2H_2, C_2H_4, and C_2H_6. Very recently, Münch and Neugebauer [62a] have discussed a possible identification of CH_3D, HCN, C_2N_2, SiH_4, or GeH_4 [62b] from spectra of Jupiter at 4.5–5.1 μm. These spectra were taken at the Cassegrain focus of the 200-in. reflector of the Hale Observatories, Mt. Palomar.

Isotopic ratios such as H/D and $^{12}C/^{13}C$ are useful for understanding the origin and evolution of the solar system. In particular, the distribution of deuterium with distance from the sun bears on the formation of the solar system. Unfortunately, deuterium has not yet been detected in the sun (or other stars, or the interstellar medium) or in any planetary atmosphere other than that of the Earth. Since the preceding sentence was written, Beer *et al.* [62c] reported an observation of CH_3D in the atmosphere of Jupiter. Whole-planet spectra were taken in the 1800–2200-cm^{-1} region, with a resolution of 0.55 cm^{-1} at the coudé focus of the 107-in. telescope of the McDonald Observatory. Neither a CH_3D abundance nor a H/D ratio was given, because of the lack of certain relevant experimental and theoretical details concerning, for example, line formation in the Jovian atmosphere.

Fox and Owen [62d] have now detected carbon-13 methane in the Jovian atmosphere.† High-resolution spectra in the 1.1-μm region were taken using the coudé spectrograph of the 82-in. Struve reflector at the McDonald Observatory. A comparison of the Jovian lines with laboratory data provided by Mantz and Rao [62e] permitted the identification of $^{13}CH_4$. Neither a $^{13}CH_4$ abundance nor a $^{12}C/^{13}C$ ratio has been deduced from the preliminary results, although it is expected that previous extensive studies of the $^{12}CH_4$ $3v_3$ band in the 1.1-μm region by Margolis and Fox [32, 38–41, 44] will be of considerable assistance.

SATURN

H_2

Beyond Jupiter, very little spectroscopic data of high resolution, or indeed any kind, are available on the planetary atmospheres. Münch and Spinrad [63] first reported a detection of the $S(0)$ and $S(1)$ lines of the 4–0 rotation–

---

† A preliminary report of this work was given by T. Owen in an invited paper, "Spectroscopic Studies of the Outer Planets," at the Ohio State University Symposium on Molecular Structure and Spectroscopy, 14–18 June, 1971, Columbus, Ohio.

vibration quadrupole H_2 band in the spectrum of Saturn. Measurement of the equivalent widths of these lines in spectra obtained by Münch and by Giver and Spinrad [64] led to two values of rotational temperature: $126 \pm 30°K$ and $103 \pm 20°K$. This work utilized the early quadrupole matrix element calculations of James and Coolidge [8]. Owen [65] rederived the temperature to be 90°K, based on the 4–0 relative intensities of Giver and Spinrad [64], but with newly calculated [20] matrix elements. In addition, he measured the equivalent width of the $S(1)$ line in the 3–0 band which, when combined with the 4–0 data, yielded a H_2 abundance of 190 ± 40 km-atm and a pressure of 1 atm. McElroy [2] has suggested that scattering in Saturn's atmosphere and collision narrowing of the H_2 lines may have an important effect on these preliminary results.

CH_4

The first, and until very recently only, estimate of the abundance of methane in Saturn's atmosphere was made by Kuiper [26] who deduced a value of 350 m-atm on the basis of a comparison of laboratory and planetary spectra in the 0.6–0.9-μm region. In 1971, Trafton [65a] and Bergstralh [65b] reported new results based on observations of the 1.1-μm CH_4 $3\nu_3$ band at the McDonald Observatory. Rotational temperatures in the range of 100–160°K and values of $\eta N \approx 40$–110 m-atm were inferred.

Giver [55] has reported a marginal spectroscopic detection of the 6450 Å NH_3 band. As there appears to be some uncertainty about this work and an earlier abundance estimate [66], Owen has suggested (as reported by McElroy [2]) that 2.5 m-atm be regarded as an upper limit for the abundance. Also, an abundance of less than 2.5 m-atm of C_2H_6 was obtained by Owen [61].

Titan, one of Saturn's ten satellites, is the only one in the solar system known to have an atmosphere. The CH_4 absorption band at 6190 Å was noted in a low-resolution spectrum of Titan reported by Kuiper [67] in 1944. Trafton [67a] has recently considered a possible identification of H_2 in Titan's atmosphere.

URANUS

H_2

Herzberg [68] first reported the identification of H_2 in the atmosphere of Uranus (and Neptune) on the basis of a broad feature observed by Kuiper [26, 69] at 8270 Å. The absorption was attributed to the pressure-induced $S(0)$ line of the 3–0 dipole band,† reproduced by Herzberg [68] in the laboratory with an 80-m path of H_2 at 100 atm pressure and a temperature of 78°K. Spinrad [71] also later identified a broad absorption feature at 6420 Å on

---

† A review of the pressure-induced infrared spectrum of molecular hydrogen and its application to the study of planetary atmospheres has been given recently by Welsh [70].

Uranus (and Neptune) as the pressure-induced $S(0)$ line of the 4–0 dipole band. Subsequently, Giver and Spinrad reported [64] the observation of the relatively narrow $S(0)$ and $S(1)$ quadrupole 4–0 lines (in the spectrum of Uranus only). Neglecting saturation, they obtained from their measured equivalent widths a temperature of $124 \pm 30°K$. Poll [72], using improved calculated line intensities [20], deduced a temperature of $98 \pm 30°K$ and an abundance of roughly 250 km-atm. Also, McElroy and Belton considered (as reported by McElroy [2]) the quadrupole lines of Giver and Spinrad [64], and obtained an abundance of about 480 km-atm (with a reflecting-layer model) and a temperature of $118 \pm 30°K$ (using a curve of growth which allowed for collision narrowing of lines). However, they [73] have recently emphasized that a simple reflecting-layer theory is inappropriate for line formation on Uranus. (It is noted [73] that the uncertainty $\pm 30°K$ above should be increased to $\pm 40°K$.) The combined quadrupole and pressure-induced dipole spectra comprise an interesting combination of data which has already yielded some results [72].

CH_4

Owen [74] has compared spectra of Uranus with high-dispersion laboratory spectra of CH_4 taken with effective absorptions of up to 5.15 km–atm in the 7500 Å region. He estimated the CH_4 abundance to be on the order of 3.5 km-atm with an uncertainty of $\pm 35\%$ at best. Fox and Ozier [74a] have recently discussed the importance of methane to pressure induced absorption in the atmospheres of the outer planets, especially Uranus and Neptune.

NEPTUNE

H_2

The broad pressure-induced features [26, 68, 71] in the spectrum of Neptune may indicate approximately the same abundance of H_2 as in the atmosphere of Uranus.

CH_4

Owen [74], by analogy with his recent estimate for Uranus, has revised Kuiper's [26] value for the abundance of CH_4 on Neptune upward to about 6 km-atm, with an associated uncertainty even larger than $\pm 35\%$.

The Inner Planets

The bulk of this section will be concerned with the planets Venus and Mars.†
Many scientifically exciting and historic discoveries were made in studies of

---

† In a very recent review [74b], Ingersoll and Leovy have compared the compositions, thermal structures, and dynamics of the lower and upper atmospheres of Venus and Mars, with consideration given to some of the problems of their evolution.

these two planets during the 1960's. Conventional high-resolution grating spectroscopy by Spinrad et al. [75] at Mt. Wilson led to the detection of water vapor in the Martian atmosphere in 1963. Janine and Pierre Connes [76–78] developed the technique of Fourier spectroscopy to the extent that near-infrared spectra of Venus and Mars were obtained with 0.08 cm^{-1} resolution [79] at the Observatoire de Saint-Michel in 1966–1967. A striking example of the achievements based on this enormous improvement in resolution was the unexpected detection of comparatively minute amounts of HCl and HF in the atmosphere of Venus [80]. Data from Venera 4 and Mariner 5,† as well as high-resolution ground-based observations to be discussed in this section, imply that the atmosphere of the planet Venus is mostly CO_2 ($\gtrsim 90\%$). Much of the data has been brought to bear on questions of atmospheric structure and dynamics. It is not intended, however, to treat these problems in the present review.

VENUS

CO_2

The expectation that the atmospheres of Venus and Earth were similar led to early attempts at spectroscopic detection of molecular oxygen and water vapor. However, high-dispersion spectra taken at Mt. Wilson during the decade starting in 1922 failed to indicate any Doppler-shifted O_2 or H_2O lines for Venus [83, 84]. In 1932, Adams and Dunham [84] observed three absorption bands with heads at 7820, 7883, and 8689 Å, with P and R branch structure. Although laboratory spectra for direct comparison were not available at that time, a quadratic fit to the lines in the Venus spectrum yielded [84] a moment of inertia close to the value for CO_2. Shortly thereafter, Adel and Dennison [85] assigned vibrational quantum numbers to the observed bands. Then, in 1934, Adel and Slipher [86, 87] reported laboratory spectra of these bands broadened at a pressure of 47 atm of CO_2 and a path length of 45 m. About fifteen years after the observations by Adams and Dunham, the CO_2 bands were reproduced in the laboratory by Herzberg [11] using a 22-m multiple-reflection tube and CO_2 pressures of 1 atm and less. With scattering ignored, it was inferred from these measurements that the equivalent of 1 km-atm of CO_2 was present above a reflecting layer in the Venus atmosphere. From a reflecting-layer model and linear absorption law

† On October 18, 1967, the USSR's Venera 4 space probe entered the atmosphere of Venus, and on the next day the USA's Mariner 5 spacecraft flew close by that planet. Scientists from the Soviet Union met with their counterparts in the United States to discuss the results and their implications at the Second Arizona Conference on Planetary Atmospheres. Short reviews were presented by Vakhnin [81], Donahue [81a], and Johnson [81b]. Also of interest is an earlier Tucson Symposium described in the work edited by Brandt and McElroy [82]. In November 1971, the USA's Mariner 9 and the USSR's Mars 2 began orbiting the planet Mars.

applied to the data of Adams and Dunham [84], various estimates around 300°K were made for the rotational temperature of the Venus atmosphere [66, 88, 89].

At the McDonald Observatory in 1947, Kuiper [26] observed Venus CO_2 absorption bands at 1–2.5 μm with spectral resolution of ~ 4 cm^{-1}. Laboratory studies in this region led to an estimate for Venus of 125 m-atm of CO_2. Resolution in the planetary rotation–vibration spectra was too low to distinguish individual rotation lines; consequently, it was not possible to derive a rotational temperature, or to consider saturation effects accurately. Since 1965, an enormous quantity of high-resolution spectra of Venus in the photographic and near-infrared regions has been obtained.

Much of the recent work at shorter wavelengths has been described by Gray Young, Schorn, Barker, and co-workers in a series of papers on high-dispersion spectroscopic studies of Venus [90–98a]. The observations were made with the coudé spectrograph of the 82-in. Struve reflector at the McDonald Observatory. The approach was to resolve the rotation lines in each rotation–vibration band, resulting in more accurate measurements of equivalent widths, and thus more precise temperature and CO_2 abundance determinations. For example, many spectra of the 10,488 Å band were obtained [96]. This band had first been identified by Herzberg† as due to CO_2. Gray Young et al. [96] interpreted the data in their 31 best plates in two ways. Before 1956, a linear absorption law had been generally assumed. However, Chamberlain and Kuiper [100] suggested that even weak absorption lines in a scattering atmosphere should follow a square-root absorption law for a continuum albedo of ~ 1. More recently, Regas [101] and McClatchey [102] showed that, for such a scattering atmosphere, weak lines could also follow a linear absorption law. Accordingly, Gray Young et al. [96] obtained an average rotational temperature of 244°K assuming a square-root absorption law; they also used curves of growth to deduce the value 237 $\pm$ 3°K. Gray Young has also studied [102a] the effective pressure for line formation in the atmosphere of Venus, using CO_2 spectra obtained earlier [92, 94–98]. It was concluded from this work [102a] that weak absorption lines are indeed formed deeper in the atmosphere.

Belton et al. [103] have independently obtained spectra of several of the bands observed by Gray Young et al. These spectra were taken at the McMath Solar Telescope of the Kitt Peak National Observatory in a photoelectric pulse-counting mode [104]. Their interpretations were based on a radiative-transfer model of line formation [105] applied to a semi-infinite, homogeneous, isotropically scattering atmosphere. The 1.05-μm Venus CO_2 band was compared to a calculated spectrum which included the instrumental profile. A temperature of 270 $\pm$ 25°K was deduced.

---

† As noted in a McDonald Observatory report by Struve [99].

In 1966, Janine and Pierre Connes obtained high-resolution ($\sim$0.08 cm^{-1}, after suitable apodization) spectra of Venus in the near-infrared (in spectral regions corresponding to atmospheric windows at 3950–5300, 5500–7200, and 7600–8500 cm^{-1}) [76–78]. This resolution represented an improvement of two orders of magnitude over earlier measurements [106]. Venus absorption lines were distinguished from those of solar and terrestrial origin by means of solar and planetary traces recorded on a single chart by an automatic plotter. The work of Connes *et al.* [107] and Pinard [108] demonstrated the practicality of their method for obtaining precise line positions and intensities. Their measurements were made relative to the ^{198}Hg 5461 Å line. Comparison of CO lines measured in the laboratory [109] with those found in the Connes' Venus spectra (reduced to vacuum and corrected for Doppler effects) indicated [80] a mean error of 0.001 cm^{-1} with a rms scatter of 0.002 cm^{-1}.

About a year before the data of Venera 4 and Mariner 5 suggested that the Venus atmosphere was predominantly CO_2, the Connes' spectra were used to infer that "CO_2 is probably the major constituent in the Venus atmosphere" [80]. An effective temperature of $240 \pm 10°$K and a CO_2 abundance of 3.3 ± 0.3 km-atm were deduced from rotation–vibration lines in a "hot" band of $^{12}C^{16}O_2$ at 5687 cm^{-1} and a band of $^{12}C^{16}O^{18}O$ at 5858 cm^{-1}. It was assumed (and verified by comparing intensities of CO_2 lines in other spectral regions) that the $^{16}O/^{18}O$ abundance ratio is the same for Venus and the Earth. Many other rotation–vibration lines not previously observed and/or resolved have been identified [110] in the Connes' spectra. For example, the $2\nu_3$ band of $^{13}C^{16}O^{18}O$ at 2.21 μm had been observed at much lower resolution by Kuiper [106] and Moroz [111] in spectra of Venus. From a study of the Connes' line positions and equivalent widths in this band, Gray Young [112] deduced a rotational temperature of $245 \pm 3°$K. More recently, Gray Young [113] has considered a band of $^{12}C^{16}O^{18}O$ identified [110] at 1.71 μm in the Connes spectra. With an assumed constant line width, as in the earlier work [112], a rotational temperature of $242 \pm 2°$K was found; but with a rotational quantum number dependence calculated [114] for linewidths of $^{12}C^{16}O_2$, the rotational temperature became $249 \pm 3°$K.

HF *and* HCl

A discussion of minor constituents in the atmosphere of Venus must include the remarkable identification of absorption lines due to HCl and HF in the Connes' spectra [80]. Rotation–vibration lines in the R branch of the 2–0 band of both H^{35}Cl and H^{37}Cl were found between 5683 and 5790 cm^{-1}. Several of these lines are shown in Fig. 5. The two series of sharp lines had an intensity ratio of about 3 to 1. The agreement in position for the Doppler-corrected Venus lines and H^{35}Cl laboratory lines [115] was better than 0.01 cm^{-1}. There was also good agreement [116] for H^{37}Cl. On the basis of the Venus equivalent widths and laboratory linewidth and intensity data [117, 118]

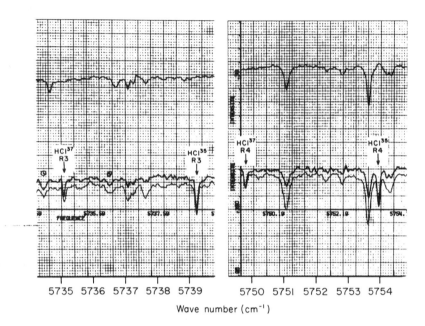

Wave number (cm⁻¹)

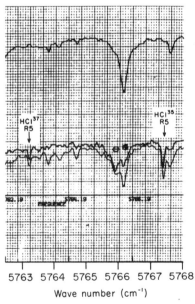

Wave number (cm⁻¹)

FIG. 5. *R* branch lines of the 2–0 rotation–vibration bands of HCl observed in the Connes' Venus spectra (courtesy of Kaplan [80]; © 1967 by the University of Chicago).

an effective amount of HCl was obtained which led to an HCl/CO_2 abundance ratio of 6×10^{-7} ($\pm 20\%$) on Venus. Lines in the 1–0 and 2–0 rotation–vibration bands [115] of HF were also observed in the Venus spectra. Figure 6 shows two lines of the 1–0 band; $R(1)$ is an extremely strong line. A study of

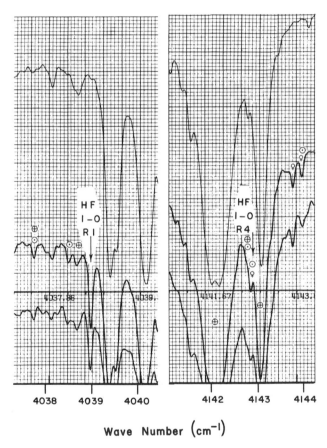

Wave Number (cm^{-1})

FIG. 6. $R(1)$ and $R(4)$ of the 1–0 rotation–vibration band of HF observed in the Connes' Venus spectra (courtesy of Kaplan [80]; © 1967 by the University of Chicago).

the equivalent widths with the use of laboratory data [119, 120] yielded an estimated (to within a factor of two) HF/CO_2 abundance ratio of 5×10^{-9}. Other gases which should have appeared in the spectra if present to more than one part in 10^6, but were not detected, were CH_4, CH_3Cl, CH_3F, C_2H_2, and HCN.

CO

Broad band spectra obtained by Sinton [121] and Moroz [111, 122] indicated the presence of CO in the Venus atmosphere. However, Kuiper [106] earlier had found no evidence of CO absorption in somewhat better spectra. The issue was settled [123] by the clear resolution of more than 30 CO lines of the 2–0 band at 2.35 μm in the Connes' spectra [79]. These lines had been measured in the laboratory with extremely high resolution [124] and are used as wavelength standards [125]. There was good evidence for the presence of the isotopic species $^{13}C^{16}O$ and $^{12}C^{18}O$, but $^{12}C^{17}O$ was not detected.

The measured equivalent widths of the CO lines in the Venus spectrum were interpreted [123] with the help of the following laboratory data: the total CO band strength [126], linewidths in self-broadened CO [127, 128], and line strengths in several CO_2 bands in the 4400–4600 cm^{-1} region [129, 130]. A "most probable" CO/CO_2 abundance ratio of 45 ($\pm$10) $\times$ 10^{-6} was obtained, independent of the radiative transfer process in the Venus clouds, assuming the CO and CO_2 to be uniformly mixed.

H_2O

No evidence for the presence of H_2O on Venus has been found [80] in the Connes' high-resolution spectra. Strong absorption by H_2O vapor in the Earth's atmosphere generally hampers the detection of this gas in other planetary atmospheres. This problem was accentuated in the Connes' Venus spectra, which were taken through a large Earth air mass.

The inference of the presence of H_2O often depends sensitively on observations of absorption features which are distinguishable by their Doppler shift from terrestrial H_2O lines. Recent studies have led to apparently conflicting conclusions: From an extensive series of observations of H_2O lines in the 8200Å region, Schorn et al. [91] reported both negative and positive results in April–June and November–December 1967, respectively. The negative result was corroborated by Owen [131] and Kuiper [132], and the positive result was also supported [133]. The data from 1963–1967, obtained by several investigators, are summarized by Schorn et al. [91]. It was suggested there that Venus H_2O vapor variations may be real, and depend on the time, the position on the planet, and the particular H_2O band observed. Some of the apparent discrepancies may also be accounted for by radiative-transfer effects in a scattering atmosphere [105].

O_2

The question of O_2 on Venus has been characterized as "provocative" [134]. Some spectroscopic observations in the 1960's indicated the presence of O_2, but negative results were obtained both before and after these (see Belton and Hunten [134] for earlier references). A sensitive test by Spinrad

and Richardson [135] indicated [134] a mixing ratio (based on a reflecting-layer model of line formation) for O_2/CO_2 of less than 1.7×10^{-4}. Belton and Hunten [134] obtained spectra of Venus in the 7630 Å region of the oxygen A band [9]. No Doppler-shifted O_2 lines were found, and an upper limit of 2–8×10^{-5} for the O_2/CO_2 mixing ratio was obtained [134, 136]. It was concluded [137] that the Venera 4 value of 1% O_2 by volume was erroneous. Later results [138, 138a] from Venera 5 and 6,† in fact, gave a limiting value of $< 0.4\%$ O_2.

MARS

H_2O

The existence of water vapor on Mars was an unsettled question until just a few years ago. Early work has been discussed by de Vaucouleurs [139]. Later unsuccessful attempts at detection by means of high-dispersion spectroscopy yielded upper limits of 80 and 35 g m^{-2} of precipitable H_2O [140, 141].‡ Recently, a detailed history of the spectroscopic search for H_2O vapor on Mars was presented by Schorn [142].

Spinrad et al. [75] reported the discovery of 11 H_2O vapor lines in a spectrogram taken at the coudé focus of the Mt. Wilson reflector on 12–13 April 1963. Their exposure, made with 5.6 Å mm^{-1} dispersion on an emulsion sensitized by ammonia, lasted 270 min. The average measured Doppler shift, $+0.42 \pm 0.02$ Å, of the Mars lines was in excellent agreement with the calculated value, $+0.414$ Å, at 8220 Å. An abundance of 14 ± 7 g m^{-2} of precipitable water was deduced by Kaplan et al. [143]. This was done on the basis of an average equivalent width for unblended H_2O lines at 8176.97, 8189.27, and 8226.96 Å in their spectrum. Laboratory strengths for four of the strongest lines were provided by Rank et al. [13]. Their measurements were made in a multiple-reflection absorption tube containing 1.85 m-atm of H_2O vapor, in a 260-m atmospheric air path at 300°K. Resolving power ranged from 67 000 to 220 000.

Also in 1963, Dollfus [144] derived a Martian H_2O abundance of 200 g m^{-2} (this result was an average over the planet, and was later reduced [145] to 45 g m^{-2}) from his observation, at the Jungfraujoch, of a broad band at 7250 cm^{-1}. Due to the fact that the 1963 detections of H_2O vapor differed considerably in amount, Schorn et al. [146] began a series of observations during

---

† It is irresistible to mention here the soft landing of Venera 7 on the surface of Venus on 15 December 1970 [138b]. Preliminary results indicate a temperature of 747 ± 20°K and a most probable pressure of 90 ± 15 kg cm^{-2} in the region of the Venera 7 landing.

‡ The total atmospheric H_2O vapor in grams (g) contained in a vertical column of one square meter (m²) cross section is referred as to 1 g m^{-2} of precipitable H_2O; 1 g m$^{-2} = 0.00124$ m-atm.

1964–1965 at the McDonald and Lick Observatories. From 19 spectrograms, taken at 4.1 Å mm^{-1} dispersion, with Doppler-shifted H_2O lines near 8200 Å, typical amounts of precipitable H_2O of the order of 10–20 g m^{-2} were obtained. The results indicated that the H_2O vapor concentration varied with time and location on the planet.

New high-dispersion (2 Å mm^{-1}) measurements of the Martian 8200 Å H_2O band were reported in 1969. All observations were made at the McDonald Observatory. Owen and Mason [147] studied their measured equivalent widths using the line strengths of Rank *et al.* [13] corrected to 230°K. They used a Voigt profile [45] in their interpretation of the absorption lines [148] and obtained 35 ± 15 g m^{-2} of precipitable H_2O. An instrumental effect noticed by Rank *et al.* [149] for weak, sharp lines observed in laboratory spectra may have affected the derived H_2O abundance.

Schorn *et al.* [150] considered two representative spectra from an extensive series of observations made in 1968–1969. Figure 7 shows density versus wavelength tracings for four of their stronger lines in the 8200 Å H_2O band. The Martian components are unmistakable. In order to interpret their data properly, Farmer [151] measured the strengths of 24 lines between 8165.54 and 8318.14 Å with an estimated accuracy of ±6%. These laboratory strengths agreed to within ±20% with those of the four lines measured previously [13]; but no systematic variation with resolution, as had appeared in the earlier

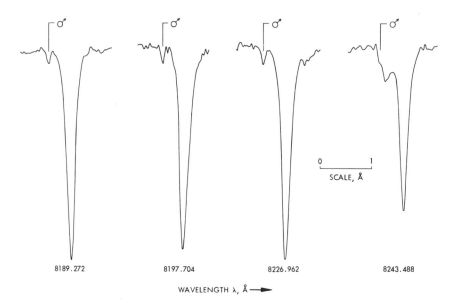

FIG. 7. Density versus wavelength tracings of some representative H_2O lines in the spectrum of Mars on 7 March 1969 (courtesy of Schorn [150]).

measurements, was observed. Assuming a Voigt profile, Schorn *et al.* [150] obtained a value of 26 ± 5 g m^{-2} of H_2O vapor in the northern hemisphere at a temperature of 225°K. For the southern hemisphere, the mean abundance was estimated to be considerably less at the same season.

Recently, Tull [152] has reported high spatial and spectral resolution measurements made at the 107-in. telescope of the McDonald Observatory in 1969. Extended laboratory studies [151] of 43 H_2O vapor line strengths in the range 8141.94–8321.59 Å, corrected to 225°K, were used to determine abundances. On March 27, the abundance of precipitable H_2O reached a maximum of about 48 g m^{-2} at 30–40° north latitude, and decreased to about 20 g m^{-2} at 30° south latitude. The same north–south decrease in abundance was indicated on April 28, but the respective amounts were only about two-thirds of those for the previous month. Spectra obtained in September indicated a decrease in abundance below the April results by at least a factor of two, tending to confirm seasonal variations reported by Schorn *et al.* [153].

CO_2

Carbon dioxide in the Martian atmosphere was detected spectroscopically by Kuiper [26] during 1947–1948 from observations of bands in the 1.6- and 2.0-μm regions. In 1963, at the time of their discovery of Martian H_2O vapor, Spinrad *et al.* [75] also reported extremely weak absorption lines for the $5v_3$ band [31] of CO_2 at 8689 Å. The Martian and laboratory wavelengths [154] were in satisfactory agreement. It was immediately suggested [75] that the detection of these lines implied a high CO_2 abundance on Mars.

Kaplan *et al.* [143] interpreted their measured equivalent widths for three unblended lines, and obtained a Martian CO_2 abundance of 55 ± 20 m-atm. Temperature and line-saturation effects were considered. Laboratory line strengths were made available by Rank *et al.* [13] who used their multiple-reflection absorption tube to reach path lengths from 2290 to 4576 m. Kaplan *et al.* [143] combined their CO_2 abundance estimates with absorption measurements by Sinton [121] and Kuiper [155] on the strongly pressure-dependent bands of CO_2 at 2.0 μm to obtain a surface pressure of 25 ± 15 mbar.† This was significantly lower than 85 mbar [139] which was the value generally accepted in 1964. Besides its intrinsic importance for understanding atmospheric structure and circulation, knowledge of the pressure at the base of the Martian atmosphere is important to the design of entry probes.

A series of spectroscopic studies [104, 156–167], suggested by Owen [157], of the Martian CO_2 bands at 8689 Å, 10 488 Å, 1.6 μm, and 2.0 μm followed to determine the CO_2 abundance and the surface pressure on Mars. Estimates of the surface pressure have ranged down to about 5 mbar. Only a few brief illustrations of these measurements and calculations will be discussed.

---

† 1 mbar ≡ 1 millibar ≡ 10^{-3} atm.

Giver *et al.* [164] and Carleton *et al.* [165] reduced their Martian CO_2 data at 1.05 μm with the help of laboratory linewidth and intensity measurements made by Boese *et al.* [168]. A multiple-reflection absorption tube of 25 m base length was used, and paths of 900 m were attained. To make high-resolution measurements of CO_2 absorption on Mars, Carleton *et al.* [165] utilized a PEPSIOS [169]† three-étalon, Fabry–Pérot spectrometer.

More recently, Gray Young [169a] has analyzed fifteen CO_2 bands, in the range 1.29–2.16 μm, of the Connes' spectra [79] to obtain a CO_2 abundance of 72.1 m-atm, a rotational temperature of 203 $\pm$ 4°K, and a best estimate for the surface pressure of 5.16 $\pm$ 0.64 mbar.

CO

The discovery of carbon monoxide in the Connes' spectra [79] of Mars was recently reported by Kaplan *et al.* [170]. They identified $^{12}C^{16}O$, $^{12}C^{18}O$, and $^{13}C^{16}O$ lines of the 2–0 band and $^{12}C^{16}O$ lines of the 3–0 band. A surface pressure of 5.3 mbar and a CO concentration of 8×10^{-4} by volume was deduced on the basis of laboratory band intensity [126] and line broadening measurements [171]. Gray Young [166] independently interpreted CO_2 and CO lines in the Connes' spectra [79] to obtain a surface pressure of 5 mbar and a CO/CO_2 abundance ratio of 1.6×10^{-4}. These results were obtained with curves of growth from measured CO_2 and CO equivalent widths and with a 2–0 CO band strength determined from laboratory measurements [172]. Gray Young [172a] has now corrected a programming error in the earlier work [166], and has found a CO abundance of 0.05–0.2 m-atm and a rotational temperature of 205 $\pm$ 7°K.

O_2

Early attempts to detect molecular oxygen on Mars have been summarized by Dunham [66], who also reported an upper limit of $O_2 <$ 200 cm-atm. From the absence of any Doppler-shifted Martian components in the telluric lines in the *A* band of O_2 at about 7600 Å, Kaplan *et al.* [143] determined $O_2 <$ 70 cm-atm. Belton and Hunten [134, 136] recently reported a possible detection of O_2 in the atmosphere of Mars on the basis of two weak absorption features in the middle of the *A* band. They considered that presssure-shifted [15] telluric lines might account for a discrepancy between the observed and expected wavelengths of one of the O_2 lines, but laboratory measurements by Margolis [173, 173a] indicated no differential pressure shift. Finally, Belton and Hunten [134] settled on $O_2 <$ 20 cm-atm, which would be the abundance if their identification is correct. Very recently, however, Margolis *et al.* [173a] concluded the earlier tentative identification of O_2 [134] was spurious. On the

† The acronym PEPSIOS denotes "poly-étalon pressure-scanned interferometric optical spectrometer."

basis of high-resolution spectra taken at the McDonald Observatory in 1969, and laboratory line-strength measurements [173b, 173c], a Martian O_2 abundance upper limit of 15 cm-atm was obtained, for an assumed temperature of 200°K.

MERCURY

CO_2, O_2, *and* H_2O

Spinrad *et al.* [174] obtained spectrograms, with 4 Å mm^{-1} dispersion, of Mercury in the 7500–8700 Å region. From the absence of R and P branch lines of the $5v_3$ CO_2 band, an upper limit of 57 m-atm was set. Lines of O_2 and H_2O, with an expected Doppler shift of 0.64 Å at 7600 Å, were not found. This led to $O_2 < 1$ m-atm, and precipitable $H_2O < 30$ g m^{-2}. Bergstralh *et al.* [175] used a Carnegie-RCA S1 image tube to obtain spectra of 3.2 Å mm^{-1} dispersion. From one of the best plates of the 12 030 Å region, it was determined that $CO_2 < 0.58$ m-atm.

Different observers [176, 177] have obtained broad band spectra of Mercury in the 1.6-μm region in an effort to detect enhancements over the terrestrial CO_2 absorption. These observations appear to give conflicting results, one positive [176] (but at the limit of sensitivity for the effect) and the other negative [177].

Future Research

In the preceding sections on the atmospheres of the outer and inner planets, several areas of laboratory and theoretical research in high-resolution infrared spectroscopy have suggested themselves. In this section, some of the needed future research will be discussed, including that with regard to the atmosphere of the most important planet, Earth, which will be considered from the point of view of air pollution and weather.

H_2

The quadrupole lines [7–9] of H_2 in the 4–0 rotation–vibration band have not yet been observed in the laboratory (see Table III). These measurements will require [20] effective absorption paths of about 50–60 km-atm. Experimental and theoretical studies of line shapes, including the effects of collision narrowing [23, 24], are desirable. As emphasized by Foltz and Rank [178], because of the extreme sharpness of the quadrupole lines, spectra of the highest possible resolution are required.

CH_4

The shortest-wavelength band of CH_4 which has been analyzed [32, 179] is $3v_3$ at 11 050 Å. High-resolution laboratory spectra in the $4v_3$ region are

quite complex [180]. However, lines at 6800 Å in the $5\nu_3$ CH_4 region have been observed in the spectra of Jupiter, Saturn, and Uranus [53]; and these features have a regular structure which appears susceptible to analysis. Only a low-resolution laboratory spectrum of this band has been reported [52]. It is desirable to have high-resolution measurements in this region at pressures of ~ 0.1 atm to permit an adequate understanding of the structure [39–41]. An estimate of the 500–1000 m-atm required implies path lengths of 5–10 km.

A determination of the pressure as well as the H_2 and He abundances from pressure-broadened CH_4 lines, as in the upper atmosphere of Jupiter [18, 19, 42, 46], depend on a knowledge of CH_4 line widths as a function of wavelength and temperature. The most extensive measurements thus far have been on lines in the rotation–vibration bands ν_3, $2\nu_3$, and $3\nu_3$ of CH_4. Self-broadening and broadening by H_2, He, N_2, and several other gases have been studied as a function of wavelength in ν_3 and $2\nu_3$ at moderate-to-high resolution [14,181–184].† Self-broadening only has been measured for $R(0)$–$R(7)$ in $3\nu_3$ [44]. All line widths were determined at room temperature. It is desirable to have data at shorter wavelengths, and for a range of temperatures at all wavelengths.

NH_3

Spectra of NH_3 in the Jovian atmosphere have been studied in the 5520 Å [57b], 6450 Å [18, 54–57], and 10 800 Å [57] regions. However, it has been difficult to deduce anything about temperature, pressure, and abundance. No analysis of the rotation–vibration bands has resulted in rotational quantum number assignments. Pressure-broadening data are not available at these wavelengths.

CO_2

Several CO_2 rotation–vibration bands which have been observed in spectra of Venus and Mars have not yet been studied in the laboratory. The transitions may be too weak, or they may be associated with less abundant isotopic variants. Many individual lines in the 7820, 7883, and 8689 Å bands have been observed [154] in laboratory spectra taken with effective absorption paths up to 5.5 km-atm. It appears, perhaps ironically, that more accurate spectroscopic constants for the 7820 and 7883 Å CO_2 bands have recently been obtained [187] on the basis of high-dispersion spectra of Venus [92, 93]. However, much line intensity data are still lacking [93]. To study bands at still shorter wavelengths will require path lengths in excess of 10 km, for moderate pressures, in the laboratory.

---

† Recently, calculations of collision-broadened line widths in ν_3 of CH_4 have been made. [185]. Also experimental and theoretical studies of collision-broadened lines in ν_4 of CH_4 have been reported [186].

EARTH

CO

Carbon monoxide is the most abundant and widely distributed air pollutant found in the Earth's atmosphere. Although the total CO emitted into the atmosphere is increasing, the background levels of CO in clean air do not appear to be increasing significantly. This presents a practical and scientifically interesting enigma [188]. Such removal reactions as

$$CO + O_2 \rightarrow CO_2 + O$$
$$CO + OH \rightarrow CO_2 + H$$
$$CO + 3H_2 \rightarrow CH_4 + H_2O$$

should be studied at low pressures and with absorption paths as long as 100 km or more. All the molecular reactants can be easily monitored by spectroscopic techniques.

CH_4

It has been suggested that the troposphere is the major region of destruction of methane, since its mixing ratio appears to be nearly constant up to the tropopause and decreases rapidly in the lower stratosphere [189]. The geochemistry of CH_4 is a complex subject [190] warranting further investigation. Reactions of the type

$$CH_4 + h\nu(\text{ultraviolet}) \rightarrow \text{dissociation products}$$

may be studied spectroscopically at very low pressures and extremely long absorption paths.

PAN

One of the specific eye irritants identified in photochemical smog is peroxyacetyl nitrate [191]. The primary photochemical processes involving PAN in urban air are not known [192]. These may be investigated spectroscopically in a simulated urban air environment, over a wide range of realistic pressures and absorption paths.

N_2

The principal constituents of the Earth's atmosphere are molecular nitrogen and oxygen (see Table I). Up to 200 km, and perhaps to 350 km, N_2 is the main component. Yet infrared absorption bands of this molecule have not been studied in the laboratory. The quadrupole rotation–vibration transitions in N_2 are estimated to be much weaker that the corresponding ones in H_2 because of the smaller vibrational anharmonicity in the former [193]. Data on line positions and intensities may be used in detecting or setting an upper limit on N_2 in atmospheres such as Jupiter's.

O_2 and O_3

Solar ultraviolet radiation is absorbed by molecular oxygen and ozone. Infrared absorption functions obtained for a broad range of pressures and amounts of absorbing gas are severely limited because data have not been obtained at the very low values of pressure and amount of absorber characteristic of the upper stratosphere and, especially, the mesosphere [194].

The study of hydrogen compounds, H_2, H_2O, and OH, including the photochemical equilibrium of H, H_2, H_2O, O, O_2, OH, and O_3, is important because of the direct effect on the thermal regime, for example through cooling due to emission by OH. The basic hindrance to the development of the theory of an oxygen–hydrogen atmosphere is the absence of data on the concentration of hydrogen-containing compounds in the mesosphere. Rocket measurements of small concentrations are extremely complex [194]. High-resolution, low-pressure, very-long-path laboratory studies will help form a sound basis for understanding the Earth's tenuous atmosphere.

Energy transport in the Earth's atmosphere is an essential ingredient in the weather problem. Much of the energy transport is determined by absorption and emission of radiation by molecular constituents of the atmosphere.

ACKNOWLEDGMENTS

I am indebted to many colleagues who have contributed to my understanding of the problems considered here. In particular, it is a pleasure to thank R. Beer, C. B. Farmer, L. D. Kaplan, J. S. Margolis, R. L. Newburn, Jr., T. Owen, R. A. Schorn, and L. D. Gray Young for useful and patient conversations, and for critical and timely comments on an early draft of this article. I take sole responsibility, however, for any errors of omission and/or commission. I also take sole responsibility, but not necessarily sole credit, for any opinions or speculations. I am grateful to several investigators for communicating to me some of their prepublication results. I appreciate the courtesy of the authors and journal editors who gave permission for the use of figures reproduced here. The support and hospitality of the Jet Propulsion Laboratory during the summer of 1970 made possible the preparation of this review.

This paper presents the results of one phase of research carried out at the Jet Propulsion Laboratory, California Institute of Technology, under Contract number NAS 7-100, sponsored by the National Aeronautics and Space Administration.

References

1. H. Spinrad and R. F. Wing, *Annu. Rev. Astron. Astrophys.* **7**, 249 (1969).
1a. S. I. Rasool, *in* "Origin of Life" (C. Ponnamperuma, ed.). Amer. Elsevier, New York, 1971.
2. M. B. McElroy, *J. Atmos. Sci.* **26**, 798 (1969).
3. R. M. Goody, *J. Atmos. Sci.* **26**, 997 (1969).
4. T. Owen, *Science* **167**, 1675 (1970).
4a. V. G. Teifel, "The Atmosphere of the Planet Jupiter," Sci. Press, Moscow, 1969; *NASA Tech. Transl.* **TT F-617** (1970) (for sale by the Clearinghouse for Fed. Sci. and Tech. Inform., Springfield, Va. 22151).

4b. V. G. Teifel, *Astron. Vestnik* **4**, No. 2, 81 (1970); also see "Physical Characteristics of the Giant Planets" (V. G. Teifel, ed.). Sci. Press, Alma-Ata, Soviet Union, 1971.

5. R. V. Wagoner, W. A. Fowler, and F. Hoyle, *Astrophys. J.* **148**, 3 (1967).

6. R. Wildt, *Veroeff. Univ.-Sternwarte Göttingen* **2**, 171 (1932).

7. G. Herzberg, *Astrophys. J.* **87**, 438 (1938).

8. H. M. James and A. S. Coolidge, *Astrophys. J.* **87**, 438 (1938).

9. G. Herzberg, "Spectra of Diatomic Molecules" (2nd ed.). Van Nostrand-Reinhold, Princeton, New Jersey, 1950.

10. G. Herzberg, *Nature* **163**, 170 (1949).

11. G. Herzberg, *in* "The Atmospheres of the Earth and Planets" (G. P. Kuiper, ed.) revised ed. Univ. Chicago Press, Chicago, Illinois, 1952.

12. C. C. Kiess, C. H. Corliss, and H. K. Kiess, *Astrophys. J.* **132**, 221 (1960).

13. D. H. Rank, U. Fink, J. V. Foltz, and T. A. Wiggins, *Astrophys. J.* **140**, 366 (1964).

14. D. H. Rank, U. Fink, and T. A. Wiggins, *Astrophys. J.* **143**, 980 (1966).

15. R. M. Goody, "Atmospheric Radiation. I. Theoretical Basis." Oxford Univ. Press (Clarendon), London and New York, 1964.

16. V. I. Moroz, "Physics of Planets." Sci. Press, Moscow, 1967; *NASA Tech. Transl.* **TT F-515** (1968), see [4a].

17. F. Zabriskie, *Astron. J.* **67**, 168 (1962).

18. H. Spinrad and L. M. Trafton, *Icarus* **2**, 19 (1963).

19. T. Owen and H. P. Mason, *Astrophys. J.* **154**, 317 (1968).

20. A. Birnbaum and J. D. Poll, *J. Atmos. Sci.* **26**, 943 (1969); also see A. Dalgarno, A. C. Allison, and J. C. Browne, *J. Atmos. Sci.* **26**, 946 (1969).

21. J. P. Emerson, J. A. Eddy, and G. A. Dulk, *Icarus* **11**, 413 (1969).

22. U. Fink and M. J. S. Belton, *J. Atmos. Sci.* **26**, 952 (1969).

23. R. H. Dicke, *Phys. Rev.* **89**, 472 (1953).

24. D. H. Rank and T. A. Wiggins, *J. Chem. Phys.* **39**, 1348 (1963).

25. L. Galatry, *Phys. Rev.* **122**, 1218 (1961).

25a. G. E. Hunt, *J. Quant. Spectrosc. Radiat. Transfer* **11**, 655 (1971).

26. G. P. Kuiper, *in* "The Atmospheres of the Earth and Planets" (G. P. Kuiper, ed.) revised ed. Univ. Chicago Press, Chicago, Illinois, 1952.

27. M. F. Walker and S. Hayes, *Publ. Astron. Soc. Pac.* **79**, 464 (1967).

28. W. A. Baum, *Science* **154**, 112 (1966).

29. T. Owen, *Astrophys. J.* **141**, 444 (1965).

30. W. H. J. Childs, *Proc. Roy. Soc. Ser. A* **153**, 555 (1936).

31. G. Herzberg, "Infrared and Raman Spectra of Polyatomic Molecules." Van Nostrand-Reinhold, Princeton, New Jersey, 1945.

32. J. S. Margolis and K. Fox, *J. Chem. Phys.* **49**, 2451 (1968).

33. E. K. Plyler, E. D. Tidwell, and L. R. Blaine, *J. Res. Nat. Bur. Stand. Sect. A* **64**, 201 (1960).

34. D. H. Rank, D. P. Eastman, G. Skorinko, and T. A. Wiggins, *J. Mol. Spectrosc.* **5**, 78 (1960).

35. K. Fox, K. T. Hecht, R. E. Meredith, and C. W. Peters, *J. Chem. Phys.* **36**, 3135 (1962).

36. K. T. Hecht, *J. Mol. Spectrosc.* **5**, 355, 390 (1960).

37. K. Fox, *J. Mol. Spectrosc.* **9**, 381 (1962).

38. J. S. Margolis and K. Fox, *Bull. Amer. Astron. Soc.* **1**, 217 (1969).

39. J. S. Margolis and K. Fox, *Astrophys. J.* **157**, 935 (1969).

40. J. S. Margolis and K. Fox, *Astrophys. J.* **158**, 1183 (1969).

41. J. S. Margolis and K. Fox, *J. Atmos. Sci.* **26**, 862 (1969).

42. J. E. Beckman, *Astrophys. J.* **149**, 453 (1967).

43. T. Owen and J. H. Woodman, *Astrophys. J. (Letters)* **154**, L21 (1968).

44. J. S. Margolis, *J. Quant. Spectrosc. Radiat. Transfer* **10**, 165 (1970).

45. J. T. Jeffries, "Spectral Line Formation." Ginn (Blaisdell), Boston, Massachusetts, 1968.
46. C. B. Farmer, *J. Atmos. Sci.* **26**, 860 (1969).
47. T. Owen, Personal communication (1969).
48. J. T. Bergstralh, *Bull. Am. Astron. Soc.* **3**, 282 (1971).
48a. J. S. Margolis, *Astrophys. J.* **167**, 553 (1971).
49. M. J. S. Belton, *Astrophys. J.* **157**, 469 (1969).
50. T. Owen, *Astrophys. J.* **142**, 782 (1965).
51. L. M. Rutherfurd, *Amer. J. Sci.* **85**, 71 (1863). (Spectra of both bands obtained at the McDonald Observatory at a dispersion of 1.25 Å mm^{-1} are reproduced by Owen [4].)
52. G. P. Kuiper, *Rept. Progr. Phys.* **13**, 247 (1950).
53. T. Owen, *Astrophys. J.* **146**, 611 (1966); also see V. G. Teifel and G. A. Kharitonova, *Sov. Astron. AJ* **13**, 865 (1970).
54. L. Giver, *Astrophys. J.* **139**, 727 (1964).
55. L. Giver, *Publ. Astron. Soc. Pac.* **77**, 128 (1965).
56. L. P. Giver, R. W. Boese, and J. H. Miller, *J. Atmos. Sci.* **26**, 941 (1969).
57. H. P. Mason, *Astrophys. Space Sci.* **7**, 424 (1970).
57a. L. P. Giver, R. W. Boese, and J. H. Miller. To be published.
57b. T. Owen, *Astrophys. J.* **164**, 211 (1971).
58. J. A. Greenspan and T. Owen, *Science* **156**, 1489 (1967).
59. E. R. Lippincott, R. V. Eck, M. O. Dayhoff, and C. Sagan, *Astrophys. J.* **147**, 753 (1967).
60. J. S. Lewis, *Icarus* **10**, 393 (1969).
61. T. Owen, *Icarus* **6**, 138 (1967).
62. R. A. Durie and G. Herzberg, *Can. J. Phys.* **38**, 806 (1960).
62a. G. Münch and G. Neugebauer, *Science* **174**, 940 (1971).
62b. R. J. Corice and K. Fox, *Icarus*. To be published.
62c. R. Beer, C. B. Farmer, R. H. Norton, J. V. Martonchik, and T. G. Barnes, *Science*. To be published.
62d. K. Fox and T. Owen. To be published.
62e. A. W. Mantz and K. N. Rao, Personal communication (1970).
63. G. Münch and H. Spinrad, *Mem. Soc. Roy. Sci. Liege* **7**, 541 (1963).
64. L. Giver and H. Spinrad, *Icarus* **5**, 586 (1966).
65. T. Owen, *Icarus* **10**, 355 (1969).
65a. L. M. Trafton, *Bull. Am. Astron. Soc.* **3**, 282 (1971).
65b. J. T. Bergstralh. To be published.
66. T. Dunham, Jr., *in* "The Atmospheres of the Earth and Planets" (G. P. Kuiper, ed.), revised ed. Univ. of Chicago Press, Chicago, Illinois, 1952.
67. G. P. Kuiper, *Astrophys. J.* **100**, 378 (1944).
67a. L. M. Trafton, *Bull. Am. Astron. Soc.* **3**, 282 (1971).
68. G. Herzberg, *Astrophys. J.* **115**, 337 (1952)
69. G. P. Kuiper, *Astrophys. J.* **109**, 540 (1949).
70. H. L. Welsh, *J. Atmos. Sci.* **26**, 835 (1969); also see A. R. W. McKellar and H. L. Welsh, *Proc. Roy. Soc. Lond.* A **322**, 421 (1971).
71. H. Spinrad, *Astrophys. J.* **138**, 1242 (1963).
72. J. D. Poll *in* "Planetary Atmospheres" (C. Sagan, T. Owen, and H. J. Smith, eds.). (I.A.U. Symposium No. 40 in Marfa, Texas, 26–31 October 1969), Springer Publ., New York, 1971.
73. M. J. S. Belton, M. B. McElroy, and M. J. Price, *Astrophys. J.* **164**, 191 (1971).
74. T. Owen, *Icarus* **6**, 108 (1967).
74a. K. Fox and I. Ozier, *Astrophys. J.* **166**, L95 (1971).

74b. A. P. Ingersoll and C. B. Leovy, *Annu. Rev. Astron. Astrophys.* **9**, 147 (1971).
75. H. Spinrad, G. Münch, and L. D. Kaplan, *Astrophys. J.(Letters)* **137**, 1319 (1963).
76. J. Connes and P. Connes, *J. Opt. Soc. Amer.* **56**, 896 (1966).
77. J. Connes and P. Connes, *in* "Infrared Astronomy" (P. J. Brancazio and A. G. W. Cameron, eds.). Gordon & Breach, New York, 1968.
78. P. Connes, *Annu. Rev. Astron. Astrophys.* **8**, 209 (1970).
79. J. Connes, P. Connes, and J. P. Maillard, "Atlas of Near Infrared Spectra of Venus, Mars, Jupiter, and Saturn." CNRS, Paris, 1969.
80. P. Connes, J. Connes, W. S. Benedict, and L. D. Kaplan, *Astrophys. J.* (*Letters*) **147**, 1230 (1967).
81. V. M. Vakhnin, *J. Atmos. Sci.* **25**, 533 (1968).
81a. T. M. Donahue, *J. Atmos. Sci.* **25**, 568 (1968).
81b. F. S. Johnson, *J. Atmos. Sci.* **25**, 658 (1968).
82. J. C. Brandt and M. B. McElroy, eds., "The Atmospheres of Mars and Venus." Gordon & Breach, New York, 1968 (Summary review was presented in that Volume by R. M. Goody).
83. C. E. St. John and S. B. Nicholson, *Phys. Rev.* **19**, 444 (1922).
84. W. S. Adams and T. Dunham, Jr., *Publ. Astron. Soc. Pac.* **44**, 243 (1932); also see the review of this work by Dunham [66].
85. A. Adel and D. M. Dennison, *Phys. Rev.* **43**, 716; **44**, 99 (1933).
86. A. Adel and V. M. Slipher, *Phys. Rev.* **46**, 240 (1934).
87. A. Adel, *Astrophys. J.* **85**, 345 (1937).
88. A. Adel, *Astrophys. J.* **86**, 337 (1937).
89. G. Herzberg, *J. Roy. Astron. Soc. Can.* **45**, 100 (1951).
90. L. D. Gray and R. A. Schorn, *Icarus* **8**, 409 (1968).
91. R. A. Schorn, E. S. Barker, L. D. Gray, and R. C. Moore, *Icarus* **10**, 98 (1969).
92. R. A. Schorn, L. D. Gray, and E. S. Barker, *Icarus* **10**, 241 (1969).
93. L. D. Gray, R. A. Schorn, and E. S. Barker, *Appl. Opt.* **8**, 2087 (1969).
94. L. D. Gray Young, R. A. Schorn, E. S. Barker, and M. MacFarlane, *Icarus* **11**, 390 (1969).
95. R. A. Schorn, L. D. Gray Young, and E. S. Barker, *Icarus* **12**, 391 (1970).
96. L. D. Gray Young, R. A. Schorn, and E. S. Barker, *Icarus* **13**, 58 (1970).
97. L. D. Gray Young, R. A. Schorn, and H. J. Smith, *Icarus* **13**, 74 (1970).
98. R. A. Schorn, L. D. Gray Young, and E. S. Barker, *Icarus* **14**, 21 (1971).
98a. L. D. Gray Young, R. A. Schorn, E. S. Barker, and A. Woszczyk, *Acta. Astron.* **21**, 329 (1971).
99. O. Struve, *Astron. J.* **52**, 146 (1947).
100. J. W. Chamberlain and G. P. Kuiper, *Astrophys. J.* **124**, 399 (1956).
101. J. Regas, Thesis, Harvard Univ., Cambridge, Massachusetts, 1967 (unpublished).
102. R. A. McClatchey, *Astrophys. J.* **148**, L93 (1967).
102a. L. D. Gray Young, *Icarus* **13**, 449 (1970).
103. M. J. S. Belton, D. M. Hunten, and R. M. Goody, *in* "The Atmospheres of Mars and Venus" (J. C. Brandt and M. B. McElroy, eds.). Gordon & Breach, New York, 1968.
104. M. J. S. Belton and D. M. Hunten, *Astrophys. J.* **145**, 454 (1966).
105. J. W. Chamberlain, *Astrophys. J.* **141**, 1184 (1965).
106. G. P. Kuiper, *Comm. Lunar Planet. Lab.* **1**, 83 (1962).
107. J. Connes, P. Connes, and J. P. Maillard, *J. Phys. (Paris) Suppl.* **28**, 120 (1967).
108. J. Pinard, *J. Phys. (Paris) Suppl.* **28**, 136 (1967); *Ann. Phys. (Paris)* **4**, 147 (1969).
109. D. H. Rank, W. B. Birtley, D. P. Eastman, and T. A. Wiggins, *J. Chem. Phys.* **32**, 296 (1960).
110. J. Connes, P. Connes, W. S. Benedict, and L. D. Gray Young. To be published.

111. V. I. Moroz, *Sov. Astron. AJ* **8**, 566 (1965).
112. L. D. Gray Young, *Icarus* **11**, 66 (1969).
113. L. D. Gray Young, *Icarus* **13**, 270 (1970).
114. G. Yamamoto, M. Tanaka, and T. Aoki, *J. Quant. Spectrosc. Radiat. Transfer* **9**, 371 (1969).
115. D. H. Rank, B. S. Rao, and T. A. Wiggins, *J. Mol. Spectrosc.* **17**, 122 (1965).
116. D. U. Webb and K. N. Rao, *Appl. Opt.* **5**, 1461 (1966).
117. D. H. Rank, D. P. Eastman, B. S. Rao, and T. A. Wiggins, *J. Mol. Spectrosc.* **10**, 34 (1963).
118. J. H. Jaffe, S. Kimel, and M. A. Hirshfeld, *Can. J. Phys.* **40**, 113 (1962).
119. W. F. Herget, W. E. Deeds, N. M. Gailar, R. J. Lovell, and A. H. Nielsen, *J. Opt. Soc. Amer.* **52**, 1113 (1962).
120. K. Narahari Rao, Personal communication to the authors of [80].
121. W. M. Sinton, *J. Quant. Spectrosc. Radiat. Transfer* **3**, 551 (1963).
122. V. I. Moroz, *Mem. Soc. Roy. Sci. Liege* **9**, 406 (1964).
123. P. Connes, J. Connes, L. D. Kaplan, and W. S. Benedict, *Astrophys. J.* **152**, 731 (1968).
124. D. H. Rank, G. Skorinko, D. P. Eastman, and T. A. Wiggins, *J. Mol. Spectrosc.* **4**, 518 (1960).
125. K. Narahari Rao, C. J. Humphreys, and D. H. Rank, "Wavelength Standards in the Infrared." Academic Press, New York, 1966.
126. C. L. Korb, R. H. Hunt, and E. K. Plyler, *J. Chem. Phys.* **48**, 4252 (1968).
127. W. S. Benedict, R. Herman, G. E. Moore, and S. Silverman, *Can. J. Phys.* **34**, 850 (1956).
128. H. J. Kostkowski and A. M. Bass, *J. Quant. Spectrosc. Radiat. Transfer* **1**, 177 (1961).
129. D. E. Burch and D. Gryvnak, Personal communication to the authors of [123].
130. R. F. Calfee and W. S. Benedict, *Nat. Bur. Stand. (U.S.) Tech. Note* **322** (1956).
131. T. Owen, *Astrophys. J.* **150**, L121 (1967).
132. G. P. Kuiper and F. F. Forbes, *Comm. Lunar Planet. Lab.* **6**, 177 (1967).
133. G. P. Kuiper, F. F. Forbes, D. L. Steinmetz, and R. I. Mitchell, *Comm. Lunar Planet. Lab.* **6**, 209 (1969).
134. M. J. S. Belton and D. M. Hunten, *Astrophys. J.* **153**, 963 (1968).
135. H. Spinrad and E. H. Richardson, *Astrophys. J.* **141**, 282 (1965).
136. M. J. S. Belton and D. M. Hunten, *Astrophys. J.* **156**, 797 (1969).
137. M. J. S. Belton, A. L. Broadfoot, and D. M. Hunten, *J. Atmos. Sci.* **25**, 582 (1968).
138. V. S. Avduevsky, M. Ya. Marov, and M. K. Rozhdestvensky, *Radio Sci.* **5**, 333 (1970).
138a. V. S. Avduevsky, M. Ya. Marov, and M. K. Rozhdestvensky, *J. Atmos. Sci.* **27**, 561 (1970).
138b. V. S. Avduevsky, M. Ya. Marov, M. K. Rozhdestvensky, N. F. Borodin, and V. V. Kerzhanovich, *J. Atmos. Sci.* **28**, 263 (1971).
139. G. de Vaucouleurs, "Physics of the Planet Mars." Faber and Faber, London, 1954.
140. C. C. Kiess, C. H. Corliss, H. K. Kiess, and E. L. R. Corliss, *Astrophys. J.* **126**, 579 (1957).
141. H. Spinrad and E. H. Richardson, *Icarus* **2**, 49 (1963).
142. R. A. Schorn *in* "Planetary Atmospheres" (C. Sagan, T. Owen, and H. J. Smith, eds.). (I.A.U. Symposium No. 40 in Marfa, Texas, 26–31 October 1969), Springer Publ., New York, 1971.
143. L. D. Kaplan, G. Münch, and H. Spinrad, *Astrophys. J.* **139**, 1 (1964).
144. A. Dollfus, *C. R. Acad. Sci.* **256**, 3009 (1963).
145. A. Dollfus, *C. R. Acad. Sci.* **261**, 1603 (1965).
146. R. A. Schorn, H. Spinrad, R. C. Moore, H. J. Smith, and L. P. Giver, *Astrophys. J.* **147**, 743 (1967).

147. T. Owen and H. P. Mason, *Science*, **165**, 893 (1969).
148. P. A. Jansson and C. L. Korb, *J. Quant. Spectrosc. Radiat. Transfer* **8**, 1399 (1968).
149. D. H. Rank, B. S. Rao, P. Sitaram, A. F. Slomba, and T. A. Wiggins, *J. Opt. Soc. Amer.* **52**, 1004 (1962).
150. R. A. Schorn, C. B. Farmer, and S. J. Little, *Icarus* **11**, 283 (1969).
151. C. B. Farmer, *Icarus* **15**, 190 (1971).
152. R. G. Tull, *Icarus* **13**, 43 (1970); also see E. S. Barker, R. A. Schorn, A. Woszczyk, R. G. Tull, and S. J. Little, *Science* **170**, 1308 (1970).
153. R. A. Schorn, H. Spinrad, R. C. Moore, H. J. Smith, and L. P. Giver, *Astrophys. J.* **147**, 743 (1967).
154. G. Herzberg and L. Herzberg, *J. Opt. Soc. Amer.* **43**, 1037 (1953).
155. G. P. Kuiper, *Mem. Soc. Roy. Sci. Liege* **9**, 365 (1963).
156. T. Owen and G. P. Kuiper, *Comm. Lunar Planet. Lab.* **2**, 113 (1964).
157. T. Owen, *Comm. Lunar Planet. Lab.* **2**, 133 (1964).
158. V. I. Moroz, *Sov. Astron. AJ* **8**, 273 (1964).
159. T. Owen, *Astrophys. J.* **146**, 257 (1966).
160. H. Spinrad, R. A. Schorn, R. Moore, L. P. Giver, and H. J. Smith, *Astrophys. J.* **146**, 331 (1966).
161. L. D. Gray, *Icarus* **5**, 390 (1966).
162. R. A. Schorn and L. D. Gray, *Astrophys. J.* **148**, 663 (1967).
163. S. S. Penner, A. Boni, and L. D. Gray, *J. Quant. Spectrosc. Radiat. Transfer* **7**, 677 (1967).
164. L. P. Giver, E. C. Y. Inn, J. H. Miller, and R. W. Boese, *Astrophys. J.* **153**, 285 (1968).
165. N. P. Carleton, A. Sharma, R. M. Goody, W. L. Liller, and F. L. Roesler, *Astrophys. J.* **155**, 323 (1969).
166. L. D. Gray Young, *Icarus* **11**, 386 (1969).
167. E. S. Barker, Thesis, Univ. of Texas, Austin, Texas, 1969 (unpublished).
168. R. W. Boese, J. H. Miller, and E. C. Y. Inn, *J. Quant. Spectrosc. Radiat. Transfer* **6**, 717 (1966); **8**, 1621 (1968).
169. J. E. Mack, D. P. McNutt, F. L. Roesler, and R. Chabbal, *Appl. Opt.* **2**, 873 (1963).
169a. L. D. Gray Young, *J. Quant. Spectrosc. Radiat. Transfer* **11**, 1075 (1971).
170. L. D. Kaplan, J. Connes, and P. Connes, *Astrophys. J.* **157**, L187 (1969).
171. D. A. Draegert and D. Williams, *J. Opt. Soc. Amer.* **58**, 1399 (1968).
172. W. S. Benedict, R. Herman, G. E. Moore, and S. Silverman, *Astrophys. J.* **135**, 277 (1962).
172a. L. D. Gray Young, *J. Quant. Spectrosc. Radiat. Transfer* **11**, 385 (1971).
173. J. S. Margolis, Personal communication to Belton and Hunten [134].
173a. J. S. Margolis, R. A. Schorn, and L. D. Gray Young, *Icarus* **15**, 197 (1971).
173b. D. E. Burch and D. A. Gryvnak, *Appl. Opt.* **8**, 1493 (1969).
173c. J. H. Miller, R. W. Boese, and L. P. Giver, *J. Quant. Spectrosc. Radiat. Transfer* **9**, 1507 (1969).
174. H. Spinrad, G. B. Field, and P. W. Hodge, *Astrophys. J.* **141**, 1155 (1965).
175. J. T. Bergstralh, L. D. Gray, and H. J. Smith, *Astrophys. J.* **149**, L137 (1967).
176. V. I. Moroz, *Sov. Astron. AJ* **8**, 882 (1965).
177. A. B. Binder and D. P. Cruickshank, *Science* **155**, 1135 (1967).
178. J. V. Foltz and D. H. Rank, *Astrophys. J. (Letters)* **138**, 1319 (1963).
179. K. Fox, To be published.
180. J. S. Margolis, Personal communication (1970).
181. H. J. Gerritsen and M. E. Heller, *Appl. Opt. Suppl.* **2**, 73 (1965).
182. H. Goldring, A. Szöke, E. Zamir, and A. Ben-Reuven, *J. Chem. Phys.* **49**, 4253 (1968).
183. G. Hubbert, T. G. Kyle, and G. J. Troup, *J. Quant. Spectrosc. Radiat. Transfer* **9**, 1469 (1969).

184. P. Varanasi, *J. Quant. Spectrosc. Radiat. Transfer.* To be published.
185. G. D. T. Tejwani, Thesis, State Univ. of New York, Stony Brook, N.Y., 1971 (unpublished); also see G. D. T. Tejwani and P. Varanasi, *J. Chem. Phys.* **55**, 1075 (1971); and G. Yamamoto and M. Hirono, *J. Quant. Spectrosc. Radiat. Transfer* **11**, 1537 (1971).
186. P. Varanasi and G. D. T. Tejwani, *J. Quant. Spectrosc. Radiat. Transfer.* To be published.
187. L. D. Gray Young, A. T. Young, and R. A. Schorn, *J. Quant. Spectrosc. Radiat. Transfer* **10**, 1291 (1970).
188. L. S. Jaffe, *J. Air Pollut. Control Assn.* **18**, 534 (1968).
189. A. E. Bainbridge and L. E. Heidt, *Tellus* **18**, 221 (1966).
190. E. A. Martell, *J. Geophys. Res.* **68**, 3759 (1963).
191. P. A. Leighton, "Photochemistry of Air Pollution." Academic Press, New York, 1961.
192. N. J. Turro, G. S. Hammond, J. N. Pitts, and D. Valentine, Jr., "Annual Survey of Photochemistry," Vol. 2. Wiley (Interscience), New York, 1970.
193. G. Herzberg, *Astrophys. J.* **87**, 428 (1938).
194. K. Ya. Kondrat'yev, ed., "Problems of Atmospheric Physics" Leningrad State Univ. Press, Leningrad, 1967; *NASA Tech. Transl.* **TT F-587** (1970), see [4a].
195. C. W. Allen, "Astrophysical Quantities" 2nd ed. Oxford Univ. Press (Athlone), London and New York, 1963.
195a. H. C. Urey, *in* "Encyclopedia of Physics," Vol. 52 (S. Flügge, ed.) Springer, Berlin, 1959.
195b. C. E. Junge, "Air Chemistry and Radioactivity," Academic Press, New York, 1963.
196. A. Dollfus, *C. R. Acad. Sci.* **256**, 3250 (1963).
197. M. Bottema, W. Plummer, and J. Strong, *Astrophys. J.* **139**, 1021 (1964).

3.2 Vibration–Rotation Structure in Asymmetric- and Symmetric-Top Molecules

Ian M. Mills

Department of Chemistry
University of Reading
Reading, England

1. Introduction

The vibration–rotation Hamiltonian was originally derived by Wilson and Howard [1], but most of the theoretical treatment relating it to observed vibration–rotation spectra was developed by Nielsen [2, 3]. Important further developments were made by Amat and co-workers [4–8]. More recently there have been several discussions of vibration–rotation theory which have added appreciably to the building up of a coherent general picture, particularly in papers by Oka and Morino [9], in Hougen's work on symmetry classification [10], in Oka's order-of-magnitude classification of the various terms [11], in Watson's work on the general Hamiltonian [12].

This article is intended primarily as a review of various topics concerned with the analysis of rotational structure in the spectra of asymmetric- and symmetric-top molecules. It is particularly intended to present a general description of the perturbation calculation by which the complete Hamiltonian is reduced to an effective rotational Hamiltonian within each vibrational state. In the process, the formulas relating many of the parameters in the effective Hamiltonian to the parameters in the original Hamiltonian are reviewed. The interpretation of asymmetric-top spectra is discussed first, since it provides a useful background to the special problems of symmetric tops. Then the symmetric-top Hamiltonian and the resulting term formulas are discussed. Finally, the particular problem of analyzing observed data to obtain axial rotational constants in symmetric tops is discussed.

2. Asymmetric Tops

Microwave rotational spectra and infrared and Raman vibration–rotation spectra at high resolution allow us to observe differences between the vibration rotation term values of a molecule. These terms may be expressed empirically as

the sum of a vibrational term which is independent of the rotational quantum numbers, and a rotational term which is largely independent of the vibrational quantum numbers:

$$T(v, J) = G(v) + F_v(J) \tag{1}$$

The rotational term values $F_v(J)$ are interpreted as the eigenvalues of an effective rotational Hamiltonian which is slightly different for each vibrational state. For an asymmetric top the form of this Hamiltonian is

$$H_{\text{rot}}/hc = A_v J_a^2 + B_v J_b^2 + C_v J_c^2 + \tfrac{1}{4} \sum_{\alpha, \beta} (\tau'_{\alpha\alpha\beta\beta})_v J_\alpha^2 J_\beta^2 + \cdots \tag{2}$$

where J_a, J_b, and J_c are components of the total angular momentum in units of $\hbar$; A_v, B_v, and C_v are the effective rotational constants; and $(\tau'_{\alpha\alpha\beta\beta})_v$ are the centrifugal distortion constants as defined by Kivelson and Wilson [13], in wave number units; α and β are summed over a, b, and c. The centrifugal distortion constants are smaller than the rotational constants by factors of the order of 10^{-4}. In principle sixth-power (and higher even power) terms in the angular momenta are also possible, but the series converges rapidly, so that these higher-order centrifugal distortion constants are generally too small to observe. The fact that only even powers of the angular momentum operators occur is related to the invariance of the Hamiltonian to time-reversal.

The relationship of the rotational constants to the energy levels and hence to the observed spectra is complicated by the fact that it is not possible to write an explicit expression for the eigenvalues of (2); this problem is discussed by King et al. [14]. The influence of the centrifugal distortion constants is further complicated by the fact that only five linear combinations of the six τ' constants are determinable from the spectrum, as discussed by Watson [15].

The effective rotational and centrifugal distortion constants are the most that can be determined from the analysis of the rotational structure in one vibrational state. Similar analysis of all vibrational states shows a vibrational dependence of the various constants, as indicated in (1) by the subscript v. This has the general form

$$B_v = B_e - \sum_r \alpha_r^B (v_r + \tfrac{1}{2}) + \sum_{r \geqslant s} \gamma_{rs}^B (v_r + \tfrac{1}{2})(v_s + \tfrac{1}{2}) + \cdots \tag{3}$$

where the sums run over all the normal modes. Similar expressions hold for the vibrational dependence of A_v and C_v. In general the α constants have a magnitude of the order 10^{-2} of the rotational constants to which they refer, and the γ constants are perhaps 10^{-2} smaller still and are rarely observed; thus the expansion in vibrational quantum numbers converges rapidly. The vibrational dependence of the $(\tau')_v$ constants would also be given by a similar equation, but in this case even the first-power dependence on the vibrational quantum numbers is generally too small to observe. To this degree of approximation we may omit the subscript v on the τ' constants.

For asymmetric tops in which vibrational degeneracies or near-degeneracies occur, the convergence of the series represented by eqs. (2) and (3) may no longer be sufficiently rapid to give a satisfactory fit to the data; a different method of analysis must then be used, as discussed below.

The above interpretation may be understood theoretically as follows. Substituting (3) into (2) shows that $-\alpha_r^{\ B}$ is the coefficient of $(v_r + \frac{1}{2})J_b^{\ 2}$ in the effective rotational Hamiltonian, just as B_e is the coefficient of $J_b^{\ 2}$, and $\tau'_{\alpha\alpha\beta\beta}$ is the coefficient of $J_\alpha^{\ 2}J_\beta^{\ 2}$. To obtain the effective rotational Hamiltonian in a particular vibrational state we must average the complete Hamiltonian over all the vibrational coordinates using the appropriate vibrational wave function so that we are left with a Hamiltonian involving only the rotational angular momentum operators. This procedure gives an approximate separation of rotation from vibration, and is analogous to the separation of vibrational from electronic degrees of freedom in the conventional discussion of the Born–Oppenheimer approximation. Our task is to understand how terms of the type $(v_r + \frac{1}{2})J_b^{\ 2}$, for example, arise from this averaging process; we then identify the coefficient of this term in the theoretical discussion with the empirical constant $-\alpha_r^{\ B}$. We now consider this procedure in greater detail.

The complete vibration–rotation Hamiltonian has been shown by Watson [12] to be given by

$$H = \sum_{\alpha, \beta} \tfrac{1}{2}\mu_{\alpha\beta}\hbar^2(J_\alpha - \pi_\alpha)(J_\beta - \pi_\beta) + \tfrac{1}{2}\sum_r P_r^2 + V(Q_r) + U \qquad (4)$$

where $\mu_{\alpha\beta}$ are the elements of the $\boldsymbol{\mu}$ tensor, which is not quite equal to the instantaneous inverse inertia tensor; π_α are the components of the vibrational angular momentum in units of $\hbar$, given by Eq. (8) below; Q_r and P_r denote the rth normal coordinate and its conjugate momentum, $P_r = -i\hbar \, \partial/\partial Q_r$; and U is a very small, mass-dependent correction to the vibrational potential energy $V(Q_r)$, which can be ignored for our purposes. The vibrational wave functions are given, in zero order of approximation, as products of harmonic oscillator functions in the normal coordinates, i.e., as eigenfunctions of the zeroth-order vibrational Hamiltonian

$$H_{\text{vib}}^0 = \sum_r \tfrac{1}{2}(P_r^2 + \lambda_r Q_r^2) \qquad (5)$$

where $\sum \frac{1}{2}\lambda_r Q_r^2$ are the quadratic terms from $V(Q_r)$. There are, however, further vibrational operators in (4), arising from the dependence of $\mu_{\alpha\beta}$ on Q_r, the π_α terms, and the higher-order terms in $V(Q_r)$.

The usual procedure is to apply a contact transformation to the hamiltonian (4) to obtain a transformed Hamiltonian

$$\tilde{H} = U^{-1}HU \qquad (6)$$

where U is unitary, such that the harmonic oscillator basis functions are the eigenfunctions of H to the desired degree of of approximation. The eigenvalues of $\tilde{H}$ are the same as those of H. We then average $\tilde{H}$ over the appropriate

vibrational basis function to obtain the effective rotational Hamiltonian in each vibrational state.

An alternative description of the same procedure is to say that we set up the matrix of the Hamiltonian (4) in the harmonic oscillator basis functions which are eigenfunctions of (5). The matrix elements will still contain the rotational angular momentum operators explicitly. We then use perturbation theory, to an appropriate order, to remove those terms in the matrix which are off-diagonal in the vibrational basis functions. The diagonal matrix elements in the modified matrix give the desired effective rotational Hamiltonian in the different vibrational states.

To apply this procedure it is necessary to expand the terms of (4) in powers of the vibrational operators P_r and Q_r and to assess the relative orders of magnitude of the various terms. The presentation which follows and which is used throughout the examples discussed in this paper is due to Dr. J. K. G. Watson. This applies in particular to the discussion of orders of magnitude and powers of vibrational and rotational operators used in picking out terms, which is different from previous presentations.

The expanded Hamiltonian is shown in Table I. The vibrational operators P_r and Q_r have been replaced by their dimensionless equivalents

$$q_r = \gamma_r^{1/2} Q_r \quad \text{and} \quad p_r = P_r / \gamma_r^{1/2} \hbar \tag{7}$$

TABLE I

TERMS IN THE ROVIBRATIONAL HAMILTONIAN, H/hc, ARRANGED BY ORDER OF MAGNITUDE AND POWER OF J

Order of magnitude	Terms in H/hc involving J^0	J^1	J^2
$\kappa^0 \nu_{\text{vib}}$	$\Sigma_r \tfrac{1}{2}\omega_r(p_r^2 + q_r^2)$	—	—
$\kappa^1 \nu_{\text{vib}}$	$+ \Sigma_{rst}(1/6)\phi_{rst} q_r q_s q_t$	—	—
$\kappa^2 \nu_{\text{vib}}$	$+ \Sigma_{rstu}(1/24)\phi_{rstu} q_r q_s q_t q_u + \Sigma_\alpha B_e^{(\alpha)}[\pi_\alpha{}^2$	$-2\pi_\alpha J_\alpha$	$+ J_\alpha{}^2]$
$\kappa^3 \nu_{\text{vib}}$	$+ \text{quintic anh} + \Sigma_{\alpha\beta r}(\hbar^2/2hc)\mu_{\alpha\beta}^{(r)} q_r[\pi_\alpha \pi_\beta$	$-(\pi_\alpha J_\beta + \pi_\beta J_\alpha)$	$+ J_\alpha J_\beta]$
$\kappa^4 \nu_{\text{vib}}$	$+ \text{sextic anh} + \Sigma_{\alpha\beta rs}(\hbar^2/2hc)\mu_{\alpha\beta}^{(r,s)} q_r q_s[\pi_\alpha \pi_\beta$	$-(\pi_\alpha J_\beta + \pi_\beta J_\alpha)$	$+ J_\alpha J_\beta]$

where $\gamma_r = \lambda_r^{1/2}/\hbar = 2\pi c\omega_r/\hbar$, ω_r being the harmonic wavenumber of the rth normal mode. The vibrational angular momenta are given by

$$\pi_\alpha = \sum_{rs} \zeta_{r,s}^{(\alpha)} Q_r P_s / \hbar = \sum_{rs} \zeta_{r,s}^{(\alpha)} q_r p_s (\omega_s/\omega_r)^{1/2} \tag{8}$$

where $\zeta_{r,s}^{(\alpha)}$ is the Coriolis zeta constant coupling Q_r to Q_s through rotation about the α axis. Thus all the operators in the table are dimensionless, and all

the coefficients have the dimensions of wavenumber. The ϕ_{rst} and ϕ_{rstu} are cubic and quartic anharmonic force constants defined by the the expansion

$$V/hc = \tfrac{1}{2}\sum_r \omega_r q_r{}^2 + \tfrac{1}{6}\sum_{rst} \phi_{rst} q_r q_s q_t + \tfrac{1}{24}\sum_{rstu} \phi_{rstu} q_r q_s q_t q_u + \cdots \quad (9)$$

where the multiple summations are unrestricted (the ϕ's differ from Nielsen's anharmonic k's by numerical factors arising from Nielsen's use of restricted sums and omission of the 1/6 and 1/24 factors). The $B_e^{(\alpha)}$ are the equilibrium rotational constants A_e, B_e, and C_e given by

$$B_e^{(\alpha)} = (\hbar^2/2hc)\mu_{\alpha\alpha}^{(e)} = \hbar^2/2hcI_\alpha \quad (10)$$

The derivatives of the μ tensor are given by Watson [12]

$$\mu_{\alpha\beta}^{(r)} = \frac{\partial \mu_{\alpha\beta}}{\partial q_r} = \frac{-a_r^{(\alpha\beta)}}{I_\alpha I_\beta}\gamma_r^{-1/2} \quad (11a)$$

$$\mu_{\alpha\beta}^{(r,s)} = \frac{\partial^2 \mu_{\alpha\beta}}{\partial q_r \partial q_s} = \sum_\xi \frac{+3(a_r^{(\alpha\xi)}a_s^{(\beta\xi)} + a_r^{(\beta\xi)}a_s^{(\alpha\xi)})}{4I_\alpha I_\beta I_\xi}(\gamma_r \gamma_s)^{-1/2} \quad (11b)$$

where

$$a_r^{(\alpha\beta)} = (\partial I_{\alpha\beta}/\partial Q_r)_e \quad (12)$$

In all these equations $I_\alpha = I_{\alpha\alpha}$ and $I_{\alpha\beta}$ are the equilibrium moments and products of inertia. The $a_r^{(\alpha\beta)}$ and $\zeta_{r,s}^{(\alpha)}$ constants are the two types of vibration–rotation interaction constant that appear in the expansion of the complete Hamiltonian; both are related to the form of the normal coordinate vectors i.e., to the harmonic force field. The a's and the ζ's are, however, related by a number of sum rules which are independent of the force field; these are discussed by Henry and Amat [4], Oka and Morino [9], Watson [12], Oka [16], Meal and Polo [17], Mills and Duncan [18] and others.

The terms in Table I have been arranged in rows according to the order of magnitude of the coefficients of the operators, following Oka [11]. Thus if ν_{vib} is a typical vibrational wave number, ϕ_{rst} and ϕ_{rstu} are taken to be of a smaller order of magnitude than ν_{vib} by the factors κ and κ^2, respectively, where κ is the Born–Oppenheimer expansion parameter $(m/M)^{1/4}$, $\approx 1/10$, m being the electron mass M a typical nuclear mass. Similarly the rotational constants and the first and second derivatives of μ are smaller than ν_{vib} by factors κ^2, κ^3, and κ^4, respectively. The columns of Table I are arranged in increasing powers of the rotational angular momenta J_α. A convenient symbolic representation of Table I has been developed by Dr. Watson, in which the terms in the Hamiltonian are written in the simplified form of Table II. In this table the symbol $h_{n,m}$ represents a term in the Hamiltonian involving operators $(q_r, p_r)^n J_\alpha^m$. Remembering that π_α involves two powers of the vibrational operators p_r or q_r, it will be seen that Table II is equivalent to Table I.

TABLE II

TERMS IN THE ROVIBRATIONAL HAMILTONIAN CLASSIFIED BY ORDER
OF MAGNITUDE AND POWERS OF (q_r, p_r) AND J_α

Order of magnitude	Powers of (q_r, p_r) and J_α		
	J^0	J^1	J^2
ν_{vib}	$h_{2,0}$	—	—
$\kappa\nu_{vib}$	$+h_{3,0}$	—	—
$\kappa^2\nu_{vib}$	$+h_{4,0}$	$+h_{2,1}$	$+h_{0,2}$
$\kappa^3\nu_{vib}$	$+h_{5,0}$	$+h_{3,1}$	$+h_{1,2}$
$\kappa^4\nu_{vib}$	$+h_{6,0}$	$+h_{4,1}$	$+h_{2,2}$

$^a h_{n,m}$ implies $(q_r, p_r)^n J_\alpha^m$.

The advantage of this classification is that it enables us to assess the relative importance of terms to be obtained in the transformed Hamiltonian from the perturbation treatment described above. For example, if two off-diagonal terms $h_{k,l}$ and $h_{m,n}$ are treated by second-order perturbation theory, they will give terms in the diagonal matrix elements of the transformed Hamiltonian

$$\langle v|h_{k,l}|v'\rangle\langle v'|h_{m,n}|v\rangle/(E_v - E_{v'})$$

which will give contributions of the type

$$\langle v|\tilde{h}_{k+m-2,l+n}|v\rangle \quad \text{and} \quad \langle v|\tilde{h}_{k+m,l+n-1}|v\rangle$$

(the power of the vibrational operators is reduced by two in the perturbation treatment); if the original terms were of magnitude $\kappa^a \nu_{vib}$ and $\kappa^b \nu_{vib}$, respectively, then the transformed term will be of magnitude $\kappa^{a+b} \nu_{vib}$.

To illustrate this procedure, consider the derivation of the expression for α_r^B in Eq. (3). We require the coefficient of $(v_r + \frac{1}{2})J_b^2$ in the transformed Hamiltonian, which is a term of the form $\tilde{h}_{2,2}$, since $(v_r + \frac{1}{2})$ results from averaging a vibrational operator of power two [for example, $\frac{1}{2}\langle v_r|q_r^2 + p_r^2|v_r\rangle = (v_r + \frac{1}{2})$]. Examining Table II we see that such terms can arise in three different ways, which we may represent symbolically as:

(a) $\tilde{h}_{2,2} = h_{2,2}$ by first-order perturbation theory.
(b) $\tilde{h}_{2,2} = (h_{2,1} \times h_{2,1})/\Delta E_{vib}$ by second-order perturbation theory.
(c) $\tilde{h}_{2,2} = (h_{3,0} \times h_{1,2})/\Delta E_{vib}$ by second-order perturbation theory.

All three contributions yield terms of order of magnitude $\kappa^4 \nu_{vib}$, i.e., of order B^2/ν_{vib}. Taking the terms from Table I, making use of Eqs. (7)–(11), and using standard formulas for the necessary vibrational matrix elements, the perturbation calculations give the formula for α_r^B as

$$-\alpha_r^{\ B} = \frac{2B^2}{\omega_r} \left[\sum_\xi \frac{3(a_r^{(b\xi)})^2}{4I_\xi} + \sum_s (\zeta_{r,s}^{(b)})^2 \frac{(3\omega_r^{\ 2} + \omega_s^{\ 2})}{\omega_r^{\ 2} - \omega_s^{\ 2}} \right.$$

$$\left. + \pi \left(\frac{c}{h}\right)^{1/2} \sum_s \phi_{rrs} a_s^{(bb)} \left(\frac{\omega_r}{\omega_s^{3/2}}\right) \right] \qquad (13)$$

The three terms in the square brackets, which correspond respectively to the terms (a), (b) and (c) above, are all dimensionless and of order of magnitude unity, so that the whole expression has the dimensions and magnitude of the factor $2B^2/\omega_r$. In applying the formula (13) it is convenient to note that $(a_r^{(bb)})^2$ has the same dimensions and magnitude as $I_e^{(b)}$, that $\pi(c/h)^{\frac{1}{2}}a_s^{(bb)}$ has the same dimensions and magnitude as $B^{-1/2}$, and that†

$$\pi(c/h)^{1/2}a_s^{(bb)} = (0.086112 \text{ cm}^{1/2})(a_s^{(bb)}/\text{u}^{1/2} \text{ Å})$$

By replacing B and b in (13) by A and a throughout, the general formula for $\alpha_r^{\ A}$ is obtained; similarly for $\alpha_r^{\ C}$.

Although I regard (13) as being expressed in the most convenient general form, the formula is often quoted in slightly different but equivalent forms, obtained by making use of the zeta sum rule [9, 12]

$$\sum_s (\zeta_{r,s}^{(\alpha)})^2 = A_{rr}^{(\alpha\alpha)} - \sum_\xi (a_r^{(\alpha\xi)})^2/4I_\xi$$

or by using Nielsen's notation for the cubic constants, according to which $\phi_{rrr} = 6k_{rrr}$, and $\phi_{rrs} = 2k_{rrs}$ if $r \neq s$.

The physical interpretation of the three terms in $\alpha_r^{\ B}$ is clear from their origin in the Hamiltonian. Thus the term (a) arises from the quadratic dependence of B (or rather μ_{bb}) on the normal coordinate q_r, which results in the mean square displacement of q_r causing a change in the effective rotational constant; (b) arises from second-order Coriolis interaction between ω_r and ω_s, which causes the rotational energy levels in the lower state to be closed up, and those in the upper state to be opened out; (c) arises from the fact that anharmonicity causes a mean square displacement of q_r to give rise to a mean first-power displacement of q_s, which in turn causes a change in the effective rotational constant. For many molecules there are important negative cubic anharmonic terms of the type ϕ_{rrr} associated with bond stretching, which reflect the anharmonicity inherent in the dissociation process for large displacements; for small molecules the corresponding terms are often the dominant contribution to α, making the right-hand side of (13) negative. This is the reason for the negative sign in the definition of α.

As a second example of the use of Tables I and II, consider the derivation of the expression for the centrifugal distortion constants. Since these are the coefficients of J^4 in (1), we require $\tilde{h}_{0,4}$ terms in the transformed Hamiltonian.

---

† 1 u = unified atomic mass unit = (1/12) mass of the ^{12}C nuclide.

Such terms can only be obtained from $(h_{1,2} \times h_{1,2})/\Delta E_{vib}$ by second-order perturbation theory; the result is a term in the transformed Hamiltonian of the form

$$\sum_{\alpha\beta\gamma\delta} \tfrac{1}{4}\tau_{\alpha\beta\gamma\delta} \hbar^4 J_\alpha J_\beta J_\gamma J_\delta \tag{14}$$

of order of magnitude $\kappa^6 v_{vib}$, i.e., of order B^3/v_{vib}^2, where

$$\tau_{\alpha\beta\gamma\delta} = -\tfrac{1}{2}\sum_r (a_r^{(\alpha\beta)} a_r^{(\gamma\delta)}/\lambda_r I_\alpha I_\beta I_\gamma I_\delta) \tag{15}$$

Kivelson and Wilson [13] (see also Watson [15]) have shown that the only terms in (14) which influence the rotational Hamiltonian in first order can be written in the form of the centrifugal distortion term in Eq. (1), where

$$\tau'_{\alpha\alpha\beta\beta} = (\hbar^4/hc)(\tau_{\alpha\alpha\beta\beta} + 2\tau_{\alpha\beta\alpha\beta} \delta_{\alpha\beta}) \tag{16}$$

Combining (15) with (16) gives the expression for the τ' constants appearing in (1). In applying the formula (15), τ is usually obtained in units u^{-2} Å^{-5} mdyn^{-1}; it is then convenient to note that

$$(\hbar^4/hc)\tau = (0.0225784 \quad cm^{-1})(\tau/u^{-2} \text{ Å}^{-5} \text{ mdyn}^{-1})$$

An important feature of these examples of the application of the perturbation treatment is the estimation of orders of magnitude, and the distinction between order of magnitude and order of perturbation theory. Thus, in the formula for α, terms derived by first- and second-order perturbation theory appear in the same order of magnitude.

A similar situation occurs for the vibrational constants x_{rs} in the formula for the vibrational term values:

$$G(v) = \sum_r \omega_r(v_r + \tfrac{1}{2}) + \sum\sum_{r\geq s} x_{rs}(v_r + \tfrac{1}{2})(v_s + \tfrac{1}{2}) + \cdots \tag{17}$$

It is well known that x_{rs} contains second-order contributions from the cubic force constants and first-order contributions from the quartic force constants of comparable magnitude. The terms in question are derived from $\tilde{h}_{4,0}$ terms in the transformed Hamiltonian, and Table II shows that these can be obtained in two ways: (i) $\tilde{h}_{4,0} = h_{4,0}$ by first-order perturbation theory, (ii) $\tilde{h}_{4,0} = (h_{3,0} \times h_{3,0})/\Delta E_{vib}$ by second-order perturbation theory.

Both contributions yield terms of magnitude $\kappa^2 v_{vib}$, i.e., of the same order of magnitude as the rotational constants in our classification. The formulas actually obtained on applying the perturbation theory are

$$x_{rr} = \tfrac{1}{16} \phi_{rrrr} - \tfrac{1}{16}\sum_s \phi_{rrs}^2 [(8\omega_r^2 - 3\omega_s^2)/\omega_s(4\omega_r^2 - \omega_s^2)] \tag{18a}$$

and for $r \neq s$

$$x_{rs} = \tfrac{1}{4}\,\phi_{rrss} - \tfrac{1}{4}\sum_t (\phi_{rrt}\,\phi_{tss}/\omega_t)$$

$$- \tfrac{1}{2}\sum_t [\phi_{rst}^2\,\omega_t(\omega_t^2 - \omega_r^2 - \omega_s^2)/\Delta_{rst}]$$

$$+ [A(\zeta_{r,s}^{(a)})^2 + B(\zeta_{r,s}^{(b)})^2 + C(\zeta_{r,s}^{(c)})^2][(\omega_r/\omega_s) + (\omega_s/\omega_r)] \qquad (18b)$$

where

$$\Delta_{rst} = (\omega_r + \omega_s + \omega_t)(\omega_r - \omega_s - \omega_t)(-\omega_r + \omega_s - \omega_t)(-\omega_r - \omega_s + \omega_t)$$

These formulas are more commonly written in terms of Nielsen's force constants k, when they take a more complex form involving restricted summations owing to the numerical factors relating the ϕ's to the k's.

Finally, we can see that the perturbation treatment which allows us to define an effective rotational Hamiltonian in each vibrational state will fail if cross terms in the matrix of H connect nearly degenerate vibrational states, because the treatment of such terms by perturbation theory is no longer adequate. Empirically, the series represented by (2) and (3) no longer converge satisfactorily. This situation is known as Coriolis resonance or anharmonic resonance, depending on whether the cross terms originate from the π_α terms or the higher terms in the expansion of $V(Q_r)$ in the hamiltonian (4).† To interpret spectra involving such resonances, it is usually necessary to diagonalize the Hamiltonian matrix for the vibration–rotation levels of the interacting states exactly, without resorting to perturbation theory, as was done by Tanaka and Morino [19] for a strong Coriolis resonance in O_3 and by Morino and Saito [20] for a strong Fermi resonance in OF_2. The general formulas used to interpret the effective rotational constants and effective vibrational term values obtained from such an analysis must be modified to exclude terms from the perturbation treatment whose effect is included explicitly in the matrix; such terms will always have a resonance denominator in the general formula [e.g., the second term in square brackets in (13) for a Coriolis resonance, the second term in (18a) and the third in (18b) for a Fermi resonance]. The modified vibration–rotation interaction constants obtained by omitting resonant terms in this way are usually denoted by an asterisk, e.g., α_r^{C*} and x_{rs}^*; their significance varies according to which terms are omitted, and should be stated explicitly whenever this symbolism is used.

† The special case of anharmonic resonance between vibrational levels (v_r, v_s) and $(v_r + 2, v_s - 1)$ due to a cubic anharmonic term $\tfrac{1}{2}\phi_{rrs}\,q_r^2 q_s$ is usually referred to as Fermi resonance.

3. Symmetric Tops

3.1. Basis Functions

Symmetric-top molecules show one simplifying feature, but a number of complicating features with respect to the preceding discussion of asymmetric tops.

The simplifying feature is that because two of the rotational constants are equal, the effective rotational Hamiltonian takes the form†

$$H_{\text{rot}}/hc = A_v J_z^2 + B_v(J_x^2 + J_y^2) + \cdots \tag{20}$$

in which the components of angular momenta are given cartesian labels according to the convention that z is the molecular axis of symmetry. The terms quadratic in J, written explicitly in (20), constitute the rigid rotor Hamiltonian of a symmetric top. Unlike Eq. (2) for the asymmetric top, explicit formulas may be written for the eigenvalues and eigenfunctions of the rigid rotor symmetric top, giving

$$F_v^0(J, k) = A_v k^2 + B_v[J(J + 1) - k^2] \tag{21}$$

where J is the quantum number of total angular momentum, k is the component of J in the molecular axis and takes values $-J \le k \le +J$ in integral steps, and m is the component in a space-fixed axis and takes similar values. In the absence of electric and magnetic fields the energy does not depend on m, nor does it depend on the sign of k, so that the rotational terms given by (21) show a $(2 - \delta_{k,0})(2J + 1)$–fold degeneracy. I shall use lower case k and m to denote the signed quantum numbers, and $K = |k|$. The rigid rotor symmetric-top wavefunctions, which we use as basis functions for the more general treatment, are thus fully specified by the quantum numbers J, k, and m; we shall write them in the Dirac form as $|J, k, m\rangle$, and may omit the quantum number m when it is not relevant. The nonzero matrix elements of the angular momentum operators in these basis functions are summarized by Hougen [10]. It should be noted that different authors use different phase conventions, and may thus use different formulas for the matrix elements; although this can make no difference to the final calculation of observable quantities, it is important to be consistent in these conventions throughout any calculation.

The effective rotational Hamiltonian of a nonrigid symmetric top has further terms, as indicated in (20) and discussed below; however, the true rotational term values may still be written as a power series expansion in J, k, and the vibrational angular momentum quantum numbers l_t (see below), the leading terms still being given by (21). This is simpler than for an asymmetric top, where there is not even an approximate closed formula for the rotational term values in terms of the rotational quantum numbers.

---

† Since, by convention, $A \ge B \ge C$, (20) is appropriate for a prolate symmetric top; for an oblate top A should be replaced by C in (20).

Complications in symmetric-top molecules arise from the fact that they necessarily have doubly degenerate vibrations, and in consequence there will always be degenerate vibrational energy levels. The zeroth-order vibrational Hamiltonian, analogous to (5), is

$$H^0_{\text{vib}} = \tfrac{1}{2} \sum_s (P_s^2 + \lambda_s Q_s^2) + \tfrac{1}{2} \sum_t [P_{t1}^2 + P_{t2}^2 + \lambda_t(Q_{t1}^2 + Q_{t2}^2)]$$

$$= \tfrac{1}{2} hc \left[\sum_s \omega_s(p_s^2 + q_s^2) + \sum_t \omega_t(p_{t1}^2 + p_{t2}^2 + q_{t1}^2 + q_{t2}^2) \right] \qquad (22)$$

where s denotes a nondegenerate and t a degenerate normal mode, a convention followed throughout the rest of this paper. The index r will be used to denote either a degenerate or a nondegenerate mode. The eigenvalues of (22) give the zeroth-order vibrational energy levels:

$$G^0(v) = \sum_s \omega_s(v_s + \tfrac{1}{2}) + \sum_t \omega_t(v_t + 1) \qquad (23)$$

The eigenfunctions of (22) may be chosen to be simultaneous eigenfunctions of the vibrational angular momentum operators

$$L_t = (Q_{t1} P_{t2} - P_{t1} Q_{t2})/\hbar = (q_{t1} p_{t2} - p_{t1} q_{t2}) \qquad (24)$$

for each degenerate mode; they are written

$$\Psi_v^0 = \prod_s \psi_{v_s}(Q_s) \prod_t \psi_{v_t, l_t}(Q_{t1}, Q_{t2})$$

$$= \prod_s |v_s\rangle \prod_t |v_t, l_t\rangle \qquad (25)$$

and they satisfy the equations

$$H^0_{\text{vib}} \Psi_v^0 = hcG^0(v)\Psi_v^0 \qquad (26)$$

and

$$L_t \psi_{v_t, l_t} = l_t \psi_{v_t, l_t} \qquad (27)$$

where l_t is an integer of the same parity as v_t, subject to $-v_t \le l_t \le +v_t$. The eigenfunction $\psi_{v_t, l_t} = |v_t, l_t\rangle$ is thus $(v_t + 1)$-fold degenerate in energy, corresponding to the different values of l_t. Matrix elements of the vibrational operators in these basis functions are given by di Lauro and Mills [21].

To a crude approximation the vibration–rotation energy levels of a symmetric top are given by the sum of the zeroth-order vibration and rotation energies in (23) and (21). In practice, however, the degeneracies associated with the quantum numbers k and l_t show a variety of splittings due to vibration–rotation interactions, and various higher-order terms in the quantum numbers are observed just as for asymmetric tops. In fact we must expect the vibration–rotation terms to be given by a power series expansion in the various quantum

numbers, with all terms allowed by symmetry present; however, the higher-power terms generally have successively smaller coefficients, so that the series converges rapidly. To interpret the spectra we need to assess the relative importance of the various terms and the relationship of the coefficients to the parameters in the original Hamiltonian.

3.2. EMPIRICAL TERM FORMULAS

The vibration–rotation terms of a symmetric-top molecule are found to fit the following formulas. As for an asymmetric top, we write

$$T(v, J) = G(v) + F_v(J) \tag{28}$$

where the vibrational term $G(v)$ involves only the vibrational quantum numbers, and the rotational terms $F_v(J)$ are eigenvalues of the effective rotational Hamiltonian for the appropriate vibrational state. The vibrational term formula is

$$
\begin{aligned}
G(v) &= G(v_s, \ldots, v_t, l_t, \ldots) \\
&= \sum_s \omega_s(v_s + \tfrac{1}{2}) + \sum_t \omega_t(v_t + 1) \\
&\quad + \sum_{s \geq s'} x_{ss'}(v_s + \tfrac{1}{2})(v_{s'} + \tfrac{1}{2}) + \sum_{s, t} x_{st}(v_s + \tfrac{1}{2})(v_t + 1) \\
&\quad + \sum_{t \geq t'} x_{tt'}(v_t + 1)(v_{t'} + 1) + \sum_{t \geq t'} g_{tt'} l_t l_{t'} + \cdots
\end{aligned} \tag{29}
$$

where the higher-order terms which are not written explicitly are at least cubic in the vibrational quantum numbers. The anharmonicity constants x_{rr}, and g_{tt}, are typically smaller than the harmonic vibration wavenumbers ω_r by a factor of the order 10^{-2}; the higher-order anharmonicity constants are smaller still by a similar factor again.

The rotational terms $F_v(J)$ may be fitted to the following formula (complications arise when there are important l-doubling terms in the effective rotational Hamiltonian, but this is discussed more specifically in Section 3.4 below):

$$
\begin{aligned}
F_v(J) &= B_v[J(J + 1) - K^2] + A_v K^2 - \sum_t 2(A\zeta_t)_v k l_t \\
&\quad - (D_J)_v J^2(J + 1)^2 - (D_{JK})_v J(J + 1)K^2 - (D_K)_v K^4 \\
&\quad + \sum_t (\eta_{tJ})_v J(J + 1)k l_t + \sum_t (\eta_{tk})_v k^3 l_t + \cdots
\end{aligned} \tag{30}
$$

The first three terms are quadratic in the angular momenta; the coefficients A_v, B_v, and $(A\zeta_t)_v$ may be thought of as effective rotational constants, although the term in $(A\zeta_t)_v$, which is only present when $l_t \neq 0$, is more often

described as a first-order Coriolis splitting of the zeroth-order degeneracy associated with l_t. Each coefficient shows a vibrational dependence given by

$$B_v = B_e - \sum_r \alpha_r{}^B (v_r + d_r/2) + \cdots \tag{31a}$$

$$A_v = A_e - \sum_r \alpha_r{}^A (v_r + d_r/2) + \cdots \tag{31b}$$

$$(A\zeta_t)_v = (A\zeta_t)_e - \sum_r \alpha_r^{A\zeta t}(v_r + d_r/2) + \cdots \tag{31c}$$

where d_r is the degeneracy of the rth normal mode. We shall find that the coefficient $(A\zeta_t)_e$ is to be interpreted as the product $A_e\zeta_{t1,t2}^{(z)}$. The constants α_r^A and α_r^B are typically smaller than A and B by a factor of the order 10^{-2}; there is not much information about the $\alpha_r^{A\zeta}$ constants, but the indications are that they are comparable to the other α's. Substituting Eqs. (31a–c) into Eq. (30) shows that $2\alpha_r^{A\zeta}$ is the coefficient of $kl_t(v_r + d_r/2)$ in the complete term formula; Maes, who was the first to recognize the importance of this term, writes $\eta_{t,r}$ for this constant [5], but I perfer the notation $2\alpha_r^{A\zeta}$ because it emphasizes the similarity in origin and order of magnitude to the other α constants. Thus the relationship of Maes' notation to that used in (31c) is

$$2\alpha_r^{A\zeta} = \eta_{t,r} \tag{32}$$

The terms in the second and third lines of (30) are quartic in the angular momenta, and the coefficients may be thought of as effective centrifugal distortion constants. They are typically smaller than the rotational constants by factors of the order of 10^{-4}; although in principle they should show a vibrational dependence according to formulas similar to (31), this has rarely been observed, and I shall ignore the vibrational dependence of centrifugal distortion and drop the subscript v on these constants. The η_{tJ} and η_{tk} constants were first introduced by Maes [5]; as for the $\alpha_r^{A\zeta}$ constants, there is little experimental information on their magnitude, but the indications are that η_{tJ} and η_{tk} are comparable to D_J, D_{JK}, and D_K in magnitude, being generally much smaller than the α's.

As for asymmetric tops, the empirical term formula implied in Eq. (28)–(31) fails when there is an accidental vibrational degeneracy or near-degeneracy in that the power series expansion in the various quantum numbers no longer converges satisfactorily.

3.3. PERTURBATION TREATMENT

The complete vibration–rotation Hamiltonian is still given by Eq. (4), as for an asymmetric-top molecule, although in a symmetric top there are relations between the coefficients imposed by symmetry, and also the sum

over normal modes must be carried over the components of degenerate coordinates separately.

The empirical vibration–rotation term formula of the preceding section is obtained by first averaging over the vibrational coordinates to obtain an effective rotational Hamiltonian, and then by replacing the latter by its eigenvalues. In the first stage, the complete Hamiltonian H is transformed, using perturbation theory, to remove terms which are vibrationally off-diagonal in the harmonic oscillator basis functions; this gives an effective Hamiltonian $\tilde{H}$ which operates only within each degenerate set of vibrational states, the degeneracy being that implied by the symmetry properties of a symmetric top. We then average $\tilde{H}$ over the vibrational coordinates to obtain the effective rotational Hamiltonian. This corresponds to the adiabatic Born–Oppenheimer separation of vibration from rotation, and gives coefficients in the rotational Hamiltonian which show a dependence on the vibrational quantum numbers [such as B_v, A_v, and $(A\zeta_t)_v$ in Eq. (30)]. Finally the rotational Hamiltonian is replaced by its eigenvalues to give the complete term formula. We now consider the various terms which arise from this procedure in greater detail.

(a) First-Order Coriolis Term

The complete Hamiltonian (Tables I and II) contains the $h_{2,1}$ term $-2A_e \pi_z J_z$. The terms from π_z which connect the two components of a doubly degenerate vibration take a particularly simple form. We have

$$\pi_z = \sum_t \zeta^{(z)}_{t1,t2}[(Q_{t1}P_{t2} - Q_{t2}P_{t1})/\hbar] + \text{other terms}$$

$$= \sum_t \zeta_t L_t + \text{other terms}$$

(33)

where $\zeta^{(z)}_{t1,t2}$ is abbreviated to ζ_t and we have used (24). The corresponding term in the Hamiltonian is thus

$$-\sum_t 2A_e\zeta_t L_t J_z$$

This is diagonal in both vibrational and rotational basis functions, giving a first-order term in the energy

$$-\sum_t 2A_e\zeta_t l_t k$$

(34)

Thus the vibrationally independent part of the coefficient of kl_t in (30), written as $(A\zeta_t)_e$ in Eq. (31), is to be identified with the product $A_e\zeta^{(z)}_{t1,t2}$. This coefficient is comparable in magnitude to the other rotational constants A_e and B_e, and may be thought of as a third rotational constant.

Although spectra are typically observed for much larger values of the rotational quantum numbers J and k than for the vibrational angular momentum quantum numbers l_t, the selection rules are such that for infrared perpendicular bands the term in $A\zeta_t$ is of comparable importance to the terms in

A and B in determining the observed rotational structure. If both A_e and $A_e\zeta_t$ could be determined independently from observed spectra, the Coriolis constant ζ_t would be determined; this would give information on the harmonic force field through the relationship of the zetas to the normal coordinate vectors. In practice the vibrational dependences of A and $A\zeta_t$ make it difficult to determine A and ζ_t independently with high precision, as discussed in Section 4.

(b) Vibrational Dependence of Rotational Constants α

The vibrational dependence of A and B is represented by the constants α_r^A and α_r^B in (31a) and (31b); for example, $-\alpha_r^B$ is the coefficient of $[J(J+1) - k^2](v_r + d_r/2)$ in the complete energy formula. These terms arise from the perturbation treatment in an exactly similar way to that described in Section 2 for asymmetric tops. The contributions are:

(a) $h_{2,2}$, first-order terms from the quadratic dependence of the $\boldsymbol{\mu}$ tensor on the normal coordinates.
(b) $(h_{2,1} \times h_{2,1})/\Delta E_{\text{vib}}$, second-order Coriolis terms.
(c) $(h_{3,0} \times h_{1,2})/\Delta E_{\text{vib}}$, second-order terms arising from the combination of cubic anharmonicity with the linear dependence of $\boldsymbol{\mu}$ on the normal coordinates.

The physical interpretation of these terms is similar to that described in Section 2 for asymmetric tops. The perturbation calculation gives the following formulas (s = nondegenerate mode, t = degenerate mode):

$$-\alpha_s^A = \frac{2A^2}{\omega_s} \left[\frac{3(a_s^{(zz)})^2}{4I_A} + \sum_{s'}{}^* (\zeta_{s,s'}^{(z)})^2 \frac{3\omega_s^2 + \omega_{s'}^2}{\omega_s^2 - \omega_{s'}^2} \right.$$
$$\left. + \pi \left(\frac{c}{h}\right)^{1/2} \sum_{s'} \phi_{sss'} a_{s'}^{(zz)} \frac{\omega_s}{(\omega_{s'})^{3/2}} \right] \tag{35}$$

$$-\alpha_t^A = \frac{2A^2}{\omega_t} \left[\frac{3(a_{t1}^{(xz)})^2}{4I_B} + \sum_{t'}{}^* (\zeta_{t1,t'2}^{(z)})^2 \frac{3\omega_t^2 + \omega_{t'}^2}{\omega_t^2 - \omega_{t'}^2} \right.$$
$$\left. + \pi \left(\frac{c}{h}\right)^{1/2} \sum_s \phi_{st1t1} a_s^{(zz)} \frac{\omega_t}{(\omega_s)^{3/2}} \right] \tag{36}$$

$$-\alpha_s^B = \frac{2B^2}{\omega_s} \left[\frac{3[(a_s^{(xx)})^2 + (a_s^{(xy)})^2]}{4I_B} \right.$$
$$+ \sum_t [(\zeta_{s,t1}^{(y)})^2 + (\zeta_{s,t1}^{(x)})^2] \frac{3\omega_s^2 + \omega_t^2}{\omega_s^2 - \omega_t^2}$$
$$\left. + \pi \left(\frac{c}{h}\right)^{1/2} \sum_{s'} \phi_{sss'} a_{s'}^{(xx)} \frac{\omega_s}{(\omega_{s'})^{3/2}} \right] \tag{37}$$

$$
-\alpha_t{}^B = \frac{2B^2}{\omega_t} \left[\frac{3(a_{t1}^{(xz)})^2}{8I_A} + \frac{3(a_{t1}^{(xx)})^2}{4I_B} \right.
$$

$$
+ \tfrac{1}{2} \sum_s [(\zeta_{s,t1}^{(y)})^2 + (\zeta_{s,t1}^{(x)})^2] \frac{3\omega_t{}^2 + \omega_s{}^2}{\omega_t{}^2 - \omega_s{}^2}
$$

$$
+ \sum_{t'}{}^* [(\zeta_{t1,t'1}^{(y)})^2 + (\zeta_{t1,t'1}^{(x)})^2] \frac{3\omega_t{}^2 + \omega_{t'}^2}{\omega_t{}^2 - \omega_{t'}^2}
$$

$$
+ \pi \left(\frac{c}{h} \right)^{1/2} \sum_s \phi_{st1t1}\, a_s^{(xx)} \frac{\omega_t}{(\omega_s)^{3/2}} \right\}
\tag{38}
$$

In these formulas, $\Sigma_{s'}{}^*$ means that the term with $s' = s$ is excluded from the summation; similarly, $\Sigma_{t'}{}^*$ means that $t' = t$ is excluded. The formulas are written in a form that applies to all symmetric-top molecules provided that the orientation of the doubly degenerate coordinates has been chosen to make $a_{t2}^{(xz)} = 0$ and $\zeta_{t1,t'1}^{(z)} = 0$ for all t and t' (these conditions would normally always be satisfied unless the molecule had no orientating symmetry elements, and no such symmetric tops have yet been studied in detail). Since only the distinction between nondegenerate and degenerate modes has been retained in the above formulas, there will often be cases where symmetry requires some of the terms included to be zero. Henry and Amat [4] have summarized the relations between $a_r^{(\alpha\beta)}$ and $\zeta_{r,r'}^{(\alpha)}$ constants which follow from symmetry for all symmetric-top point groups.

As for Eq. (13), the terms in the square brackets are dimensionless and of order of magnitude unity, giving the α constants the dimensions and magnitude of the first factor in each case; they are thus of order $\kappa^4 v_{\text{vib}}$ (or B^2/v_{vib}) in magnitude. The contributions from the terms (a), (b), and (c) described above are given in order.

For prolate symmetric tops with only H atoms off-axis, such as methyl halides or methyl cyanide, the rotational constants are such that $A \gg B$. In this case $\alpha_r{}^A \gg \alpha_r{}^B$, for all r, owing to the factor $2A^2/\omega_r$ or $2B^2/\omega_r$ in the formula. For oblate symmetric tops $B > C$, but the difference is never so great: the extreme case occurs for a planar, oblate symmetric top, where $B = 2C$.

(c) Vibrational Dependence of $A\zeta_t$

The vibrational dependence of $A\zeta_t$ is represented by the constant $\alpha_r^{A\zeta_t}$ in Eq. (31c). These terms arise from the perturbation treatment in a similar manner to the more familiar constants $\alpha_r{}^A$ and $\alpha_r{}^B$, and are of the same order of magnitude, but the formulas are appreciably more complex. We require $\tilde{h}_{4,1}$ terms in the transformed Hamiltonian, and from Table II we see that the following terms can contribute to the formulas for $\alpha_r^{A\zeta_t}$:

(a) $h_{4,1}$, first-order terms from the perturbation treatment.

(b) $(h_{2,1} \times h_{2,1})/\Delta E_{\text{vib}}$, second order terms.†

(c) $(h_{4,0} \times h_{2,1})/\Delta E_{\text{vib}}$, second-order terms.

(d) $(h_{3,0} \times h_{3,1})/\Delta E_{\text{vib}}$, second-order terms.

(e) $(h_{3,0} \times h_{3,0} \times h_{2,1})/(\Delta E_{\text{vib}})^2$, third-order terms.

All contributions are of order of magnitude $\kappa^4 v_{\text{vib}}$ in the transformed Hamiltonian. Both cubic and quartic anharmonic force constants appear in the final expression [cubic terms in (d) and (e) and quartic terms in (c)], in contrast to the formulas for α_r^A and α_r^B, which contain only cubic anharmonic constants.

The perturbation calculation to produce the final expression is complex. The only published formulas for $\alpha_r^{A\zeta_t}$ are given by Maes [5] in the appendix to his paper; they are given in such a general form that they are not really usable in numerical calculations without considerable further work. In his original thesis Maes gives simplications of this formulas for C_{3v} molecules with no A_2 vibrations. We are at present repeating the perturbation calculation in this laboratory as a check on Maes' formulas. I shall not quote the formulas here.

No numerical calculations of $\alpha_r^{A\zeta_t}$ coefficients have been reported, nor have any $\alpha_r^{A\zeta_t}$ been determined empirically from observed spectra, up to the present time. Nonetheless, it should be realized that symmetric-top energy levels will generally include terms of this kind, and that their importance is comparable to the terms in α_r^A and α_r^B. Moreover, the formulas show that in prolate symmetric tops ($A \gg B$) $\alpha_r^{A\zeta_t}$ must be expected to be comparable to α_r^A rather than to α_r^B. Finally it should be realized that many of the terms (b)–(d) arising from second- and third-order perturbation theory will have resonance denominators, so that accidental vibrational degeneracies may give rise to resonant terms in the expressions for $\alpha_r^{A\zeta_t}$; in such cases observed spectra will show anomalously high vibrational dependence of $A\zeta_t$ (assuming that the observed energy levels can still be fitted to a power series expansion in the quantum numbers).

(d) Centrifugal Distortion Constants

The centrifugal distortion constants D_J, D_{JK}, and D_K arise from $\tilde{h}_{0,4}$ terms in the transformed Hamiltonian. The only contributions to these terms come from the second-order perturbation treatment of $(h_{1,2} \times h_{1,2})/\Delta E_{\text{vib}}$ terms from Table II. The formulas have been given by Wilson [22]; for a general symmetric top they may be written

---

† These terms, which are at first unexpected, arise from the fact that it is possible to drop *either* two powers of q or p, *or* one power of J, in the perturbation treatment. In the contact transformation this is related to the difference between the commutation relations $[q, p] = i\hbar$ and $[J_x, J_y] = -i\hbar J_z$.

$$D_J = -\tfrac{1}{4}\tau'_{xxxx} \tag{39}$$

$$D_{JK} = -2D_J - \tfrac{1}{2}\tau'_{xxzz} \tag{40}$$

$$D_K = D_J - \tfrac{1}{4}\tau'_{zzzz} + \tfrac{1}{2}\tau'_{xxzz} \tag{41}$$

where the expression for $\tau'_{\alpha\alpha\beta\beta}$ is given in (16) and (15). For planar oblate symmetric tops (such as BF_3 or C_6H_6) the τ's are related such that $2\tau_{zzzz} = \tau_{xxzz}$ and $\tau_{xzxz} = 0$; this results in only two of the three D's being independent, such that

$$D_{JK} = -\tfrac{2}{3}(D_J + 2D_K) \tag{42}$$

The centrifugal distortion constants η_{tJ} and η_{tK} which occur in the rotational term formulas for excited degenerate vibrational states arise from $\tilde{h}_{2,3}$ terms in the transformed Hamiltonian. Table II shows that contributions to these terms will come from $(h_{3,1} \times h_{1,2})/\Delta E_{vib}$, $(h_{2,1} \times h_{2,2})/\Delta E_{vib}$, $(h_{1,2} \times 1,2)/\Delta E_{vib}$, and $(h_{3,0} \times h_{2,1} \times h_{1,2})/\Delta E^2_{vib}$, through second- and third-order perturbation theory; they will thus involve the cubic anharmonic force constants.† The order of magnitude of these coefficients will be $\kappa^6 v_{vib}$, as for D_J, D_{JK}, and D_K. Maes [5] originally drew attention to the importance of these terms, but no formulas relating η_{tJ} and η_{tK} directly to the force field have yet been published. Several authors have introduced these constants into the interpretation of microwave and infrared spectra of excited degenerate vibrational states [7, 23, 24].

(e) Vibrational Anharmonic Constants

The vibrational anharmonic coefficients which appear in the vibrational term formula (29) arise from purely vibrational terms. The $x_{rr'}$ and $g_{tt'}$ coefficients are derived from $\tilde{h}_{4,0}$ terms in the transformed Hamiltonian and are of magnitude $\kappa^4 v_{vib}$; as for an asymmetric top, both first-order and second-order perturbation terms contribute. For a symmetric top the general formulas are as follows

$$x_{ss} = \tfrac{1}{16}\phi_{ssss} - \tfrac{1}{16}\sum_{s'}[\phi^2_{sss'}(8\omega_s^2 - 3\omega_{s'}^2)/\omega_{s'}(4\omega_s^2 - \omega_{s'}^2)] \tag{43}$$

$$x_{ss'} = \tfrac{1}{4}\phi_{sss's'} - \tfrac{1}{4}\sum_{s''}(\phi_{sss''}\phi_{s''s's'}/\omega_{s''})$$
$$- \tfrac{1}{2}\sum_{s''}(\phi^2_{ss's''}\omega_{s''}(\omega_{s''}^2 - \omega_s^2 - \omega_{s'}^2)/\Delta_{ss's''}]$$
$$+ A(\zeta^{(z)}_{s,s'})^2[(\omega_s/\omega_{s'}) + (\omega_{s'}/\omega_s)] \tag{44}$$

---

† I am grateful to Dr. J. M. Brown for drawing my attention to the third order terms.

$$x_{st} = \tfrac{1}{4}\,\phi_{sstt} - \tfrac{1}{4}\sum_{s'}(\phi_{sss'}\,\phi_{s'tt}/\omega_{s'})$$

$$-\tfrac{1}{2}\sum_{t'}[\phi_{stt'}^2\,\omega_{t'}(\omega_{t'}^2 - \omega_s{}^2 - \omega_t{}^2)/\Delta_{stt'}]$$

$$+\, B[(\zeta_{s,t1}^{(x)})^2 + (\zeta_{s,t1}^{(y)})^2][(\omega_s/\omega_t) + (\omega_t/\omega_s)] \qquad (45)$$

$$x_{tt'} = \tfrac{1}{4}\,\phi_{ttt't'}^* - \tfrac{1}{4}\sum_{s}(\phi_{stt}\,\phi_{st't'}/\omega_s)$$

$$-\tfrac{1}{4}\sum_{s}[\phi_{stt'}^2\,\omega_s(\omega_s{}^2 - \omega_t{}^2 - \omega_{t'}^2)/\Delta_{stt'}]$$

$$-\tfrac{1}{2}\sum_{t''}[\phi_{tt't''}^2\,\omega_{t'}(\omega_{t''}^2 - \omega_t{}^2 - \omega_{t'}^2)/\Delta_{tt't''}]$$

$$+\,[\tfrac{1}{2}\,A(\zeta_{t1,t'2}^{(z)})^2 + B(\zeta_{t1,t'1}^{(y)})^2][(\omega_t/\omega_{t'}) + (\omega_{t'}/\omega_t)] \qquad (46)$$

$$x_{tt} = \tfrac{1}{16}\,\phi_{tttt} - \tfrac{1}{16}\sum_{s}[\phi_{stt}^2(8\omega_t{}^2 - 3\omega_s{}^2)/\omega_s(4\omega_t{}^2 - \omega_s{}^2)]$$

$$-\tfrac{1}{16}\sum_{t'}[\phi_{ttt'}^2(8\omega_t{}^2 - 3\omega_{t'}^2)/\omega_{t'}(4\omega_t{}^2 - \omega_{t'}^2)] \qquad (47)$$

$$g_{tt} = -\tfrac{1}{48}\,\phi_{tttt} - \tfrac{1}{16}\sum_{s}[\phi_{stt}^2\,\omega_s/(4\omega_t{}^2 - \omega_s{}^2)]$$

$$+\tfrac{1}{16}\sum_{t'}[\phi_{ttt'}^2(8\omega_t{}^2 - \omega_{t'}^2)/\omega_{t'}(4\omega_t{}^2 - \omega_{t'}^2)]$$

$$+\, A(\zeta_{t1,t2}^{(z)})^2 \qquad (48)$$

$$g_{tt'} = +\tfrac{1}{2}\sum_{s}(\phi_{stt'}^2\,\omega_s\,\omega_t\,\omega_{t'}/\Delta_{stt'}) - \sum_{t''}(\phi_{tt't''}^2\,\omega_s\,\omega_{t'}\,\omega_{t''}/\Delta_{tt't''})$$

$$-\, 2B(\zeta_{t1,t'1}^{(y)})^2 + A(\zeta_{t1,t'2}^{(z)})^2 + 2A\zeta_{t1,t2}^{(z)}\,\zeta_{t'1,t'2}^{(z)} \qquad (49)$$

In these expressions

$$\Delta_{rr'r''} = (\omega_r + \omega_{r'} + \omega_{r''})(\omega_r - \omega_{r'} - \omega_{r''})(\omega_{r'} - \omega_{r''} - \omega_r)(\omega_{r''} - \omega_r - \omega_{r'})$$

and

$$\phi_{ttt't'}^* = \tfrac{1}{2}(\phi_{t1t1t'1t'1} + \phi_{t1t1t'2t'2}).$$

The numerical subscripts on t for the other cubic and quartic anharmonic force constants are as follows: $\phi_{stt'} = \phi_{st1t'1} = \phi_{st2t'2}$; $\phi_{tt't''} = \phi_{t1t'1t''1} = -\phi_{t1t'2t''2} = -\phi_{t2t'1t''2} = -\phi_{t2t'2t''1}$; $\phi_{tttt} = \phi_{t1t1t1t1} = 3\phi_{t1t1t2t2} = \phi_{t2t2t2t2}$. All of the summations in Eq. (43)–(49) are unrestricted, so that $\Sigma_{s'}$ includes the term with $s' = s$ and $\Sigma_{t'}$ includes the term with $t' = t$, etc.; however the index s runs *only* over nondegenerate modes and the index t runs *only* over degenerate modes. Also (44), (46), and (49) hold *only* for the case $s \neq s'$, $t \neq t'$.

The formulas (43)–(49) have been published previously by several authors;

however, they have generally been written in terms of Nielsen's force constants $k_{rr'r''}$ rather than the corresponding force constants $\phi_{rr'r''}$ defined in Eq. (9), and this results in superficially more complex expressions in which the terms with $s' = s$ and $t' = t$ have to be written separately from the general summation because the numerical factor is different for these terms when Nielsen's ks' are used. (For example, $\phi_{ss's''} = k_{ss's''}$ when $s \neq s' \neq s'' \neq s$, but $\phi_{sss'} = 2k_{sss'}$ when $s \neq s'$, and $\phi_{sss} = 6k_{sss}$.) Also, Nielsen's expression for the vibrational anharmonic constants [2, 3] of the type $x_{ss'}$ are apparently unsymmetrical in s and s', owing to the fact that he does *not* restrict $s \geqslant s'$ in the third term on the right-hand side of Eq. (29); these differences make it necessary to take the greatest care in comparing formulas. Even allowing for all these differences, some of the terms in Eq. (43)–(49) are apparently missing from Nielsen's formulas. Morino *et al.* [25] have also published formulas for the vibrational anharmonic constants: their results are in agreement with Eq. (43)–(49) except that their formulas appear to be missing the term $A(\zeta_{t1,t2}^z)^2$ from g_{tt} and the term $A\zeta_{t1,t2}^{(z)}\zeta_{t'1,t'2}^{(z)}$ from $g_{tt'}$.

3.4. *l*-DOUBLING CONSTANTS

The empirical term formulas given by (30) for the rotational energy levels in a vibrational state actually represent the diagonal matrix elements of the transformed Hamiltonian obtained from the perturbation treatment, and the discussion of the preceding section is concerned only with diagonal matrix elements of $\tilde{H}$ in the rigid, symmetric rotor basis functions. In fact there are a few matrix elements of $\tilde{H}$ which are off-diagonal in the rotational quantum numbers, and to this extent the empirical term formula (30) is inadequate. The most important of these off-diagonal matrix elements, and the only ones discussed here, are those associated with *l*-doubling and *l*-resonance effects in excited degenerate vibrational states. These have been discussed, in particular, by Grenier-Besson [6], Oka [11], and by Cartwright and Mills [26].

There are three different types of rotational *l*-doubling interactions which may arise in an excited degenerate vibrational state of a symmetric top, involving three different *l*-doubling constants, the differences being associated with the selection rules in k and l_t which govern the nonzero off-diagonal matrix elements. These are as follows:

(a) $\Delta l_t = \pm 2$, $\Delta k = \pm 2$, denoted $q_t^{(+)}$-type interactions by Cartwright and Mills [26], discussed below.
(b) $\Delta l_t = \pm 2$, $\Delta k = \mp 2$, denoted $q_t^{(-)}$-type interactions.
(c) $\Delta l_t = \pm 2$, $\Delta k = \mp 1$, denoted r_t-type interactions.

The effects (b) and (c) can only occur in certain point groups, owing to symmetry restrictions, and have rarely been observed: they are discussed in the literature [6, 26, 27], and will not be considered further here.

The effect (a) is the most familiar type of l-doubling interaction, and the l-doubling constant $q_t^{(+)}$, which may be written simply q_t when there is no danger of confusion with effect (b), defines the magnitude of the off-diagonal matrix elements according to the equation

$$\langle v_t, l_t + 1, J, k + 1 \mid \tilde{H}/hc \mid v_t, l_t - 1, J, k - 1 \rangle$$
$$= (\rho/4)q_t^{(+)}\{[(v_t + 1)^2 - l_t^2][J(J + 1) - k(k + 1)][J(J + 1) - k(k - 1)]\}^{1/2}$$

(50)

In this equation ρ is a sign index, equal to $+1$ or -1, discussed below, and $q_t(= q_t^{(+)})$ is the l-doubling constant [note that Grenier-Besson [6] uses the symbol $F^t = 4q_t^{(+)}$ for the l-doubling constant in (50)]. Interactions of this type occur in the excited states of all E_1 species vibrations (g, u, $'$, or $''$) of all symmetric-top point groups; for molecules with a threefold primary axis they occur for all degenerate vibrations.

A particular difficulty arises in defining the sign of the l-doubling constant q_t, since it only appears in off-diagonal matrix elements of the transformed Hamiltonian. The sign of the matrix element (50) depends on the relative phases of the basis functions $|v_t, l_t, J, k\rangle$, and different authors use different phase conventions. Cartwright and Mills [26] have discussed this problem specifically, and propose a convention for the infrared-active degenerate vibrations of symmetric tops which is related to the rovibrational symmetry species of the $k = l_t = \pm 1$ pairs of levels in the presence of l-doubling (see below). I shall follow this convention, which agrees with the implicit assumptions of most other workers. Using Hougen's phase conventions for the rotational basis functions [10] and the usual phase conventions for the degenerate vibrational basis functions [26], we thus find $\rho = -1$ in Eq. (50).

The effect of the matrix elements (50) on the energy levels and the observed spectrum is as follows. The constants q_t prove to be of the same order of magnitude as α_t^B constants, so that whenever the matrix elements couple levels differing in energy by the order of magnitude of a rotational constant the effects are very small and may often be neglected. Grenier-Besson and Amat [7] have shown how they may be accounted for by second-order perturbation theory in such a situation. There are, however, two situations where the effects become more important. The first is known as l-doubling: the $k = l_t = \pm 1$ pairs of wave functions in $v_t = 1, 3, 5, \ldots$ vibrational states are always directly coupled by the matrix element (50), and since they would otherwise be degenerate, they become split by twice the magnitude of the matrix element. In this way we find a splitting of these levels in the $v_t = 1$ vibrational state of $q_t J(J + 1)$. The rotational term formula for these pairs of levels thus becomes

$$F_{v_t=1}(J) = (B_v \pm \tfrac{1}{2}q_t)J(J + 1) + A_v - B_v - 2(A\zeta_t)_v + \text{centrifugal terms} \quad (51)$$

The selection rules show that, following the sign and phase conventions discussed above, the allowed transitions in an infrared perpendicular fundamental band go to one or other of the two split levels as follows [26]:

$$B_{eif} = B_v + \tfrac{1}{2}q_t \qquad \text{for } P \text{ and } R \text{ branch transitions} \qquad (52a)$$

$$B_{eff} = B_v - \tfrac{1}{2}q_t \qquad \text{for } Q \text{ branch transitions} \qquad (52b)$$

where B_{eff} is the coefficient of $J(J + 1)$ in the term formula (51).

The second important effect of the matrix elements (50) is known as *l*-resonance; this occurs when the rotational constants happen to have such values that the interacting energy levels are approximately accidentally degenerate for *all* rotational quantum numbers. The effects are discussed in the literature [24, 26, 28], and have been observed for a number of oblate symmetric tops.

The empirical determination of *l*-doubling constants from observed spectra has only been achieved thus far for a few symetric-top molecules. It has generally been done *either* from observation and analysis of the P, Q, and R structure of the $K = 1{-}0$ subband of the infrared perpendicular fundamental, using (52), *or* from observation and analysis of the microwave spectrum in the $v_t = 1$ excited state. In the latter case one may either observe the usual $J + 1$ $\leftarrow J$ rotational transitions, for which the *l*-doubled levels give rise to subsidiary peaks on the high- and low-frequency sides of the other k transitions split by $2q_t(J + 1)$ (see, for example, Grenier-Besson and Amat's analysis of CH_3CN [7]), or one may observe direct transitions between the *l*-doubled levels of a given J (see Lafferty's observations on CH_3CN [29]). Neither of the microwave methods allows one to determine the *sign* of the *l*-doubling constant, in contrast to the infrared method.

Finally, we must consider how matrix elements of the type in Eq. (50) arise in the transformed Hamiltonian as a result of the general perturbation treatment. From the selection rules $\Delta l_t = \pm 2$, $\Delta k = \pm 2$ we see that we require terms in $\tilde{H}$ of the type $(q_{t1} \pm iq_{t2})^2 (J_x \mp iJ_y)^2$, since these operators have the correct shift properties in the quantum numbers. This is an $\tilde{h}_{2,2}$ term in the notation of Table II. It follows that the *l*-doubling constants q_t arise in the same general way as the α_t constants, and contributions of the type (a), (b), and (c) in Section 3.3(b) are to be expected for q_t just as for α_t. The perturbation calculation has been described by both Grenier-Bession [6] and Oka [11]. The result gives the following formula for q_t ($= q_t^{(+)}$) for C_{3v} molecules:

$$q_t = \frac{2B^2}{\omega_t} \left\{ -\frac{3(a_{t1}^{(xz)})^2}{4I_A} + \sum_s [(\zeta_{s,t1}^{(y)})^2 - (\zeta_{s,t1}^{(x)})^2] \frac{3\omega_t^2 + \omega_s^2}{\omega_t^2 - \omega_s^2} \right.$$

$$\left. + 2\pi \left(\frac{c}{h}\right)^{1/2} \sum_{t'} \phi_{t1t1t'1} a_{t'1}^{(yy)} \frac{\omega_t}{(\omega_{t'})^{3/2}} \right\} \qquad (53)$$

This formula assumes σ_v orientation of the degenerate coordinates (see [21]) and assumes the sign and phase conventions discussed above (and in [26]). It may be applied to a molecule belonging to any symmetric-top point group of which C_{3v} is a subgroup by imposing the symmetry restrictions on the a, ϕ, and ζ constants implied by the higher symmetry. Molecules with fourfold axes require a different formula—see [6] (the formula (53) is not applicable in this case, as was erroneously implied in [26]).

It should be added that l-doubling constants must be expected to show both a dependence on the vibrational quantum numbers v_r and the rotational quantum numbers J and k of the form

$$q_t = q_t^{(e)} + \delta q_t^{(J)} J(J + 1) + \delta q_t^{(k)}(k - l_t)^2 + \sum_r \delta q_t^{(r)}(v_r + d_r/2) + \cdots$$

Some of these effects have been observed in precise microwave determinations; however, they are expected to be of a smaller order of magnitude than the leading term $q_t^{(e)}$ and no theoretical expressions for these terms have been derived for symmetric-top molecules. The formula (53) should strictly be applied only to the leading term $q_t^{(e)}$.

4. Discussion

In Sections 2 and 3 I have reviewed some of the formulas for the rovibrational interaction constants and energy levels of both asymmetric-top and symmetric-top molecules. These formulas may be used, in conjunction with appropriate selection rules and intensity formulas, to predict rotation and rotation–vibration spectra. The input to such a calculation would be the atomic masses, the equilibrium structure, and the force field; the terms which I have included in this review involve both the quadratic force constants and the cubic and quartic anharmonic force constants.

Conversely, one might hope to deduce from observed spectra the equilibrium structure, and both the harmonic and the cubic and quartic anharmonic force constants. However, this reverse calculation is incomparably more difficult, owing to problems of indeterminacy, as is well known.

There is one aspect of the indeterminacy problem which I shall discuss further here: namely the problem of determining the axial rotation constant A (or C) for symmetric-top molecules. It is unfortunate that the spectroscopic selection rules generally forbid the observation of transitions which might allow us to determine A_0 in the ground vibrational state, or indeed A_v in any vibrational state, for a symmetric-top molecule. The result is that although B_v, B_0, and B_e may frequently be determined to a few parts in 10^5, the corresponding information on the axial rotational constant is almost invariably subject to uncertainties of the order of 1 or 2%.

One method of estimating A which has been widely used is to study all of the infrared perpendicular fundamentals of the molecule at high resolution and thus to determine the linear coefficient in the spacing of the subband origins for each fundamental:

$$[A - (A\zeta_t) - B]_{v_t = 1} \tag{54}$$

If B is known, and the vibrational dependence of A, $A\zeta_t$, and B, is neglected, the quantities (54) may be solved in conjunction with the linear zeta sum rule to determine A and the ζ_t's separately. The vibrational dependence of both B and A can be determined if the spectra are fully resolved, but there is no method of obtaining the vibrational dependence of $A\zeta_t$ from fundamentals alone, and unless the data are corrected for the influence of all the coefficients $\alpha_r^{A\zeta_t}$, results obtained from the zeta sum rule must be regarded as uncertain to within a few per cent.

A more powerful method of analysis is obtained by combining observations on fundamental and overtone bands. In C_{3v} molecules the fundamental v_t, $l_t = 1$, $\pm 1 - 0$, 0 and the overtone v_t, $l_t = 2$, $\pm 2 - 0$, 0 both give rise to allowed perpendicular bands. From the fundamental the combination of constants in (54) may be determined; similarly from the first overtone the combination

$$[A + 2(A\zeta_t) - B]_{v_t = 2} \tag{55}$$

may be determined. Since B_0 and α_t^B can generally be determined from the J structure of the band (or from microwave spectra), and since α_t^A can be determined from the degradation of the subband origins, the quantities (54) and (55) can be corrected to give the derived quantities

$$x = A_0 - (A\zeta_t)_{v_t = 1} = A_0 - (A\zeta_t)_0 + \alpha_r^{Art} \tag{56}$$

$$y = A_0 + 2(A\zeta_t)_{v_t = 2} = A_0 + 2(A\zeta_t)_0 - 4\alpha_t^{A\zeta_t} \tag{57}$$

This analysis may in practice be complicated by problems of separating centrifugal contributions to the data, but since these involve higher powers of the rotational quantum numbers they are in principle separable. From (56) and (57) we obtain

$$A_0 - \tfrac{2}{3}\alpha_t^{A\zeta_t} = (2x + y)/3 \tag{58}$$

$$(A\zeta_t)_0 - \tfrac{5}{3}\alpha_t^{A\zeta_t} = (y - x)/3 \tag{59}$$

This is as close as one can come to a determination of A_0 without further data. Barnett and Edwards [30] have applied this method to v_4 and $2v_4$ of CH_3Br and CH_3I; they constrained $\alpha_4^{A\zeta_4}$ ($= \tfrac{1}{2}\eta_{44}$) to be zero in their analysis and so obtained a solution for A_0. If we remove this constraint, we should interpret their results on CH_3I, for example, to give

$$A_0 - \tfrac{2}{3}\alpha_4^{A\zeta_4} = 5.134 \pm 0.003 \text{ cm}^{-1} \tag{60}$$

Apart from the two general methods of determining A_0 described above, there are particular cases where other methods have succeeded. For NF_3, which is an oblate top, the equilibrium structure has been determined from the experimental values of B_e for $^{14}NF_3$ and $^{15}NF_3$, and this has been used to calculate C_e [28]. For molecules belonging to the D_{2d} point group a peculiarity of the Raman selection rules allows one to determine A_0 directly by combining infrared and Raman data [31]; the method has been applied to allene, but not with very high resolution. For CH_3I Maki and Hexter [32] originally observed that a resonance between v_5 and $v_3 + v_6$ gives rise to weak lines in the 1400 cm^{-1} band which can be used to isolate a ground-state combination difference in k, from which A_0 can be determined.† Matsuura et al. [33] have observed this spectrum with high resolution; their analysis gives for CH_3I

$$A_0 = 5.1744 \pm 0.0022 \quad \text{cm}^{-1} \tag{61}$$

Combining this with Barnett and Edwards' result in Eq. (60), we obtain for CH_3I

$$\alpha_4^{A\zeta4} = +0.060 \pm 0.005 \quad \text{cm}^{-1} \tag{62}$$

This result is of the expected order of magnitude. It may be compared with other results obtained by Barnett and Edwards from the analysis of v_4 and $2v_4$ for CH_3I;

$$\alpha_4^A = +0.0311 \pm 0.0009 \quad \text{cm}^{-1} \tag{63a}$$

$$\alpha_4^B = -0.000122 \pm 0.000003 \quad \text{cm}^{-1} \tag{63b}$$

$$(A\zeta_4)_0 = +0.40 \pm 0.01 \quad \text{cm}^{-1} \tag{63c}$$

$$\zeta_4 \, (= \zeta_{4a,4b}) \approx +0.08 \pm 0.03 \tag{63d}$$

I have obtained the result in (63c) by combining Barnett and Edwards' observation of the quantity in (59) with the result in (62). Finally, I have obtained the approximate result in (63d) by dividing $(A\zeta_4)_0$ by A_0, but it should be noted that this ignores the zero-point corrections to these two quantities, which are not all known, and which should be made before obtaining ζ_4. The resulting uncertainty in ζ_4 is hard to estimate, but it must be in the region of ± 0.03.

The conclusion of this discussion is that the difficulties of determining axial rotational constants of symmetric-top molecules are likely to remain with us, and that the most precise determinations are likely to be obtained from the analysis of accidental resonances similar to that in CH_3I. The difficulty of determining zeta constants with a precision better than about ± 0.03 is equally great.

---

† A similar method has been used by Olsen [32a] to obtain A_0 for CH_3D, although this is not yet published.

ACKNOWLEDGMENTS

I am grateful to the successive generations of research students with whom I have struggled to understand this subject, and particularly to Dr. J. K. G. Watson, whose ideas are reflected in much of the presentation in Sections 2 and 3. I would like to thank Dr. J. M. Brown for reading and criticizing the manuscript.

References

1. E. B. Wilson and J. B. Howard, *J. Chem. Phys.* **4**, 260 (1936); B. T. Darling and D. M. Dennison, *Phys. Rev.* **57**, 128 (1940).
2. H. H. Nielsen, *Rev. Mod. Phys.* **23**, 90 (1951).
3. H. H. Nielsen, *In* "Handbuck der Physik" (S. Flügge, ed.), Vol. 38. Springer-Verlag Berlin and New York, 1959.
4. G. Amat and L. Henry, *Cah. Phys.* **12**, 273 (1958); L. Henry and G. Amat. *Ibid* **14**, 230. (1960).
5. S. Maes, *Cah. Phys.* **14**, 125, 164 (1960).
6. M. L. Grenier-Besson, *J. Phys. Radium*, **21**, 555 (1960).
7. M. L. Grenier-Besson and G. Amat, *J. Mol. Spectrosc.* **8**, 22 (1962).
8. S. Maes and G. Amat, *Can. J. Phys.* **43**, 321 (1965).
9. T. Oka and Y. Morino, *J. Mol. Spectrosc.* **6**, 472 (1961); and later papers.
10. J. T. Hougen, *J. Chem. Phys.* **37**, 1433 (1962).
11. T. Oka, *J. Chem. Phys.* **47**, 5410 (1967).
12. J. K. G. Watson, *Mol. Phys.* **15**, 479 (1968).
13. D. Kivelson and E. B. Wilson, **20**, 1575 (1952).
14. G. W. King, R. M. Hainer, and P. C. Cross, *J. Chem. Phys.* **11**, 27 (1943).
15. J. K. G. Watson, *J. Chem. Phys.* **45**, 1360 (1966); **46**, 1935 (1967).
16. T. Oka, *J. Mol. Spectrosc.* **29**, 84 (1969).
17. J. H. Meal and S. R. Polo, *J. Chem. Phys.* **24**, 1119 (1956).
18. I. M. Mills and J. L. Duncan, *J. Mol. Spectrosc.* **9**, 244 (1962).
19. T. Tanaka and Y. Morino, *J. Mol. Spectrosc.* **33**, 538 (1970).
20. Y. Morino and S. Saito, *J. Mol. Spectrosc.* **19**, 435 (1966).
21. C. di Lauro and I. M. Mills, *J. Mol. Spectrosc.* **21**, 386 (1966).
22. E. B. Wilson, *J. Chem. Phys.* **27**, 986 (1957).
23. A. P. Cox, A. H. Brittain, and M. J. Whittle, *J. Mol. Spectrosc.* **35**, 49 (1970).
24. C. Costain, *Symp. Mol. Spectrosc., Columbus*, 1967, Paper G.15. To be published.
25. Y. Morino, K. Kuchitsu, and S. Yamamoto, *Spectrochim. Acta (Part A)*, **24**, 335 (1968).
26. G. Cartwright and I. M. Mills, *J. Mol. Spectrosc.* **34**, 415 (1970).
27. J. de Heer, *Phys. Rev.* **83**, 741 (1951).
28. M. Otake, C. Matsumura, and Y. Morino, *J. Mol. Spectrosc.* **28**, 316 (1968); M. Otake, E. Hirota, and Y. Morino, *Ibid.* **28**, 325 (1968); E. Hirota and Y. Morino, *Ibid.* **33**, 460. (1970).
29. W. J. Lafferty, *J. Mol. Spectrosc.* **25**, 359 (1968).
30. T. L. Barnett and T. H. Edwards, *J. Mol. Spectrosc.* **20**, 347, 352 (1966); **23**, 302 (1967).
31. I. M. Mills, *Mol. Phys.* **8**, 363 (1964).
32. A. G. Maki and R. M. Hexter, *Symp. Mol. Spectrosc., Colombus, 1966*; *J. Chem. Phys.* **53**, 453 (1970).
32a. W. B. Olsen, to be published.
33. H. Matsuura, T. Nakagawa, and J. Overend, *J. Chem. Phys.* **53**, 2540 (1970).

3.3   Molecular Laser Emissions in the Infrared[†]

K. Narahari Rao

Department of Physics
The Ohio State University
Columbus, Ohio

A. W. Mantz

Air Force Avionics Laboratory
Wright Patterson Air Force Base
Ohio

I. Introduction

Molecular lasers have been studied from diverse points of view. Initially, much emphasis was placed on the production of stabilized sources yielding high power outputs. However, during recent years some efforts have also been directed toward establishing accurate values for the spectral positions of laser lines. Wherever it was possible to achieve a measure of success in such measurements, the experimental data proved to be immensely useful for molecular spectroscopists. Some laser lines provided information not available before because the transitions involved are between energy levels not ordinarily reached by studies employing conventional absorption and emission techniques. Therefore, they have enabled a deeper understanding of the extent of applicability of theory to experimental results. The discussions related to the CO and CO_2 laser emissions appearing in a subsequent section of this article illustrate the importance of accurately measured laser data in the determination of molecular structures.

II. References

The bibliography appearing at the end of this article furnishes for each of the molecular species given not only the usual information pertaining to the journals and the dates of publication, but also the titles of the articles, with the

[†] Only vibration rotation transitions in the ground electronic state are considered in this article. No electronic transitions are included.

belief that these titles can provide a brief insight into the nature of research presented in the communications. Papers which appeared through December 1970 have been cited. The references for each molecule have been collected according to the year in which the articles appeared in publications. In a particular year the journals are arranged in alphabetical order according to the list†:

Applied Optics
Applied Physics Letters
Bulletin of the American Physical Society
Canadian Journal of Physics
Chemical Physics Letters
Comptes Rendus
Electronics Letters
International Journal of Chemical Kinetics
Japanese Journal of Applied Physics
Journal of Applied Physics
Journal of Chemical Physics
Journal of Molecular Spectroscopy
Journal of the Optical Society of America
Journal of Quantum Electronics
JETP Letters
Nature
Optical Communications
Optics and Spectroscopy
Physical Review
Physical Review Letters
Physics Letters
Proceedings of the IEEE
Proceedings of the Physical Society
Soviet Physics JETP

III. Basic Observational Data

The wave numbers of the molecular laser emissions observed in the infrared are collected and presented in Tables I–XIV. These data pertain to the pure rotational and vibration–rotation transitions in the ground electronic states of

† References to articles related to CO, CO_2, N_2O, HCl, and HCN laser studies published in Journal de Chimie Physique appear on p. 177 with serial numbers 294–306.

diatomic molecules ($^{12}C^{16}O$, hydrogen halides and their isotopic varieties, and $^{14}N^{16}O$), linear polyatomic molecules ($^{12}C^{16}O_2$, $^{13}C^{16}O_2$, and $^{14}C^{16}O_2$; $H^{12}C^{14}N$ and $D^{12}C^{14}N$; $^{14}N_2^{16}O$, $^{12}C^{32}S_2$, and $^{16}O^{12}C^{32}S$), and asymmetric-top molecules ($H_2^{16}O$, $H_2^{18}O$, and $D_2^{16}O$). Several unidentified laser lines are listed in Table XIV.

GENERAL REMARKS FOR ALL TABLES

An asterisk indicates that the line has more than one assignment. Sources of the data are given as footnotes to the tables. The reference numbers given in these footnotes are the serial numbers given in the Bibliography at the end of this article.

A FEW SPECIFIC COMMENTS

Related to Table IX

Molecular spectroscopic terminology used is what one has been customarily accustomed to. In the case of the carbon dioxide bands Amat and collaborators† have considered theoretically more cogent designations to account for the strong perturbations taking place between energy levels; the correspondence between this notation and the one appearing in Table IX is as follows:

Band in Table IX		New notation (for theoretical reasons)		New notation (modified)	
Upper state	Lower state	Upper state	Lower state	Upper state	Lower state
$v_1 v_2{}^l v_3$	$v_1 v_2{}^l v_3$				
$0\ 0^0\ 1$	$1\ 0^0\ 0$	00^01	$(10^00, 02^00)_I$	00^01	$(10^00)_I$
$0\ 1^1\ 1$	$1\ 1^1\ 0$	01^11	$(11^10, 03^10)_I$	01^11	$(11^10)_I$
$1\ 0^0\ 2$	$1\ 0^0\ 1$	$(10^02, 02^02)_I$	$(10^01, 02^01)_I$	$(10^02)_I$	$(10^01)_I$

Related to Table XIV

The BCl_3 laser transitions with line numbers 1–8 have been identified as respectively due to the bands $(2v_3{}^{10} - 3v_2{}^{10})$, $(2v_3{}^{11} - 3v_2{}^{11})$, $(v_3{}^{10} - v_1{}^{10})$, $(v_3{}^{10} - v_2{}^{10})$, $(v_3{}^{11} - v_2{}^{11})$, $(v_3{}^{11} - v_1{}^{11})$, $(3v_2{}^{10} - v_3{}^{10})$, and $(3v_2{}^{11} - v_3{}^{11})$; the superscripts 10 and 11 refer to the ^{10}B and ^{11}B isotopes.

† See, for instance, the work of Oberly et al. [1].

TABLE I

WAVE NUMBERS (vac cm^{-1}) OF CO LASER LINES*

4-3 Band	
P(13)	2012.70
P(14)	2008.56
P(15)	2004.38
P(16)	2000.11

5-4 Band	
P(9)	2003.29
P(10)	1999.14
P(11)	1995.14
P(12)	1991.01
P(13)	1986.918
P(14)	1982.766
P(15)	1978.609[a]
P(16)	1974.357[a]
P(17)	1970.159[a]
P(18)	1965.853

6-5 Band	
P(7)	1985.17
P(8)	1981.19
P(9)	1977.27
P(10)	1973.310[a]
P(11)	1969.304[a]
P(12)	1965.249
P(13)	1961.166
P(14)	1957.070[a]
P(15)	1952.888[a]
P(16)	1948.730
P(17)	1944.510
P(18)	1940.251[a]
P(19)	1936.002

7-6 Band	
P(7)	1959.2
P(8)	1955.47
P(9)	1951.50
P(10)	1947.496[a]
P(11)	1943.540
P(12)	1939.504[a]
P(13)	1935.484
P(14)	1931.380[a]
P(15)	1927.282[a]
P(16)	1923.169[a]
P(17)	1919.0
P(18)	1914.8
P(19)	1910.6
P(20)	1906.3

8-7 Band	
P(7)	1933.4
P(8)	1929.64
P(9)	1925.700
P(10)	1921.814
P(11)	1917.884[a]
P(12)	1913.892
P(13)	1909.907[a]
P(14)	1905.834
P(15)	1901.779

8-7 Band (Cont.)	
P(16)	1897.668
P(17)	1893.518
P(18)	1889.365[a]
P(19)	1885.1
P(20)	1880.897†
P(21)	1876.629†
P(22)	1872.329†

9-8 Band	
P(7)	1907.72
P(8)	1903.815[a]
P(9)	1900.043
P(10)	1896.193[a]
P(11)	1892.270
P(12)	1888.320
P(13)	1884.369
P(14)	1880.330[a]
P(15)	1876.314
P(16)	1872.251
P(17)	1868.118[a]
P(18)	1864.002
P(19)	1859.9
P(20)	1855.615†
P(21)	1851.382†
P(22)	1847.2

10-9 Band	
P(7)	1882.12
P(8)	1878.26
P(9)	1874.446
P(10)	1870.636[a]
P(11)	1866.748
P(12)	1862.833
P(13)	1858.918[a]
P(14)	1854.927
P(15)	1850.918
P(16)	1846.917[a]
P(17)	1842.821
P(18)	
P(19)	1834.577†
P(20)	1830.5
P(21)	1826.3
P(22)	1822.1

11-10 Band	
P(6)	1860.23
P(7)	1856.50
P(8)	1852.729
P(9)	1848.958
P(10)	1845.147
P(11)	1841.315
P(12)	1837.427
P(13)	1833.527
P(14)	1829.605
P(15)	1825.620
P(16)	1821.623
P(17)	1817.606[a]
P(18)	1813.514†

11-10 Band (Cont.)	
P(19)	1809.416†
P(20)	1805.3

12-11 Band	
P(6)	1834.63
P(7)	1830.99
P(8)	1827.241
P(9)	1823.528[a]
P(10)	1819.742
P(11)	1815.939
P(12)	1812.116
P(13)	1808.233
P(14)	1804.332
P(15)	1800.414
P(16)	1796.449
P(17)	
P(18)	1788.398†
P(19)	1784.334†

13-12 Band	
P(6)	1809.17
P(7)	1805.54
P(8)	1801.866
P(9)	1798.152
P(10)	1794.452[a]
P(11)	1790.668
P(12)	1786.854
P(13)	1783.034
P(14)	1779.172
P(15)	1775.248[a]
P(16)	
P(17)	1767.359†
P(18)	1763.363†
P(19)	1759.334†

14-13 Band	
P(6)	1783.74
P(7)	1780.184
P(8)	1776.550
P(9)	1772.898
P(10)	1769.189
P(11)	1765.459
P(12)	1761.712
P(13)	1757.907
P(14)	1754.055[a]
P(15)	1750.205
P(16)	1746.329[a]

15-14 Band	
P(6)	1758.47
P(7)	1754.928
P(8)	
P(9)	1747.709
P(10)	1744.036
P(11)	1740.362
P(12)	1736.636[a]
P(13)	1732.853
P(14)	1729.056

15-14 Band (Cont.)	
P(15)	1725.242
P(16)	1721.374

16-15 Band	
P(5)	1736.77
P(6)	
P(7)	1729.73
P(8)	1726.211
P(9)	1722.603
P(10)	1718.980
P(11)	1715.333
P(12)	1711.634
P(13)	1707.891
P(14)	1704.128

17-16 Band	
P(7)	1704.684
P(8)	1701.166
P(9)	1697.596
P(10)	1693.998
P(11)	1690.378
P(12)	1686.721
P(13)	1683.017
P(14)	1679.293
P(15)	
P(16)	1671.748

18-17 Band	
P(7)	1679.674
P(8)	1676.192
P(9)	1672.668
P(10)	1669.104
P(11)	1665.505
P(12)	1661.884
P(13)	1658.234
P(14)	
P(15)	1650.810

19-18 Band	
P(7)	1654.760
P(8)	1651.298
P(9)	1647.804
P(10)	1644.288
P(11)	1640.752[a]
P(12)	1637.149
P(13)	1633.516
P(14)	1629.915[a]
P(15)	1626.182

20-19 Band	
P(5)	1636.68
P(6)	1633.309
P(7)	1629.853[a]
P(8)	1626.512
P(9)	1623.068
P(10)	1619.572
P(11)	1616.042
P(12)	1612.480

TABLE I *(continued)*

20-19 Band (Cont.)		24-23 Band		27-26 Band (Cont.)		32-31 Band	
P(13)	1608.889	P(5)	1537.91	P(12)	1442.157	P(5)	1343.84
P(14)	1605.278	P(6)	1534.73	P(13)	1439.242^a	P(6)	1340.90
P(15)	1601.804^a	P(7)	1531.439	P(14)	1436.095^a	P(7)	1337.96
		P(8)	1528.164			P(8)	1334.97
21-20 Band		P(9)	1524.824^a	**28-27 Band**		P(9)	1331.93
P(5)	1611.82	P(10)		P(5)	1440.42	P(10)	1328.78
P(6)	1608.528	P(11)	1518.100	P(6)	1437.31		
P(7)	1605.190	P(12)	1514.696	P(7)	1434.20	**33-32 Band**	
P(8)	1601.802	P(13)	1511.268^a	P(8)	1431.034^a	P(6)	1316.95
P(9)	1598.380			P(9)	1427.870^a	P(7)	1314.01
P(10)	1594.938	**25-24 Band**		P(10)	1424.633	P(8)	1311.02
P(11)	1591.429	P(5)	1513.389	P(11)	1421.43	P(9)	1308.01
P(12)	1587.925	P(6)	1510.261^a			P(10)	1304.98
P(13)	1584.347	P(7)		**29-28 Band**			
P(14)	1580.524^a	P(8)	1503.763	P(5)	1416.15	**34-33 Band**	
P(15)	1577.152	P(9)	1499.497^a	P(6)	1413.10	P(6)	1293.00
		P(10)	1497.159	P(7)	1410.01	P(7)	1290.10
22-21 Band		P(11)	1493.836	P(8)	1406.92	P(8)	1287.16
P(5)	1587.14	P(12)	1490.431	P(9)	1403.75	P(9)	1284.19
P(6)	1583.824			P(10)	1400.60	P(10)	1281.15
P(7)	1580.524	**26-25 Band**		P(11)	1397.40		
P(8)	1577.18	P(5)	1489.01			**35-34 Band**	
P(9)	1573.784	P(6)	1485.83	**30-29 Band**		P(6)	1269.09
P(10)	1570.371	P(7)	1482.660	P(5)	1391.98	P(7)	1266.25
P(11)	1566.909	P(8)	1479.452	P(6)	1389.01	P(8)	1263.34
P(12)	1563.453^a	P(9)		P(7)	1385.92	P(9)	1260.41
P(13)		P(10)	1472.931	P(8)	1382.89		
P(14)	1556.365	P(11)	1469.589^a	P(9)	1379.73	**36-35 Band**	
		P(12)	1466.259	P(10)	1376.63	P(5)	1248.03
23-22 Band		P(13)	1462.878			P(6)	1245.23
P(5)	1562.44			**31-30 Band**		P(7)	1242.36
P(6)	1559.214	**27-26 Band**		P(5)	1367.91	P(8)	1239.52
P(7)	1555.957	P(4)	1467.73	P(6)	1364.89	P(9)	1236.58
P(8)	1552.624	P(5)		P(7)	1361.92		
P(9)	1549.282	P(6)	1461.50	P(8)	1358.88	**37-36 Band**	
P(10)	1545.898	P(7)		P(9)	1355.81	P(6)	1221.31
P(11)	1542.462	P(8)	1455.25	P(10)	1352.71	P(7)	1218.51
P(12)		P(9)	1451.98	P(11)	1349.55	P(8)	1215.71
P(13)	1535.534	P(10)	1448.77				
P(14)	1532.033	P(11)	1445.463				

* *Sources of data*: The wave numbers quoted to three decimal places are from bibliography ref. [30], except the ones with a dagger (†) next to them, which have been taken from bibl. ref. [24]. The two-decimal entries are from bibl. ref. [29]. The wave numbers quoted to the tenth of a decimal place are from bibl. ref. [12], except for the $P(7)$ line of the 7–6 band, which is from bibl. ref. [7].

^{a} Possible interference here due to H_2O or CO_2 lines resulting from 3-m air path outside the vacuum spectrograph.

TABLE II

Wave Numbers (vac cm⁻¹) of the Pure Rotational Laser Transitions in HCl and HBr[a]

$H^{35}Cl$						$H^{37}Cl$		
Vibrational Level v=0			Vibrational Level v=1			Vibrational Level v=0		
J'-J"	Set #1	Set #2[†]	J'-J"	Set #1	Set #2	J'-J"	Set #1	Set #2[‡]
18-17		363.53	20-19	389.045		28-27 *		538.94
19-18	382.465		21-20	406.780		29-28		555.65
20-19	401.016		22-21	424.259		32-31		600.82
21-20	419.313		23-22	441.473		Vibrational Level v=1		
22-21	437.375		24-23	458.448		21-20	406.211	
23-22	455.154		25-24	475.126		28-27		522.33
24-23	472.688		26-25	491.510		29-28		537.84
25-24	489.942		27-26	507.608		33-32		596.48
28-27	539.898		29-28 *		538.94	Line unassigned		381.00
29-28	555.944	556.33	30-29		554.48			
30-29	571.680	571.92	31-30		568.99			
31-30	587.060	587.03	32-31		583.94			
32-31	602.102		Vibrational Level v=2					
33-32	616.807		22-21	411.222				
39-38	697.186		27-26	476.211				
40-39	709.250		29-28		521.30			
41-40	720.875							

HBr

Vibrational Level v=0				Vibrational Level v=1		
J'-J"	$H^{79}Br$	$H^{81}Br$		J'-J"	$H^{79}Br$	$H^{81}Br$
19-18		307.99		19-18		299.32
20-19		323.12		20-19		313.98
29-28		451.75		21-20		328.46
30-29	465.10			31-30	464.12	
31-30	478.56	477.35		34-33		500.30
32-31	491.16					
34-33		515.49				
Vibrational Level v=2				Vibrational Level v=3		
16-15		246.76		23-22		335.73
20-19	304.89					
21-20		318.80				
30-29		437.54				
31-30	449.92			Line unassigned	426.69	

[a] *Sources of data*: Set #1 in HCl is from bibl. ref. [41] and the rest of the data are from bibl. ref. [61].

† Both the lines at 505.49 and at 504.52 for $H^{35}Cl$ have the assignment {$v = 3$, $J'-J"$ is 29-28}.

‡ Both the lines at 522.33 and at 522.96 for $H^{37}Cl$ have the assignment {$v = 0$, $J'-J"$ is 27-26}.

TABLE III

WAVE NUMBERS (vac cm^{-1}) OF HCl AND HBr LASER LINES[a]

H^{35}Cl

	1-0 Band			2-1 Band (Continued)	
	Set #1	Set #2		Set #1	Set #2
P(9)		2678.1	P(8)	2604.09	
P(10)		2651.8	P(9)	2579.42	
P(11)		2626.1	P(10)	2554.34	
P(12)		2599.4		3-2 Band	
P(13)		2572.0			
	2-1 Band		P(4)	2596.79	2596.7
			P(5)	2574.70	2574.7
P(4)	2697.52		P(6)	2552.26	
P(5)	2675.01	2675.2	P(7)	2529.31	
P(6)	2651.82	2651.8	P(8)	2505.68	
P(7)	2628.13	2628.1	P(9)	2481.69	

H^{37}Cl

	2-1 Band			3-2 Band	
P(5)	2673.23		P(6)	2550.70	
P(6)	2650.08		P(7)	2527.79	
P(7)	2626.45				
P(8)	2602.48				

HBr

	1-0 Band				3-2 Band		
H^{79}Br		H^{81}Br		H^{79}Br		H^{81}Br	
P(4)	2489.40	P(4)	2489.05	P(4)	2312.15	P(4)	2311.85
P(5)	2470.97	P(5)	2470.63	P(5)	2294.68	P(5)	2294.39
P(6)	2452.03	P(6)	2451.68	P(6)	2276.61	P(6)	2276.32
P(7)	2432.70	P(7)	2432.36	P(7)	2258.29	P(7)	2258.00
P(8)	2412.99	P(8)	2412.68	P(8)	2239.52	P(8)	2239.26
		P(9)	2392.56	P(9)	2220.20	P(9)	2219.92
	2-1 Band				4-3 Band		
P(4)	2400.78	P(4)	2400.47	P(5)	2206.07	P(5)	2205.81
P(5)	2382.68	P(5)	2382.35	P(6)	2188.61	P(6)	2188.35
P(6)	2364.36			P(7)	2170.61	P(7)	2170.35
P(7)	2345.58	P(7)	2345.26	P(8)	2152.27	P(8)	2152.04
P(8)	2326.23	P(8)	2325.92				
P(9)	2306.60	P(9)	2306.30				

[a] *Sources of data*: Set #1 in H^{35}Cl and the entire HBr measurements are from bibl. ref. [41]. Set #2 in H^{35}Cl is from bibl. ref. [40].

TABLE IV

WAVE NUMBERS (vac cm^{-1}) OF DCl AND DBr LASER LINES[a]

$D^{35}Cl$		$D^{37}Cl$		$D^{79}Br$		$D^{81}Br$	
2-1 Band							
P(5)	1982.35	P(5)	1979.65				
P(6)	1970.72	P(6)	1968.08				
P(7)	1958.90	P(7)	1956.25				
P(8)	1946.94	P(8)	1944.35			P(8)	1722.67
P(9)	1934.67						
3-2 Band							
P(4)	1941.35						
P(5)	1930.10	P(5)	1927.56	P(5)	1705.91	P(5)	1705.43
P(6)	1918.73	P(6)	1916.24	P(6)	1696.98	P(6)	1696.52
P(7)	1907.13	P(7)	1904.67	P(7)	1687.89	P(7)	1687.45
P(8)	1895.37	P(8)	1892.91	P(8)	1678.60	P(8)	1678.13
P(9)	1883.35						
P(10)	1871.15						
P(11)	1858.77						
4-3 Band							
P(5)	1878.13			P(5)	1660.88	P(5)	1660.45
P(6)	1867.01	P(6)	1864.65	P(6)	1652.10	P(6)	1651.69
P(7)	1855.66	P(7)	1853.36	P(7)	1643.18	P(7)	1642.76
		P(8)	1841.79	P(8)	1634.00	P(8)	1633.57
P(9)	1832.27			P(9)	1624.80	P(9)	1624.39
P(10)	1820.34			P(10)	1615.42	P(10)	1615.03
P(11)	1808.20			P(11)	1605.85	P(11)	1605.43
5-4 Band							
P(6)	1815.38					P(6)	1606.75
P(7)	1804.31			P(7)	1598.32	P(7)	1597.93
P(8)	1792.89			P(8)	1589.41	P(8)	1589.01
P(9)	1781.36			P(9)	1580.31	P(9)	1579.92

[a] *Source of data*: Bibl. ref. [41].

TABLE V

WAVE NUMBERS (vac cm^{-1}) OF THE PURE ROTATIONAL LASER
TRANSITIONS IN HF[a]

Vibrational Level v=0			Vibrational Level v=2		
J'-J"	Set #1	Set #2	J'-J"	Set #1	Set #2
14-13		552.944	13-12	477.57	
15-14		589.102	16-15		577.201
16-15	624.16		17-16		608.125
18-17	692.49		20-19	699.88	
19-18	725.47		21-20 *	728.45	
20-19	757.52	757.346	22-21	756.37	
21-20	788.76	789.328	29-28	924.93	
22-21	819.12	819.471	30-29	945.01	
23-22	848.50	849.401	Vibrational Level v=3		
24-23	876.94	876.962			
25-24	904.38	904.732	13-12	458.96	
26-25	930.76		14-13	491.37	
27-26	956.23		15-14	523.21	
28-27	980.60		17-16		584.966
Vibrational Level v=1			28-27 *	866.49	
12-11	460.86		Vibrational Level v=4		
13-12	496.68		30-29 *	866.49	
14-13	531.89				
15-14		566.733			
16-15		600.420			
18-17	665.94				
20-19 *	728.45				
21-20	758.28				
22-21	787.37	789.141			
23-22	815.53	815.461			
24-23		842.957			

[a] *Sources of data*: Set #1 is from bibl. ref. [39] and set #2 is from bibl. ref. [61].

TABLE VI

Wave Numbers (vac cm^{-1}) of HF Laser Lines[a]

1-0 Band				3-2 Band (Continued)			
	Line Positions				Line Positions		
	Set #1	Set #2	Set #3		Set #1	Set #2	Set #3
P(4)			3787.9	P(7)	3327.73		
P(5)			3741.1	P(8)	3280.64		
P(6)	3693.50		3694.1	P(9)		3230	
P(7)	3644.16		3644.3	P(12)		3084	
P(8)	3593.80			**4-3 Band**			
P(9)	3542.20						
P(10)	3489.59			R(4)		3620	
P(11)	3436.12			R(1)		3529	
P(12)	3381.50			P(2)		3386	
P(13)	3326.21			P(8)		3130	
P(14)	3269.90			P(9)		3084	
P(15)	3212.80			**5-4 Band**			
2-1 Band				R(0)		3334	
P(2)	3708.86			P(2)		3230	
P(3)	3666.38			P(4)		3149	
P(4)	3622.71	3620	3623.2	P(5)		3111	
P(5)	3577.47	3572	3577.8	P(6)		3070	
P(6)	3531.31	3529	3531.1	P(7)		3025	
P(7)	3483.63	3482	3483.1	**6-5 Band**			
P(8)	3435.17	3434					
P(9)	3385.34	3386		P(1)		3111	
P(10)	3334.55	3334		P(4)		2999	
P(11)	3282.86	3284		P(5)		2960	
P(12)	3230.18	3230					
P(13)	3176.60						
P(14)	3122.14						
P(15)	3067.22						
3-2 Band							
P(2)	3544.51						
P(3)	3503.80						
P(4)	3461.54						
P(5)	3418.16	3416					
P(6)	3373.46						

[a] *Sources of data*: Set #1 is from bibl. ref. [38]; set #2 is from [62]; and set #3 is from [55].

TABLE VII

WAVE NUMBERS (vac cm^{-1}) OF DF LASER LINES[a]

	1-0 Band			3-2 Band	
	Set #1	Set #2		Set #1	Set #2
P(8)		2717.4	P(3)	2662.17	
P(9)		2691.1	P(4)	2640.04	
P(10)		2665.2	P(5)	2617.41	
P(11)		2638.5	P(6)	2594.23	
P(12)	2611.10	2611.0	P(7)	2570.51	
P(15)	2527.06		P(8)	2546.37	2546.5
P(16)	2498.02		P(9)	2521.81	2522.1
			P(10)	2496.61	2496.9
	2-1 Band		P(11)	2471.34	2471.6
P(3)	2750.05		P(12)	2445.29	
P(4)	2727.38		P(14)	2392.46	
P(5)	2703.98				
P(6)	2680.28			4-3 Band	
P(7)	2655.97		P(5)	2532.50	
P(8)	2631.09	2631.6	P(6)	2509.86	
P(9)	2605.87	2605.5	P(7)	2486.83	
P(10)	2580.16	2580.0			
P(11)	2553.97	2553.6			
P(12)	2527.47	2527.2			
P(13)	2500.32				
P(16)	2417.27				
P(17)	2388.79				

[a] *Sources of data*: Set #1 is from bibl. ref. [38] and set #2 is from [55].

TABLE VIII

WAVE NUMBERS (vac cm^{-1}) OF NO LASER LINES[a]

6-5 Band — P(J-1/2)

$^2\Pi_{1/2}$		$^2\Pi_{3/2}$	
		P(7)	1710.52
P(8)	1707.98	P(8)	1706.95
		P(9)	1703.41
P(10)	1700.99		
P(12)	1693.88	P(12)	1692.53

7-6 Band

$^2\Pi_{1/2}$		$^2\Pi_{3/2}$	
		P(7)	1682.84
		P(8)	1679.37
P(9)	1676.96	P(9)	1675.81
P(10)	1673.46	P(10)	1672.27
P(11)	1669.96	P(11)	1668.59
P(12)	1666.39	P(12)	1665.18
		P(13)	1661.36
P(14)	1659.29	P(14)	1657.71
P(15)	1655.58		

8-7 Band

$^2\Pi_{1/2}$		$^2\Pi_{3/2}$	
		P(7)	1655.12
		P(8)	1651.72
P(9)	1649.40	P(9)	1648.19
		P(10)	1644.71
P(11)	1642.47	P(11)	1641.13
P(12)	1638.95		
		P(13)	1633.87
P(15)	1628.22		

9-8 Band — P(J-1/2)

$^2\Pi_{1/2}$		$^2\Pi_{3/2}$	
P(8)	1625.02	P(8)	1624.00
P(9)	1621.72		
P(10)	1618.34	P(10)	1617.12
P(11)	1614.95	P(11)	1613.63
P(12)	1611.48	P(12)	1610.06
P(13)	1607.94	P(13)	1606.46
P(14)	1604.42		

10-9 Band

$^2\Pi_{1/2}$		$^2\Pi_{3/2}$	
		P(6)	1603.06
		P(7)	1599.71
P(8)	1597.39	P(8)	1596.30
		P(9)	1592.91
P(10)	1590.71	P(10)	1589.50
P(11)	1587.36	P(11)	1586.02
P(12)	1583.88	P(12)	1582.50
P(13)	1580.43	P(13)	1578.89

11-10 Band

$^2\Pi_{1/2}$		$^2\Pi_{3/2}$	
		P(8)	1568.29
		P(9)	1565.09
P(10)	1562.99	P(10)	1561.74
P(12)	1556.14	P(12)	1554.71

[a] *Source of data*: Bibl. ref. [65].

TABLE IX

WAVE NUMBERS (vac cm^{-1}) OF CO_2 LASER LINES[a]

$00^0 1$-$10^0 0$ BAND OF $^{12}C^{16}O_2$

J	R(J)		P(J)	
	Set #1	Set #2	Set #1	Set #2
4	964.74	964.76967	957.76	957.80124
6	966.18	966.25105	956.16	956.18568
8	967.73	967.70792	954.52	954.54580
10	969.09	969.14023	952.88	952.88157
12	970.50	970.54793	951.16	951.19299
14	971.91	971.93094	949.44	949.48003
16	973.24	973.28921	947.73	947.74271
18	974.61	974.62263	945.94	945.98096
20	975.90	975.93112	944.15	944.19476
22	977.18	977.21461	942.37	942.38407
24	978.47	978.47298	940.51	940.54883
26	979.67	979.70612	938.66	938.68898
28	980.87	980.91391	936.77	936.80447
30	982.08	982.09624	934.88	934.89522
32	983.19	983.25298	932.92	932.96114
34	984.35	984.38399	930.97	931.00217
36	985.42	985.48911	928.94	929.01820
38	986.49	986.56822	926.96	927.00913
40	987.56	987.62115	924.90	924.97486
42	988.63	988.64773	922.85	922.91528
44	989.61	989.64779	920.77	920.83025
46	990.54	990.62115	918.65	918.71966
48	991.47	991.56763	916.51	916.58337
50	992.46	992.48702	914.41	914.42123
52	993.34	993.37916	912.16	912.23311
54	994.18	994.24379	909.92	910.01884
56			907.73	907.77825

[a] *Sources of data*: Set #1 is from bibl. ref. [88]; Set #2 is from [202].

TABLE IX (continued)[a]

$$00^0 1\text{-}02^0 0 \text{ BAND OF } ^{12}C^{16}O_2$$

J	R(J)		P(J)	
	Set #1	Set #2	Set #1	Set #2
4	1067.50	1067.53908	1060.61	1060.57065
6	1068.89	1069.01407	1059.04	1058.94872
8	1070.43	1070.46228	1057.30	1057.30016
10	1071.87	1071.88374	1055.58	1055.62508
12	1073.28	1073.27846	1053.91	1053.92352
14	1074.63	1074.64647	1052.13	1052.19556
16	1076.00	1075.98779	1050.47	1050.44130
18	1077.30	1077.30249	1048.66	1048.66083
20	1078.57	1078.59062	1046.85	1046.85425
22	1079.85	1079.85223	1045.04	1045.02168
24	1081.08	1081.08740	1043.19	1043.16325
26	1082.29	1082.29622	1041.29	1041.27908
28	1083.48	1083.47878	1039.34	1039.36932
30	1084.63	1084.63516	1037.40	1037.43413
32	1085.74	1085.76549	1035.46	1035.47365
34	1086.84	1086.86987	1033.48	1033.48805
36	1087.90	1087.94846	1031.56	1031.47754
38	1088.97	1089.00136	1029.44	1029.44226
40	1090.04	1090.02875	1027.38	1027.38245
42	1090.99	1091.03076	1025.27	1025.29829
44	1092.00	1092.00755	1023.17	1023.19002
46	1093.01	1092.95932	1021.03	1021.05783
48	1093.85	1093.88623	1018.85	1018.90199
50	1094.81	1094.78850	1016.67	1016.72270
52	1095.71	1095.66629	1014.46	1014.52025
54			1012.25	1012.29488
56			1010.00	1010.04687
58			1007.76	1007.77650
60			1005.38	1005.48406

[a] Sources of data: Set #1 is from bibl. ref. [88]; set #2 is from [202].

TABLE IX (*continued*)[b]

$01^1 1 - 11^1 0$ BAND OF $^{12}C^{16}O_2$

	Set #1	Set #2		Set #2
P(19)	911.335	911.29	P(35)	896.42
P(20)	910.282		P(36)	894.97
P(21)	909.551	909.50	P(37)	894.53
P(22)	908.459		P(38)	893.02
P(23)	907.747	907.73	P(39)	892.58
P(24)	906.621	906.62	P(40)	890.99
P(25)	905.927	905.92	P(41)	890.51
P(26)	904.741	904.69	P(42)	888.93
P(27)	904.081	904.08	P(43)	888.53
P(28)	902.840	902.85	P(44)	886.76
P(29)	902.204	902.12	P(45)	886.49
P(30)	900.916	900.90		
P(31)	900.314	900.33		
P(32)	898.974	899.00		
P(33)	898.409	898.35		
P(34)	897.008	896.98		

	$10^0 2 - 10^0 1$ BAND
P(7)	2296.25
P(9)	2294.62
P(11)	2292.94
P(13)	2291.25
P(15)	2289.51
P(17)	2287.76
P(19)	2286.00
P(21)	2284.20
P(23)	2282.38
P(25)	2280.53
R(11)	2310.73
R(13)	2312.18
R(17)	2314.64

	$^{13}C^{16}O_2$ $00^0 1 - 10^0 0$ BAND	$^{14}C^{16}O_2$ $00^0 1 - 10^0 0$ BAND
R(22)		882.78
R(20)	928.66	881.47
R(18)	927.35	880.04
R(16)	925.95	878.68
R(14)	924.54	877.26
P(12)	903.81	
P(14)	902.09	854.94
P(16)	900.39	853.18
P(18)	898.65	851.50
P(20)	896.91	849.76
P(22)	895.14	848.03
P(24)	893.38	846.25
P(26)	891.56	844.48
P(28)	889.75	

[b] *Sources of data*: Bibl. refs. [88, 91, 135].

TABLE X

WAVE NUMBERS (vac cm^{-1}) OF HCN AND DCN LASER LINES[a]

HCN				
UPPER STATE LEVELS		LOWER STATE LEVELS		
$(v_1 v_2^{\ell} v_3)'$	J'	$(v_1 v_2^{\ell} v_3)''$	J''	
$04^0 0$	9	$04^0 0$	8	26.84360
$11^{1c} 0$	10	$04^0 0$	9	29.712539
$04^0 0$	10	$04^0 0$	9	29.83444
$11^{1c} 0$	11	$04^0 0$	10	32.16603
$11^{1c} 0$	11	$11^{1c} 0$	10	32.28786
$11^{1c} 0$	12	$11^{1c} 0$	11	35.2
$12^0 0$	25	$05^{1c} 0$	24	74.111
$12^0 0$	26	$05^{1c} 0$	25	76.430
$12^{2d} 0$	26	$05^{1d} 0$	25	77.743
$12^{2d} 0$	27	$05^{1d} 0$	26	79.262
DCN				
$09^{1c} 0$	20	$09^{1c} 0$	19	48.9267
$09^{1c} 0$	21	$09^{1c} 0$	20	51.344
$22^0 0$	21	$09^{1c} 0$	20	51.3604
$22^0 0$	22	$22^0 0$	21	52.6294
$22^0 0$	22	$09^{1c} 0$	21	52.6457
$22^0 0$	23	$22^0 0$	22	55.009

[a] *Sources of data*: Bibl. refs. [224, 227, 228, 232].

TABLE XI

Wave Numbers (vac cm^{-1}) of N_2O, CS_2, and OCS Laser Lines[a]

$00^01\text{-}10^00$ Band							
N_2O				CS_2		OCS	
P(5)	934.6	R(8)	946.1	P(28)	870.90	P(18)	1195.82
P(6)	933.7	R(9)	946.9	P(30)	870.38	P(19)	1195.40
P(7)	932.9	R(10)	947.7	P(32)	869.85	P(20)	1194.95
P(8)	932.0	R(11)	948.6	P(34)	869.33	P(21)	1194.52
P(9)	931.2	R(12)	949.4	P(36)	868.82	P(22)	1194.09
P(10)	930.3	R(13)	950.2	P(38)	868.31	P(23)	1193.62
P(11)	929.4	R(14)	951.0	P(40)	867.80	P(24)	1193.19
P(12)	928.52	R(15)	951.7	P(42)	867.27	P(25)	1192.76
P(13)	927.65	R(16)	952.6	P(44)	866.73	P(26)	1192.32
P(14)	926.78	R(17)	953.3	P(46)	866.20	P(27)	1191.89
P(15)	925.88	R(18)	954.1			P(28)	1191.46
P(16)	925.01	R(19)	954.8			P(29)	1191.02
P(17)	924.12	R(20)	955.7			P(30)	1190.49
P(18)	923.26	R(21)	956.4			P(31)	1190.14
P(19)	922.37	R(22)	957.1			P(32)	1189.70
P(20)	921.46	R(23)	957.8			P(33)	1189.27
P(21)	920.57	R(24)	958.5			P(34)	1188.82
P(22)	919.66	R(25)	959.3			P(35)	1188.40
P(23)	918.75	R(26)	960.0			P(36)	1187.95
P(24)	917.84	R(27)	960.8			P(37)	1187.46
P(25)	916.92	R(28)	961.5			P(38)	1187.04
P(26)	916.00	R(29)	962.3				
P(27)	915.08	R(30)	963.0			R(15)	1209.59
P(28)	914.16	R(31)	963.7			R(16)	1209.99
P(29)	913.23	R(32)	964.4			R(17)	1210.32
P(30)	912.31	R(33)	965.1			R(18)	1210.73
P(31)	911.38					R(19)	1211.08
P(32)	910.43					R(20)	1211.48
P(33)	909.50					R(21)	1211.86
P(34)	908.53					R(24)	1213.02
P(35)	907.58					R(25)	1213.35
P(36)	906.65					R(26)	1213.76
P(37)	905.66						
R(4)	942.9						
R(5)	943.7						
R(6)	944.5						
R(7)	945.3						

[a] *Sources of data*: N_2O: Two-decimal entries are from bibl. ref. [234]. Single-decimal entries are from [235, 240]. CS_2: [241]. OCS: [245].

TABLE XII

WAVE NUMBERS (vac cm^{-1}) OF THE PURE ROTATIONAL TRANSITIONS IN
$H_2^{16}O$, $H_2^{18}O$, AND $D_2^{16}O$ [a]

$H_2^{16}O$							$D_2^{16}O$						
Vibrational Level 010							**Vibrational Level 020**						
J'	K'_a	K'_c	J''	K''_a	K''_c		J'	K'_a	K'_c	J''	K''_a	K''_c	
13	11	2	13	10	3	273.18	11	4	7	11	3	8	58.80
13	11	2	12	10	3	590.60	11	6	6	11	5	7	118.89
Vibrational Level 020							10	6	5	10	5	6	119.43
							11	7	5	11	6	6	137.44
8	3	5	8	2	6	86.72	10	7	3	10	6	4 *	138.07
8	4	4	8	3	5	126.44	10	7	4	10	6	5 *	138.07
5	4	1	5	3	2	146.32	10	6	4	9	5	5	243.94
4	4	1	4	3	2 *	148.88	11	7	5	10	6	4	273.78
9	5	4	9	4	5	173.01	**Vibrational Level 100**						
5	5	0	5	4	1	181.53							
6	5	2	6	4	3	181.82	13	6	8	13	5	9	92.67
6	6	1	6	5	2	209.70							
9	6	3	9	5	4	211.67							
4	4	1	3	3	0	246.08			UNIDENTIFIED LINES				
12	3	10	11	2	9 *	285.58		$H_2^{16}O$			$D_2^{16}O$		
5	5	0	4	4	1	303.73							
8	4	4	7	3	5	352.66		110.42			96.78		
6	6	1	5	5	0	356.46		111.18			101.01		
9	6	3	8	5	4	432.3		114.52			127.94		
Vibrational Level 100								115.87			131.05		
								149.45			163.45		
9	5	4	9	4	5	115.64		149.52			182.72		
8	1	7	8	0	8	136.24		182.31			197.20		
7	3	4	6	2	5 *	285.58		185.49			204.92		
Vibrational Level 001								205.44			379.36		
								211.01					
6	4	2	6	3	3	83.28		217.82					
		$H_2^{18}O$						219.70					
								235.24					
Vibrational Level 020								262.56					
5	5	0	5	4	1	178.16		289.02					
6	6	1	6	5	2	205.74		836.1					
5	5	0	4	4	1	300.23		845.3					
								2096.4					
								4387.60					

[a] *Source of data*: Bibl. ref. [275].

TABLE XIII

WAVE NUMBERS (vac cm^{-1}) OF $H_2{}^{16}O$, $H_2{}^{18}O$, AND $D_2{}^{16}O$ LASER LINES[a]

100-020 Band of $H_2{}^{16}O$

J'	K'_a	K'_c	J"	K''_a	K''_c	
5	2	3	5	5	0	45.407494
9	5	4	9	6	3	111.39
8	5	3	8	6	2	114.32
7	5	2	7	6	1	116.87
8	0	8	8	3	5	127.48
8	1	7	8	4	4	137.26
6	2	5	5	5	0	* 148.88
9	1	9	8	4	4	173.43
7	4	3	7	5	2	203.83
9	4	5	9	5	4	207.5
13	1	13	12	2	10	247.2
12	0	12	11	3	9	264.21
12	1	12	11	2	9	279.07
5	1	4	4	4	1	302.76
6	4	2	5	5	1	351.48
8	0	8	7	3	5	353.73
7	4	3	6	5	2	375.09
8	4	4	7	5	3	400.54
9	4	5	8	5	4	427.99

020-010 Band of $H_2{}^{16}O$

6	6	1	7	7	0	1297.19
5	5	0	6	6	1	1316.38
4	4	1	5	5	0	1340.70

001-020 Band of $H_2{}^{16}O$

6	4	2	6	6	1	84.323417
6	3	3	6	5	2	210.67
7	4	4	6	6	1	251.92
6	3	3	5	5	0	357.51

100-020 Band of $H_2{}^{18}O$

J'	K'_a	K'_c	J"	K''_a	K''_c	
8	4	5	8	5	4	202.31
7	4	4	7	5	3	205.07
6	4	3	6	5	2	206.76
12	1	12	11	2	9	282.62
6	4	3	5	5	0	353.42
7	4	4	6	5	1	376.01
8	4	5	7	5	2	397.42

100-020 Band of $D_2{}^{16}O$

11	0	11	11	3	8	58.25
13	6	8	13	7	7	89.49
12	6	6	12	7	5	90.51
11	6	5	11	7	4	91.84
11	6	6	11	7	5	92.823
12	1	12	11	4	7	118.65
13	5	9	13	6	8	134.18
12	5	8	12	6	7	136.35
11	5	7	11	6	6	138.99
16	0	16	15	1	15	175.96
12	6	6	11	7	5	239.28
9	5	5	8	6	2	252.97
10	5	6	9	6	3	264.13
10	5	5	9	6	4	264.63
11	5	7	10	6	4	275.30
11	5	6	10	6	5	277.04
12	5	8	11	6	5	285.05
13	5	9	12	6	6	295.02

[a] *Source of data*: Bibl. ref. [275].

TABLE XIV

WAVE NUMBERS (cm^{-1}) OF LASER LINES OBSERVED IN MOLECULAR
DISCHARGES BUT NOT STUDIED EXTENSIVELY[a]

CN		C_2H_2	SO_2
4-3 Band		$(\nu_2-\nu_5)$ Q Branch Lines	
	(air cm^{-1})	(vac. cm^{-1})	(vac. cm^{-1})
P(9)	1929.08	1244.70	70.98
P(10)	1925.09	1244.46	66.14
P(11)	1921.07	1244.09	51.89
		1243.64	46.44
		1243.12	

BCl$_3$		NH$_3$			
Line No.	(cm^{-1})	Line Identifications			
1	546.4	Vib. Levels	Rot. Transitions		(vac. cm^{-1})
2	531.9	$v_1v_2v_3v_4$	(J',K')	(J",K")	
3	523.6				
4	515.5	(0 1 0 0)	(8,7)$_s$	(7,7)$_a$	122.7
5	495.0				
6	485.4	(0 1 0 0)	(7,7)$_a$	(7,7)$_s$	379.7
7	446.4				
8	434.8				

UNIDENTIFIED LINES (VAC.CM^{-1})

In ICN Discharge	In NH$_3$ Discharge	In ^{15}NH$_3$ plus CH$_4$ Discharge	In Dimethyl-amine Discharge
12.91	465.744	90.711	139.084
14.80	443.616	88.253	136.796
18.56	443.203	72.063	131.418
18.60	422.386	60.551	129.868
26.83	401.316		122.618
29.68	380.489		103.733
32.16	312.979		101.325
32.26			98.759
84.03			89.233
			86.109
			49.737
			47.393
			44.853

[a] *Sources of data*: CN–bibl. ref. [281]; C_2H_2–[283]; SO_2–[285];
BCl$_3$–[287]; NH$_3$–[288, 290]; unidentified lines–[214, 215, 228].

IV. Laser Spectra and Molecular Structure

Two specific examples will be discussed to illustrate the usefulness of laser data to molecular spectroscopy. One of these is related to the evaluation of the potential function for the ground electronic state of the carbon monoxide molecule. The other one deals with the determination of precise values for the rotational constants of the vibrational states involved in some of the laser transitions of the carbon dioxide molecule.

RKR POTENTIAL OF CO

The ground electronic state $X\,^1\Sigma^+$ of the CO molecule has been one of the most extensively studied molecular states among diatomic molecules. The numerous spectroscopic studies of the CO bands published prior to 1966 have been summarized by Krupenie [2]. Until recently, the analysis of the CO $A\,^1\Pi$–$X\,^1\Sigma^+$ electronic bands by Gerö and Schmid [3] was the only basis of the data for $8 \leq v \leq 24$. However, advances made during recent years in molecular laser technology have enabled the observation of infrared transitions between high vibrational levels and accurate spectral positions are now available for vibrational levels through $v = 28$ (see Table I). It has been shown that these high-v data are consistent with the measurements made by well-established methods for the absorption bands involving $v \leq 6$. These new laser measurements supplant the earlier electronic data. In addition, the excellent agreement between the grating data for the $P(13)$ line of the 7–6 band (1935.484 cm^{-1}) and the absolute frequency measurement [4] for the same line (580 24 341 MHz or 1935.4834 cm^{-1}; $c = 2.9979250 \times 10^{10}$ cm sec^{-1} was used for the conversion from MHz to cm^{-1}) adds additional credence to the calibration techniques [5] employed for determining the spectral positions of the nearly 200 CO laser lines observed in the infrared. These high-precision measurements encourage us to apply the Rydberg–Klein–Rees method [6] to the ground electronic state of the CO molecule in order to construct a potential curve to high vibrational levels.

The Rydberg–Klein–Rees method has been a means for determining empirical potential curves for diatomic molecules from experimental data for the vibrational term values $G(v)$ and rotational constants $B(v)$. The theory for this technique is known; essentially, we evaluate the classical turning points $r_{\min}(v, J = 0)$ and $r_{\max}(v, J = 0)$. It can be shown that

$$r_{\max} = [f^2 + (f/g)]^{1/2} + f \tag{1}$$

$$r_{\min} = [f^2 + (f/g)]^{1/2} - f \tag{2}$$

where

$$f = \frac{1}{2}[r_{\max} - r_{\min}] = \frac{\hbar}{(2hc\mu)^{1/2}} \int_{v_{\min}}^{v} \frac{dv'}{[G(v) - G(v')]^{1/2}} \tag{3}$$

$$g = \frac{1}{2}\left(\frac{1}{r_{min}} - \frac{1}{r_{max}}\right) = \frac{(2hc\mu)^{1/2}}{\hbar} \int_{v_{min}}^{v} \frac{B(v')\,dv'}{[G(v) - G(v')]^{1/2}} \tag{4}$$

In (3) and (4) the lower limit of integration v_{min} is that value of v where $E(v, J = 0) = Y_{00} + G(v)$ vanishes [7]. Y_{00} is given in [8]

$$Y_{00} = \frac{B_e}{4} + \frac{\alpha_e \omega_e}{12 B_e} + \frac{(\alpha_e \omega_e)^2}{144 B_e^3} - \frac{\omega_e x_e}{4} \tag{5}$$

For the CO X $^1\Sigma^+$ state, the value of v_{min} is -0.50009. The upper limit of integration v causes a singularity in the evaluation of these integrals. This numerical problem can be treated by a variety of means. Zeleznik [9] has noted that the singularity may be removed by a change of variable. After integrating Eqs. (3) and (4) by parts, Watson [10] has shown that the functions f and g become

$$f = \frac{\hbar}{(2hc\mu)^{1/2}} \left\{ \frac{[2[G(v) + Y_{00}]^{1/2}}{\omega_e} + 4 \int_{v_{min}}^{v} \frac{[G(v) - G(v')]^{1/2}}{\omega_{v'}^2} (\omega x)_{v'}\,dv' \right\} \tag{6}$$

$$g = \frac{(2hc\mu)^{1/2}}{\hbar} \left\{ 2[G(v) + Y_{00}]^{1/2} \frac{B_e}{\omega_e} + 2 \int_{v_{min}}^{v} \frac{[G(v) - G(v')]^{1/2}}{\omega_{v'}^2} \right.$$

$$\left. \times [2B(v')(\omega x)_{v'} - \alpha_{v'} \omega_{v'}]\,dv' \right\} \tag{7}$$

where $\alpha_{v'}$, $\omega_{v'}$, and $(\omega x)_{v'}$ are introduced by means of

$$\frac{dB(v')}{dv'} = -\alpha_{v'}; \qquad \frac{dG(v')}{dv'} = \omega_{v'}; \qquad -\frac{1}{2}\frac{d^2 G(v')}{dv'^2} = (\omega x)_{v'} \tag{8}$$

On the other hand, Albritton *et al.* [11] have evaluated these integrals numerically, where each integral is broken up into a succession of integrals, Simpson's rule is applied up to the region of the singularity, and Gaussian quadrature is used in the region of the singularity.

The computer programs used in both of these alternative formulations led to identical results. In fact, the values obtained from the two approaches differed by $<5 \times 10^{-7}$ Å for r_{min} and $<10 \times 10^{-7}$ Å for r_{max}. This agreement between the two approaches and other tests performed suggest that we now have [12] a reasonably unique RKR potential for the ground electronic state of the CO molecule.

GROUND STATE MOLECULAR CONSTANTS FOR $^{12}C^{16}O$

The molecular constants appearing in the expressions for term values given in the following equations were obtained by using a least squares program incorporating double-precision arithmetic to fit the present (see Table I, the

three decimal entries up to $v = 28$) and previously available experimental results [13–15]; the observational data were assigned weights inversely proportional to $(\Delta v)^2$, Δv representing the quoted uncertainties. Lines having possible interference due to atmospheric absorptions (those marked by superscript a in Table I) resulting from the 3-m air path outside the monochromator section were not used in the evaluations. Also, no attempt was made to include the measurements of the rf emission spectra [16], sunspot spectra [17], or chemical laser spectra [18, 19].

$$
\begin{aligned}
G(v) &= Y_{10}(v + \tfrac{1}{2}) + Y_{20}(v + \tfrac{1}{2})^2 + Y_{30}(v + \tfrac{1}{2})^3 \\
&\quad + Y_{40}(v + \tfrac{1}{2})^4 + Y_{50}(v + \tfrac{1}{2})^5 + Y_{60}(v + \tfrac{1}{2})^6 + \cdots \\
&= \omega_e(v + \tfrac{1}{2}) - \omega_e x_e(v + \tfrac{1}{2})^2 + \omega_e y_e(v + \tfrac{1}{2})^3 \\
&\quad - \omega_e z_e(v + \tfrac{1}{2})^4 + \omega_e a_e(v + \tfrac{1}{2})^5 - \omega_e b_e(v + \tfrac{1}{2})^6 + \cdots \\
&= 2169.81801(v + \tfrac{1}{2}) - 13.2906899(v + \tfrac{1}{2})^2 \\
&\quad + 1.09777979 \times 10^{-2}(v + \tfrac{1}{2})^3 + 2.29371618 \times 10^{-5}(v + \tfrac{1}{2})^4 \\
&\quad + 2.10035541 \times 10^{-6}(v + \tfrac{1}{2})^5 - 4.49979099 \times 10^{-8}(v + \tfrac{1}{2})^6 + \cdots
\end{aligned}
\tag{9}
$$

$$
\begin{aligned}
F(J) &= [Y_{01} + Y_{11}(v + \tfrac{1}{2}) + Y_{21}(v + \tfrac{1}{2})^2]J(J + 1) \\
&\quad + [Y_{02} + Y_{12}(v + \tfrac{1}{2})]J^2(J + 1)^2 \\
&= [B_e - \alpha_e(v + \tfrac{1}{2}) + \gamma_e(v + \tfrac{1}{2})^2]J(J + 1) \\
&\quad - [D_e - \beta_e(v + \tfrac{1}{2})]J^2(J + 1)^2 \\
&= [(1.93126515) - (1.75054229 \times 10^{-2})(v + \tfrac{1}{2}) + (1.81117949 \times 10^{-7}) \\
&\quad \times (v + \tfrac{1}{2})^2]J(J + 1) + [(-6.10370612 \times 10^{-6}) + (1.41301891 \times 10^{-9}) \\
&\quad \times (v + \tfrac{1}{2})]J^2(J + 1)^2
\end{aligned}
\tag{10}
$$

The Y's are the Dunham coefficients [20], and the other constants follow the standard notation [21]. The number of significant figures quoted for the molecular constants is to avoid round off errors in the numerical integrations required for evaluating the potential at high-v values.

MOLECULAR CONSTANTS OF $^{12}C^{16}O_2$

The measurements made [22] for the cw beating of pairs of the carbon dioxide laser lines near 10 μm (see Table IX for the basic observational data) have enabled the evaluation of some of the molecular constants of $^{12}C^{16}O_2$ with a precision not achieved before. These constants, expressed in cm^{-1}, are

$B_{00^01} = 3.8714044,$ $D_{00^01} = 13.252 \times 10^{-8}$

$B_{00^01} - B_{10^00} = -3047.389 \times 10^{-6},$ $B_{00^01} - B_{02^00} = -3340.757 \times 10^{-6}$

$D_{00^01} - D_{10^00} = 1.8366 \times 10^{-8},$ $D_{00^01} - D_{02^00} = -2.3816 \times 10^{-8}$

It is interesting also to note that the laser measurements, for the first time, led to an experimental value [23] for the 00^02 level of $^{12}C^{16}O_2$. The observational data for the levels like 00^01 (2349.142 cm^{-1}), 00^02 (4673.311 cm^{-1}), and 00^03 (6972.555 cm^{-1}) would indeed be very valuable in the evaluation of some of the molecular constants for CO_2.

Finally, the energy level separations relevant to CO_2 laser excitations derived from published results [1, 24] are

$$00^01 - 10^00 = 960.955 \quad cm^{-1} \qquad 00^01 - 02^00 = 1063.730 \quad cm^{-1}.$$

In conclusion, it may be commented that in addition to the specific examples discussed above, the work related to the identifications of the transitions involved in the laser excitations of hydrogen cyanide and water vapor has also demonstrated the usefulness of having available precisely measured spectral positions for laser emissions. It seems that molecular laser spectroscopy will continue to provide new challenges and deeper understanding of the structures of small molecules.

ACKNOWLEDGMENTS

One of us (KNR) would like to express his gratitude to the National Science Foundation and the Office of Naval Research for support of research programs which formed the basis for some of the material appearing in this article. Thanks are also due to Professor Ross McFarlane, Cornell University, Ithaca, New York, for reading the manuscript and making valuable suggestions.

References†

1. R. Oberly, K. Narahari Rao, Y. H. Hahn, and T. K. McCubbin, Jr., *J. Mol. Spectrosc.* **25**, 138 (1968).
2. P. H. Krupenie, "The Band Spectrum of Carbon Monoxide." U.S. NSRDS -5, Nat. Bur. Stand. 1966.
3. L. Gerö, *Z. Phys.* **100**, 374 (1936); R. Schmid and L. Gerö, *Ibid.* **101**, 343 (1936).
4. D. R. Sokoloff, A. Sanchez, R. M. Osgood, and A. Javan, *Appl. Phys. Lett.* **17**, 257 (1970).
5. K. Narahari Rao, T. J. Coburn, J. S. Garing, K. Rossmann, and H. H. Nielsen, *J. Opt. Soc. Amer.* **49**, 221 (1959).
6. R. Rydberg, *Z. Phys.* **73**, 376 (1931); **80**, 514 (1933); O. Klein, *Ibid.* **76**, 226 (1932); A. L. G. Rees, *Proc. Phys. Soc. London* **59**, 998 (1947).
7. E. W. Kaiser, *J. Chem. Phys.* **53**, 1686 (1970).
8. G. Herzberg and A. Monfils, *J. Mol. Spectrosc.* **5**, 482 (1960).
9. F. J. Zeleznik, *J. Chem. Phys.* **42**, 2836 (1965).
10. J. K. G. Watson, Unpublished work (1970).
11. D. L. Albritton, A. L. Schmeltekopf, and R. N. Zare, "Diatomic Franck-Condon Factors," Harper, New York, To be published.

† References cited in the text are listed here.

12. A. W. Mantz, J. K. G. Watson, K. Narahari Rao, D. L. Albritton, A. L. Schmeltekopf, and R. N. Zare, *J. Mol. Spectrosc.* **39**, 180 (1971).
13. K. Narahari Rao, C. J. Humphreys, and D. H. Rank, "Wavelength Standards in the Infrared." Academic Press, New York, 1966.
14. D. H. Rank, A. G. St. Pierre, and T. A. Wiggins, *J. Mol. Spectrosc.* **18**, 418 (1965).
15. J. M. Weinberg, E. S. Fishburne, and K. Narahari Rao, *J. Mol. Spectrosc.* **18**, 428 (1965).
16. H. M. Mould, W. C. Price, and G. R. Wilkinson, *Spectrochim. Acta* **16**, 479 (1960).
17. D. N. B. Hall, *Symp. Mol. Spectrosc., Columbus, 1969*, Paper E1.
18. M. A. Pollack, *Appl. Phys. Lett.* **8**, 237 (1966).
19. D. W. Gregg and S. J. Thomas, *J. Appl. Phys.* **39**, 4399 (1968).
20. J. L. Dunham, *Phys. Rev.* **41**, 721 (1932).
21. G. Herzberg, "Spectra of Diatomic Molecules." Van Nostrand-Reinhold, Princeton, New Jersey, 1950.
22. T. J. Bridges and T. Y. Chang, *Phys. Rev. Lett.* **22**, 811 (1969).
23. T. K. McCubbin, Jr. and Y. H. Hahn, *J. Opt. Soc. Amer.* **57**, 1373 (1967).
24. H. R. Gordon and T. K. McCubbin, Jr., *J. Mol. Spectrosc.* **18**, 73 (1965).

Bibliography†

Carbon Monoxide

1. F. Legay and N. Legay-Sommaire, Luminescence infrarouge de l'oxyde de carbone excité par l'azote activé. *C.R. Acad. Sci.* **257** 2644 (1963).
2. R. C. Millikan, Vibrational fluorescence of carbon monoxide. *J. Chem. Phys.* **38**, 2855 (1963).
3. R. C. Millikan and D. R. White, Vibrational energy exchange between N_2 and CO. The vibrational relaxation of nitrogen. *J. Chem. Phys.* **39**, 98 (1963).
4. L. E. S. Mathias and J. T. Parker, Visible laser oscillations from carbon monoxide. *Phys. Lett.* **7**, 194 (1963).
5. P. K. Cheo and H. G. Cooper, Excitation mechanisms of population inversion in CO and N_2 pulsed lasers. *Appl. Phys. Lett.* **5**, 42 (1964).
6. H. G. Cooper and P. K. Cheo, Dependence of the recovery time of the pulsed carbon monoxide laser on gas pressure and tube bore. *Appl. Phys. Lett.* **5**, 44 (1964).
7. C. K. N. Patel and R. J. Kerl, Laser oscillation on $X^1\Sigma^+$ vibrational-rotational transitions of CO. *Appl. Phys. Lett.* **5**, 81 (1964).
8. H. G. Cooper and P. K. Cheo, Recovery time of the CO-pulsed laser. *Bull. Amer. Phys. Soc.* II, **9**, 500 (1964).
9. N. Legay-Sommaire and F. Legay, Luminescence infrarouge des gaz excités par l'azote activé I. Oxyde de carbone. *J. Phys. (Paris)* **25**, 917 (1964).
10. C. K. N. Patel, CW laser on vibrational-rotational transitions of CO. *Appl. Phys. Lett.* **7**, 246 (1965).
11. N. Legay-Sommaire, L. Henry, and F. Legay, Réalisation d'un laser utilisant l'énergie de vibration des gaz excités par l'azote activé (CO, CO_2, et N_2O). *C. R. Acad. Sci.* **260**, 3339 (1965).
12. R. A. McFarlane and J. A. Howe, Stimulated emission in the system CO/CO_2. *Phys. Lett.* **19**, 208 (1965).
13. M. A. Pollack, Laser oscillation in chemically formed CO. *Appl. Phys. Lett.* **8**, 237 (1966); erratum, *Appl. Phys. Lett.* **9**, 74 (1966).

† References cited in table footnotes are listed here. In addition, all other articles published on infrared molecular laser emissions are included here.

14. C. K. N. Patel, Vibrational-rotational laser action in carbon monoxide. *Phys. Rev.* **141**, 71 (1966).
15. G. Karl, P. Kruus, and J. C. Polanyi, Infrared-emission studies of electronic-to-vibrational energy transfer. II. Hg + CO. *J. Chem. Phys.* **46**, 224 (1967).
16. F. Legay, Étudé d'un laser à CO-N₂ par une méthode de modulation. *C. R. Acad. Sci.* **266**, 554 (1968).
17. F. Legay, N. Legay-Sommaire, and M. G. Taïeb, Étude du laser à CO-N₂: sélection des raies, évaluation de l'amplification et des populations vibrationnelles. *C. R. Acad. Sci.* **266**, 855 (1968).
18. R. M. Osgood, Jr. and W. C. Eppers, Jr., High power CO-N₂-He laser. *Appl. Phys. Lett.* **13**, 409 (1968).
19. D. W. Gregg and S. J. Thomas, Analysis of the CS₂-O₂ chemical laser showing new lines and selective excitation. *J. Appl. Phys.* **39**, 4399 (1968).
20. R. M. Osgood, Jr., E. R. Nichols, W. C. Eppers, Jr., and R. D. Petty, Q-Switching of the carbon monoxide laser. *Appl. Phys. Lett.* **15**, 69 (1969).
21. C. Wittig, J. C. Hassler, and P. D. Coleman, Carbon monoxide chemical laser utilizing a fast flow system. *Appl. Phys. Lett.* **16**, 117 (1970).
22. M. M. Mann, M. L. Bhaumik, and W. B. Lacina, Room-temperature CO laser. *Appl. Phys. Lett.* **16**, 430 (1970).
23. W. Q. Jeffers and C. E. Wiswall, A transverse flow CO chemical laser. *Appl. Phys. Lett.* **17**, 67 (1970).
24. M. L. Bhaumik, High efficiency CO laser at room temperature. *Appl. Phys. Lett.* **17**, 188 (1970).
25. W. J. Graham, J. Kershenstein, J. T. Jensen, Jr., and K. Kershenstein, Pulsed behavior and inversion mechanism in the carbon monoxide laser. *Appl. Phys. Lett.* **17**, 194 (1970).
26. R. L. McKenzie, Laser power at 5 μm from the supersonic expansion of carbon monoxide. *Appl. Phys. Lett.* **17**, 462 (1970).
27. D. R. Sokoloff, A. Sanchez, R. M. Osgood, and A. Javan, Extension of laser harmonic frequency mixing into the 5μ region, *Appl. Phys. Lett.* **17**, 257 (1970).
28. J. T. Yardley, Vibrational energy transfer in CO-He lasers, *J. Chem. Phys.* **52**, 3983 (1970).
29. J. T. Yardley, Laser action in highly-excited vibrational levels of CO. *J. Mol. Spectrosc.* **35**, 314 (1970).
30. A. W. Mantz, E. R. Nichols, B. D. Alpert, and K. Narahari Rao, CO laser spectra studied with a 10-meter vacuum infrared grating spectrograph. *J. Mol. Spectrosc.* **35**, 325 (1970).
31. W. C. Eppers, Jr., R. M. Osgood, Jr., and P. R. Greason, 75-Watt CW carbon monoxide laser. *IEEE J.* **QE-6**, 4 (1970).
32. R. M. Osgood, Jr., W. C. Eppers, Jr., and E. R. Nichols, An investigation of the high-power CO laser. *IEEE J.* **QE-6**, 145 (1970).
33. M. L. Bhaumik, W. B. Lacina, and M. M. Mann, Enhancement of CO laser efficiency by addition of xenon. *IEEE J.* **QE-6**, 575 (1970).
34. M. D. Baranov, V. M. Kaslin, and G. G. Petrash, Pulsed laser action on CO electronic transitions with cooling of the gas. *Sov. Phys. JETP* **30**, 205 (1970).

Hydrogen Halides

35. J. K. Cashion and J. C. Polanyi, Resolved infrared emission spectrum of the reaction atomic H · plus Cl₂ . *J. Chem. Phys.* **30**, 1097 (1959).
36. J. R. Airey, R. R. Getty, J. C. Polanyi, and D. R. Snelling, Absolute efficiency of conversion of heat of the reaction H + Cl₂ into vibration. *J. Chem. Phys.* **41**, 3255 (1964).

37. J. V. V. Kasper and G. C. Pimentel, HCl chemical laser. *Phys. Rev. Lett.* **14**, 352 (1965).
38. T. F. Deutsch, Molecular laser action in hydrogen and deuterium halides. *Appl. Phys. Lett.* **10**, 234 (1967).
39. T. F. Deutsch, Laser emission from HF rotational transitions. *Appl. Phys. Lett.* **11**, 18 (1967).
40. J. R. Airey, A new pulsed I-R chemical laser. *IEEE J.* **QE-3**, 208 (1967).
41. T. F. Deutsch, New infrared laser transitions in HCl, HBr, DCl, and DBr. *IEEE J.* **QE-3**, 419 (1967).
42. K. G. Anlauf, D. H. Maylotte, P. D. Pacey, and J. C. Polanyi, Vibrational population-inversion and stimulated emission from the continuous-mixing of chemical reagents. *Phys. Lett. A* **24**, 208 (1967).
43. H.-L. Chen, J. C. Stephenson, and C. B. Moore, Laser-excited vibrational fluorescence of HCl and the HCl-CO$_2$ laser. *Chem. Phys. Lett.* **8**, 593 (1968).
44. C. B. Moore, An electrically pulsed HCl laser. *IEEE J.* **QE-4**, 52 (1968).
45. N. V. Karlov, Yu. B. Konev, Yu. N. Petrov, A. M. Prokhorov, and O. M. Stel'makh, Laser based on boron trichloride. *JETP Lett.* **8**, 12 (1968).
46. T. A. Cool, T. J. Falk, and R. R. Stephens, DF-CO$_2$ and HF-CO$_2$ continuous-wave chemical lasers. *Appl. Phys. Lett.* **15**, 318 (1969).
47. J. H. Parker and G. C. Pimental, Vibrational energy distribution through chemical laser studies. I. Fluorine atoms plus hydrogen or methane. *J. Chem. Phys.* **51**, 91 (1969).
48. R. W. F. Gross, R. R. Giedt, and T. A. Jacobs, Stimulated emission behind overdriven detonation waves in F$_2$O-H$_2$ mixtures. *J. Chem. Phys.* **51**, 1250 (1969).
49. N. G. Basov, V. V. Gromov, E. L. Koshelev, E. P. Markin, and A. N. Oraevskii, Generation spectrum of a chemical laser using a mixture of H$_2$ and Cl$_2$. *JETP Lett.* **9**, 147 (1969).
50. O. M. Batovskii, G. K. Vasil'ev, E. F. Makarov, and V. L. Tal'roze, Chemical laser operating on branched chain reaction of fluorine with hydrogen. *JETP Lett.* **9**, 200 (1969).
51. V. S. Burmasov, G. G. Dolgov-Savel'ev, V. A. Polyakov, and G. M. Chumak, Quantum yield of generation of an H$_2$ + F$_2$ mixture. *JETP Lett.* **10**, 28 (1969).
52. T. A. Cool and R. R. Stephens, Efficient purely chemical cw laser operation. *Appl. Phys. Lett.* **16**, 55 (1970).
53. D. J. Spencer, H. Mirels, T. A. Jacobs, and R. W. E. Gross, Preliminary performance of a cw chemical laser. *Appl. Phys. Lett.* **16**, 235 (1970).
54. D. J. Spencer, H. Mirels, and T. A. Jacobs, Comparison of HF and DF continuous chemical lasers: I. Power. *Appl. Phys. Lett.* **16**, 384 (1970).
55. M. A. Kwok, R. R. Giedt, and R. W. F. Gross, Comparison of HF and DF continuous chemical lasers: II. Spectroscopy. *Appl. Phys. Lett.* **16**, 386 (1970).
56. J. J. Hinchen and C. M. Banas, CW HF electric-discharge mixing laser. *Appl. Phys. Lett.* **17**, 386 (1970).
57. C. J. Buczeks, R. J. Freiberg, J. J. Hinchen, P. P. Chenausky, and R. J. Wayne, Premixed CW chemical laser. *Appl. Phys. Lett.* **17**, 514 (1970).
58. S. W. Mayer, M. A. Kwok, R. W. F. Gross, and D. J. Spencer, Isotope separation with the CW hydrogen fluoride laser. *Appl. Phys. Lett.* **17**, 516 (1970).
59. J. R. Airey, Report on the International Symposium on chemical lasers. *Int. J. Chem. Kinet.* **2**, 65 (1970).
60. J. B. Anderson, Energy requirements for chemical reaction: H + HF → H$_2$ + F*. *J. Chem. Phys.* **52**, 3849 (1970).
61. D. P. Akitt and J. T. Yardley, Far-infrared laser emission in gas discharges containing boron trihalides. *IEEE J.* **QE-6**, 113 (1970).
62. N. G. Basov, L. V. Kulakov, E. P. Markin, A. I. Nikitin, and A. N. Oraevskii, Emission spectrum of a chemical laser using an H$_2$ + F$_2$ mixture, *JETP Lett.* **9**, 375 (1970).

Nitric Oxide

63. M. Huber, Laser transition with predissociating lower state in the NO molecule. *Phys. Lett.* **12**, 102 (1964).
64. M. A. Pollack, Molecular laser action in nitric oxide by photodissociation of NOCl. *Appl. Phys. Lett.* **9**, 94 (1966).
65. T. F. Deutsch, NO molecular laser. *Appl. Phys. Lett.* **9**, 295 (1966).

Carbon Dioxide

66. F. Legay and N. Legay-Sommaire, Luminescence infrarouge de l'oxyde de carbone excité par l'azote activé. *C. R. Acad. Sci.* **257**, 2644 (1963).
67. F. Legay and P. Barchewitz, Émission infrarouge du gaz carbonique et du protoxyde d'azote provoquée par l'azote activé. *C. R. Acad. Sci.* **256**, 5305 (1963).
68. F. Legay and N. Legay-Sommaire, Sur les possibilités de réalisation d'un maser optique utilisant l'energie de vibration des gaz excités par l'azote activé. *C. R. Acad. Sci.* **259**, 99 (1964).
69. C. K. N. Patel, Continuous-wave laser action on vibrational-rotational transitions of CO_2. *Phys. Rev. A* **136**, 1187 (1964).
70. C. K. N. Patel, Interpretation of CO_2 optical maser experiments. *Phys. Rev. Lett.* **12**, 588 (1964); errata, *Phys. Rev. Lett.* **12**, 684 (1964).
71. C. K. N. Patel, Selective excitation through vibrational energy transfer and optical maser action in N_2-CO_2. *Phys. Rev. Lett.* **13**, 617 (1964).
72. C. K. N. Patel, CW high power N_2-CO_2 laser. *Appl. Phys. Lett.* **7**, 15 (1965).
73. J. A. Howe, Effect of foreign gases on the CO_2 laser: R-branch transitions. *Appl. Phys. Lett.* **7**, 21 (1965).
74. T. J. Bridges and C. K. N. Patel, High-power Brewster window laser at 10.6 microns. *Appl. Phys. Lett.* **7**, 244 (1965).
75. G. Moeller and J. D. Rigden, High-power laser action in CO_2-He mixtures. *Appl. Phys. Lett.* **7**, 274 (1965).
76. C. K. N. Patel, P. K. Tien, and J. H. McFee, CW high-power CO_2-N_2-He laser. *Appl. Phys. Lett.* **7**, 290 (1965).
77. W. B. McKnight, Excitation mechanisms in pulsed CO_2 lasers. *J. Appl. Phys.* **40**, 2810 (1965).
78. W. J. Witteman, Increasing continuous laser-action on CO_2 rotational vibrational transitions through selective depopulation of the lower laser level by means of water vapour. *Phys. Lett.* **18**, 125 (1965).
79. R. A. McFarlane and J. A. Howe, Stimulated emission in the system CO/CO_2. *Phys. Lett.* **19**, 208 (1965).
80. G. B. Jacobs, CO_2 laser self-modulation characteristics. *Appl. Opt.* **5**, 1960 (1966).
81. M. A. Kovacs, G. W. Flynn, and A. Javan, Q switching of molecular laser transitions. *Appl. Phys. Lett.* **8**, 62 (1966).
82. G. W. Flynn, M. A. Kovacs, C. K. Rhodes, and A. Javan, Vibrational and rotational studies using Q switching of molecular gas lasers. *Appl. Phys. Lett.* **8**, 63 (1966).
83. G. Moeller and J. D. Rigden, Observation of laser action in the R-branch of CO_2 and N_2O vibrational spectra. *Appl. Phys. Lett.* **8**, 69 (1966).
84. T. K. McCubbin, Jr., R. Darone, and J. Sorrell, Determination of vibration-rotational line strengths and widths in CO_2 using a CO_2-N_2 laser. *Appl. Phys. Lett.* **8**, 118 (1966).
85. B. F. Jacoby and R. K. Long, High Resolution absorption measurement in CO_2 with a tuned laser. *Appl. Phys. Lett.* **8**, 202 (1966).
86. E. T. Gerry and D. A. Leonard, Measurement of 10.6-μ CO_2 laser transition probability and optical broadening cross sections. *Appl. Phys. Lett.* **8**, 227 (1966).
87. T. Deutsch, G. DeMars, and D. T. Wilson, Performance of high-power N_2-CO_2 lasers. *Bull. Amer. Phys. Soc.* **11**, 128 (1966).

88. C. Frapard, P. Laures, M. Roulot, X. Ziegler, and N. Legay-Sommaire, Mise en evidence de 85 oscillations laser nouvelles sur trois transitions vibrationnelles de l'anhydride carbonique, *C.R. Acad. Sci. B* **262**, 1340 (1966).

89. B. Hartmann, and B. Kleman, Laser lines from CO_2 in the 11–18 micron region, *Can. J. Phys.* **44**, 1609 (1966).

90. H. Statz, C. L. Tang, and G. F. Koster, Transition probabilities between laser states in carbon dioxide. *J. Appl. Phys.* **37**, 4278 (1966).

91. J. A. Howe and R. A. McFarlane, New emission systems in CO_2. Part I. Π–Π transitions. *J. Mol. Spectrosc.* **19**, 224 (1966).

92. J. D. Rigden and G. Moeller, Recent developments in CO_2 lasers. *IEEE J.* **QE-2**, 365, (1966).

93. M. J. Weber and T. F. Deutsch, Pulsed and steady-state infrared emission studies of CO_2 laser systems. *IEEE J.* **QE-2**, 369 (1966).

94. G. W. Flynn, L. O. Hocker, A. Javan, M. A. Kovacs, and C. K. Rhodes, Progress and applications of Q-switching techniques using molecular gas lasers. *IEEE J.* **QE-2**, 378 (1966).

95. R. A. Brandewie, W. T. Haswell, III, and R. H. Harada, Heterodyne detection and linewidth measurement with high power CO_2 lasers. *IEEE J.* **QE-2**, 756 (1966).

96. V. K. Konyukhov and A. M. Prokhorov, Population inversion in adiabatic expansion of a gas mixture. *JETP Lett.* **3**, 286 (1966).

97. N. N. Sobolev and V. V. Sokovikov, A mechanism ensuring level population inversion in CO_2 lasers. *JETP Lett.* **4**, 204 (1966).

98. W. J. Witteman, Inversion mechanisms, population densities and coupling-out of a high-power molecular laser, *Philips Res. Rep.* **21**, 73 (1966).

99. I. Wieder and G. B. McCurdy, Isotope shifts and the role of Fermi resonance in the CO_2 infrared maser. *Phys. Rev. Lett.* **16**, 565 (1966).

100. L. O. Hocker, M. A. Kovacs, C. K. Rhodes, G. W. Flynn, and A. Javan, Vibrational relaxation measurements in CO_2 using an induced-fluorescence technique. *Phys. Rev. Lett.* **17**, 233 (1966).

101. D. Rosenberger, The influence of hydrogen on the output of a N_2–CO_2 laser. *Phys. Lett.* **21**, 520 (1966).

102. G. J. Dezenberg and J. A. Merritt, The use of a multipath cell as a CO_2–N_2 gas laser amplifier and oscillator. *Appl. Opt.* **6**, 1541 (1967).

103. M. A. Kovacs, C. K. Rhodes, A. Szöke, and A. Javan, Measurement of some molecular vibrational-rotational parameters with an infrared heterodyning technique. *Appl. Phys. Lett.* **10**, 108 (1967).

104. R. A. Crane and A. L. Waksberg, Visible side-light emission properties of a CO_2–N_2–He plasma induced by the CO_2 laser radiation field. *Appl. Phys. Lett.* **10**, 237 (1967).

105. P. K. Cheo, Relaxation of the 10.6 μ CO_2 laser levels by collisions with H_2. *Appl. Phys. Lett.* **11**, 38 (1967).

106. O. R. Wood and S. E. Schwarz, Passive Q-switching of a CO_2 laser. *Appl. Phys. Lett.* **11**, 88 (1967).

107. D. F. Hotz and J. W. Austin, Gain saturation flux and stimulated emission cross section for the 10.6 μ line of CO_2. *Appl. Phys. Lett.* **11**, 60 (1967); errata, *Appl. Phys. Lett.* **11**, 141 (1967).

108. N. N. Sobolev and V. V. Sokovikov, Influence of rate of disintegration of the lower laser level on the power of a CO_2 laser. *JETP Lett.* **5**, 99 (1967).

109. A. G. Sviridov, N. N. Sobolev, and G. G. Tselikov, Plasma gas temperatures in the discharges used for CO_2 lasers. *JETP Lett.* **6**, 62 (1967).

110. M. Shimazu, Y. Suzaki, M. Takatsuji, and K. Takami, Q-switched CO_2 laser and the detection with the pyroelectric thermal detector. *Jap. J. Appl. Phys.* **6**, 120 (1967).

111. G. B. Jacobs and H. C. Bowers, Extension of CO_2-laser wavelength range with isotopes. *J. Appl. Phys.* **38**, 2692 (1967).

112. A. I. Carswell and J. I. Wood, Plasma properties of a CO_2 laser discharge. *J. Appl. Phys.* **38**, 3028 (1967).

113. P. K. Cheo, Effects of CO_2, He, and N_2 on the lifetimes of the 00^01 and 10^00 CO_2 laser levels and on pulsed gain at 10.6 μ. *J. Appl. Phys.* **38**, 3563 (1967).

114. T. K. McCubbin, Jr., and Y. H. Hahn, Infrared emission of CO_2-N_2 and CO_2-N_2-He plasmas. *J. Opt. Soc. Amer.* **57**, 1373 (1967).

115. P. K. Cheo and H. G. Cooper, Gain Characteristics of CO_2 laser amplifiers at 10.6 microns. *IEEE J.* **QE-3**, 79 (1967).

116. H. Kogelnik and T. J. Bridges, A nonresonant multipass CO_2-laser amplifier. *IEEE J.* **QE-3**, 95 (1967).

117. T. F. Deutsch, Gain and fluorescence characteristics of flowing CO_2 laser systems. *IEEE J.* **QE-3**, 151 (1967).

118. T. J. Bridges and E. G. Burkhardt, Observation of the output of a CO_2 laser by a high-resolution thermographic screen. *IEEE J*, **QE-3**, 168 (1967).

119. C. Freed, Stability measurements of CO_2-N_2-He lasers at 10.6 μm wavelength. *IEEE J.* **QE-3**, 203 (1967).

120. T. J. Bridges and A. R. Strnad, Rapid scan spectrometer for CO_2 laser studies. *IEEE J.* **QE-3**, 335 (1967).

121. R. J. Carbone, Long-term operation of a sealed CO_2 laser. *IEEE J.* **QE-3**, 373 (1967).

122. G. Makhov and I. Wieder, Vibrational excitation of CO_2 by transfer from thermally excited nitrogen. *IEEE J.* **QE-3**, 378 (1967).

123. T. G. Roberts, G. J. Hutcheson, J. J. Ehrlich, W. L. Hales, and T. A. Barr, Jr., High-power N_2-CO_2-He laser development. *IEEE J.* **QE-3**, 605 (1967).

124. P. H. Lee and M. L. Skolnick, Interferometric methods for measuring dispersion in CO_2 laser oscillations and amplifiers. *IEEE J.* **QE-3**, 609 (1967).

125. P. K. Cheo, Effects of gas flow on gain of 10.6 μ CO_2 laser amplifiers. *IEEE J.* **QE-3**, 683 (1967).

126. R. A. Paananen, A $CO_2-N_2-He-Xe$ laser. *Proc. IEEE J.* **QE-3**, 2035 (1967).

127. P. A. Bokhan, On a possibility of using non-contracted discharge to enhance the power of a CO_2-N_2-He laser. *Opt. Spectrosc. (USSR)* **25**, 225 (1967).

128. I. Wieder, Flame pumping and infrared maser action in CO_2. *Phys. Lett. A* **24**, 759 (1967).

129. R. D. Sharma and C. A. Brau, Near-resonant vibrational energy transfer in N_2-CO_2 mixtures. *Phys. Rev. Lett.* **19**, 1273 (1967).

130. G. J. Mullaney, W. H. Christiansen, and D. A. Russell, Fog dissipation using a CO_2 laser. *Appl. Phys. Lett.* **13**, 145 (1968).

131. D. F. Hotz and J. N. Ferrer, Intrinsic flux limits for continuous and Q-pulse gain for the 10.6-μ line of CO_2. *J. Appl. Phys.* **39**, 1797 (1968).

132. N. Djeu, T. Kan, C. R. Miller, and G. J. Wolga, Sequential Q-switching of vibration-rotation transitions in the CO_2 gas laser. *J. Appl. Phys.* **39**, 2157 (1968).

133. I. Burak, J. I. Steinfeld, and D. G. Sutton, CO_2 laser output tuning by selective intra-cavity absorption. *J. Appl. Phys.* **39**, 4464 (1968).

134. J. C. Siddoway, Calculated and observed laser transitions using $^{14}C^{16}O_2$. *J. Appl. Phys.* **39**, 4854 (1968).

135. D. R. Rao, L. O. Hocker, A. Javan, and K. Knable, Spectroscopic studies of 4.3 μ transient laser oscillations in CO_2. *J. Mol. Spectrosc.* **25**, 410 (1968).

136. N. Djeu, T. Kan, and G. J. Wolga, Gain distribution, population densities and rotational temperature for the $(00^01)-(10^00)$ rotation-vibration transitions in a flowing CO_2-N_2-He laser. *IEEE J.* **QE-4**, 256 (1968).

137. C. Freed, Design and short-term stability of single-frequency CO_2 lasers. *IEEE J.* **QE-4**, 404 (1968).
138. D. Meyerhofer, Q-switching of the CO_2 laser. *IEEE J.* **QE-4**, 762 (1968).
139. H. W. Mocker, Rotational level competition in CO_2 lasers. *IEEE J.* **QE-4**, 769 (1968).
140. E. T. Antropov, I. A. Silin-Bekchurin, N. N. Sobolev, and V. V. Sokovikov, Gain measurement in the CO_2 laser discharge. *IEEE J.* **QE-4**, 790 (1968).
141. B. F. Gordietz, N. N. Sobolev, V. V. Sokovikov, and L. A. Shelepin, Population inversion of the vibrational levels in CO_2 lasers. *IEEE J.* **QE-4**, 796 (1968).
142. N. V. Karlov, G. P. Kuzmin, Yu. N. Petrov, and A. M. Prokhorov, Q-switching of a CO_2 laser with a saturating filter based on boron trichloride. *JETP Lett.* **7**, 134 (1968).
143. J. A. F. Alexander, J. T. Houghton, and W. B. McKnight, Collisional relaxation from the ν_3 vibration of CO_2. *J. Phys. London B* **1**, 1225 (1968).
144. N. V. Karlov, G. P. Kuzmin, A. M. Prokhorov, and V. I. Shemyakin, Influence of the choice of the instant of Q-switching in pulsed pumping of a CO_2 laser on the intensity of the generated pulses. *Sov. Phys. JETP* **27**, 704 (1968).
145. P. Hanst and J. A. Morreal, A wavelength-selective, repetitively pulsed CO_2 laser. *Appl. Opt.* **8**, 109 (1969).
146. J. H. McCoy, D. B. Rensch, and R. K. Long, Water vapor continuum absorption of carbon dioxide laser radiation near 10μ. *Appl. Opt.* **8**, 1471 (1969).
147. A. D. Devir and U. P. Oppenheim, Line width determination in the 9.4-μ and 10.4-μ bands of CO_2 using a CO_2 laser. *Appl. Opt.* **8**, 2121 (1969).
148. R. L. Abrams and A. Dienes, Cross saturation of 10.6-μ signals in SF_6. *Appl. Phys. Lett.* **14**, 237 (1969).
149. W. L. Nighan and J. H. Bennett, Electron energy distribution functions and vibrational excitation rates in CO_2 laser mixtures. *Appl. Phys. Lett.* **14**, 240 (1969).
150. P. Rabinowitz, R. Keller, and J. T. LaTourrette, 'Lamb Dip' spectroscopy applied to SF_6. *Appl. Phys. Lett.* **14**, 376 (1969).
151. F. Shimizu, Absorption of CO_2 laser lines by SF_6. *Appl. Phys. Lett.* **14**, 378 (1969).
152. F. T. Chan and C. L. Tang, Rotational transition of CO_2 molecule by collisions. *J. Appl. Phys.* **40**, 2806 (1969).
153. W. B. McKnight, Excitation mechanisms in pulsed CO_2 lasers. *J. Appl. Phys.* **40**, 2810 (1969).
154. T. A. Cool, Power and gain characteristics of high speed flow lasers. *J. Appl. Phys.* **40**, 3563 (1969).
155. N. Karube, E. Yamaka, and F. Nakao, Decomposition of CO_2 molecules in a sealed CO_2 laser. *J. Appl. Phys.* **40**, 3883 (1969).
156. A. M. Ronn and L. J. Schoen, Effect of substituting $^{15}N_2$ for $^{14}N_2$ in the CO_2–N_2 and N_2O–N_2 laser systems. *J. Appl. Phys.* **41**, 2246 (1969).
157. T. K. McCubbin, Jr., J. G. Pantiz, and R. I. Ely, Temperature dependence of the collision broadened widths of the lines in the 10.4μ CO_2 band. *J. Opt. Soc. Amer.* **59**, 496 (1969).
158. R. J. Carbone, Characteristics of a single-frequency sealed-off CO_2 amplifier. *IEEE J.* **QE-5**, 48 (1969).
159. R. Bleekrode, A study of the spontaneous emission from CO_2–N_2–He–H_2 laser discharges $C^3\Pi_u$–$B^3\Pi_g$ emission bands of N_2. *IEEE J.* **QE-5**, 57 (1969).
160. N. V. Karlov, Yu. B. Konev, G. P. Koozmin, and A. M. Prokhorov, Pulsed CO_2 laser with double modulation. *IEEE J.* **QE-5**, 137 (1969).
161. R. L. Abrams and W. B. Gandrud, A variable 10.6μ attenuator. *IEEE J.* **QE-5**, 212 (1969).

162. C. P. Christensen, C. Freed, and H. Haus, Gain saturation and diffusion in CO_2 lasers. *IEEE J.* **QE-5**, 276 (1969).
163. T. Kan, H. T. Powell, and G. J. Wolga, Observation of the central tuning dip in N_2O and CO_2 molecular lasers. *IEEE J.* **QE-5**, 299 (1969).
164. W. B. McKnight, Considerations on high peak powers from CO_2 and CO_2-mixture lasers. *IEEE J.* **QE-5**, 420 (1969).
165. G. W. Day, O. L. Gaddy, and K. C. Jungling, Investigation of a Q-switched pulsed discharge CO_2 laser. *IEEE J.* **QE-5**, 423 (1969).
166. R. L. Abrams, Characteristics of $10.6-\mu$ chirped pulses. *IEEE J.* **QE-5**, 522 (1969).
167. W. F. Krupke and W. R. Sooy, Properties of an unstable confocal resonator CO_2 laser system. *IEEE J.* **QE-5**, 575 (1969).
168. D. C. Smith, Thermal defocusing of CO_2 laser radiation in gases. *IEEE J.* **QE-5**, 600 (1969).
169. N. V. Karlov, Yu. B. Konev, G. P. Koozmin, and A. M. Prokhorov, Pulsed CO_2 laser with double modulation. *IEEE J.* **QE-5**, 137, (1969).
170. V. K. Konyukhov, I. V. Matrosov, A. M. Prokhorov, D. T. Shalunov, and N. N. Shirokov, Vibrational relaxation of CO_2 and N_2 molecules in an expanding supersonic gas jet. *JETP Lett.* **9**, 53 (1969).
171. S. S. Alimpiev, N. V. Karlov, Yu. B. Konev, G. P. Kuzmin, and R. P. Petrov, Influence of dissociation of the inversion on a CO_2 laser with pulsed pumping. *JETP Lett.* **9**, 223 (1969).
172. N. G. Basov, I. N. Kompanets, O. N. Kompanets, V. S. Letokhov, and V. V. Nikitin, Narrow resonances in the saturation of absorption of SF_6 by CO_2-laser emission. *JETP Lett.* **9**, 345 (1969).
173. N. E. Alekseevskiĭ, Pressure dependence of the temperature of the transition of the compound Bi_2K into the superconducting state. *JETP Lett.* **9**, 347 (1969).
174. V. S. Arakelyan, N. V. Karlov, and A. M. Prokhorov, Self-synchronization of transverse modes of a CO_2 laser. *JETP Lett.* **10**, 178 (1969).
175. V. N. Ivanov and L. F. Erybasheva, A study of the spectra of molecular-laser gas mixtures. *Opt. Spectrosc. (USSR)* **28**, 287 (1969).
176. R. D. Sharma, Near-resonant vibrational energy transfer among isotopes of CO_2. *Phys. Rev.* **177**, 102 (1969).
177. T. J. Bridges and T. Y. Chang, Accurate rotational constants of $C^{12}O_2^{16}$ from measurement of cw beats in bulk GaAs between CO_2 vibrational-rotational laser lines. *Phys. Rev. Lett.* **22**, 811 (1969).
178. A. M. Danishevskiĭ, I. M. Fishman, and I. D. Yaroshetskiĭ, Investigation of the laser effect in CO_2 during pulsed excitation. *Sov. Phys. JETP* **28**, 421 (1969).
179. G. Hillman, J. Tulip, and H. Seguin, Pulse repetition rate control and stabilization in a passively Q-switched CO_2 laser. *Appl. Opt.* **9**, 515 (1970).
180. G. J. Dezenberg, E. L. Roy, and J. A. Merritt, Properties of a 15-cm i.d. multipath CO_2 laser amplifier and oscillator. *Appl. Opt.* **9**, 516 (1970).
181. W. I. Dobrov and E. R. Washwell, CO_2 laser pumping by a dc-tesla coil combination. *Appl. Opt.* **9**, 1485 (1970).
182. S. Marcus and J. H. McCoy, Self-mode locking and saturation-pulse sharpening in a rotating-mirror Q-switched CO_2 laser. *Appl. Phys. Lett.* **16**, 11 (1970).
183. D. M. Kuehn and D. J. Monson, Experiments with a CO_2 gas-dynamic laser. *Appl. Phys. Lett.* **16**, 48 (1970).
184. L. J. Schoen and A. M. Ronn, Simultaneous oscillation on two isotopic lines in CO_2 and N_2O lasers. *Appl. Phys. Lett,* **16**, 119 (1970).
185. B. R. Bronfin, L. R. Boedeker, and J. P. Cheyer, Thermal laser excitation by mixing in a highly convective flow. *Appl. Phys. Lett.* **16**, 214 (1970).

186. K. M. Evenson, J. S. Wells, and L. M. Matarrese, Absolute frequency measurements of the CO_2 cw laser at 28 THz (10.6 μm). *Appl. Phys. Lett.* **16**, 251 (1970).

187. C. J. Buczek, R. J. Wayne, P. Chenausky, and R. J. Freiberg, Magnetically stabilized cross-field CO_2 laser. *Appl. Phys. Lett.* **16**, 321 (1970).

188. F. Shimizu, Q-switching of N_2O and CO_2 lasers by Stark effect of ammonia. *Appl. Phys. Lett.* **16**, 368 (1970).

189. A. J. Beaulieu, Transversely excited atmospheric pressure CO_2 lasers. *Appl. Phys. Lett.* **16**, 504 (1970).

190. C. Freed and A. Javan, Standing-wave saturation resonances in the CO_2 10.6μ transitions observed in a low-pressure room-temperature absorber gas. *Appl. Phys. Lett.* **17**, 53 (1970).

191. J. R. Kenemuth, G. B. Hogge, and P. V. Avizonis, Thermal blooming of a 10.6μ laser beam in CO_2. *Appl. Phys. Lett.* **17**, 220 (1970).

192. O. R. Wood, R. L. Abrams, and T. J. Bridges, Mode locking of a transversely excited atmospheric pressure CO_2 laser. *Appl. Phys. Lett.* **17**, 376 (1970).

193. D. L. Lyon, E. V. George, and H. A. Haus, Observation of spontaneous mode locking in a high-pressure CO_2 laser. *Appl. Phys. Lett.* **17**, 474 (1970).

194. A. Mooradian, S. R. J. Brueck, and F. A. Blum, Continuous spin-flip Raman scattering in InSb. *Appl. Phys. Lett.* **17**, 481 (1970).

195. N. Karube and E. Yamaka, Mass-spectrometric studies of a sealed CO_2 laser. *J. Appl. Phys.* **41**, 2031 (1970).

196. A. M. Ronn and L. J. Schoen, Effect of substituting $^{15}N_2$ for $^{14}N_2$ in the CO_2–N_2 and N_2O–N_2 laser systems. *J. Appl. Phys.* **41**, 2246 (1970).

197. J. Freudenthal, Collision processes in a CO_2 laser plasma. *J. Appl. Phys.* **41**, 2447 (1970).

198. J. Freudenthal, Deposits in a sealed-off CO_2 laser-type discharge. *IEEE J.* **QE-6**, 507 (1970).

199. K. A. Laurie and M. M. Hale, Folded-path atmospheric pressure CO_2 laser. *IEEE J.* **QE-6**, 530 (1970).

200. N. V. Karlov, Yu. N. Petrov, A. M. Prokhorov, and O. M. Stelmakh, Dissociation of boron trichloride molecules by CO_2 laser radiation. *JETP Lett.* **11**, 135 (1970).

201. N. A. Generalov, V. P. Zimakov, G. I. Kozlov, V. A. Masyukov, and Yu. P. Raizer, Gas breakdown under the influence of longwave infrared radiation of a CO_2 laser. *JETP Lett.* **11**, 228 (1970).

202. T. Y. Chang, Accurate frequencies and wavelengths of CO_2 laser lines, *Opt. Commun.* **2**, 77 (1970).

203. P. K. Cheo and C. H. Wang, Propagation of a cavity-dumped CO_2 laser pulse through SF_6. *Phys. Rev. A* **1**, 225 (1970).

204. D. J. Booth and W. E. K. Gibbs, Carbon-dioxide dissociation in a pulsed CO_2–N_2 laser mixture. *Phys. Lett. A* **31**, 241 (1970).

205. A. S. Biryukov, B. F. Gordiets, and L. A. Shelepin, Vibrational relaxation and population inversion in the CO_2 molecule in nonstationary conditions. *Sov. Phys. JETP* **30**, 321 (1970).

Hydrogen Cyanide

206. H. A. Gebbie, N. W. B. Stone, and F. D. Findlay, A stimulated emission source at 0.34 millimetre wave-length. *Nature (London)* **202**, 685 (1964).

207. L. N. Large and H. Hill, A compact pulsed gas laser for the far infrared. *Appl. Opt.* **4**, 625 (1965).

208. L. E. S. Mathias, A. Crocker, and M. S. Wills, Laser oscillations at sub-millimetre wavelengths from pulsed gas discharges in compounds of hydrogen, carbon and nitrogen. *Electron. Lett.* **1**, 45 (1965).

209. H. P. Broida, K. M. Evenson, and T. T. Kikuchi, Comments on the mechanism of the 337-micron CN laser. *J. Appl. Phys.* **36**, 3355 (1965).
210. G. W. Chantry, H. A. Gebbie, and J. E. Chamberlain, A suggested mechanism for the 337μ CN maser. *Nature (London)*, **205**, 377 (1965).
211. W. W. Müller and G. T. Flesher, Continuous wave submillimeter oscillation in H_2O, D_2O and CH_3CN. *Appl. Phys. Lett.* **8**, 217 (1966).
212. H. A. Gebbie, N. W. B. Stone, W. Slough, and J. E. Chamberlain, Sub-millimetre maser amplification and continuous wave emission. *Nature (London)* **211**, 62 (1966).
213. H. Steffen, J. Steffen, J. F. Moser, and F. K. Kneubühl, Stimulated emission up to 0.538 mm wavelength from cyanic compounds. *Phys. Lett.* **20**, 20 (1966).
214. H. Steffen, J. Steffen, J. F. Moser, and F. K. Kneubühl, Comments on a new laser emission at 0.774 mm wavelength from ICN. *Phys. Lett.* **21**, 425 (1966).
215. H. Steffen, P. Schwaller, J. F. Moser, and F. K. Kneubühl, Mechanism of the sub-millimeter laser emissions from the CN-radical. *Phys. Lett.* **23**, 313 (1966).
216. W. Prettl and L. Genzel, Notes on the submillimeter laser emission from cyanic compounds. *Phys. Lett.* **23**, 443 (1966).
217. G. T. Flesher and W. M. Müller, Submillimeter gas laser. *Proc. IEEE* **54**, 543 (1966).
218. L. O. Hocker, A. Javan, D. R. Rao, L. Frenkel, and T. Sullivan, Absolute frequency measurement and spectroscopy of gas laser transitions in the far infrared. *Appl. Phys. Lett.* **10**, 147 (1967).
219. V. Sochor and E. Brannen, Time dependence of the power output at 337μ in a CN laser. *Appl. Phys. Lett.* **10**, 232 (1967).
220. D. R. Lide, Jr. and A. G. Maki, On the explanation of the so-called CN laser. *Appl. Phys. Lett.* **11**, 62 (1967).
221. S. Kon, M. Yamanaka, J. Yamamoto, and H. Yoshinaga, Experiments on a far infra-red CN laser. *Jap. J. Appl. Phys.* **6**, 612 (1967).
222. M. Lichtenstein, V. J. Corcoran, and J. J. Gallagher, Observation of HCN millimeter absorption in cyanide laser discharge. *IEEE J.* **QE-3**, 696 (1967).
223. L. O. Hocker, D. R. Rao, and A. Javan, Absolute frequency measurement of the 190μ and 194μ gas laser transitions. *Phys. Lett. A* **24**, 690 (1967).
224. L. O. Hocker and A. Javan, Absolute frequency measurements on new CW HCN submillimeter laser lines. *Phys. Lett. A* **25**, 489 (1967).
225. R. Turner, A. K. Hochberg, and T. O. Poehler, Multiple pulse emission from a HCN laser. *Appl. Phys. Lett.* **12**, 104 (1968).
226. A. G. Maki, Assignment of some DCN and HCN laser lines. *Appl. Phys. Lett.* **12**, 122 (1968).
227. L. O. Hocker and A. Javan, Absolute frequency measurements of new CW DCN submillimeter laser lines. *Appl. Phys. Lett.* **12**, 124 (1968).
228. L. E. S. Mathias, A. Crocker, and M. S. Wills, Spectroscopic measurements on the laser emission from discharges in compounds of hydrogen, carbon, and nitrogen. *IEEE J.* **QE-4**, 205 (1968).
229. L. O. Hocker and A. Javan, Laser harmonic frequency mixing of two different far IR laser lines up to 118μ. *Phys. Lett. A* **26**, 255 (1968).
230. V. J. Corcoran, W. T. Smith, and J. J. Gallagher, CW gain characteristics of the 890 GHz HCN laser line. *IEEE J.* **QE-5**, 292 (1969).
231. V. J. Corcoran, R. E. Cupp, and J. J. Gallagher, Frequency lock of the hydrogen cyanide laser to a microwave frequency standard. *IEEE J.* **QE-5**, 424 (1969).
232. R. E. Cupp, V. J. Corcoran, and J. J. Gallagher. Line narrowing in a phase-locked laser. *IEEE J.* **QE-6**, 241 (1970).

Nitrous Oxide
233. L. E. S. Mathias, A. Crocker, and M. S. Wills, Laser oscillations from nitrous oxide at wavelengths around 10.9μ. *Phys. Lett.* **13**, 303 (1964).

234. C. K. N. Patel, CW laser action in N_2O (N_2–N_2O system). *Appl. Phys. Lett.* **6**, 12 (1965).
235. J. A. Howe, R branch laser action in N_2O. *Phys. Lett.* **17**, 252 (1965).
236. G. Moeller and J. D. Rigden, Observation of laser action in the R-branch of CO_2 and N_2O vibrational spectra. *Appl. Phys. Lett.* **8**, 69 (1966).
237. F. Shimizu, Q-switching of N_2O and CO_2 lasers by Stark effect of ammonia. *Appl. Phys. Lett.* **16**, 368 (1970).
238. A. M. Ronn and L. J. Schoen, Effect of substituting $^{15}N_2$ for $^{14}N_2$ in the CO_2–N_2 and N_2O–N_2 laser systems. *J. Appl. Phys.* **41**, 2246 (1970).
239. N. Djeu and G. J. Wolga, Observation of new laser transitions in N_2O. *IEEE J.* **QE-5**, 50 (1969).
240. U. P. Oppenheim and P. Melman, Spectroscopic studies with a tunable N_2O laser. *J. Opt. Soc. Amer.* **60**, 332 (1970).

Carbon Disulfide
241. C. K. N. Patel, CW laser oscillation in an N_2–CS_2 system. *Appl. Phys. Lett.* **7**, 273 (1965).
242. A. G. Maki, Interpretation of the CS_2 laser transitions. *Appl. Phys. Lett.* **11**, 204 (1967).
243. N. Legay-Sommaire, Interpretation and mechanism of the CS_2–N_2 laser. *Appl. Phys. Lett.* **12**, 34 (1968).
244. D. W. Gregg and S. J. Thomas, Analysis of the CS_2–O_2 chemical laser showing new lines and selective excitation. *J. Appl. Phys.* **39**, 4399 (1968).

Carbonyl Sulfide
245. T. F. Deutsch, OCS molecular laser. *Appl. Phys. Lett.* **8**, 334 (1966).
246. R. S. Winton and W. Gordy, High precision millimeter-wave spectroscopy with the Lamb dip. *Phys. Lett. A* **32**, 219 (1970).

Water Vapor
247. H. A. Gebbie, N. W. B. Stone, F. D. Findlay, and J. A. Robb, Interferometric observations on far infra-red stimulated emission sources. *Nature* (*London*) **202**, 169 (1964).
248. A. Crocker, H. A. Gebbie, M. F. Kimmitt, and L. E. S. Mathias, Stimulated emission in the far infra-red. *Nature* (*London*) **201**, 250 (1964).
249. L. E. S. Mathias and A. Crocker, Stimulated emission in the far infra-red from water vapour and deuterium oxide discharges. *Phys. Lett.* **13**, 35 (1964).
250. W. J. Witteman and R. Bleekrode, Pulsed and continuous molecular far infra-red gas laser. *Phys. Lett.* **13**, 126 (1964).
251. W. W. Müller and G. T. Flesher, Continuous wave submillimeter oscillation in H_2O, D_2O, and CH_3CN. *Appl. Phys. Lett.* **8**, 217 (1966); Errata, *Appl. Phys. Lett.* **9**, 218 (1966).
252. D. P. Akitt, W. Q. Jeffers, and P. D. Coleman, Water vapor gas laser operating at 118-microns wavelength. *Proc. IEEE* **54**, 547 (1966).
253. W. Q. Jeffers and P. D. Coleman, Spiking and time behavior of a pulsed water-vapor laser. *Appl. Phys. Lett.* **10**, 7 (1967).
254. W. M. Müller and G. T. Flesher, Continuous-wave submillimeter oscillation in discharges containing C, N, and H or D. *Appl. Phys. Lett.* **10**, 93 (1967).
255. M. A. Pollack, T. J. Bridges, and A. R. Strnad, Central tuning dip in a submillimeter molecular laser. *Appl. Phys. Lett.* **10**, 182 (1967).
256. M. A. Pollack, T. J. Bridges, and W. J. Tomlinson, Competitive and cascade coupling between transitions in the CW water vapor laser. *Appl. Phys. Lett.* **10**, 253 (1967).
257. W. J. Tomlinson, M. A. Pollack, and R. L. Fork, Zeeman effect studies of the water-vapor laser oscillating on the $118.65\mu m$ transition. *Appl. Phys. Lett.* **11**, 150 (1967).

258. W. Q. Jeffers, Single wavelength operation of a pulsed water-vapor laser. *Appl. Phys. Lett.* **11**, 178 (1967).

259. L. Frenkel, T. Sullivan, M. A. Pollack, and T. J. Bridges, Absolute frequency measurement of the 118.6-μm water-vapor laser transition. *Appl. Phys. Lett.* **11**, 344 (1967).

260. A. Minoh, T. Shimizu, S. Kobayashi, and K. Shimoda, Far-infrared and submillimeter maser oscillators with H_2O and D_2O. *Jap. J. Appl. Phys.* **6**, 921 (1967).

261. S. F. Dyubko, V. A. Svich, and R. A. Valitov, Submillimeter CW gas laser. *JETP Lett.* **6**, 80 (1967).

262. L. O. Hocker, D. R. Rao, and A. Javan, Absolute frequency measurement of the 190μ and 194μ gas laser transitions. *Phys. Lett. A* **24**, 690 (1967).

263. W. Q. Jeffers and P. D. Coleman, The far infrared stimulated emission spectrum of D_2O. *Proc. IEEE* **55**, 1222 (1967).

264. B. Hartmann and B. Kleman, On the origin of the water-vapor laser lines. *Appl. Phys. Lett.* **12**, 168 (1968).

265. W. S. Benedict, Identification of water vapor laser lines. *Appl. Phys. Lett.* **12**, 170 (1968).

266. M. A. Pollack and W. J. Tomlinson, Molecular level parameters and proposed identifications for the CW water-vapor laser. *Appl. Phys. Lett.* **12**, 173 (1968).

267. W. Q. Jeffers, An experimental test of proposed water-vapor laser transition assignments. *Appl. Phys. Lett.* **13**, 104 (1968).

268. W. Q. Jeffers and P. D. Coleman, Relaxation phenomena in the water vapor laser. *Appl. Phys. Lett.* **13**, 250 (1968).

269. T. Kasuya and K. Shimoda, Notes on the identification of water laser lines. *Jap. J. Appl. Phys.* **7**, 782 (1968).

270. B. Hartmann, B. Kleman, and G. Spangstedt, Water vapor laser lines in the 7-μm region. *IEEE J.* **QE-4**, 296 (1968).

271. M. A. Pollack, L. Frenkel, and T. Sullivan, Absolute frequency measurement of the 220 μm water vapor laser transition. *Phys. Lett. A* **26**, 381 (1968).

272. R. Turner and T. O. Poehler, Emission from HCN and H_2O lasers in the 4 to 13 μm region. *Phys. Lett. A* **27**, 479 (1968).

273. R. A. McFarlane and L. H. Fretz, High power operation of pulsed water-vapor laser and precision wavelength measurement of the strongest component. *Appl. Phys. Lett.* **14**, 385 (1969).

274. D. P. Akitt and W. Q. Jeffers, Correlation effects in H_2O and D_2O laser transitions. *J. Appl. Phys.* **40**, 429 (1969).

275. W. S. Benedict, M. A. Pollack, and W. J. Tomlinson, III, The water-vapor laser. *IEEE J.* **QE-5**, 108 (1969).

276. T. M. Hard, F. A. Haak, and O. M. Stafsudd, Simultaneous HCN and H_2O laser emission in mixtures containing H, C, N, and O. *IEEE J.* **QE-5**, 132 (1969).

277. M. A. Pollack, Far infrared laser gain resulting from rotational perturbations. *IEEE J.* **QE-5**, 558 (1969).

278. W. J. Sarjeant and E. Brannen, Enhancement of laser action in H_2O by the addition of helium. *IEEE J.* **QE-5**, 620 (1969).

279. K. M. Evenson, J. S. Wells, L. M. Matarrese, and L. B. Elwell, Absolute frequency measurements of the 28- and 78-μm cw water vapor laser lines. *Appl. Phys. Lett.* **16**, 159 (1970).

280. K. M. Evenson, J. S. Wells, and H. E. Radford, Infrared resonance of OH with the H_2O laser: A galactic maser pump? *Phys. Rev. Lett.* **25**, 199 (1970).

CN *Radical*

281. M. A. Pollack, Laser action in optically-pumped CN. *Appl. Phys. Lett.* **9**, 230 (1966).

282. H. Steffen, J. F. Moser, and F. K. Kneubühl, Resonator modes and splitting of the 0.337 mm emission of the CN laser. *J. Appl. Phys.* **38**, 3410 (1967).

Acetylene

283. C. F. Shelton and F. T. Byrne, Laser emission near 8μ from a $H_2-C_2H_2-He$ mixture. *Appl. Phys. Lett.* **17**, 436 (1970).

Sulfur Dioxide and Hydrogen Sulfide

284. S. F. Dyubko, V. A. Svich, and R. A. Valitov, SO_2 submillimeter laser generating at wavelengths 0.141 and 0.193 mm. *JETP Lett.* **7**, 320 (1968).
285. T. M. Hard, Sulfur dioxide submillimeter laser. *Appl. Phys. Lett.* **14**, 130 (1969).
286. J. C. Hassler and P. D. Coleman, Far infrared lasing in H_2S, OCS, and SO_2. *Appl. Phys. Lett.* **14**, 135 (1969).

Boron Trichloride

287. N. V. Karlov, Yu. B. Konev, Yu. N. Petrov, A. M. Prokhorov, and O. M. Stel'makh, Laser based on boron trichloride. *JETP Lett.* **8**, 12 (1968).

Ammonia

288. L. E. S. Mathias, A. Crocker, and M. S. Wills, Laser oscillations at wavelengths between 21 and 32μ from a pulsed discharge through ammonia. *Phys. Lett.* **14**, 33 (1965).
289. J. L. Jenkins and P. E. Wagner, Microwave echoes in gaseous NH_3. *Appl. Phys. Lett.* **13**, 308 (1968).
290. T. Y. Chang, T. J. Bridges, and E. G. Burkhardt, CW laser action at 81.5 and 263.4 μm in optically pumped ammonia gas. *Appl. Phys. Lett.* **17**, 357 (1970).
291. R. G. Brewer and J. D. Swalen, Analysis of laser spectroscopy of ammonia. *J. Chem. Phys.* **52**, 2774 (1970).

CO_2 *Pumped Laser Systems*

292. T. Y. Chang and T. J. Bridges, Laser action at 452, 496 and 541 μm in optically pumped CH_3F. *Opt. Commun.* **1**, 423 (1970).
293. T. Y. Chang, T. J. Bridges, and E. G. Burkhardt, cw submillimeter laser action in optically pumped methyl fluoride, methyl alcohol, and vinyl chloride gases, *Appl. Phys. Lett.* **17**, 249 (1970).

Molecular Species: CO, CO_2, N_2O, HCl *and* HCN (*References from Journal de Chimie Physique*)

294. R. Abouaf and F. Legay, Cinétique de la vibroluminescence de CO, CO_2, N_2O excités par l'azote activé. *J. Chim. Phys.* **63**, 1393 (1966).
295. F. Legay, Excitation des molécules par transfert d'énergie vibrationnelle en phase gazeuse. *J. Chim. Phys.* **64**, 9 (1967).
296. L. Doyennette, M. Margottin-Maclow, and L. Henry, Relaxation vibrationnelle de l'oxyde de carbone. *J. Chim. Phys.* **64**, 33 (1967).
297. J. P. Kennealy, A. T. Stair, Jr., and M. H. Bruce, Kinetic behavior of the $N_2{}^+-CO$ infrared vibraluminescent system. *J. Chim. Phys.* **64**, 43 (1967).
298. A. T. Stair, Jr., J. P. Kennealy, and R. E. Murphy, A study of some inelastic processes using nitrogen and carbon monoxide. *J. Chim. Phys.* **64**, 52 (1967).
299. A. Hadni, R. Thomas, and J. Weber, Lasers pour l'infrarouge lointain. *J. Chim. Phys.* **64**, 71 (1967).
300. H. A. Gebbie, N. W. B. Stone, J. E. Chamberlain, W. Slough, and W. A. Sheraton, Generation of C.W. stimulated submillimetre waves. *J. Chim. Phys.* **64**, 80 (1967).
301. C. K. N. Patel, Recent developments in CO_2 and other molecular lasers. *J. Chim. Phys.* **64**, 82 (1967).
302. C. Rossetti, R. Farrenq, and P. Barchewitz, Lasers moléculaires a excitation haute fréquence; coefficient d'amplification et d'absorption dans les gaz excités vibrationnellement. *J. Chim. Phys.* **64**, 93 (1967).

303. P. Laures and X. Ziegler, Lasers moléculaires de grande puissance en fonctionnement continu et en impulsions. *J. Chim. Phys.* **64**, 100 (1967).
304. W. J. Witteman, Dependence of radiation production and population densities on the thermal relaxation processes in a high power molecular laser. *J. Chim. Phys.* **64**, 107 (1967).
305. F. Cabre and L. Henry, Formation des molécules d'acide chlorhydrique sur des niveaux vibrationnels excités; étude de la relaxation. *J. Chim. Phys.* **64**, 119 (1967).
306. R. Joeckle and M. Peyron, Chimiluminescence infrarouge de l'oxyde de carbone excité par l'azote activé. *J. Chim. Phys.* **67**, 1175 (1970).

CHAPTER 4

ELECTRONIC SPECTRA

4.1 Progress in Electronic Spectroscopy of Polyatomic Molecules[†]

K. Keith Innes

State University of New York
Binghamton, New York

Introduction and Scope

Many methods of characterizing electronic energy levels of polyatomic molecules have been introduced and/or significantly improved during the past 25 years. For example, optical spectroscopy—still the most generally useful method—has seen the introduction and widespread usage of high-quality, commercial diffraction gratings that make it possible to resolve rotational fine structure in the band spectra of rather large molecules on a routine basis. There is no doubt that these methods are largely responsible for the growth of the share of all of electronic spectroscopy in the program of contributed papers of the Columbus Symposium from about 10% in 1950 and before to more than 30% in 1960 and since.

In the present review, there is not space to be comprehensive in the descriptions of these methods or in the effects that they have had on the understanding of all polyatomic molecules. For the reader interested in comprehensive and critical discussion of observed spectra, the recent books by Herzberg[‡] [1] and by McGlynn *et al.* [2] (and references therein) are recommended. For those interested in general and reasonably up-to-date coverage of experimental methods, reference should be made to Samson's book [3]

---

† This work was supported by the National Science Foundation.
‡ 1971 Nobel Prize in Chemistry.

if the interest is in rapidly developing vacuum-ultraviolet techniques, and otherwise to appropriate volumes of continuing series (for example, Marton [4]). Some more specialized reviews are mentioned in the following sections.

The flavor of the period can be captured best by summarizing the present understanding of electronic states of a sampling of molecules that have been important both to theorists and to experimentalists during the past 25 years. We shall concentrate on work that has contributed to knowledge of the symmetry species and/or molecular geometries for excited states of the molecules selected.† Publications through 1970, and mostly since 1945, have been considered. However, we shall strive to minimize duplication of the discussions contained in the references given already. Occasional reinterpretations of existing data, a few unreported negative results, and some suggestions for further work will be offered.

Choosing an experimental technique for characterization of a new molecular electronic system is increasingly complex. It is no longer a question of emission versus absorption spectroscopy. Several new electron spectroscopies as well as new and older optical spectroscopies must be considered. We shall see that, for almost any one of the molecules discussed here, important contributions to the present understanding of electronic states have been made by two or more techniques. From the discussions taken collectively, the particular strengths of all techniques currently in use should stand out.

Notation will follow Mulliken's recommendations [7].

Triatomic Dihydrides
BH_2, CH_2, NH_2,
OH_2, AlH_2, SiH_2,
PH_2, SH_2, AsH_2

This important series of molecules has been relatively well-characterized by rotational analyses of high-resolution spectra. For example, Johns [8] has been able to show that the one excited state of the water molecule susceptible to such treatment is a $^1B_1$ state, for which the inertial constants and geometrical parameters differ from those of the $^1A_1$ ground state by less than 13%. Because this sort of analysis and result is emphasized in Herzberg's detailed treatise [1], we here discuss only some major themes.

These molecules are asymmetric tops in most of their states, so that *emission* spectra, even when they can be obtained (NH_2 in flames, PH_2 in discharges), are discouragingly complex. However, all but two of the nine

---

† These limitations have the effects of excluding discussion of much important work performed during the past 25 years (for example, see Dieke [5]) as well as of burgeoning fields of present activity (for example, see Eisinger [6]).

molecules are rather short-lived free radicals whose *absorption* spectra could be resolved only by means of flash photolysis [9]. The required applications of this technique have been reported almost exclusively by G. Herzberg, J. W. C. Johns, D. A. Ramsay, and their former colleagues.

Triatomic dihydrides have provided many examples of changes of shape on electronic excitation. Accordingly, they have made possible critical experimental tests of one of the several diagrams in which molecular orbital energy was plotted against bond angle by Walsh in 1953 [10], *before any of the rotational analyses were complete*. The "Walsh diagrams" have survived these and other tests, impressively.

Related to the changes of shape have been the discoveries in these spectra of two gross effects not previously observed in molecular spectroscopy, namely the Renner splitting of electronic degeneracy in linear molecules [11] and quasilinearity [12, 13]. The theories required for the analysis of spectra exhibiting either effect have been developed [14–16] and applied to these and many other molecules. (For example, later in this review, quasilinearity enters the discussion of excited states of the HCP molecule.)

Triplet and *gerade* excited states are seldom revealed by conventional methods of absorption spectroscopy, since connections with the ground state are forbidden in first order. Observations are especially difficult in the far-ultraviolet region, where the allowed electric dipole transitions are very strong. Of the several unconventional methods, so far only electron impact spectroscopy has been applied to a triatomic dihydride. Subjecting the water molecule to 30–60-eV impact energies, one may observe not only the lowest-energy (7.3 eV) peak absorption of radiation by the vapor [1], but also much structure extending from a shoulder at 6.1 eV to 4.5 eV [17–19]. Probably the latter corresponds to promotion to a triplet excited state.

It seems likely that double-photon spectroscopy eventually will reveal triatomic dihydride transitions which are forbidden for single-photon interactions, e.g., g–g transitions. However, to date, the method has been applied only to a few aromatic molecules. Accordingly, discussion is deferred to later sections.

To give an idea of the continuing interest in these species, we note other papers that have appeared since the publication of Herzberg's book: BH_2 [20], CH_2 [21], OH_2 [22], SiH_2 [23, 24], PH_2 [25, 26], SH_2 [27], AsH_2 [28].

Carbon Dioxide, Carbon Disulfide, and Their Ions CO_2, CO_2^+, CS_2, CS_2^+

These molecules (and a number of closely related ones such as BO_2 and NCO) also have been characterized mainly by fine structure analysis. They differ from the triatomic dihydrides in the important role that emission

spectra have played in the understanding of ground and excited states. Again, many of the results outlined here can be studied in greater detail in Herzberg's book [1].

The emission spectrum of CO_2^+ is rare in recalling "prehistory" at the University of Chicago where Bueso-Sanllehi [29] analyzed a $^2\Sigma_u^+ - ^2\Pi_g$ transition and Mrozowski [30, 31] analyzed $^2\Pi_u - ^2\Pi_g$ bands. Only the $^2\Sigma_u^+ - ^2\Pi_g$ analog has been analyzed for CS_2^+ [32]. The lower state is in every case taken to be the ground state and, as may be noted from the state designations, the molecule ions are linear and symmetric in each observed state.

Rotational analysis of the complex absorption of CS_2 in the region 4000–3500 Å extended over the period 1941–1964. It was suspected early and gradually proven that the molecule, linear in the ground state, was angular in this excited state [1]. The excited-state identification ($^3A_2$) only became clear upon analysis of the Zeeman effect on the fine structure [33]. Less extensive rotational analysis of another and stronger absorption in the region 2200–1800 Å showed that the transition moment is parallel to the axis of smallest inertia (a), that is, that the upper state is $^1B_2$ [34].

Very recently, the first successfully interpreted level-crossing experiment with a polyatomic molecule led to determination of the product of the radiative lifetime and the Landé g factor of the heavily perturbed second excited state (3200 Å) of CS_2 [35].

It is not surprising that the analog of the spin-forbidden $^3A_2 - ^1\Sigma_g^+$ transition of CS_2 is not seen in absorption in the lighter CO_2 molecule. The first known absorption by CO_2 rises gradually from 1750 Å to a maximum at 1475 Å. Probably the 0–0 band is too weak to be observed and the maximum of intensity corresponds to a large upper-state vibrational quantum number. Therefore, the Franck–Condon principle implies a change of shape, as was found for CS_2. Unfortunately, the absorption bands are diffuse and some understanding of vibrational and rotational structural detail has been possible only for the near-ultraviolet *emission* from low vibrational levels of the same excited state [36]. Though the structure is exceedingly complex, it seems consistent with identification of the upper state as $^1B_2$.

All the foregoing experimental results are in accord with Walsh's orbital energy diagram for AB_2 molecules [10]. However, this diagram is based largely on the prior knowledge that while CO_2^+ and CO_2 are linear in their ground states, NO_2 is not. Its success is accordingly not as startling as was that of the AH_2 diagram.

Rydberg series have been observed for most of the molecules to be discussed in this review. Usually, diffuseness of the spectra has precluded identification of the corresponding excited states. However, the ground states of CO_2^+ and CS_2^+ have been characterized by the work already described. It is therefore only necessary to observe a Rydberg series of CO_2 (or CS_2) with an

ionization limit which shows a doubling equal to the spacing of the two components of the $^2\Pi_g$ ground state of CO_2^+ (or CS_2^+) in order to identify the latter as the "excited state" of CO_2 (or CS_2). This has been done at 111 060 and 111 240 cm^{-1} for the CO_2 absorption spectrum [37]. Similarly, higher Rydberg limits of CO_2 have been found to correspond to the known *excited* states of CO_2^+, and Rydberg limits in the absorption spectrum of CS_2 agree with the known states of CS_2^+ [1].

The unambiguous ionization data of the preceding paragraph allow critical tests of data from the newly capitalized technique of photoelectron spectroscopy. Peak separations of photoelectron spectra of CO_2 and CS_2 must correspond to level differences of CO_2^+ and CS_2^+ [38].

Acetylene
C₂H₂

No emission spectrum has been attributed with certainty to the acetylene molecule, but the ultraviolet absorption spectrum is rich. It is fairly typical of polyatomic absorptions in beginning with a weak, sharp system at lowest energies (in this case below about 50 000 cm^{-1}) and continuing with stronger, more diffuse systems at higher energies (compare Fig. 1). Further typical behavior is that the strongest absorption is assigned to fairly long Rydberg series whose bands are sharper than any except those of the lowest-energy system.

Although the Rydberg states of acetylene could be located in Price's early and extensive studies of such states [39], no excited states could be characterized as to point-group symmetry, molecular geometry, and vibrational assignments until after 1950. Then, it was proved by analysis of vibrational and rotational structure of the bands between 2500 and 2100 Å that in the excited state the carbon–carbon bond is 15% longer than in the ground state [40, 41]. This result might seem normal in light of many years of experience with rather fully analyzed spectra of diatomic molecules. At the time, the unique and surprising aspect of the analyses was that the excited-state molecule was found (from the derived moments of inertia) to be *trans* bent (planar). However, this change of shape on electronic excitation proved to have been a harbinger as other small molecules (such as those already discussed) were studied in the later 1950's. Indeed, for acetylene itself, *vibrational* structures of two other band systems suggest changes of shape [42].

The observed rotational selection rules for the 2500 Å absorption were $\Delta K = \pm 1$, where K is the approximate quantum number for rotation about the (nearly prolate) top axis of the excited-state molecule. A small surfeit of rotational lines following the selection rules of $\Delta K = 0$ and ± 2 was later shown quantitatively to be the natural result of the appreciable "switching" of the inertial axis system attendant to such a large change of geometry [43].

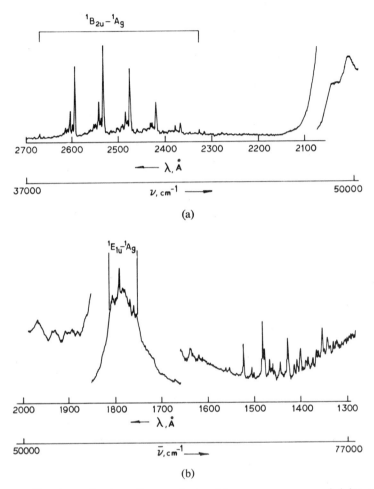

FIG. 1. The electronic absorption spectrum of benzene vapor, recorded by a 1-m, double-beam spectrometer. Breaks in the curve indicate changes of absorbing path. The strongest absorption, at 1800 Å, required a pressure-path of only 0.4 Torr-cm, while the weakest absorption detected, at 2600 Å, required 30 Torr-cm. As explained in the text, the experimental assignments of the sharp bands at 1800 Å and at 2600 Å are based on rotational analyses of analogous bands of simple substituted benzenes. The sharp bands at 1800 Å are superimposed on a strong continuum and are the "parents" of a Rydberg series that can be seen converging to the ionization potential at 1342 Å (9.247 eV).

In further detail, the rotational selection rules are those of band type C, which proves that the transition moment direction is perpendicular to the plane of the excited-state molecule. The excited electronic state must accordingly be ^1A_u.

A good example of strides made in vacuum-ultraviolet spectroscopy

during the past 25 years is the work of Herzberg on the only other rotational analysis to date of the acetylene transitions. He found that the Rydberg transition at 1250 Å is $^1\Pi_u$–$^1\Sigma_g{}^+$, that is, the transition moment polarization is perpendicular to the molecular axis, and there is no change of shape or "switching of axes" [44].

Recently, electron-impact spectroscopy has revealed transitions not found in the earlier, optical work. Electrons at low energies show two forbidden transitions, both assumed to be triplet–singlet, at 5.2 and 6.1 eV [45]. Electrons at intermediate energies reveal peaks at 6.35 and 6.49 eV which show a large decrease in intensity with scattering angle. These peaks are thought *not* to correspond to triplet–singlet transitions [46].

Boron Trifluoride
BF₃

Although electronic states of the 31-electron free radical BOF_2 have been characterized [47], *no conventional electronic spectrum has been assigned to BF_3*, a molecule with 32 electrons. It has remained for photoelectron spectroscopy to offer information about the highest occupied orbitals of BF_3 [48, 49]. Of course, the differences of peaks in the photoelectron spectra are characteristic of $BF_3{}^+$, so that it is of some interest to compare them with those found in the emission spectrum of the isoelectronic species, BOF_2.

A likely interpretation of the BOF_2 spectrum [47] which has been advanced by Dixon *et al.* [50] is that the ground ($^2B_2$) and first excited ($^2B_1$) states are separated by 0.7 eV. This compares closely with the first difference in the photoelectron spectrum of BF_3. From the agreement, we conclude that analogous states are involved. Now, BOF_2 belongs to point group C_{2v}, while $BF_3{}^+$ may be assumed to belong to point group D_{3h}. The ground state of $BF_3{}^+$ may therefore be either $^2E'$ or $^2A_2{}'$, while its first excited state may be either $^2E''$ or $^2A_2{}''$. This is in agreement with the correlations of Walsh [10] and with recent quantum calculations [51], though not with the deductions of Bassett and Lloyd [49] who have concluded that the reverse order of states is correct. Their conclusion was based on relative intensities of the first two peaks of their photoelectron spectrum. However, especially on account of overlap of these two peaks, we prefer the assignments based on the energy separation of the peaks.

Formaldehyde
H₂CO

Formaldehyde has two excited electronic states which exhibit sufficiently fine structure to permit the kind of characterization wanted here. (Higher,

Rydberg states are also observed, with some vibrational detail.) Those two states offer examples of many different and important phenomena, some of them only very recently understood in detail.

Fundamental understanding of the finer details of the spectrum really began after Walsh concluded from his far-reaching considerations of molecular orbitals [10] that the first orbital promotion should render the formaldehyde molecule slightly nonplanar, such that inversion doubling energy levels might be observed. Brand [52] achieved an essential understanding of the irregular vibrational structure of the stronger of the two systems (3500 Å) on this basis (see Fig. 2). Robinson [54] showed more directly that the molecule

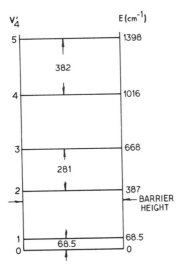

FIG. 2. Scale drawing of inversion doublets as observed in the excited $^1A_2$ state of the 3500 Å bands of D_2CO [53]. If the data are fitted to a potential function of the form $V(Q_4) = \frac{1}{2}\lambda Q_4^2 + A \exp(-a^2 Q_4^2)$, the height of the barrier to inversion through a planar configuration is $339\ cm^{-1}$ (See also Jones and Coon [53a]).

was nonplanar in the upper state of the stronger system by focusing attention on the inertial defect, $\Delta = I_c - I_a - I_b$, which he found to be negative. Robinson and DiGiorgio found the characteristic inversion doublets also for the upper state of the weaker, 3800 Å system [55].

Later rotational analysis [56] and a study of the electric field splitting of some rotational lines [57] showed that the weak 0–0 band of the 3500 Å system arises from a *magnetic dipole* transition moment parallel to the carbon–oxygen bond, the first example to be established in a polyatomic molecule. Most of the intensity of this "forbidden" system is vibrationally induced by mixing with at least two higher-lying electronic transitions (the Herzberg–Teller effect). Accordingly, each of the three possible band types (A, B, and C) is observed and each of the six fundamental vibrational frequencies of the excited $^1A_2$ state† could be established [53].

---

† The symmetry classification of energy levels for this nonrigid molecule is somewhat subtle but has been discussed by Job *et al.* [53].

The 3800 Å transition was long assumed to be the triplet analog of the 3500 Å transition. However, it was not until 1964 that the theory of rotational transitions associated with a triplet–singlet transition of an asymmetric top was published, by Hougen [58]. He found that for $\Delta S \neq 0$, unlike $\Delta S = 0$, the apparent band type is *not* simply related to the transition moment polarization. (The polarization depends upon the singlet state from which the triplet gains singlet character, via spin–orbit mixing [59, 60]). Hougen gave appropriate rotational selection rules and intensity expressions. Raynes [61] was then able to complete the rotational analysis of the 3800 Å system, showing that the electronic assignment is $^3A_2$–$^1A_1$ and that the intensity is in this case "borrowed" by spin–orbit mixing of the $^3A_2$ state and a $^1A_1$ excited state.

Recently, electric field (Stark) splittings have been measured in both band systems of formaldehyde, and electric-field-induced intensity has been studied in the singlet–singlet system. The dipole moment derived from the data for the $^1A_2$ state is 1.5 D [62, 63], while that derived for the $^3A_2$ state is 1.3 D [64]. These values are lower than the ground-state dipole moment by about 40%, in qualitative agreement with the assignment of the excited states to a π^*–n excitation [65].

Although the fluorescence emission of formaldehyde vapor from the $^1A_2$ state was useful in Brand's vibrational analysis of the 3500 Å transition, it has been little studied since. Now that many $^1A_2$ rovibronic levels are assigned, lasers should be tuned to a variety of the levels so that lifetimes can be measured as functions of quantum numbers.† In addition, rotational analyses of fluorescence bands would offer an unusual opportunity to study strong perturbations among high vibrational levels of a molecular ground state.

Ethylene
C₂H₄

No emission spectrum of the ethylene molecule has been identified, but its absorption spectrum has been the subject of much speculation and some striking experiments. Gas-phase experiments have included high-resolution vacuum-ultraviolet and photoelectron spectroscopy, electron-impact spectroscopy, and a low-resolution absorption spectrum of a mixture of C_2H_4 and O_2, at 50 and 25 atm pressure, respectively. Condensed-phase experiments have included observation of a weak long-wavelength limit of absorption at 3400 Å by use of a 1m absorbing path of the liquid, and studies of single crystals of ethylene and of an alkane-substituted ethylene [66]. Except for the last of these, all have been summarized in useful detail by Merer and Mulliken [67], who give also an extensive review of the quantum theory of the ethylene molecule, and more than 100 references.

---

† Note added in proof: Initiation of such work on H_2CO has been reported. See C. B. Moore and E. S. Yeung, *J. Amer. Chem. Soc.* **93**, 2059 (1971).

There is no unambiguous experimental evidence about the orbital assignments of the diffuse bands of the two lowest-energy absorptions of ethylene.† (Controversy about the vibrational structure in the higher-energy system has been summarized [69] and may not yet be settled [70].) However, maximum intensities are observed very far from the estimated origins. It therefore is assumed that there is a large difference of geometry between excited-state and ground-state molecules, consistent with a transition between valence-shell states.

A more satisfactory empirical picture may be summarized for the Rydberg transition that starts at 1750 Å, owing to the facts that the bands are sharper than those seen at lower energies and that the 0–0 band is one of the strongest of the system. A reasonable vibrational analysis has been published [71]. Activity of the out-of-plane twisting vibration has been confirmed, and vibrational spacings and intensities have been analyzed. They indicate that the ethylene molecule is nonplanar (point group D_2) at equilibrium in the upper electronic state, being twisted by about 25°, with a potential barrier of about 290 cm^{-1} to inversion through the planar configuration (compare Fig. 2). In addition, activity of the C—C stretching vibration indicates that the C—C bond length increases by 6% in this transition. The additional possible complication that the two CCH$_2$ groups are each pyramidal rather than planar, that is, that the excited-state molecule belongs to point group C_1, was not discussed [71].

A fairly secure determination of the polarization of the 1750 Å transition has been achieved [71] as follows; although the 0–0 bands of C_2H_4 and C_2D_4 exhibit no useful rotational features, the 2–0 bands of v_2, which, according to this vibrational assignment, have the same polarization as the 0–0 bands, each exhibit two heads. The spacings and estimated relative intensities of the two heads seem to agree best with a vibronic transition moment perpendicular to the plane of the ground-state molecule. If this can be substantiated by detailed computer simulation of the observed band contour (a method discussed at the end of the section on benzene), and it can be understood why the two 0–0 bands do not show double heads, the transition may be assigned as $^1B_{3u}$–^1A_g. The Rydberg orbital assignment is discussed by Merer and Mulliken [67].

It is of interest that in very recent studies of polarized reflection spectra of single crystals of bicyclohexylidene [66], no strong absorption polarized perpendicular to the plane (or indeed to the C—C bond) was detected above 1724 Å. We will not discuss other spectra of substituted ethylenes since they have been reviewed thoroughly [67].

---

† Unfortunately, the diffuseness is even more marked in the spectra of simple substituted ethylenes. For example, cis-difluoroethylene exhibits only continua in the two longest-wave absorptions observed, namely 1775–2100 Å and 1550–1670 Å [68] (see also [67]).

As for acetylene, electron-impact spectroscopy has revealed a transition of C_2H_4 not found in the earlier, optical work. It lies at 7.45 eV and has been attributed to an electric quadrupole transition [46, 72]. In addition, the triplet–singlet transition observed optically only under strenuous conditions seems to have been found in electron-impact spectra [73, 74].

Ethane
C_2H_6

Until 1966, it was generally believed that the ultraviolet absorption spectrum of gaseous ethane, which begins near 1400 Å, was structureless [1]. Two papers since then emphasized that, actually, ethane is the only one of the *n*-alkane molecules that *does* show sharp features in this region [75, 76].† It was found that the 0–0 band of C_2D_6 exhibits a distinctive rotational contour [78]. Computer simulation of the contour proved that the transition moment lies perpendicular to the C—C bond; the electronic transition is $^1E_u-^1A_g$ [78]. Electronic angular momentum was detected in the excited state. Further, it was deduced from the linewidths needed to reproduce the observed contour that the lifetime of C_2D_6 in the zero level of the excited state is about 10^{-11} sec. The transition is unique so far in being associated with the promotion of a C—H bonding electron. This is assumed to account for a large reduction in the C—H stretching frequency (with a consequent 731 cm^{-1} shift of 0–0 band on per-deutero substitution), as well as for the short lifetime.

Electron impact spectra of C_2H_6 and C_2D_6 have been reported in the 50–180-eV range of impact energies and at scattering angles to 9° [79]. These seem similar to the optical absorptions except that the rotational contour of C_2D_6 could not be resolved. Indeed, the conclusions from a quite detailed consideration of vibrational structure are consistent with those of the preceding paragraph. It should be emphasized, however, that not enough information has been obtained from the combined efforts of optical and electron spectroscopy to determine completely the geometric structure of the ethane molecule in any excited electronic state.

Benzene
C_6H_6

The emission and absorption spectra of this important molecule were discussed thoroughly by Herzberg [1] and also by Dunn [80]. Most of the 120 references of the latter review deal with excited electronic states; yet the only experimentally secure conclusions were: (1) The first, very weak absorption,

---

† Very recently, it has been reported that cyclopentane and cyclohexane bands near 1750 Å exhibit rotational contours [77].

at 3400 Å, is to a triplet state [2, 80a]. (2) The second absorption system, at 2600 Å (see Fig. 1, certainly the most famous polyatomic spectrum), is symmetry-forbidden, the classic case of vibronically allowed structure arranged about a missing 0–0 band [81, 82, 83]. The transition very probably is $^1B_{2u}-^1A_g$, but the best evidence for this is found not in benzene itself but in substituted benzenes, for which the substitutional perturbations seem slight. For example, in chlorobenzene the 0–0 band is active and has been studied for the vapor [84, 85] and (with polarized light) for the crystal [86]. The band type (vapor) requires, and the polarization (crystal) is consistent with, a transition moment in-plane and perpendicular to the axis of symmetry. For benzene, the excited-state molecule remains a planar symmetric rotor in which the major difference from the ground state is a carbon–carbon distance which is 0.037 Å longer. This follows both from Franck–Condon analysis of relative intensities in the main vibrational progression [87] and from rotational analysis [88]. (3) Rydberg series (see Fig. 1), which are found between 1750 and 1350 Å, extrapolate to an ionization potential 9.247 eV [89], in agreement with the value found by photoionization [90] and, later, by photoelectron spectroscopy [91].

We now summarize in somewhat greater detail the definitive activity of the four or five years since the earlier reviews [1, 80] were completed.

Colson and Bernstein [92] have found another excited state by studying the absorption spectrum of a crystal at 4.2°K. The addition of O_2 causes intensification of absorption, an effect that is expected if we assume that the excited state is triplet [80]. This new state lies about 7500 cm^{-1} above the lowest triplet and just below the lowest excited singlet state. Low-energy electron-impact studies agree with this location for a second triplet state [93, 94]. A third triplet state has been located in triplet–triplet absorption experiments [95].

Vibrational structure of a 2100 Å system has been studied in greater detail than before, for both benzene and deuterated benzenes, and both in solid Ar, Kr, Xe, and N_2 at 4–20°K [96] and as a vapor at 200°K [97]. Analysis suggests the assignment $^1B_{1u}-^1A_g$. The negative result of no two-photon spectrum in this region argues also (by elimination of the two-photon-allowed $^1E_{2g}-^1A_g$ alternative) for a $^1B_{1u}$ excited state [98]. Electron-impact studies [46] suggest that there may be *two* electronic transitions in this region.

It is commonly assumed that Rydberg bands move to high energies, that is, "disappear" into inaccessible regions of the spectrum, or are otherwise modified, when the molecules in question are frozen into a cold, dense solution. Indeed, the "disappearance" of intensity upon condensation is often taken as a sufficient condition for assignment to a Rydberg transition and vice versa. It appears, however, that the principle should be applied cautiously; experimental evidence for the observation of Rydberg transitions of benzene in solid Ar, Kr, and Xe has been presented recently [99].

As was mentioned earlier, bands of benzene vapor are assigned unambiguously to Rydberg transitions by extrapolation to an independently known ionization potential (Fig. 1). Unfortunately, the bands are too diffuse for rotational analysis. Again, one must make use of a substituted compound to define the transition moment direction. In pyrazine-d_4 (1,4-diazabenzene-d_4), the Rydberg parent of Fig. 1 is not shifted by the "substitution," while the strong continuum under it in the figure is shifted to 1600 Å, an energy nearly 1 eV higher than in benzene. The 0–0 band exhibits a distinct rotational contour which has been shown by computer simulation to correspond to a transition $^1B_{2u}-^1A_g$, with a moment in-plane and perpendicular to the line of the two nitrogen atoms [100]. In the absence of specific evidence for benzene, we conclude by analogy that the 1800 Å transition of benzene is $^1E_{1u}-^1A_g$.

Several times earlier in this review [78, 84, 85, 88] we have mentioned computer simulation of band contours (see also the caption of Fig. 3). This is a technique which has had a rapid growth during the past seven years and therefore merits explanation here. Its importance arises from the general failure to resolve individual rotational transitions in the bands of large and/or predissociated molecules. Such a band often may be analyzed for the polarization of the transition moment and information about the excited-state molecular geometry, even if only two or three peaks of the band are resolved. A computer is desirable for the process of computing band contours (using various combinations of rotational selection rules and moments of inertia) until one is obtained which closely resembles the observed contour. If the molecule is a large, asymmetric rotor, the computer is *required*. The first asymmetric rotor computer program for this purpose was written by Parkin [101], and several other versions have been put to good use since. The pyrazine-d_4 band analysis of the preceding paragraph was the first application of Parkin's program. This excited pyrazine-d_4 molecule has the three undesirable qualities that make full resolution of fine structure impossible and computer simulation essential; it is a large, predissociated, asymmetric rotor.

A useful review of band contour analyses of aromatic molecules has been written by Ross [102].

Methinophosphide and Pyrazine
HCP and p-C₄H₄N₂

From the examples considered so far, it could be correctly concluded that it is rare for more than one of the many excited electronic states of a polyatomic molecule to have been characterized experimentally, even to the extent of our modest requirement of identification of state symmetry species. To underline the ideal scope of electronic spectroscopy it seems worthwhile to emphasize briefly the two molecules for which the largest number of states

have been so characterized, namely HCP (the phosphorous analog of HCN) and *p*-diazabenzene. Not the least striking aspect of these molecules is that their spectra had not even been reported at the time of the first Columbus meeting. In fact, the first *preparation* of HCP was reported in 1961.

These examples are useful also because of the contrast in their spectroscopic histories. Seven excited states of HCP all have been assigned by the classic and unambiguous method of high-resolution, gas-phase spectroscopy, and are reported by Johns *et al.* in a single paper [103] which also contains information about the molecular geometry and vibrations of each state. We summarize in Table I. One of the more interesting aspects of HCP is its "quasilinear"

TABLE I

Molecular shape	State symmetry	Energy (v_{vac}, cm^{-1})
Nonlinear	$^1A'$	40 247.6
Linear	$^3\Pi_i$	35 976.3
Linear	$^1\Pi$	35 926.9
Nonlinear	$^1A''$	34 745.6
Linear	$^3\Sigma^-$	31 023.9
Linear	$^3\Pi_r$	30 430
Linear	$^3\Sigma^+$	24 440
Linear	$^1\Sigma^+$	0

character in some of the excited states; some vibrational bending displacements are so large that it probably will be possible to fit the observed levels only through the use of a recently published theory which uses a curvilinear bending coordinate rather than the usual rectilinear one [15].

By contrast, in order to assign seven excited states of pyrazine, it has been necessary to combine the results of many papers and the methods of both vapor-phase and solid-state spectroscopy. For example, although rotational fine structure fixes the transition moment of the 3200 Å absorption as perpendicular to the molecular plane, the 2600 Å transition exhibits no rotational structure. However, the direction of the 2600 Å transition moment *relative* to the known direction of that for the 3700 Å transition has been determined by a method of photoselection of absorbing (and subsequently phosphorescing) molecules from a random sample in a rigid glass. It is found that the transition moment for 3700 Å emission is perpendicular to that for 2600 Å absorption, which requires that the latter be perpendicular to the line of the nitrogen atoms, corresponding to a $^1B_{2u}$–^1A_g transition [104].†

† The work is summarized in the context of a description of the method of photoselection by Goodman and Hollas [105]. The original point of view of the experiment was to determine the transition moment direction for the 3700 Å transition, *assuming* that at 2600 Å. However, there is now independent evidence about the moment at 3700 Å [106–111], so that it is interesting instead to use the result to remove the assumption about the 2600 Å transition.

Complete summaries of the analyses for pyrazine and other azines have been published [112]. Important problems remain, just as for HCP. In addition, because of the several methods used, some controversies arise. One that has been considered recently is the possibility that the molecular geometry in the excited state of the 3200 Å system is not planar [113]. The evidence considered is the 3200 Å fluorescence spectrum of pyrazine in a benzene host crystal, measured at 4.2°K; there is observed an unexpected peak which must be attributed to two quanta of an antisymmetric mode. Earlier, this band was recorded also in the "hot" bands of the high-resolution absorption spectrum of the vapor [114, 115], where it could be given an unambiguous assignment to $2v_5''$, that is, two quanta of an out-of-plane hydrogen-bending vibration. The observation of $2v_5''$ was interpreted by Hochstrasser and Marzzacco as implying a tendency to nonplanarity in the excited state [113]. However, there is an even more likely interpretation, namely Fermi resonance in the ground state. If one uses the vapor-phase observations [116–118], high Franck–Condon intensity in a totally symmetric mode $(v_{6a}'' + v_{9a}'')$ is found within 11 cm^{-1} of the 0–2 band of v_5 of pyrazine-d_0 and within 27 cm^{-1} of the 0–2 band of pyrazine-d_4. Indeed, the observed intensities indicate that $3v_{6a}''$, at slightly lower frequencies, also is involved in the resonance.

More positive evidence is found by consideration of the high-dispersion measurements of bands on both sides of the 0–0 band [117]. Fortunately, v_5 is active in mixing the excited electronic state, ${}^eB_{3u}$, with a second excited state, ${}^eB_{1u}$, so that transitions with $\Delta v = \pm 1$ are allowed by the Herzberg–Teller selection rules [1]. The 1–0 and 0–1 bands are strong and of different type from the 0–0 band, as expected. Other $\Delta v = \pm 1$ bands are relatively weak, but stand out from the thousands of weak bands because of their contrasting rotational structure. Vibrational intervals are thus well-defined in both states, as set out in Table II. For example, consider the (2–1) band of Table II:

TABLE II

DESLANDRES TABLE FOR TYPE A AND ASSOCIATED TYPE C BANDS^a
PYRAZINE-d_0 (v_5)

v_5'	$v_5'' = 0$	$v_5'' = 1$	$v_5'' = 2$
	919.2	919.5	
0	30 875.8 $(C, 50)$	29 956.6 $(A, 3)$	29 037.1 $(C, 0)$
	382.6	383.9	383.5
1	31 258.4 $(A, 20)$	30 340.5 $(C, 4)$	29 420.6 $(A, 0)$
	387.0	385.8	(386)
2	31 645.4 $(C, 3)$	30 726.3 $(A, 2)$	—
			(390)
3	—	—	30 197.4 $(A, 0)$

^{a} Frequencies (v_{vac}, cm^{-1}) are those of the sharpest edges in the bands. Band types and estimated relative intensities are in parentheses.

The closest alternative choices from bands of the correct type are at frequencies 62 cm^{-1} lower or 286 cm^{-1} higher than the frequency chosen, 30,726 cm^{-1}.

Clearly, the 2–0 band of the table is no stronger than is expected for a frequency which is reduced from 919 cm^{-1} in the ground state to 383 cm^{-1} in the excited state. In addition, the upper-state differences show only a moderate and regular anharmonicity. (Contrast Fig. 2, a well-established case of nonplanarity.) We conclude that the activity of v_5 does not arise from nonplanarity of the molecule. All that is known in detail about the geometry change is that the nitrogen atoms are about 5 % closer together in the excited state than in the ground state [119].

A second remaining problem about pyrazine is the need for identification of an observed ionization potential with the nitrogen lone-pair electrons. Even photoelectron spectroscopy has so far not managed an unambiguous identification [120, 121].

Naphthalene
$C_{10}H_8$

Because of the low vapor pressures of the polycyclic aromatic molecules, their vapor-phase absorption spectra are seldom displayed. However, Morris and co-workers recently measured the vapor spectrum of $C_{10}H_8$ between 30 000 and 70 000 cm^{-1}. Singlet–singlet transitions with observed 0–0 bands at 32 020, 35 910, and 47 530 cm^{-1} were shown [122]. The transition probabilities expressed as f-values are 0.002, 0.102, and 1.3, respectively. Below 2000 Å, each of five Rydberg series was found to converge to the ionization potential 8.13$_6$ eV [123].

The knowledge of triplet states of naphthalene has been reviewed critically [2]. Their approximate locations are 21 000, 45 000, and 60 000 cm^{-1}. The first is observed by EPR or in phosphorescence emission, in condensed phases. The others are observed in triplet–triplet absorption experiments, starting from the lowest triplet level, at 21 000 cm^{-1}. These triplet–triplet experiments are still revealing new excited states, for example one at 38,500 cm^{-1} [124].

Very recently, the singlet manifold has been extended. Pulsed laser spectroscopy has made possible absorption spectroscopy between excited-state singlets [125]. A new *gerade* state, at about 55 300 cm^{-1}, is indicated. An electron-impact spectrum [93] shows a strong peak at 5.4 eV or 44 000 cm^{-1} which could correspond to the second triplet noted above. However, two-photon spectroscopy of liquid 1-*chloro*naphthalene has revealed states of even parity at 37 700 cm^{-1} and 42 600 cm^{-1} [98]. The *gerade* state of naphthalene corresponding to the second of these may be the electron-impact state, in which case it would of course *not* be a triplet state.

Having listed all electronic energy values so far established for naphthalene, we turn now to our major preoccupation, which is with more positive electronic assignments and information about changes of geometry.

The 21 000-cm^{-1} transition is well-established as $^3B_{1u}$–^1A_g, most convincingly by EPR spectroscopy of the excited state [126], but also through measurements of the polarization of phosphorescence [127, 128]. All such studies have been of samples in rigid media, where the lifetime for emission to the ground state is a few seconds [2] and the three components of the triplet state (in the absence of a magnetic field) lie at -0.066, $+0.019$, and 0.047 cm^{-1} [2].

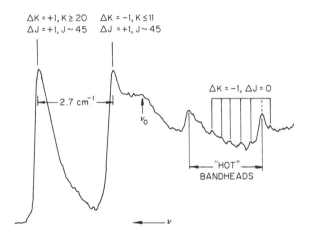

FIG. 3. Rotational structure in the 1–0 band of naphthalene at 32,458 cm^{-1}: reproduced from a microphotometer tracing of a photograph made with a commercial 3.4-m spectrograph. The detailed assignments indicated by leading lines are results of a band contour analysis [130]. Since the molecule is an asymmetric rotor, the prolate symmetric rotor quantum number K is used only as a convenient index. Nearly 10^5 rotational transitions contribute to this 1 Å section of the naphthalene spectrum! They follow selection rules which prove that the vibronic transition moment lies along the central carbon–carbon bond (perpendicular to the electronic transition moment).

McClure [129] studied two transitions by dissolving less than 0.5 mole% $C_{10}H_8$ in the transparent solvent tetramethyl benzene (durene). At 77°K the $C_{10}H_8$ molecules have known orientations in the crystal so that the directions of absorption of polarized light can be meaningful. McClure found that the 32 000-cm^{-1} transition was polarized perpendicular to the central C—C bond and in the plane of the molecule ($^1B_{2u}$–^1A_g) and that the 36 000-cm^{-1} transition is polarized parallel to that C—C bond ($^1B_{1u}$–^1A_g). The first result is confirmed by band contour analysis [130, 131] (see Fig. 3). Although such confirmation is very desirable (on account of possible perturbations by "host" crystals), it does not seem possible for the 0–0 band of the 36 000-cm^{-1}

system because of a diffuseness [132] which is rather characteristic of the second singlet–singlet absorption systems of large polyatomic molecules.

On the basis of measured vibrational intensities in the systems, simplified Franck–Condon calculations for the 32 000- and 36 000-cm^{-1} transitions of $C_{10}H_8$ were carried out by McCoy and Ross [133]. Sign and magnitude choices for changes of internuclear distances were made with the help of orbital theory. The small and irregular changes in C—C bond lengths suggested by their calculations will not be discussed in detail. However, when band contours were calculated assuming the McCoy–Ross model for the $^1B_{2u}$ excited state, impressive reproductions of the observed contours (e.g., Fig. 3) were obtained [130]. From this experience, one may gain some confidence in the Franck–Condon results not only for naphthalene but for the similar systems of anthracene that were considered [133].

Vibrational assignments were of course a prerequisite for the Franck–Condon calculations. This was particularly crucial for the 32 000-cm^{-1} system, for which most of the intensity is vibrationally induced. Fortunately, the assignments were well-based in that case [131]. The vibrational structure in the 36 000-cm^{-1} system is much less well understood [132] for reasons that cast some doubt on a Franck–Condon analysis; McClure and Wessel have recently studied irregularities of vibrational structure in the vicinity of this 0–0 band and have concluded that they are caused by perturbations of the vibronic levels of the $^1B_{1u}$ state by those of the $^1B_{2u}$ state [134]. (The apparent diffuseness in this region may have the same cause.)

It does not seem to have been noted that data exist for the 32 000-cm^{-1} transition which make possible a test of the theory of temperature dependence of vibrationally induced intensity [135, 136]. Since this test should help us to estimate more prescisely the ratio of induced to "allowed" intensity, we consider it briefly. The dependence has the form: $f(T) = f_0 + f_1 \coth(hc\nu/2kT)$, in which f_0 is independent of temperature and f_1/f_0 represents the ratio at 0°K of the vibronic intensity to the purely electronic intensity. The frequency of the vibration that induces intensity is denoted by ν (cm^{-1}), in this case 506 cm^{-1} [131]. The f-values for 93, 193, 293, and 333°K may be calculated from curves measured for solutions of naphthalene in alcohol [137], and they fit the equation for $f(T)$ to within 2%. The ratio f_1/f_0 is found to be 3.4, which is reasonable judged by previous estimates based on relative intensities of vibrational bands within the system, near room temperature [131] and at 20°K [129].

The 45 000-cm^{-1} excited state has been studied by triplet–triplet polarization measurements of naphthalene in durene crystals [138], and by photoselection [139], and found to be $^3B_{3g}$.

Some indication that the 47 530-cm^{-1} state is $^1B_{2u}$ has been found in polarization studies of crystalline naphthalene absorption [140]. However, it appears that this will be difficult to check; photographs of the absorption

bands of the vapor have been made using a 21-ft, concave grating spectrograph. With the exception of very broad and diffuse bands at 2170 Å and 2060 Å, only continuous absorption was found [141]. No band contour analysis was possible.

Although no detailed assignments of Rydberg systems of naphthalene have been reported, some apparent sharp edges of Rydberg bands have been interpreted in terms of interesting perturbations between intravalence ($\pi^*-\pi$) and extravalence (Rydberg) excitations [142].

Anthracene
$C_{14}H_{10}$

Spectra of the vapor of anthracene [143–146] have yielded little fundamental information about its excited electronic states: only that the f-values of the first two singlet–singlet transitions, at 3800 and 2500 Å, are 0.02 and 0.93, respectively [144], and that the ionization potential (from Rydberg bands) is 7.15 eV [143]. However, no molecule has been studied more frequently as a pure or mixed solid. Often, crystals have been studied because of interest in intermolecular effects on electronic states rather than in the states of the free molecule [147]. Discussion here will be confined to that smaller body of work which leads to conclusions about the free molecule.

The 2500 Å system of anthracene was examined in absorption with polarized light in the pure crystal by Craig [148]. Observed crystal splittings and intensities were accounted for in detail by assignment of the system as $^1B_{2u}-^1A_g$. Similarly, the weaker, 3800 Å transition was found to be $^1B_{1u}-^1A_g$ [149]. These two transitions often are described as long-axis (y) polarized and short-axis (z) polarized, respectively.

An emission spectrum at 6800 Å is attributed to the lowest-lying triplet state of anthracene [2]. Recently, a study of the Zeeman effect on the 0–0 band of a single crystal has been reported [150]. The excited state was found to be $^3B_{1u}$.

Anthracene has served as a testing ground for slowly developing techniques of the optical absorption spectroscopy of molecules in excited triplet [151–156] and singlet [156] states. For the triplet–triplet absorption of anthracene in benzophenone at 4425 Å, a measured polarization ratio indicates long-axis polarization, that is, that the transition is $^3B_{3g}-^3B_{1u}$ [155]. Kliger and Albrecht [156] found that a frequency doubled ruby laser, exciting anthracene at 3472 Å, allows observation of a singlet–singlet absorption of a polarized beam from a xenon flash lamp. From the preceding paragraphs, we know that the laser must have excited anthracene into the $^1B_{1u}$ state. It was found that the absorption from the $^1B_{1u}$ state is polarized parallel to the fluorescence from it. Thus, the new singlet state, lying 6.2 eV above the ground state, must be

assigned as ^1A_g. It should be emphasized that the new ^1A_g state would be observable by direct transition from the ground state only in double-photon absorption or by electron-impact spectroscopy.

Conclusion and Outlook

In any single year, progress in electronic spectroscopy is likely to be termed steady but not spectacular. A survey of the past 25 years has been more reassuring. We have seen that almost all detailed knowledge of excited electronic states of polyatomic molecules so far achieved has been produced in those years.

It should be clear from the examples discussed that progress in this field was controlled by advances in instrumentation. Of foremost importance were advances in diffraction grating spectrographs [157] and electron spectrometers [158, 159]. Also very important were the amassing of detailed knowledge of electronic ground states [160, 161] and the development and application of recording spectrophotometers, flash photolysis [9], cryogenics, electron spin resonance [2], and high-speed computers [102].

One should not, however, slight the contributions of theorists of this period, neither those concerned with the theoretical apparatus necessary for the interpretation of raw experimental data (such as rotational fine structure), nor those concerned with systematizing knowledge of electronic structures of molecules. Although it is true that much basic theory was developed in the 1930's, notably by Mulliken† and Teller and their colleagues [1], we have seen that appreciable extensions have been essential to the understanding of the more recent and detailed results. A notable example of extension of the interpretive apparatus was the work of Hougen, Pople, and Longuet-Higgins on the Renner–Teller effect [14]. Outstanding systematization of electronic structure and spectra can be found in the contributions of Kasha [162], Platt [163], and Walsh [10] to the literature of the first decade of our history.

It may be expected that progress in the future will have prerequisites similar to those just described. Indeed, some of the instrumental developments are already underway; applications of lasers and fast recording systems to studies of excited electronic states are assured. It seems that easily the most promising of these for optical transitions is saturated absorption or "Lamb-dip" spectroscopy [164–166]. Since, by this technique, linewidths may be achieved which are but a small fraction of those heretofore observed, further information should be extractable from many of the spectra discussed above. In addition, ability and courage to deal with larger molecules than before may develop among high-resolution spectroscopists. Along similar, if more modest, lines it may be hoped that the potential of the Fabry–Perot etalon as a very high-resolution and high-luminosity device will be realized at last [167].

† 1966 Nobel Prize in Chemistry.

For full exploitation of these new experiments, there may be needed new developments in the theory of line shapes, particularly in the case of saturated absorption.

There exist fluorescence techniques which, like saturated absorption, feature absence of Doppler broadening and the consequent possibility of observation of fine and hyperfine structure, with or without laser excitation [168, 169]. Some of these techniques have been applied recently to diatomic molecules (see also Mills and Zare [35], on CS_2), but it seems unlikely that they will have the *general* applicability to polyatomic molecules of the two methods of the preceding paragraph.

Among lower-resolution experiments that one may hope will be useful in the characterization of excited electronic states of rather simple molecules, typical examples are circular dichroism and magnetic circular dichroism [170]. Recently, the former has been extended to wavelengths below 1700 Å [171]. These examples are also typical in needing further development of the theory for unambiguous interpretation of measurements.

Already, both theorists and experimentalists are organizing a determined attack on the problem of decay of electronic excitation in polyatomic molecules [134]. Ideally, this effort should result in detailed understanding of such topics as predissociation and chemical isomerization.

Finally, it is noted that during the past 10 years quantum mechanical calculations of some excited-state properties of some diatomic molecules have achieved surprising reliability. May we hope that it will be possible to say the same of calculations for some polyatomic molecules within the coming 25 years?

References

1. G. Herzberg, "Molecular Spectra and Molecular Structure." III. "Electronic Spectra and Electronic Structure of Polyatomic Molecules." Van Nostrand-Reinhold, Princeton, New Jersey, 1966.
2. S. P. McGlynn, T. Azumi, and M. Kinoshita, "Molecular Spectroscopy of the Triplet State." Prentice-Hall, Englewood Cliffs, New Jersey, 1969.
3. J. A. R. Samson, "Techniques of Vacuum Ultraviolet Spectroscopy." Wiley, New York, 1967.
4. L. Marton, ed. *Methods Exp. Phys.* 3 (1962); 4 (1967).
5. G. H. Dieke, "Spectra and Energy Levels of Rare Earth Ions in Crystals." Wiley (Interscience), New York, 1968.
6. J. Eisinger, *Nature (London)*, **226**, 113 (1970).
7. R. S. Mulliken, *J. Chem. Phys.* **23**, 1997 (1955).
8. J. W. C. Johns, *Can. J. Phys.* **41**, 209 (1963).
9. G. Porter, *Nobel Lecture Chem.* (1967).
10. A. D. Walsh, *J. Chem. Soc.* pp. 2260, 2266, 2288, 2296, 2301, 2306 (1953); see also, *Annu. Rep. Progr. Chem.* **63**, (1966).
11. K. Dressler and D. A. Ramsay, *J. Chem. Phys.* **27**, 971 (1957).
12. D. A. Ramsay, *Nature (London)*, **178**, 374 (1956).
13. R. N. Dixon, *Trans. Faraday Soc.* **60**, 1363 (1964).

14. J. T. Hougen, Interactions between electronic, vibrational and rotational motions. *In* "Physical Chemistry, An Advanced Treatise" (D. Henderson, ed.), Vol. IV. Academic Press, New York, 1970.
15. J. T. Hougen, P. R. Bunker, and J. W. C. Johns, *J. Mol. Spectrosc.* **34**, 136 (1970); J. Pliva, *Collect. Czech. Chem. Commun.* **23**, 1839, 1846 (1958).
16. J. W. C. Johns, *Can. J. Phys.* **45**, 2639 (1967).
17. A. Skerbele, M. A. Dillon, and E. N. Lassettre, *J. Chem. Phys.* **49**, 5042 (1968).
18. H. Larzul, F. Gélebart, and A. Johannin-Gilles, *C. R. Acad. Sci.* **261**, 4701 (1965).
19. D. Lewis and W. H. Hamill, *J. Chem. Phys.* **51**, 456 (1969).
20. G. Herzberg and J. W. C. Johns, *Proc. Roy. Soc. Ser. A* **298**, 142 (1967).
21. G. Herzberg and J. W. C. Johns, *Proc. Roy. Soc. Ser. A* **295**, 107 (1966).
22. C. R. Brundle and D. W. Turner, *Proc. Roy. Soc. Ser. A* **307**, 27 (1968) (Photoelectron spectrum).
23. I. Dubois, G. Herzberg, and R. D. Verma, *J. Chem. Phys.* **47**, 4262 (1967).
24. I. Dubois, *Can. J. Phys.* **46**, 2485 (1968).
25. R. N. Dixon, G. Duxbury, and D. A. Ramsay, *Proc. Roy. Soc. Ser. A* **296**, 137 (1967).
26. B. Pascat, J. M. Berthou, J. C. Prudhomme, H. Guenebaut, and D. A. Ramsay, *J. Chim. Phys. Physicochim. Biol.* **65**, 2022 (1968) (Emission spectrum).
27. J. Delwiche and P. Natalis, *Chem. Phys. Lett.* **5**, 564 (1970) (Photoelectron spectrum).
28. R. N. Dixon, G. Duxbury, and H. M. Lamberton, *Proc. Roy. Soc. Ser. A* **305**, 271 (1968).
29. F. Bueso-Sanllehi, *Phys. Rev.* **60**, 556 (1941).
30. S. Mrozowski, *Phys. Rev.* **60**, 730 (1941); **62**, 270 (1942); **72**, 682, 691 (1947).
31. S. Mrozowski, *Rev. Mod. Phys.* **14**, 216 (1942).
32. J. H. Callomon, *Proc. Roy. Soc. Ser. A* **244**, 220 (1958).
33. A. E. Douglas and E. R. V. Milton, *J. Chem. Phys.* **41**, 357 (1964).
34. A. E. Douglas and I. Zanon, *Can. J. Phys.* **42**, 627 (1964).
35. J. W. Mills and R. N. Zare, *Chem. Phys. Lett.* **5**, 37 (1970).
36. R. N. Dixon, *Discuss. Faraday Soc.* **35**, 105 (1963); *Proc. Roy. Soc. Ser. A* **275**, 431 (1963).
37. Y. Tanaka, A. S. Jursa, and F. J. LeBlanc, *J. Chem. Phys.* **32**, 1199 (1960).
38. M. I. Al-Joboury, D. P. May, and D. W. Turner, *J. Chem. Soc.* p. 6350 (1965); *J. Chem. Phys.* **46**, 1156 (1967).
39. W. C. Price, *Phys. Rev.* **47**, 444 (1935).
40. C. K. Ingold and G. W. King, *J. Chem. Soc.* p. 2702 (1953).
41. K. K. Innes, *J. Chem. Phys.* **22**, 863 (1954).
42. P. G. Wilkinson, *J. Mol. Spectrosc.* **2**, 387 (1958).
43. J. T. Hougen and J. K. G. Watson, *Can. J. Phys.* **43**, 298 (1965).
44. G. Herzberg, *Discuss. Faraday Soc.* **35**, 7 (1963).
45. S. Trajmar, J. K. Rice, P. S. P. Wei, and A. Kupperman, *Chem. Phys. Lett.* **1**, 703 (1967).
46. E. N. Lassettre, A. Skerbele, M. A. Dillon, and K. J. Ross, *J. Chem. Phys.* **48**, 5066 (1968).
47. C. W. Mathews and K. K. Innes, *J. Mol. Spectrosc.* **15**, 199 (1965); **19**, 203 (1966).
48. R. J. Boyd and D. C. Frost, *Chem. Phys. Lett.* **1**, 649 (1968).
49. P. J. Bassett and D. R. Lloyd, *Chem. Commun.* p. 36 (1970).
50. R. N. Dixon, G. Duxbury, R. C. Mitchell, and J. P. Simons, *Proc. Roy. Soc. Ser. A* **300**, 405 (1967).
51. D. R. Armstrong and P. G. Perkins, *Chem. Commun.* p. 856 (1969).
52. J. C. D. Brand, *J. Chem. Soc.* p. 858 (1956).
53. V. A. Job, V. Sethuraman, and K. K. Innes, *J. Mol. Spectrosc.* **30**, 365 (1969); **33**, 189 (1970).

53a. V. T. Jones and J. B. Coon, *J. Mol. Spectrosc.* **31**, 137 (1969).
54. G. W. Robinson, *Can. J. Phys.* **34**, 699 (1956).
55. G. W. Robinson and V. E. DiGiorgio, *Can. J. Chem.* **36**, 13 (1958); *J. Chem. Phys.* **31**, 1678 (1959).
56. J. H. Callomon and K. K. Innes, *J. Mol. Spectrosc.* **10**, 166 (1963).
57. J. R. Lombardi, D. E. Freeman, and W. Klemperer, *J. Chem. Phys.* **46**, 2746 (1967).
58. J. T. Hougen, *Can. J. Phys.* **42**, 433 (1964).
59. D. S. McClure, *J. Chem. Phys.* **17**, 665 (1949).
60. S. I. Weissman, *J. Chem. Phys.* **18**, 232 (1950).
61. W. T. Raynes, *J. Chem. Phys.* **44**, 2755 (1966).
62. D. E. Freeman and W. Klemperer, *J. Chem. Phys.* **45**, 52 (1966).
63. N. J. Bridge, D. A. Haner, and D. A. Dows, *J. Chem. Phys.* **48**, 4196 (1968).
64. A. D. Buckingham, D. A. Ramsay, and J. Tyrrell, *Can. J. Phys.* **48**, 1242 (1970).
65. R. S. Mulliken, *J. Chem. Phys.* **3**, 564 (1935).
66. P. A. Snyder and L. B. Clark, *J. Chem. Phys.* **52**, 998 (1970).
67. A. J. Merer and R. S. Mulliken, *Chem. Rev.* **69**, 639 (1969).
68. W. L. Greer and K. K. Innes, Unpublished work (1964).
69. A. J. Merer and R. S. Mulliken, *J. Chem. Phys.* **50**, 1026 (1969).
70. R. McDiarmid, *J. Chem. Phys.* **50**, 1794 (1969).
71. A. J. Merer and L. Schoonveld, *Can. J. Phys.* **47**, 1731 (1969).
72. K. J. Ross and E. N. Lassettre, *J. Chem. Phys.* **44**, 4633 (1966).
73. A. Kupperman and L. M. Raff, *Discuss. Faraday Soc.* **35**, 30 (1963).
74. J. P. Doering and A. J. Williams, III, *J. Chem. Phys.* **47**, 4180 (1967).
75. J. W. Raymonda and W. T. Simpson, *J. Chem. Phys.* **47**, 430 (1967).
76. B. A. Lombos, P. Sauvageau, and C. Sandorfy, *J. Mol. Spectrosc.* **24**, 253 (1967).
77. S. Bell, R. Davidson, G. D. Gray, and P. A. Warsop, *Chem. Phys. Lett.* **5**, 214 (1970).
78. E. F. Pearson and K. K. Innes, *J. Mol. Spectrosc.* **30**, 232 (1969).
79. E. N. Lassettre, A. Skerbele, and M. A. Dillon, *J. Chem. Phys.* **49**, 2382 (1968).
80. T. M. Dunn, The spectrum and structure of benzene. *In* " Studies of Chemical Structure and Reactivity " (J. H. Ridd, ed.). Methuen, London, 1966.
80a. M. S. de Groot and J. H. van der Waals, *Mol. Phys.* **6**, 545 (1963).
81. A. Sklar, *J. Chem. Phys.* **5**, 669 (1937).
82. H. Sponer, G. Nordheim, A. Sklar, and E. Teller, *J. Chem. Phys.* **7**, 207 (1939).
83. C. K. Ingold, H. G. Poole, and A. P. Best, *J. Chem. Soc.* pp. 406, 417, 427, 433, 440, 456, 461, 475, 483, 491, 508 (1948).
84. T. Cvitas and J. M. Hollas, *Mol. Phys.* **18**, 101 (1970).
85. H. D. Bist, V. N. Sarin, A. Ojha, and Y. S. Jain, *Spectrochim. Acta Part A* **26**, 841 (1970); *Appl. Spectrosc.* **24**, 292 (1970).
86. G. V. Klimusheva, A. F. Prikhot'ko, and G. M. Soroka, *Opt. Spektrosk.* **25**, 361 (1968).
87. D. P. Craig, *J. Chem. Soc.* p. 2146 (1950).
88. J. H. Callomon, T. M. Dunn, and I. M. Mills, *Phil. Trans. Roy. Soc. London Ser. A* **259**, 499 (1966).
89. P. G. Wilkinson, *Can. J. Phys.* **34**, 596 (1956).
90. K. Watanabe, *J. Chem. Phys.* **22**, 1564 (1954).
91. F. I. Vilesov, B. L. Kurbatov, and A. N. Terenin, *Sov. Phys. Dokl.* **6**, 490 (1961).
92. S. D. Colson and E. R. Bernstein, *J. Chem. Phys.* **43**, 2661 (1965).
93. R. N. Compton, R. H. Huebner, P. W. Reinhardt, and L. G. Christophorou, *J. Chem. Phys.* **48**, 901 (1968).
94. J. P. Doering, *J. Chem. Phys.* **51**, 2866 (1969).
95. T. S. Godfrey and G. Porter, *Trans. Faraday Soc.* **62**, 7 (1966).
96. B. Katz, M. Brith, B. Sharf, and J. Jortner, *J. Chem. Phys.* **52**, 88 (1970).

97. J. H. Smith, D. M. Burland, and G. W. Robinson, To be published.
98. P. R. Monson and W. M. McClain, *J. Chem. Phys.* **53**, 29 (1970).
99. B. Katz, M. Brith, B. Sharf, and J. Jortner, *J. Chem. Phys.* **50**, 5195 (1969).
100. J. E. Parkin and K. K. Innes, *J. Mol. Spectrosc.* **15**, 407 (1965).
101. J. E. Parkin, *J. Mol. Spectrosc.* **15**, 483 (1965).
102. I. G. Ross, *Advan. Chem. Phys.* **20**, 341 (1971).
103. J. W. C. Johns, H. F. Shurvell, and J. K. Tyler, *Can. J. Phys.* **47**, 893 (1969).
104. V. G. Krishna and L. Goodman, *J. Chem. Phys.* **36**, 2217 (1962).
105. L. Goodman and J. M. Hollas, Electronic spectra of polyatomic molecules. *In* " Physical Chemistry, An Advanced Treatise " (D. Henderson, ed.), Vol. III. Academic Press, New York, 1969.
106. A. E. Douglas, *Discuss. Faraday Soc.* **35**, 235 (1963).
107. L. E. Giddings and K. K. Innes, *Discuss. Faraday Soc.* **35**, 192, 237 (1963).
108. M. Chowdhury and D. S. McClure, *Symp. Mol. Struct. Spectrosc, Columbus, Ohio, 1964*; R. M. Hochstrasser and T. -S. Lin, *J. Chem. Phys.* **53**, 2676 (1970).
109. B. S. Snowden and W. H. Eberhardt, *J Mol. Spectrosc.* **18**, 372 (1965).
110. L. Cheng and A. L. Kwiram, *Chem. Phys. Lett.* **4**, 457 (1969).
111. M. Sharnoff, *Chem. Phys. Lett.* **2**, 498 (1968).
112. K. K. Innes, J. P. Byrne, and I. G. Ross, *J. Mol. Spectrosc.* **22**, 125 (1967); K. K. Innes, *Amer. J. Phys.* **34**, 306 (1966).
113. R. M. Hochstrasser and C. A. Marzzacco, *in* " Molecular Luminescence " (E. C. Lim, ed.). Benjamin, New York, 1969.
114. K. K. Innes, J. D. Simmons, and S. G. Tilford, *J. Mol. Spectrosc.* **11**, 257 (1963).
115. K. K. Innes and J. A. Merritt, *J. Mol. Spectrosc.* **23**, 281 (1967).
116. J. D. Simmons, Ph.D. Thesis, Vanderbilt Univ., Nashville, Tennessee, 1963.
117. S. G. Tilford, Ph.D. Thesis, Vanderbilt Univ., Nashville, Tennessee, 1962.
118. M. Ito, R. Shimada, T. Kuraishi, and W. Mizushima, *J. Chem. Phys.* **26**, 1508 (1957).
119. K. K. Innes, *Proc. Int. Conf. Spectrosc., Bombay, 1968*, p. 135, Department of Atomic Energy, Government of India; A. H. Kalantar and K. K. Innes, To be published.
120. A. D. Baker, D. Betteridge, N. R. Kemp, and R. E. Kirby, *Chem. Commun.* p. 286 (1970).
121. L. Asbrink, E. Lindholm, and O. Edqvist, *Chem. Phys. Lett.* **5**, 609 (1970).
122. G. A. George and G. C. Morris, *J. Mol. Spectrosc.* **26**, 67 (1968).
123. J. G. Angus, B. J. Christ, and G. C. Morris, *Aust. J. Chem.* **21**, 2153 (1968).
124. W. H. Melhuish, *J. Chem. Phys.* **50**, 2779 (1969).
125. R. Bonneau, J. Faure, and J. Joussot-Dubien, *Chem. Phys. Lett.* **2**, 65 (1968). [Observed also in nanosecond, pulse radiolysis experiments by J. K. Thomas, *J. Chem. Phys.* **51**, 770 (1969)].
126. C. A. Hutchinson, Jr. and B. W. Mangum, *J. Chem. Phys.* **29**, 952 (1958); **34**, 908 (1961). Confirmed recently in an interpretation of the Zeeman effect on the visible absorption system, by R. H. Clarke and R. M. Hochstrasser, *J. Chem. Phys.* **49**, 3313 (1968).
127. H.-J. Czekalla, W. Liptay, and E. Döllefield, *Ber. Bunsenges. Phys. Chem.* **68**, 80 (1964).
128. R. M. Hochstrasser and S. K. Lower, *J. Chem. Phys.* **40**, 1041 (1964).
129. D. S. McClure, *J. Chem. Phys.* **22**, 1668 (1954); **24**, 1 (1956).
130. K. K. Innes, J. E. Parkin, D. K. Ervin, J. M. Hollas, and I. G. Ross, *J. Mol. Spectrosc.* **16**, 406 (1965).
131. D. P. Craig, J. M. Hollas, M. F. Redies, and S. C. Wait, *Phil. Trans. Roy. Soc. London Ser. A* **253**, 543 (1961).
132. H. Sponer and C. D. Cooper, *J. Chem. Phys.* **23**, 646 (1955).

133. E. F. McCoy and I. G. Ross, *Aust. J. Chem.* **15**, 573 (1962).
134. D. S. McClure and J. Wessel, quoted by J. Jortner, S. A. Rice, and R. M. Hochstrasser, *Advan. Photochem.* **7**, 175 (1969).
135. A. C. Albrecht, *J. Chem. Phys.* **33**, 169 (1960); *Int. Spectrosc. Conf, Tokyo, Japan, 1962*, Paper B-313.
136. L. L. Lohr, Jr., *J. Chem. Phys.* **50**, 4596 (1969).
137. R. Passerini and I. G. Ross, *J. Chem. Phys.* **22**, 1012, Fig. 1 (1954).
138. D. P. Craig and G. Fischer, *Proc. Chem. Soc. London* p. 176 (1964).
139. M. A. El-Sayed and T. Pavlopoulos, *J. Chem. Phys.* **39**, 834 (1963); see, in addition, *J. Chem. Phys.* **53**, 4230 (1970).
140. A. Bree and T. Thirunamachandran, *Mol. Phys.* **5**, 397 (1962).
141. E. F. Pearson, Ph.D. Thesis, Vanderbilt Univ., Nashville, Tennessee (1969).
142. J. Jortner and G. C. Morris, *J. Chem. Phys.* **51**, 3689 (1970).
143. J. G. Angus and G. C. Morris, *J. Mol. Spectrosc.* **21**, 310 (1966).
144. J. Ferguson, L. W. Reeves, and W. G. Schneider, *Can. J. Chem.* **35**, 117 (1957).
145. J. P. Byrne and I. G. Ross, *Can. J. Chem.* **43**, 3253 (1965).
146. J. E. Haebig, *J. Mol. Spectrosc.* **25**, 117 (1968).
147. W. H. Wright, *Chem. Rev.* **67**, 581 (1967).
148. D. P. Craig, *J. Chem. Soc.* p. 539 (1955), see also L. Clark, *J. Chem. Phys.* **51**, 5719 (1969); **53**, 4093 (1970).
149. D. P. Craig and P. C. Hobbins, *J. Chem. Soc.* p. 2309 (1955).
150. R. H. Clarke and R. M. Hochstrasser, *J. Chem. Phys.* **46**, 4532 (1967); see also R. H. Clarke, *J. Chem. Phys.* **52**, 2328 (1970).
151. D. S. McClure, *J. Chem. Phys.* **19**, 670 (1951).
152. D. P. Craig and I. G. Ross, *J. Chem. Soc.* p. 1589 (1954).
153. G. Porter and F. J. Wright, *Trans. Faraday Soc.* **51**, 1205 (1955).
154. M. W. Windsor, The triplet state: *Proc. Int. Symp. Univ. of Beirut, February 1967* (A. B. Zahlan, *et al.*, ed.). Cambridge Univ. Press, London and New York, 1967.
155. R. M. Hochstrasser and A. P. Marchetti, *Chem. Phys. Lett.* **1**, 597 (1968).
156. D. S. Kliger and A. C. Albrecht, *J. Chem. Phys.* **50**, 4109 (1969); **53**, 4059 (1970).
157. R. C. M. Learner, *J. Sci. Instrum.* [2] **1**, 589 (1968).
158. R. S. Berry, *Annu. Rev. Phys. Chem.* **20**, 357 (1969).
159. K. Siegbahn, "ESCA Applied to Free Molecules." North-Holland Publ., Amsterdam, 1969.
160. J. E. Wollrab, "Rotational Spectra and Molecular Structure." Academic Press, New York, 1967.
161. E. B. Wilson, Jr., J. C. Decius, and P. C. Cross, "Molecular Vibrations." McGraw-Hill, New York, 1955.
162. M. Kasha, *Discuss. Faraday Soc.* **9**, 14 (1950).
163. J. R. Platt, "Systematics of the Electronic Spectra of Conjugated Molecules: A Source Book—Papers of the Chicago Group 1949–64." Wiley, New York, 1964.
164. G. R. Hanes and C. E. Dahlstrom, *Appl. Phys. Lett.* **14**, 362 (1969).
165. M. Kroll, *Phys. Rev. Lett.* **23**, 631 (1969).
166. P. R. Bunker, *In* "Molecular Spectroscopy: Modern Research" (K. N. Rao and C. W. Mathews, eds.). Academic Press, New York, 1972.
167. M. Kroll and K. K. Innes, *J. Mol. Spectrosc.* **36**, 295 (1970).
168. A. Corney and G. W. Series, *Proc. Phys. Soc. London* **83**, 207, 213 (1964).
169. W. W. Smith and A. Gallagher, *Phys. Rev.* **145**, 26 (1966).
170. P. N. Schatz and A. J. McCaffery, *Quart. Rev. Chem. Soc.* **23**, 552 (1969).
171. O. Schnepp, E. F. Pearson, and E. Sharman, *J. Chem. Phys.* **52**, 6424 (1970); *Rev. Sci. Instrum.* **41**, 1136 (1970).

Note Added in Proof†

H_2O
1. J. W. C. Johns, *Can. J. Phys.* **49**, 944 (1971). Cf. [8].
2. S. Trajmar, W. Williams, and A. Kupperman, *J. Chem. Phys.* **54**, 2274 (1971).
3. D. M. Bishop and A. A. Wu, *J. Chem. Phys.* **54**, 2917 (1971).

H_2S
J. Delwiche and P. Natalis, *Int. J. Mass Spectrom. Ion Phys.* **5**, 443 (1970). Cf. [27].

CH_2
G. Herzberg and J. W. C. Johns, *J. Chem. Phys.* **54**, 2276 (1971). Cf. [21].

PH_2
J. Berthou and B. Pascat, *C.R. Acad. Sci. C* **271** (14), 799 (1970).

CO_2
D. Andrick and F. H. Read, *J. Phys. B* **4**, 389 (1971).

CS_2
1. R. M. Hochstrasser and D. A. Wiersma, *J. Chem. Phys.* **54**, 4165 (1971).
2. L. Bajema, M. Gouterman, and B. Meyer, *J. Phys. Chem.* **75**, 2204 (1971).
3. V. Y. Foo, C. E. Brion, and J. B. Hasted, *Proc. Roy. Soc. Ser. A* **322**, 535 (1971). (Also CO_2).

$CO_2{}^+$
T. T. Basiev, Y. I. Malakhov, and S. N. Tsys, *Opt. Spektrosk.* **30**, 421 (1971).

C_2H_2
A. N. Petelin, *Opt. Spektrosk.* **29**, 1153 (1970).

BF_3
1. D. R. Lloyd and P. J. Bassett, *J. Chem. Soc. A* p. 1551 (1971). Cf. [49].
2. T. E. H. Walker and J. A. Horsley, *Mol. Phys.* **21**, 939 (1971).
3. W. Hayes and F. C. Brown, *J. Phys. B* **4** (10), L85 (1971).

H_2CO
1. M. J. Weiss, C. E. Kuyatt, and S. Mielczarek, *J. Chem. Phys.* **54**, 4147 (1971).
2. J. Solomon, C. Jonah, P. Chandra, and R. Bersohn, *J. Chem. Phys.* **55**, 1908 (1971).
3. S. D. Peyerimhoff, R. J. Buenker, W. E. Kammer, and H. Hsu, *Chem. Phys. Lett.* **8**, 129 (1971).
4. G. H. Kirby and K. Miller, *J. Mol. Struct.* **8**, 373 (1971).
5. C. G. Stevens, A. M. Garcia, and J. C. D. Brand, *J. Amer. Chem. Soc.* **93**, 7098 (1971).
6. J. E. Mentall, E. P. Gentieu, M. Krauss, and D. Neumann, *J. Chem. Phys.* **55**, 5471 (1971).

C_2H_4
1. M. J. Hubin–Franskin, and J. E. Collin, *Int. J. Mass Spectrom. Ion Phys.* **5**, 163 (1970). Cf. [72–74].
2. G. R. Branton, D. C. Frost, T. Makita, C. A. McDowell, and I. A. Stenhouse, *Phil. Trans. Roy. Soc. London, ser. A* **268**, 77 (1970).
3. H. Basch, V. McKoy, and T. Shibuya, *J. Chem. Phys.* **53**, 1628 (1970); **54**, 1738 (1971).
4. R. J. Buenker, S. D. Peyerimhoff, W. E. Kammer, *J. Chem. Phys.* **55**, 814 (1971).

† We take this opportunity to add to the currency of the bibliographies for the molecules discussed in this review.

C_2H_6

1. E. E. Koch and M. Skibowski, *Chem. Phys. Lett.* **9**, 429 (1971).
2. A. D. Baker, D. Betteridge, N. R. Kemp, and R. E. Kirby, *J. Mol. Struct.* **8**, 75 (1971).

C_6H_6

1. J. G. Angus and G. C. Morris, *Mol. Cryst. Liquid Cryst.* **11**, 309 (1970). Cf. [99].
2. A. A. Givaiz, M. A. El-Sayed, and D. S. Tinti, *Chem. Phys. Lett.* **9**, 454 (1971).
3. M. Brith, R. Lubart, and I. T. Steinberger, *J. Chem. Phys.* **54**, 5104 (1971).
4. C. S. Parmenter and G. H. Atkinson, *J. Phys. Chem.* **75**, 1564, 1572 (1971).
5. J. H. van der Waals, A. M. D. Berghius, and M. S. de Groot, *Mol. Phys.* **21**, 497 (1971).

HCP

J. G. Moehlmann, A. Hartford, and J. R. Lombardi. To be published. Cf. [103].

$P-C_4H_4N_2$

1. L. H. Hall, Jr. and M. A. El-Sayed, *J. Chem. Phys.* **54**, 4958 (1971).
2. A. D. Baker and D. W. Turner, *Phil. Trans. Roy. Soc. London, Ser. A* **268**, 131 (1970). Cf. [120, 121].
3. R. Gleiter, E. Heilbronner, and V. Hornung, *Angew. Chem. Int. Ed. Engl.* **9**, 901 (1970). Cf. [120, 121].
4. L. H. Hall, Jr., D. Owens, and M. A. El-Sayed, *Molec. Phys.* **20**, 1025 (1971).
5. M. Hackmeyer and J. L. Whitten, *J. Chem. Phys.* **54**, 3739 (1971).
6. C. Fridh, L. Åsbrink, B. Ö. Jonsson, and E. Lindholm. To be published. Cf. [121].

$C_{10}H_8$

1. J. G. Angus and G. C. Morris, *Mol. Cryst. Liquid Cryst.* **11**, 257 (1970). *Aust. J. Chem.* **24**, 173 (1971). Cf. [123].
2. T. Pavlopoulos, *J. Chem. Phys.* **53**, 4230 (1970). Cf. [139].
3. J. M. Hollas and S. N. Thakur, *Mol. Phys.* **22**, 203 (1971). Cf. [130].

$C_{14}H_{10}$

1. C. Ting, *J. Chin. Chem. Soc. (Taipei)* **17**, 128 (1970). Cf. [150].
2. B. E. Cook and P. G. Le Comber, *J. Phys. Chem. Solids* **32**, 1321 (1971).
3. J. P. Larkindale and D. J. Simkin, *J. Chem. Phys.* **55**, 5668 (1971).

General

1. D. W. Turner, C. Baker, A. D. Baker, and C. R. Brundle, "Molecular Photoelectron Spectroscopy." Wiley (Interscience), New York, 1970.
2. K. Sarka, *J. Mol. Spectrosc.* **38**, 545 (1971). Cf. [15].
3. P. R. Bunker and J. M. R. Stone, *J. Mol. Spectrosc.* To be published. Cf. [15].
4. J. P. Byrne and I. G. Ross, *Aust. J. Chem.* **24**, 1107 (1971).
5. W. Gordy and R. L. Cook, "Microwave Molecular Spectra." Wiley (Interscience), New York, 1970.
6. R. W. Redding, *J. Mol. Spectrosc.* **38**, 396 (1971).
7. C. di Lauro, *J. Mol. Spectrosc.* **40**, 103 (1971).
8. G. Herzberg, "The Spectra and Structures of Simple Free Radicals," Cornell Univ. Press, Ithaca, New York, 1971.
9. B. Meyer, "Low-Temperature Spectroscopy," Amer. Elsevier, New York, 1971.
10. A. A. Lamola (ed.), "Creation and Detection of the Excited State," Marcel Dekker, New York, 1971.

4.2 Rotational Line Strengths: The O_2^+ b $^4\Sigma_g^-$–a $^4\Pi_u$ Band System[†]

Richard N. Zare

Department of Chemistry
Columbia University
New York, New York

Introduction

In 1928, Condon [1] presented a quantum formulation of what has become known as the Franck–Condon principle.[‡] He was able to show that the intensity distribution of the vibrational bands within an electronic transition was largely controlled by the square modulus of the vibrational overlap integral, the so-called Franck–Condon factor. It is interesting to note that in the same year Hill and Van Vleck [2] derived a determinental equation for the energy levels of diatomic molecules intermediate between Hund's case (a) and case (b). The eigenvalue–eigenvector solutions to this equation were used to calculate line strength factors that control the intensities of the rotational lines within an individual vibrational band. Hill and Van Vleck's results were originally for doublet electronic states, but could be easily generalized to electronic states of any multiplicity (see, for example, Budó and others [3]). Thus, no longer than two years after the birth of the new quantum mechanics of de Broglie, Schrödinger, Born, Heisenberg, and Jordan, the theoretical basis underlying the intensity features of diatomic spectra had been developed. It is sobering to realize that during the more than 40 years since that time there have been relatively few quantitative comparisons between theory and experiment.

No doubt, in large measure this lack has been caused by the difficulty of obtaining reliable intensity data and the labor involved in performing realistic numerical calculations from theory. Moreover, it might be objected that surely the principles of quantum mechanics had been tested more rigorously

---

[†] Dedicated to E. U. Condon on the occasion of his retirement from formal teaching duties at the University of Colorado.

[‡] For an enjoyable account of this discovery see Condon [1a].

long ago by other means, and based on these celebrated successes, the theoretical predictions of molecular intensity factors must be essentially correct. However, this would overlook the fact that what is really being tested is not quantum mechanics so much as the validity of the Born–Oppenheimer approximation [4]† by which we separate the nuclear and electronic motions of the molecule. If we recall that the fine structure splittings of multiplet states come about from relativistic and magnetic interactions that lie outside the usual Born–Opppenheimer framework [4],† then we realize that there is good reason to expect that theory will fail at some level of comparison with experiment, and that the deviations can be used to give us better insight into the real molecular dynamics. Moreover, quantitative intensity studies and their proper theoretical interpretation are potentially of much importance since they provide direct information about the populations of particular molecular quantum states, and hence, the kinetics or thermodynamics of the molecular source under study.

We present here for the O_2^+ a $^4\Sigma_g^-$–b $^4\Pi_u$ first negative band system a comparison of the rotational line strengths deduced from the relative plate blackenings reported by Nevin [6] and by Nevin and Murphy [7] with those calculated numerically from the Hill–Van Vleck treatment. A computer program has been written that, in addition to the spin–orbit interaction, takes into account the spin–spin interaction, the spin–rotation interaction, and the centrifugal distortion. However, the latter effects are shown to exert little influence on the magnitude of the rotational line strengths. If appropriate sums of the rotational line strengths are compared, the agreement between theory and experiment appears to be surprisingly good, indeed far better than might have been expected, considering the crudeness of the experimental intensity estimates. Unfortunately, the quality of the intensity data precludes a more detailed comparison, but it is hoped that this work will serve to stimulate similar studies now that rotational line strengths can be calculated by computer in a relatively effortless manner.

The Rotational Structure of the O_2^+ First Negative Bands

When an electric discharge is passed through oxygen at low pressure, a visible band system results in the negative glow region of the discharge, the so-called first negative band system of ionized oxygen. Under low resolution, these bands appear to have two heads: one, well-defined,‡ degraded to the violet; the other, less well-defined, about 30 cm^{-1} to shorter wavelengths than the first. Based on probable electronic configurations of the O_2^+ molecule,

---

† For a modern account with emphasis on open-shell molecules see the work of Miller *et al.* [5].

‡ Band wavelengths are referred to this head.

Mulliken [8] was the first to suggest that the O_2^+ first negative bands might be a $^4\Sigma_g^- - ^4\Pi_u$ transition. In a series of two papers, Nevin [6] undertook a rotational analysis of these bands using the second and third orders of a 21-ft grating spectrograph having a resolving power of 180 000 and 200 000, respectively. The spectrum was excited by a discharge through helium mixed with small amounts of oxygen. Photographic plates were taken of the (0, 1) $\lambda = 6438$ Å band, the (0, 0) $\lambda = 6026$ Å band, the (1, 0) $\lambda = 5632$ Å band, and the (0, 2) $\lambda = 6856$ Å band. All 48 branches predicted to occur for a $^4\Sigma-^4\Pi$ transition were identified, although 8 pairs of branches are found essentially to coincide. Nevin and Murphy [7] performed a similar analysis on the (0, 3) $\lambda = 7348$ Å band, and subsequently, Weniger [9]† extended the rotational analysis of this band system to include higher vibrational levels of both the upper and lower states.

Figure 1 illustrates some of the branch designations of this $^4\Sigma_g^- - ^4\Pi_u$ transition by means of a schematic energy level diagram. The upper $^4\Sigma$ state, in which the component Λ of the electronic angular momentum along the internuclear axis is zero, is said to belong to Hund's case (b). The resultant spin $S = \frac{3}{2}$ is coupled loosely to the rotational axis of the molecule. Thus, each upper-state rotational level consists of four closely spaced components corresponding to $J = N + \frac{3}{2}$, $J = N + \frac{1}{2}$, $J = N - \frac{1}{2}$, and $J = N - \frac{3}{2}$, where J is the quantum number of the total angular momentum of the molecule and N is the quantum number of the angular momentum exclusive of spin. These four components are respectively denoted by $F_1'(N + \frac{3}{2})$, $F_2'(N + \frac{1}{2})$, $F_3'(N - \frac{1}{2})$, and $F_4'(N - \frac{3}{2})$.

In the lower $^4\Pi$ state for which $\Lambda = 1$, either Hund's case (a) or case (b) is possible according to whether $S = \frac{3}{2}$ is coupled to the internuclear axis or to the rotational axis. In case (a) notation, the component of S along the internuclear axis is denoted by Σ and has the values $\pm\frac{1}{2}$, $\pm\frac{3}{2}$. The total projection $\Omega = |\Lambda + \Sigma|$ assumes the possible values $\frac{1}{2}$, $\frac{3}{2}$, and $\frac{5}{2}$, and J takes the corresponding values Ω, $\Omega + 1$, $\Omega + 2$, etc. Because of the spin–orbit interaction, phenomenologically represented by $A\Lambda\Sigma$, the $^4\Pi$ state is split into four sublevels traditionally denoted by $^4\Pi_{-1/2}$, $^4\Pi_{1/2}$, $^4\Pi_{3/2}$, and $^4\Pi_{5/2}$, where the subscript refers to the value of $\Lambda + \Sigma$. The O_2^+ a $^4\Pi_u$ state, like many other multiplet electronic states, shows the characteristic behavior that at low J its coupling approximates case (a), in which S is tightly coupled to the internuclear axis, while with increasing J, the electronic spin S gradually uncouples from the internuclear axis and couples to the rotational axis, approaching Hund's case (b). In the intermediate case, the notation of either case (a) or case (b) is appropriate. For case (a), the sublevel designations are as discussed above, whereas for case (b), the rotational levels corresponding to a

---

† Some plate blackening estimates are presented for the stronger branches of the (0, 3) and (1, 4) bands, but the data are not extensive enough to permit a derivation of the rotational line strengths using the procedure described in the text.

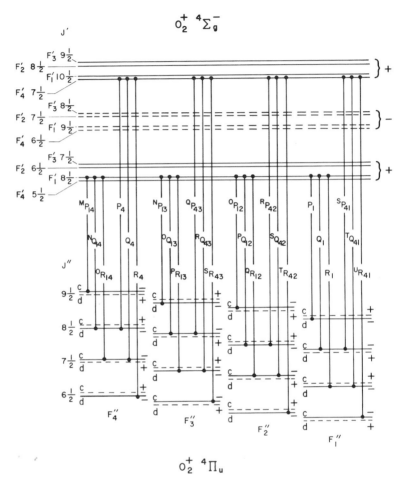

FIG. 1. Rotational energy level structure of the O_2^+ first negative bands. Transitions are shown for the 24 branches that originate from the F_1' and F_4' components of the upper state. The dashed horizontal lines correspond to missing energy levels.

given N are denoted by $F_1''(N + \frac{3}{2})$, $F_2''(N + \frac{1}{2})$, $F_3''(N - \frac{1}{2})$, and $F_4''(N - \frac{3}{2})$, as in the $^4\Pi$ state. If the $^4\Pi$ state is regular, i.e., $A \geq 0$, then F_4'' corresponds to $^4\Pi_{5/2}$ and F_1'' to $^4\Pi_{-1/2}$, while if the state is inverted, i.e., $A < 0$, then F_4'' corresponds to $^4\Pi_{-1/2}$ and F_1'' to $^4\Pi_{5/2}$. In addition to the above splittings, each sublevel is found to be slightly doubled because of the interaction between the magnetic field caused by the molecular rotation and the field along the internuclear axis. This small effect is referred to as Λ-type doubling. The upper Λ component is classified as the c level, and the lower Λ component as the d level.

In a homonuclear molecule, because of its symmetry properties, alternate

rotational levels have different statistical weights. For the O_2^+ homonuclear molecule, composed of nuclei with no nuclear spin, this causes an important simplification in the energy level pattern; namely, alternate rotational levels in the $^4\Sigma_g^-$ state and alternate c and d levels in the $^4\Pi_u$ state do not occur. These missing levels are shown in Fig. 1 by dashed lines. In the observation of the O_2^+ a $^4\Sigma_g^-$–b $^4\Pi_u$ spectrum, it is found that $F_1'(N)$ is blended with $F_4''(N)$, and $F_2'(N)$ with $F_3'(N)$, as shown in Fig. 1. The effect of this is to make 8 pairs of branches originating from the F_2' and the F_3' components coincide in position, reducing the total number of observed branches from 48 to 40 However, branches originating from the F_1' and F_4' components of the $^4\Sigma$ state are not overlapped (since they cannot connect to the same F'' rotational level of the ground state), and all 24 such branches, as shown in Fig. 1, have been identified by Nevin.

Of all the electronic transitions for which rotational analyses are available, the O_2^+ first negative bands occupy the unique position of being the only known instance of a $^4\Sigma$–$^4\Pi$ transition—indeed, the only case known involving a $^4\Pi$ multiplet state. Consequently, the experimentally measured fine structure splittings, and their dependence on J, have become a topic of lively theoretical interest [3]. We do not wish to enter into a full discussion of the various and sundry theoretical refinements that have been proposed to account for the observed energy level patterns, but rather to note what role perturbations from nearby electronic states may play. The presence of other electronic states mixed into the wave functions of the states under study is of particular interest to us since such mixing may be presumed to affect the rotational line intensity distribution as well. For the O_2^+ b $^4\Sigma_g^-$ state, spin–orbit mixing with $^4\Pi$, $^2\Pi$, $^2\Sigma$, and other $^4\Pi$ electronic states has been examined by Budó and Kovács [10] and by Kovács [11], who found that in first approximation the effect of these perturbations is to alter the value of the spin–spin interaction parameter, but to leave the dependence on the rotational quantum number unchanged. Thus, it is difficult to determine strictly from a rotational analysis of the O_2^+ b $^4\Sigma_g^-$ state to what extent the effective spin–spin parameter is caused by the "true" spin–spin interaction and to what extent by perturbations.

For the O_2^+ a $^4\Pi_u$ state, the situation is somewhat less ambiguous. The spin–orbit interaction causes a perturbation of the $^4\Pi$ state by the $^2\Pi$, $^4\Delta$, and $^2\Delta$ states [12]. If spin–orbit interaction with two close $^2\Pi_u$ states as well as spin–spin interaction are simultaneously taken into account, Budó and Kovács [12] and Kovács and Weniger [13] have shown that this gives a quite satisfactory explanation of the anomalous multiplet splittings occuring in the O_2^+ a $^4\Pi_u$ state, and their work clearly suggests the influence of the nearby A $^2\Pi_u$ and an unidentified $^2\Pi_u$ electronic state in causing the multiplet splittings. The small Λ-type doublings in this lower state appear to be also well accounted for in terms of perturbations caused by the $^4\Sigma$ and $^2\Sigma$ electronic states [14].

Experimental Line Strengths

Consider an electric dipole transition between the ith fine structure component of the upper state and the jth fine structure component of the lower state.† The intensity (energy sec^{-1}) in emission of the vibration rotation line $iv'J' \rightarrow jv''J''$ with a frequency v is proportional to the product of the population $N_{iv'J'}$ of the excited-state level and the Einstein coefficient of spontaneous emission,

$$I^{iv'J'}_{jv''J''} = KhvN_{iv'J'} A^{iv'J'}_{jv''J''} \tag{1}$$

where K is a constant expressing the solid angle subtended by the detector, its quantum efficiency, etc. The Einstein A coefficient may in turn be related to the matrix element of the transition dipole moment by

$$A^{iv'J'}_{jv''J''} = \frac{64\pi v^3}{3h(2J'+1)} \sum_{M', M''} |R^{iv'J'}_{jv''J''}|^2 \tag{2}$$

where the summation is over all possible combinations of degenerate magnetic sublevels.

According to the Born–Oppenheimer separation, the total molecular wave function for the upper state may be written in first approximation as the simple product of an electronic term, a vibrational term,‡ and a rotational term:

$$\psi_{n'iv'J'M'} = |n'\rangle |v'\rangle |iJ'M'\rangle \tag{3a}$$

with a similar expression for the lower state,

$$\psi_{n''jv''J''M''} = |n''\rangle |v''\rangle |jJ''M''\rangle \tag{3b}$$

The transition dipole matrix element may then be factored into the product of two terms. Thus, Eq. (2) takes the form

$$A^{iv'J'}_{jv''J''} = [64\pi v^3/3h(2J'+1)]S_{v'v''} S^{ij}_{J'J''} \tag{4}$$

where

$$S_{v'v''} = |\langle v'| R^{n'n''}_e |v''\rangle|^2 \tag{5}$$

is called the *vibrational band strength* (which is simply proportional to the Franck–Condon factor $\langle v'|v''\rangle^2$ if the electronic transition moment $R^{n'n''}_e$ is independent of internuclear distance), and

† For a review of molecular intensity relationships (see Tatum [15] and Schadee [16]). Note that these two authors adopt different conventions for handling Λ-type doubling and for normalizing their rotational line strengths.

‡ Strictly speaking, the radial wavefunction that represents the vibrational motion of the molecule depends on the rotational state J through the influence of vibration–rotation interaction (see Zare [17]). However, for nonhydride molecules these effects are usually quite small.

$$S_{J'J''}^{ij} = 3 \sum_{M', M''} |\langle iJ'M'|z|jJ''M''\rangle|^2 \tag{6}$$

is called the *rotational line strength*. The $S_{J'J''}^{ij}$ factors may be shown to satisfy the sum rules

$$\sum_{i, J'} S_{J'J''}^{ij} = 2J'' + 1 \tag{7a}$$

and

$$\sum_{j, J''} S_{J'J''}^{ij} = 2J' + 1 \tag{7b}$$

We are particularly interested in the intensities of the lines of different branches within the same (v', v'') band. Let us suppose that, over the width of the band, the frequency v is essentially constant and thus may be incorporated into K. Then, by combining Eqs. (1), (4), and (7), we obtain the following relationship expressing the ratio of the intensity of a single vibration–rotation line emitted from the level $iv'J'$ to the sum of the intensities of all the emission lines originating from $iv'J'$:

$$I_{jv''J''}^{iv'J'} \bigg/ \sum_{j, J''} I_{jv''J''}^{iv'J'} = S_{J'J''}^{ij} / 2J' + 1 \tag{8}$$

Note that Eq. (8) permits the rotational line strengths to be calculated directly from relative intensity data and requires no knowledge of the excited-state populations.

In the course of the rotational analysis of the O_2^+ first negative bands by Nevin [6] and by Nevin and Murphy [7], extensive tables were prepared listing the wave number positions of all the observed lines in each branch. Beside each entry is placed an intensity estimate ranging in unit steps from 0 to 10, but with occasional entries of 20 or 25. These relative intensity measurements serve no role in their subsequent rotational analysis and are presented with no comment as to how they were obtained .Thus it is unclear whether they are microdensitometer readings or simply eyeball estimates of plate blackenings, and it is unclear what corrections, if any, were made for the response of the film. Indeed, this is typical of most intensity data available in the literature that are generated not as ends in themselves, but rather as by-products of positional studies for which they serve the purpose of characteristic identification markers.

Using Eq. (8), rotational line strengths are found for the lines of the 24 branches shown in Fig. 1 from the relative intensity estimates of Nevin and Nevin and Murphy. However, inspection of the results shows that these experimental line strengths have a noisy, irregular appearance that does not change smoothly with J, as is to be expected. In order to present this massive amount of data in a compressed form that would allow a simple test against theory, we have elected not to report the rotational line strength for each (alternate) value of J'', but rather to give the sum of the line strengths for

each branch over the range $J'' = 2\frac{1}{2}$ through $J'' = 26\frac{1}{2}$, i.e., the sum is over the values $J'' = 2\frac{1}{2}$, $4\frac{1}{2}$, ..., $26\frac{1}{2}$ for the Q lines originating from the F_1' component and the P and R lines from the F_4' component, and the sum is over the values $J'' = 3\frac{1}{2}$, $5\frac{1}{2}$, ..., $25\frac{1}{2}$ for the P and R lines originating from the F_1' component and the Q lines from the F_4' component. This has the effect of smoothing out the local variations in the data.

The resulting line strength sums are presented in Table I. We also have computed in Table I the average of the sums of the four bands for which data

TABLE I

ROTATIONAL LINE STRENGTH SUMS OF THE O_2^+ FIRST NEGATIVE BANDS FOR J'' RANGING FROM 2.5 TO 26.5, AS DERIVED FROM MEASURED RELATIVE INTENSITIES

Branch designation	Vibrational band				Average
	(0, 0)	(0, 1)	(1, 0)	(0, 3)	
$^OR_{14}$	4.0	0.6	0.0	0.5	1.3
$^NQ_{14}$	1.3	1.0	3.9	5.7	3.0
$^MP_{14}$	0.4	0.9	0.4	0.0	0.4
$^PR_{13}$	15.3	5.9	6.7	17.3	11.4
$^OQ_{13}$	41.1	44.8	27.5	26.9	35.1
$^NP_{13}$	3.7	4.0	11.5	11.4	7.7
$^QR_{12}$	44.7	33.5	39.3	36.9	36.1
$^PQ_{12}$	62.7	53.7	57.1	67.5	60.3
$^OP_{12}$	36.9	39.9	36.0	41.6	38.6
R_1	47.6	50.6	50.9	33.3	45.6
Q_1	70.4	101.4	83.9	77.2	83.2
P_1	46.2	45.4	56.6	46.7	48.7
R_4	51.0	65.7	65.5	56.6	59.7
Q_4	77.9	75.4	64.2	69.2	71.7
P_4	56.7	48.5	34.4	60.6	50.1
$^SR_{43}$	35.4	24.4	43.9	44.5	37.1
$^RQ_{43}$	56.9	72.6	57.1	58.6	61.3
$^QP_{43}$	44.2	46.5	49.4	31.3	42.9
$^TR_{42}$	15.0	6.2	11.3	6.8	9.8
$^SQ_{42}$	22.3	21.4	16.1	21.0	20.4
$^RP_{42}$	9.7	11.3	24.3	20.0	16.3
$^UR_{41}$	0.0	0.0	1.1	2.3	0.9
$^TQ_{41}$	3.6	2.3	6.0	2.6	3.6
$^SP_{41}$	0.8	6.7	4.2	0.0	2.9

are available. An examination of the entries of Table I shows that there is no obvious trend discernible between the sums for the different vibrational bands; the vibrational dependence of the rotational line strengths thus appears to be smaller than our experimental uncertainties in these sums. Consequently, for

comparison purposes, we use our averaged sums as the "best" representation of the rotational line strength sums for the O_2^+ first negative bands. The sums in Table I were somewhat arbitrarily terminated at $J'' = 26\frac{1}{2}$ because the lines of a number of branches were not followed in the rotational analysis to much higher rotational quantum numbers.

Comparison with Calculated Line Strengths

The task of theory is the evaluation of Eq. (6) for the lines of all the branches occurring in the rotational structure of a (v', v'') band. If both the upper and lower states are well described by Hund's case (a) coupling, then the solutions to Eq. (6) are well known. For such states, the rotational wave functions are symmetric-top wave functions $J\Omega M$ and the rotational line strengths are the so-called Hönl–London factors, named after the two workers who first derived them [18]. Specifically, for a $J'\Omega' \rightarrow J''\Omega''$ transition, the line strengths are given by

$$
S_{J'J''}^{\Omega'\Omega''} = 3\delta_{S'S''}\delta_{\Sigma'\Sigma''} \sum_{M,M''} |\langle J'\Omega'M'|z|J''\Omega''M''\rangle|^2
$$

$$
= \delta_{S'S''}\delta_{\Sigma'\Sigma''}(2J'+1)(2J''+1)\begin{pmatrix} J' & 1 & J'' \\ \Omega' & \Omega''-\Omega' & -\Omega'' \end{pmatrix}^2 \tag{9}
$$

where the last quantity in parentheses is a $3j$ symbol and the Kronecker δ's express the selection rules, $\Delta S = 0$ and $\Delta\Sigma = 0$, for electric-dipole-allowed transitions in Hund's case (a).

In the more general case, the rotational wave function for a particular component of a multiplet electronic state may be expressed as a linear combination of symmetric-top wave functions. For example, the upper state $|iJ'M'\rangle$ may be written

$$
|iJ'M'\rangle = \sum_{\Omega'} T_{\Omega'J'}^i |J'\Omega'M'\rangle \tag{10}
$$

where in Eq. (10), $\Omega' = \Lambda' + \Sigma$, and Σ ranges in integral steps from $-S$ to $+S$. Similarly, the lower-state rotational wave function $|jJ''M''\rangle$ may be written

$$
|jJ''M''\rangle = \sum_{\Omega''} T_{\Omega''J''}^j |J''\Omega''M''\rangle \tag{11}
$$

Substituting Eqs. (10) and (11) into Eq. (6), we obtain, with the help of Eq. (9), the following general expression for the rotational line strength for the $iJ'M' \leftrightarrow jJ''M''$ transition:

$$
S_{J'J''}^{ij} = (2J'+1)(2J''+1)\left| \sum_{\Sigma=-S}^{S} T_{\Lambda'+\Sigma,J'}^i T_{\Lambda''+\Sigma,J''}^j \right.
$$

$$
\left. \times \begin{pmatrix} J' & 1 & J'' \\ \Lambda'+\Sigma & \Lambda''-\Lambda' & -\Lambda''-\Sigma'' \end{pmatrix} \right|^2 \tag{12}
$$

Thus, the calculation of rotational line strengths for electronic states whose coupling is intermediate between Hund's case (a) and case (b) reduces to the problem of finding the values of the coefficients $T^i_{\Omega'J'}$ and $T^j_{\Omega''J''}$ appearing in Eqs. (10) and (11). As Hill and Van Vleck [2] showed, this is equivalent to finding the vectors of the unitary transformation matrix that diagonalizes the molecular Hamiltonian using the case (a) rotational wave functions as a basis set.

We shall make the traditional assumption that the effects of spin–orbit, spin–spin, and spin–rotation interaction may be taken into account by introducing phenomenological parameters into the form of the rotational Hamiltonian whose values are determined by a best least squares fit to the observed energy levels. The molecular Hamiltonian excluding terms that connect states with different values of Λ or other electronic multiplets has the form

$$\mathscr{H} = \mathscr{H}_0 + \mathscr{H}_R + \mathscr{H}_{SO} + \mathscr{H}_{SS} + \mathscr{H}_{SR} \tag{13}$$

where

$$\mathscr{H}_R = B(r)(\mathbf{J}^2 - \mathbf{J}_z^2 + \mathbf{S}^2 - \mathbf{S}_z^2) - B(r)(\mathbf{J}_+\mathbf{S}_- + \mathbf{J}_-\mathbf{S}_+) \tag{14}$$

$$\mathscr{H}_{SO} = A(r)\mathbf{L}_z \cdot \mathbf{S}_z \tag{15}$$

$$\mathscr{H}_{SS} = \varepsilon(r)(3\mathbf{S}_z^2 - \mathbf{S}^2) \tag{16}$$

$$\mathscr{H}_{SR} = \gamma(r)(\mathbf{J}_z \cdot \mathbf{S}_z - \mathbf{S}^2) + \tfrac{1}{2}\gamma(r)(\mathbf{J}_+\mathbf{S}_- + \mathbf{J}_-\mathbf{S}_+) \tag{17}$$

Here, the mechanical–rotational, spin–orbit, spin–spin, and spin–rotation operators are denoted by B, A, ε, and γ, respectively, $\mathbf{J}_\pm = \mathbf{J}_x \pm i\mathbf{J}_y$, and $\mathbf{S}_\pm = \mathbf{S}_x \pm i\mathbf{S}_y$ are the raising and lowering operators of $\mathbf{J}$ and $\mathbf{S}$, and $\mathbf{L}_z$ is the component of the electronic angular momentum along the internuclear axis taken to define the z direction.

Fortunately, the form of all of the matrix elements for H between case (a) wave functions have been previously derived elsewhere [3, 4, 5, 19] and the results are summarized in Table II. Strictly speaking, the mechanical–rotational, spin–orbit, spin–spin, and spin–rotation operators all depend on the internuclear distance r and thus the matrix elements $(\mathbf{0})_{\Sigma\Sigma}$, $(\mathbf{0})_{\Sigma, \Sigma\pm1}$, and $(\mathbf{0})_{\Sigma\Sigma\pm2}$ in Table II refer to the appropriate radial integrals of the operators $\mathbf{0}$ for the (v, J) state. However, the v and J dependences of the matrix elements of these operators are seldom known, except for $B(r)$ and, sometimes, $A(r)$, and must therefore be neglected in practice. For accurate work, we use [19]

$$(B)_{\Sigma, \Sigma} = B_v - D_v[J(J + 1) - \Omega^2 + 3S(S + 1) - 3\Sigma^2]$$
$$+ 2D_v\{[S(S + 1) - \Sigma^2]^2 - \Omega\Sigma\}/[J(J + 1) - \Omega^2 + S(S + 1) - \Sigma^2] \tag{18}$$

$$(A)_{\Sigma, \Sigma} = A_v \tag{19}$$

TABLE II

Case (a) Matrix Elements of the Molecular Hamiltonian Given in Eq. (13)

Diagonal terms

$(\mathcal{H}_0)_{\Sigma\Sigma} = \nu_0$ (the band origin)

$(\mathcal{H}_R)_{\Sigma\Sigma} = (B)_{\Sigma\Sigma}[J(J+1) - \Omega^2 + S(S+1) - \Sigma^2]$

$(\mathcal{H}_{SO})_{\Sigma\Sigma} = (A)_{\Sigma\Sigma}\Lambda\Sigma$

$(\mathcal{H}_{SS})_{\Sigma\Sigma} = (\varepsilon)_{\Sigma\Sigma}[3\Sigma^2 - S(S+1)]$

$(\mathcal{H}_{SR})_{\Sigma\Sigma} = (\gamma)_{\Sigma\Sigma}[\Omega\Sigma - S(S+1)]$

Nondiagonal terms

$(\mathcal{H}_R)_{\Sigma,\Sigma\pm1} = (B)_{\Sigma,\Sigma\pm1}[J(J+1) - \Omega(\Omega\pm1)]^{1/2}[S(S+1) - \Sigma(\Sigma\pm1)]^{1/2}$

$(\mathcal{H}_R)_{\Sigma,\Sigma\pm2} = (B)_{\Sigma,\Sigma\pm2}[J(J+1) - \Omega(\Omega\pm1)]^{1/2}[S(S+1) - \Sigma(\Sigma\pm1)]^{1/2}$

$(\mathcal{H}_{SR})_{\Sigma,\Sigma\pm1} = -\frac{1}{2}(\gamma)_{\Sigma,\Sigma\pm1}[J(J+1) - \Omega(\Omega\pm1)]^{1/2}[S(S+1) - \Sigma(\Sigma\pm1)]^{1/2}$

and

$$(B)_{\Sigma,\Sigma\pm1} = B_v - 2D_v[J(J+1) - \Omega(\Omega\pm1) + S(S+1) - \Sigma(\Sigma\pm1) - 1] \quad (20)$$

$$(B)_{\Sigma,\Sigma\pm2} = -D_v[J(J+1) - (\Omega\pm1)(\Omega\pm2)]^{1/2}[S(S+1) - (\Sigma\pm1)(\Sigma\pm2)]^{1/2} \quad (21)$$

Here, A_v, B_v, and D_v are the spin–orbit, rotational, and centrifugal distortion constants for the vibrational level v.

The molecular Hamiltonian given in Eq. (13) satisfies the Schrödinger equation

$$\mathcal{H}|qvJ\rangle + E_{qvJ}|qvJ\rangle \quad (22)$$

for the fine structure energy level E_{qvJ} with associated wave function $|qvJ\rangle$. Let us expand $|qvJ\rangle$ in terms of the case (a) wave functions $|vJ\Omega = \Lambda + \Sigma\rangle$,

$$|qvJ\rangle = \sum_{\Omega} T^q_{\Omega J}|vJ\Omega\rangle \quad (23)$$

By substituting Eq. (23) into (22), multiplying on the left by $\langle|vJ\Omega' = \Lambda + \Sigma'|$, and integrating over all space, we obtain a system of $2S + 1$ linear equations for the coefficients $T^q_{\Omega J}$:

$$\sum_{\Sigma=-S}^{S} [(\mathcal{H})_{\Sigma,\Sigma'} - E_{qJM}]T^q_{\Lambda+\Sigma,J} = 0 \quad (24)$$

For this set of simultaneous equations to have a nontrivial solution, its determinant must vanish:

$$|(\mathcal{H})_{\Sigma,\Sigma'} - E_{qJM}\delta_{\Sigma,\Sigma'}| = 0 \quad (25)$$

and the $2S + 1$ eigenvalues of this secular equation provide the energy levels of the $2S + 1$ fine structure components q in intermediate coupling. Associated

with each eigenvalue E_{qvJ} of the matrix $(\mathscr{H})_{\Sigma,\Sigma'}$ is the eigenvector $T^q_{\Lambda+\Sigma,J}$ that diagonalizes $(\mathscr{H})_{\Sigma,\Sigma'}$. By substituting the value of E_{qvJ} into Eq. (24), the coefficients $T^q_{\Lambda+\Sigma,J}$ may be determined subject to the condition that

$$\sum_{\Sigma=-S}^{S} (T^q_{\Lambda+\Sigma,J})^2 = 1 \qquad (26)$$

Thus, rotational line strengths may be calculated for a molecular transition based solely on a knowledge of the fine structure energy level splittings in the upper and lower states, and this procedure outlined above has formed the basis of almost all rotational line strength calculations [3]. However, past workers have exclusively sought algebraic solutions to the secular determinant given by Eq. (25). Consequently, no general treatment for molecular multiplet states for $S \geq 1$ has been developed, and for $S \leq 1$, the determinantal equations have been simplified for the purposes of calculating line strengths to include only diagonal and nondiagonal terms containing the constants A_v and B_v. The resultant algebraic formulas are nevertheless incredibly complex, subject to errors in typography and transcription, and extremely arduous to apply in practice.† To overcome these difficulties, we have written a simple computer program [19] that accepts values of B_v, D_v, A_v, ε, and γ for each state, sets up the appropriate $(2S + 1) \times (2S + 1)$ secular determinant, and solves for the eigenvalues and corresponding eigenvectors. This is accomplished for both the upper and lower states, and with the use of Eq. (12), rotational line strengths are automatically computed for lines in all of the branches.

This computer program has been applied to the O_2^+ first negative bands. As a first trial, we set the constants D_v, ε, and γ to zero for both states. The values of the rotational constants for both states were chosen as $B' = 1.27626$ cm^{-1} and $B'' = 1.09681$ cm^{-1}, respectively [6]. For the upper b $^4\Sigma_g^-$ state, the coupling scheme is case (b) and the spin–orbit constant A' is of course equal to zero; for the lower a $^4\Pi_u$ state, the best value [13] of the spin–orbit constant appears to be $A'' = 47.792$ cm^{-1}. However, it is of interest to examine the nature of the rotational line strengths calculated, assuming that the lower

---

† The recent monograph by Kovács [3] presents for the first time in the literature general algebraic expressions for doublet transitions and triplet transitions where both the upper and lower electronic states may belong to a coupling case intermediate between Hund's case (a) and case (b). Despite the painstaking care evident throughout the preparation of this book, careful inspection of Kovács' line strength expressions shows that while his Tables 3.6, 3.7, and 3.10 appear to be free of error, his Table 3.8 should be altered as follows:

1. In his expression for $^SR_{21}(J)$ replace $C_2(J + 1)$ by $C_2'(J + 1)$.
2. In his expression for $^SQ_{31}(J)$ replace $C_3''(J)$ by $C_3'(J)$, and replace $(J - 1)$ by $(J - \Lambda)$.
3. In his expression for $^SR_{32}(J)$ replace $u_3'(J + 1)$ by $u_3'^+(J + 1)$.

Some further checks were also made on his algebraic expressions for higher multiplicity transitions and they were found in some cases not to satisfy the sum rules for rotational line strengths [see Eqs. (7a) and (7b)].

$^4\Pi$ state could be well-approximated by one of the limiting Hund's coupling cases. Accordingly, we let A'' approach the values $-\infty$, 0, and $+\infty$, corresponding to inverted case (a) coupling, case (b) coupling, and regular case (a) coupling. The results of the sums of the line strengths calculated for these idealized coupling cases are presented in Table III. Comparison of the entries of Table III with the corresponding entires in Table I shows no sensible

TABLE III

CALCULATED ROTATIONAL LINE STRENGTH SUMS OF THE $O_2{}^+$ FIRST NEGATIVE BANDS FOR J'' RANGING FROM 2.5 TO 26.5, BASED ON DIFFERENT PURE HUND'S CASE COUPLINGS

Branch designation	Inverted case (a)	Case (b)	Regular case (a)	Branch designation	Inverted case (a)	Case (b)	Regular case (a)
$^OR_{14}$	14.5	0.0	9.6	R_4	12.9	94.6	8.9
$^NQ_{14}$	26.8	0.0	26.2	Q_4	20.3	178.6	19.9
$^MP_{14}$	10.4	0.0	16.0	P_4	9.3	99.4	13.5
$^PR_{13}$	33.7	0.0_1	29.6	$^SR_{43}$	38.8	0.0	34.0
$^OQ_{13}$	70.7	0.0	70.2	$^RQ_{43}$	69.8	0.6	69.3
$^NP_{13}$	31.3	0.0	35.8	$^QP_{43}$	36.5	1.8	41.9
$^QR_{12}$	29.6	1.7	33.7	$^TR_{42}$	34.0	0.0	38.8
$^PQ_{12}$	70.2	1.5	70.7	$^SQ_{42}$	69.3	0.0	69.8
$^OP_{12}$	35.8	0.0	31.3	$^RP_{42}$	41.9	0.0_2	36.5
R_1	9.6	85.7	14.5	$^UR_{41}$	8.9	0.0	12.9
Q_1	26.2	192.4	26.8	$^TQ_{41}$	19.9	0.0	20.3
P_1	16.0	101.4	10.4	$^SP_{41}$	13.5	0.0	9.3

agreement with the theoretical predictions based on calculations that ignore the effects of intermediate coupling.

Next, the rotational line strengths were recalculated using the experimentally derived value of the spin–orbit parameter $A'' = 47.792$ cm^{-1}, and the results are listed in the second column of Table IV. In the third column of Table IV, we give the results of the full intermediate coupling calculation for the $O_2{}^+$ b $^4\Sigma_g{}^-$–a $^4\Pi_u$ transition where we have included for both states the effects of spin–spin, spin–rotation, and centrifugal distortion.† Finally, the last column of Table IV contains for comparison purposes the averaged sums found in Table I, based on the measured relative intensities.

Inspection of Table IV shows that for the $O_2{}^+$ first negative bands there is little difference between the rotational line strengths calculated in intermediate

† The values used for these parameters were $D' = 5.91 \times 10^{-6}$cm^{-1}, $\varepsilon' = 0.1487$ cm^{-1}, $\gamma' = -6.6 \times 10^{-4}$cm^{-1}, $D'' = 4.83 \times 10^{-6}$cm^{-1}, $\varepsilon'' = 0.1487$ cm^{-1}, and $\gamma'' = 0.0$ cm^{-1}. They are most appropriate for the (0, 0) band. The values of ε'' and γ'' are those recommended by Kovács and Weniger [13].

TABLE IV

COMPARISON OF CALCULATED AND OBSERVED ROTATIONAL LINE STRENGTH SUMS OF THE O_2^+ FIRST NEGATIVE BANDS FOR J'' RANGING FROM 2.5 TO 26.5

Branch designation	Simple intermediate coupling calculation	Full intermediate coupling calculation	" Best " experimental value
$^O R_{14}$	1.9	1.9	1.3
$^N Q_{14}$	2.8	2.8	3.0
$^M P_{14}$	0.8	0.8	0.4
$^P R_{13}$	11.3	11.8	11.4
$^O Q_{13}$	19.9	20.9	35.1
$^N P_{13}$	7.7	8.1	7.7
$^Q R_{12}$	33.5	34.1	36.1
$^P Q_{12}$	70.1	72.0	60.3
$^O P_{12}$	32.2	33.1	38.6
R_1	40.7	39.6	45.6
Q_1	101.0	98.2	83.2
P_1	52.8	51.5	48.7
R_4	55.6	53.8	59.7
Q_4	95.4	92.3	71.7
P_4	49.8	50.0	50.1
$^S R_{43}$	31.6	32.8	37.1
$^R Q_{43}$	64.7	66.7	61.3
$^Q P_{43}$	37.4	38.5	42.9
$^T R_{42}$	7.0	7.4	9.8
$^S Q_{42}$	17.6	18.5	20.4
$^R P_{42}$	12.5	13.1	16.3
$^U R_{41}$	0.5	0.6	0.9
$^T Q_{41}$	1.6	1.8	3.6
$^S P_{41}$	1.5	1.6	2.9

coupling employing only the values of A_v and B_v and those calculated in intermediate coupling using all the splitting parameters. This conclusion may be expected to be of general validity and has the practical significance that, if electronic perturbations can be ignored, fairly reliable rotational line strengths may be calculated for a number of molecular band systems for which values of the spin–spin, the spin–rotation, and the centrifugal distortion constants are unknown or only known to poor accuracy. Examination of the second and third columns of Table IV with the last column also shows that there is remarkable agreement between the " best " experimental line strength sums and those theoretically predicted from intermediate coupling calculations, not that this comparison is entirely free of egregious exceptions. However, we are likely to delude ourselves if we attempt to interpret the deviations that do occur, until better relative intensity measurements become available.

References

1. E. U. Condon, *Phys. Rev.* **32**, 858 (1928).

1a. E. U. Condon, *Amer. J. Phys.* **15**, 365 (1947).

2. E. L. Hill and J. H. Van Vleck, *Phys. Rev.* **32**, 250 (1928); see also J. H. Van Vleck, *Phys. Rev.* **33**, 467 (1929).

3. A. Budó, *Z. Phys.* **96**, 219 (1935); **105**, 73 (1937); W. H. Brandt, *Phys. Rev.* **50**, 778 (1936); K. S. Rao, *Indian J. Phys.* **26**, 47, 254 (1952); M. Ninomiya, *J. Phys. Soc. Jap.* **10**, 829 (1955); G. N. Yurkov and G. A. Khachkuruzov, *Opt. Spectrosc. (USSR)* **25**, 459 (1968); **27**, 493, 496 (1969); for a review consult I. Kovács, "Rotational Structure in the Spectra of Diatomic Molecules." Akadémiai Kiadó, Budapest, Hungary, 1969.

4. M. Born and J. R. Oppenheimer, *Ann. Phys.* **84**, 457 (1927).

5. T. A. Miller, D. H. Levy, and A. Carrington, *Advan. Chem. Phys.* **18**, 149–248 (1970).

6. T. E. Nevin, *Phil. Trans. Roy. Soc. London* **237**, 471 (1938); *Proc. Roy. Soc. Ser. A* **174**, 371 (1940).

7. T. E. Nevin and T. Murphy, *Proc. Roy. Irish Acad.* **46**, 23 (1941).

8. R. S. Mulliken, *Rev. Mod. Phys.* **4**, 56 (1932).

9. S. Weniger, *J. Phys. Radium* **23**, 225 (1962).

10. A. Budó and I. Kovács, *Hung. Acta Phys.* **1**, 1 (1948); *Phys. Rev.* **73**, 1120 (1948).

11. I. Kovács, *Acta Phys.* **15**, 337 (1963).

12. A. Budó and I. Kovács, *Acta Phys.* **4**, 273 (1954); see also I. Kovács, *Acta Phys.* **10**, 255 (1959).

13. I. Kovács and S. Weniger, *J. Phys. Radium* **23**, 377 (1962).

14. A. Budó and I. Kovács, *Z. Phys.* **65**, 122 (1944).

15. J. B. Tatum, *Astrophys. J. Suppl. Ser.* **16**, 21 (1967).

16. A. Schadee, *J. Quant. Spectrosc. Radiat. Transfer* **7**, 169 (1967).

17. R. N. Zare, *J. Chem. Phys.* **40**, 1934 (1964).

18. H. Hönl and F. London, *Z. Phys.* **33**, 803 (1925).

19. D. L. Albritton, A. L. Schmeltekopf, and R. N. Zare, "Diatomic Intensity Factors." Harper, New York, To be published.

4.3 A Chrestomathy of Energy Transfer Research on Iodine

J. I. Steinfeld†

Department of Chemistry
Massachusetts Institute of Technology
Cambridge, Massachusetts

Fifty-nine years ago, the transformation of the visible iodine fluorescence from a resonance spectrum to a band spectrum was first reported by Franck and Wood [1]. Once the principles of vibration–rotation spectroscopy were established, it was quickly realized that the details of these "transfer bands" could yield a great deal of information on vibrationally and rotationally inelastic processes occurring within the electronically excited molecule upon a collision with another gas molecule. The elucidation of accurate cross sections for these processes, however, could not be obtained until only recently. Since all these results have already or will shortly appear in the literature, we will limit ourselves here to a brief review and index of this work.

The basic principle behind this method is the use of monochromatic radiation to excite a single vibration–rotation state which, in the absence of added foreign gases, gives a resonance fluorescence spectrum. The selectivity possible in this way is illustrated in Fig. 1, which shows the overlap of the narrow central component of the green mercury emission line at 5460.74 Å with the 25–0, $P(33)$ line of the visible iodine absorption spectrum [2]. The use of optical lasers as excitation sources has greatly extended the range of experimental possibilities, in iodine as well as in other systems.

The appearance of a vibrationally and rotationally transferred fluorescence spectrum is shown in Fig. 2. The specific rates of the transferring processes are obtained from careful analysis of the sideband intensities, which requires accurate photometric measurements; yet, it was not until Brown's work on the sodium D-line excited fluorescence in 1964 [4] that photelectric detection was applied to this system. In order to derive the magnitudes of the cross sections from these rates, an accurate value for the radiative lifetime of the molecule must be known; this was also not available until 1963 [5], and is still not completely known for all the vibrational states of iodine.

† Alfred P. Sloan Research Fellow.

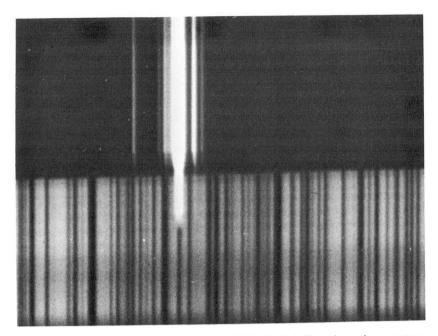

FIG. 1. High-resolution spectrum of the visible B–X iodine absorption spectrum, showing the overlap of the mercury emission line at 5460.74 Å with a single feature of the spectrum. The entire range covered by this figure is about 1 Å [2].

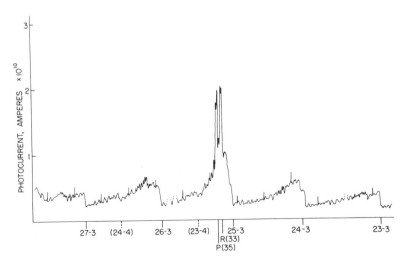

FIG. 2. Portion of the mercury-excited iodine fluorescence spectrum in the presence of added helium, showing the development of vibration-rotation transfer bands [3].

Following the work on the $v' = 15$ state excited by the D lines a complete photometric analysis of the mercury-green-line-excited $v' = 25$ fluorescence was carried out [3], and subsequently, the fluorescence from $v' = 43$, excited by the argon ion laser 5145.36 Å line [6], and from the $v' = 51$ level, excited by the cadmium 5086 Å line [7]. The $v' = 43$ fluorescence is shown in Fig. 3; a long, overlapping progression of bands is seen, indicating extensive vibrational energy transfer. Each of these bands demonstrates extensive rotational relaxation, as shown in Fig. 4.

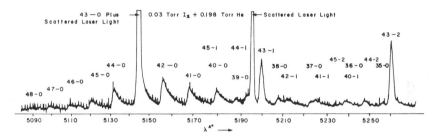

FIG. 3. Portion of the argon-laser-excited iodine fluorescence spectrum in the presence of added helium. An extensive series of overlapping transfer bands is developed in this case, in which the vibrational spacing is much smaller than available thermal energy [6].

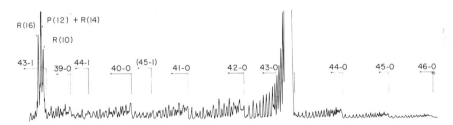

FIG. 4. High-resolution scan of a portion of the fluorescence spectrum shown in Fig. 3, from the 46–0 band through the 43–1 band, showing rotational structure of the resonance band and fully developed rotational relaxation in the transfer bands. The relaxing gas in this case was primarily air [7a]. (Spectrum by D. Hatzenbuhler, Michigan State Univ.)

The rotationally and vibrationally inelastic cross sections obtained from these studies are listed in Tables I, II, and III. Not repeated here are cross sections for quenching by collision-induced predissociation [8] or by action of a magnetic field [9].

These data now provide an extensive map of energy transfer efficiencies over the vibrational levels of a simple (albeit electronically excited) diatomic molecule. We see that these efficiencies are high, although their relative magnitudes, at least, can be predicted fairly well by simple first-order models [10].

TABLE I   VIBRATIONAL ENERGY TRANSFER IN $I_2(B\,^3\Pi_{0_u}{}^+)$

Inelastic cross section for given buffer gas (Å²)

	³He	⁴He	Ne	Ar	Kr	Xe	H₂	D₂	N₂	O₂	NO	CO₂	CH₃Cl	SO₂	NH₃	I₂	Ref.
$v' = 15$																	[4]
$\sigma^2(15, 14)$	—	1.58	1.24	1.89	1.23	1.01	2.10	2.59	2.69	2.65	2.34	—	—	—	—	—	
$\Sigma_v \sigma^2(15, v)$	—	3.71	4.41	5.44	3.30	3.60	4.95	9.2	10.9	12.6	12.0	—	—	—	—	—	
$v' = 25$																	[3]
$\sigma^2(25, 23)$	0.42	0.51	—	—	—	—	0.6	—	—	—	—	—	—	—	—	—	
$\sigma^2(25, 24)$	2.41	2.75	4.5	—	6.0	4.9	2.4	—	—	—	—	6.9	9.9	14.6	—	—	
$\sigma^2(25, 26)$	1.45	1.73	—	—	—	—	1.9	—	—	—	—	5.5	6.5	8.6	—	—	
$\sigma^2(25, 27)$	0.32	0.43	—	—	—	—	—	—	—	—	—	—	—	—	—	—	
$\Sigma_v \sigma^2(25, v)$	4.5	5.55	8.6	16.9	16.1	12.2	4.8	—	—	15.5	—	17.8	22.0	25.4	9.9	—	
$v' = 43$																	[6]
$\sigma^2(43, 35)$	—	0.028	0.064	0.054	0.093	0.043	0.013	—	—	—	—	0.047	—	—	—	0.052	
$\sigma^2(43, 36)$	—	0.033	0.106	0.094	0.15	0.057	0.022	—	—	—	—	0.081	—	—	—	0.086	
$\sigma^2(43, 37)$	—	0.081	0.159	0.204	0.34	0.152	0.029	—	—	—	—	0.107	—	—	—	0.115	
$\sigma^2(43, 38)$	—	0.098	0.263	0.36	0.49	0.26	0.051	—	—	—	—	0.185	—	—	—	0.20	
$\sigma^2(43, 39)$	—	0.228	0.63	0.97	1.23	0.70	0.14	—	—	—	—	0.51	—	—	—	0.55	
$\sigma^2(43, 40)$	—	0.57	1.16	1.67	2.09	1.32	0.29	—	—	—	—	1.05	—	—	—	1.13	
$\sigma^2(43, 41)$	—	1.22	2.64	3.47	4.56	3.30	0.73	—	—	—	—	2.64	—	—	—	2.86	
$\sigma^2(43, 42)$	—	2.28	5.07	7.07	9.12	7.53	1.59	—	—	—	—	5.80	—	—	—	6.31	
$\sigma^2(43, 44)$	—	1.83	4.33	5.89	7.61	6.26	1.32	—	—	—	—	4.79	—	—	—	5.20	
$\sigma^2(43, 45)$	—	0.67	1.58	2.22	2.81	2.12	0.46	—	—	—	—	1.65	—	—	—	1.82	
$\sigma^2(43, 46)$	—	0.203	0.53	0.64	0.80	0.57	0.12	—	—	—	—	0.43	—	—	—	0.48	
$\sigma^2(43, 47)$	—	0.093	0.21	0.25	0.325	0.233	0.051	—	—	—	—	0.19	—	—	—	0.20	
$\sigma^2(43, 48)$	—	0.030	0.068	0.096	0.126	0.062	0.014	—	—	—	—	0.053	—	—	—	0.052	
$\Sigma_v \sigma^2(43, v)$	—	7.36	16.8	23.0	29.8	22.6	4.81	—	—	—	—	17.5	—	—	—	19.0	
$v' = 51$																	[7]
$\Sigma_v \sigma^2(51, v)$	—	3.8															

TABLE II

Rotational Energy Transfer in $I_2(B\ ^3\Pi_{0_{u^+}})$ with $\Delta_v = 0$

| | Inelastic cross section for given buffer gas (Å^2) | | | | | | | | | | | | | | | | |
	^{3}He	^{4}He	Ne	Ar	Kr	Xe	H_2	D_2	N_2	D_2	NO	CO_2	CH_3Cl	SO_2	NH_3	I_2	Ref.
$v' = 15$, $J' = 37$ and 44	—	4.9	13.4	17	20	19.5	3.6	7.3	17.6	19	11	—	—	—	—	—	[4]
$v' = 25$, $J' = 34$	10.8	14.5	14.5	21.5	29.9	37.0	12.8	—	—	23	—	69.0	54.0	42.0	15.0	38.0	[3]
$v' = 43$, $J' = 11$ and 15	—	1.63	2.65	5.17	6.9	6.7	1.17	—	—	—	—	9.2	—	—	—	5.3	[6]

TABLE III

ROTATIONAL ENERGY TRANSFER IN $I_2(B\ ^3\Pi_{0_u}{}^+)$, $v'_{initial} = 25$, $J'_{initial} = 34$

Partial inelastic cross section for given buffer gas and vibrational state change[a]
[Mb($= 10^{-18}$ cm^2)]

ΔJ	^{3}He $\Delta_v = -2$	-1	0	$+1$	$+2$	^{4}He $\Delta_v = -1$	0	$+1$	Kr $(\Delta_a = 0)$	I_2 $(\Delta_v = 0)$
-34	—	0.07	0.07	0.10	0.02	0.03	0.12	0.03	0.43	1.32
-32	—	0.08	0.15	0.12	0.03	0.05	0.14	0.05	0.65	1.61
-30	—	0.10	0.20	0.14	0.03	0.10	0.21	0.09	0.86	1.9
-28	—	0.13	0.25	0.17	0.04	0.14	0.26	0.14	1.08	2.3
-26	0.01	0.17	0.37	0.20	0.05	0.17	0.34	0.19	1.5	2.6
-24	0.02	0.20	0.48	0.24	0.06	0.23	0.45	0.24	1.7	2.8
-22	0.02	0.29	0.70	0.31	0.07	0.28	0.69	0.29	2.4	3.0
-20	0.03	0.36	0.90	0.34	0.08	0.38	0.88	0.36	2.8	3.3
-18	0.05	0.51	1.21	0.39	0.09	0.52	1.22	0.47	3.4	3.7
-16	0.07	0.63	1.76	0.44	0.10	0.68	1.65	0.54	4.7	4.2
-14	0.08	0.89	2.7	0.46	0.10	0.89	2.3	0.61	6.2	5.6
-12	0.13	0.97	3.9	0.55	0.11	1.04	3.4	0.71	8.2	8.4
-10	0.20	1.16	5.4	0.65	0.12	1.18	4.5	0.87	10.5	11.7
-8	0.25	1.45	6.9	0.80	0.12	1.46	7.0	0.95	13.3	16.3
-6	0.29	1.81	8.9	0.91	0,13	1.8	9.5	1.08	17.4	25.8
-4	0.32	1.96	11.2	0.98	0.14	1.9	13.5	1.18	24.8	32.8
-2	0.36	2.0	12.8	1.02	0.15	2.0	20.0	1.25	46.4	38.4
0	0.38	2.1	—	1.11	0.17	2.2	—	1.27	—	—
$+2$	0.34	1.95	12.8	1.02	0.15	2.0	20.0	1.18	46.4	41.9
$+4$	0.32	1.67	11.8	0.96	0.14	1.8	14.1	1.11	25.2	38.1
$+6$	0.29	1.32	9.4	0.80	0.13	1.56	9.9	0.82	17.9	32.8
$+8$	0.24	1.04	7.8	0.61	0.12	1.34	7.0	0.73	14.2	25.8
$+10$	0.20	0.90	5.4	0.58	0.12	1.06	5.2	0.66	10.3	11.7
$+12$	0.19	0.70	4.4	0.48	0.12	0.83	3.8	0.56	8.4	8.5
$+14$	0.15	0.65	3.0	0.41	0.11	0.66	2.8	0.47	6.5	5.6
$+16$	0.12	0.54	2.0	0.31	0.10	0.56	1.9	0.36	5.0	4.2
$+18$	0.10	0.44	1.32	0.25	0.10	0.42	1.39	0.30	3.9	3.7
$+20$	0.07	0.37	1.11	0.15	0.09	0.33	1.05	0.23	3.2	3.3
$+22$	0.05	0.29	0.86	0.12	0.09	0.28	0.75	0.17	2.6	2.8
$+24$	0.03	0.22	0.55	0.12	0.09	0.23	0.57	0.16	2.0	2.6
$+26$	0.02	0.20	0.43	0.10	0.08	0.17	0.45	0.10	1.6	2.1
$+28$	0.02	0.14	0.31	0.08	0.08	0.14	0.37	0.09	1.3	1.6
$+30$	0.02	0.12	0.21	0.07	0.08	0.12	0.24	0.07	0.95	1.4
$+32$	0.01	0.10	0.15	0.05	0.07	0.10	0.19	0.05	0.75	1.17
$+34$	0.01	0.08	0.14	0.03	0.07	0.09	0.16	0.05	0.65	1.17
$+36$	—	0.07	0.10	0.03	0.06	0.07	0.14	0.03	0.56	0.88
$+38$	—	0.05	0.07	0.03	0.06	0.05	0.12	0.02	0.43	0.88
$+40$	—	0.05	0.05	0.02	0.05	0.05	0.10	0.02	0.35	0.70

[a] From Steinfeld and Klemperer [3].

TABLE III (*continued*)

Partial inelastic cross section for given buffer gas and vibrational state change[a]
$[Mb(= 10^{-18} \text{ cm}^2)]$

ΔJ	$\Delta_v = -2$	-1	0	$+1$	$+2$	$\Delta_v = -1$	0	$+1$	Kr ($\Delta_v = 0$)	I_2 ($\Delta_v = 0$)
		³He					⁴He		Kr	I_2
$+42$	—	0.03	0.03	0.02	0.04	0.04	0.09	0.01	0.28	0.70
$+44$	—	0.03	0.03	0.01	0.03	0.04	0.07	0.01	0.26	0.59
$+46$	—	0.02	0.02	0.01	0.02	0.03	0.07	—	0.19	0.47
$+48$	—	0.02	0.02	—	0.02	0.02	0.05	—	0.17	0.44
$+50$	—	0.02	0.01	—	0.01	0.02	0.05	—	0.13	0.23
$+52$	—	0.01	0.01	—	0.01	0.02	0.04	—	0.11	0.15
$+54$	—	0.01	—	—	—	0.01	0.03	—	0.09	0.09
$+56$	—	—	—	—	—	0.01	0.02	—	0.06	0.03
$+58$	—	—	—	—	—	—	0.02	—	0.04	—
$+60$	—	—	—	—	—	—	0.01	—	0.02	—
$+62$	—	—	—	—	—	—	0.01	—	—	—
$+64$	—	—	—	—	—	—	—	—	—	—

[a] From Steinfeld and Klemperer [3].

Vibrational deactivation is accompanied by extensive rotational relaxation. Near the top of the potential well, stepwise vibrational transitions may be replaced by direct dissociation into the continuum. These and other observations are now being tested by trajectory analysis [11], and should form the basis for a good insight into the nature of the redistribution of energy in collisions.

ACKNOWLEDGMENTS

I would like to thank the agencies which have supported this work—principally, the National Science Foundation and the Petroleum Research Fund of the American Chemical Society—and those individuals who have been associated with me in carrying it out—namely Robert L. Brown, Jim Campbell, Eugene Degenkolb, Robert Frank, Lorrie Jones, Prof. William Klemperer, Richard Kurzel, Mike Lesk, Neil Schweid, Judy Selwyn, Dr. Ed. Wasserman, Natalie Weiss, and Prof. Richard Zare.

References

1. J. Franck, *Verh. Deut. Phys. Ges.* **14**, 419 (1912); R. W. Wood and J. W. Franck, *Ibid.* **13**, 84; *Phys. Z.* **12**, 81; *Phil. Mag.* **21**, 265 (1911).
2. J. I. Steinfeld, R. N. Zare, L. Jones, M. Lesk, and W. Klemperer, *J. Chem. Phys.* **42**, 25 (1965).
3. J. I. Steinfeld and W. Klemperer, *J. Chem. Phys.* **42**, 3475 (1965).
4. R. L. Brown and W. Klemperer, *J. Chem. Phys.* **41**, 3072 (1964).

5. L. Brewer, R. A. Berg, and G. M. Rosenblatt, *J. Chem. Phys.* **38**, 1381 (1963).

6. J. I. Steinfeld and R. B. Kurzel, *J. Chem. Phys.* **53**, 3293 (1970).

7. J. I. Steinfeld and A. N. Schweid, *J. Chem. Phys.* **53**, 3304 (1970).

7a. D. Hatzenbuhler, G. Leroi, J. Steinfeld, and R. Kurzel, *J. Chem. Phys.* **55**, 4822 (1971).

8. J. I. Steinfeld, *Accounts Chem. Res.* **3**, 313 (1970).

9. E. O. Degenkolb, J. I. Steinfeld, E. Wasserman, and W. Klemperer, *J. Chem. Phys.* **51**, 615 (1969).

10. J. I. Steinfeld, *J. Chim. Phys.* **64**, 17 (1967).

11. D. Feldman, D. G. Sutton, and J. I. Steinfeld, *Proc. Intl. Conf. Phys. Electronic Atomic Collisions, 7th, July 1971*, p. 638. North-Holland Publ. Amsterdam.

4.4 Nuclear Hyperfine Structure in the Electronic Spectra of Diatomic Molecules

T. M. Dunn

Department of Chemistry
University of Michigan
Ann Arbor, Michigan

A. Introduction

1. ATOMS

The earliest detection of nuclear hyperfine structure (as distinct from effects due to isotopic mass shifts) in atomic electronic spectra [1–3] dates back to the final decade of the nineteenth century following the construction of both Fabry–Perot and Gehrcke–Lummer interferometers. These studies were restricted to the observation of complex stucture within what appeared to be single atomic lines when viewed using spectrographs of relatively low resolving powers. Such observations were extended, and to some extent classified, by the work of Janicki [4] and Wali-Mohammed [5], but the recognition of the nature and origin of these hyperfine "flag" patterns as associated with a small nuclear magnetic moment was not forthcoming until the work of Pauli [6] in 1924 and Russell *et al.* [7] in 1927 (see Fig. 1).

The first successful theoretical treatment and analysis followed rapidly late in 1927 and early in 1928 when, in a pair of papers, Goudsmit and Back [8] analyzed and discussed the hyperfine structure found in the atomic spectrum of bismuth in terms of the vector model. Application of vector coupling methods led them to formulate a Landé interval rule for hyperfine energy levels by analogy with that obtained for the coupling of the electron orbital and spin angular momenta L and S to yield the total electronic angular momentum J. By analogy, they defined

$$\mathbf{F} = \mathbf{I} + \mathbf{J}$$

$\mathbf{I}$ being defined as the nuclear spin momentum and $\mathbf{F}$ as the total atomic angular momentum. Application of the well-known cosine coupling relationships leads to the hyperfine energy

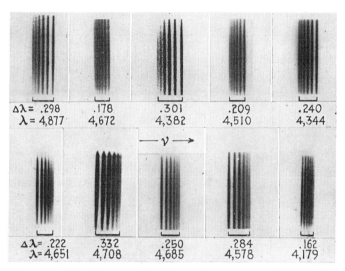

$\Delta\lambda= .298$ .178   .301   .209   .240
$\lambda = 4,877$ 4,672   4,382   4,510   4,344

$\longrightarrow \nu \longrightarrow$

$\Delta\lambda= .222$ .332   .250   .284   .162
$\lambda=4,651$ 4,708   4,685   4,578   4,179

FIG. 1. Hyperfine "flag" patterns in the atomic spectrum of praeseodymium. The photograph is a reproduction of the figure given by White [7a] and we are indebted to him and to the American Physical Society for permission to reproduce it.

$$W_F = \tfrac{1}{2}A_F[F(F+1) - I(I+1) - J(J+1)]$$

where A_F is the coupling coefficient pertinent to the complete hyperfine multiplet ranging over all values of F from $J + I$ to $J - I$ and distinguished here from its spin–orbit coupling analog A_J by the subscript. The hyperfine interval rule quickly follows by the usual substitution of F and $F + 1$ for constant J and I in the above formula, and subtraction yields

$$\Delta W(F + 1, - F) = A_F(F + 1)$$

Such an energy level pattern persists into most diatomic molecular spectra exhibiting hyperfine structure since the nuclear moment is almost never coupled to any internal (internuclear) axis and is, therefore, quantized only in the external (laboratory) coordinate frame. In this respect, it differs considerably from the more usual effects of spin–orbit coupling in molecules, at least as manifested by those molecules with Hund's case (a) coupling, where the molecular term intervals become simple integral multiples of A_Ω since, for such cases,

$$W_\Omega = \tfrac{1}{2}A_\Omega[\Omega^2 - \Lambda^2 - \Sigma^2]$$

2. MOLECULES

The observation of nuclear hyperfine structure in electronic molecular spectra is more clearly documented than for the atomic case, but even here

there are some obscure aspects. As perhaps might have been anticipated, the earliest effects were both sought and found in metal hydride spectra, for reasons which will be apparent from Table I when coupled with the favorable reciprocal moments of inertia of such compounds.

TABLE I

STABLE NUCLIDES WITH $\mu' \geq |0.5|$

Atom	Mass number	Abundance	I	μ'	Q
Nb	93	100	9/2	6.14	—
[Tc]	99	0	9/2	5.66	—
In	113	4.3	9/2	5.50	1
In	115	95.7	9/2	5.50	1
V	51	99.75	7/2	5.14	—
Sc	45	100	7/2	4.75	—
Co	59	100	7/2	4.64	0.5
Bi	209	100	9/2	4.04	−0.4
Pr	141	100	5/2	3.8	—
La	138	0.089	5	3.68	0.9
Al	27	100	5/2	3.64	—
Mn	55	100	5/2	3.46	0.4
Eu	151	48	5/2	3.42	1.2
Sb	121	57	5/2	3.34	−0.6
V	50	0.25	6	3.34	0.3
Ho	165	100	7/2	3.3	±2
Li	7	92.6	3/2	3.26	—
Re	187	63	5/2	3.18	2.6
Re	185	37	5/2	3.14	2.8
Lu	176	2.6	5–7	2.8	8
H	1	99.985	1/2	2.79	—
I	127	100	5/2	2.79	−0.7
La	139	99.91	7/2	2.76	—
B	11	81	3/2	2.69	—
Cs	133	100	7/2	2.56	—
Sb	123	43	7/2	2.53	−0.8
Ga	71	39.8	3/2	2.55	—
Cu	65	31	3/2	2.38	—
Cu	63	69	3/2	2.22	—
Na	23	100	3/2	2.22	—
Br	79	50.5	3/2	2.10	0.33
Ta	181	99.988	7/2	2.1	3
Ga	69	60.2	3/2	2.01	—
Lu	175	97.4	7/2	2	6
O	17	0.037	5/2	−1.89	—
Eu	153	52	5/2	1.50	2.5
Er	167	23	7/2	0.5	±10
Hg	201	13	3/2	−0.61	0.5
Hg	199	17	1/2	0.50	—

The earliest claim for the detection of hyperfine effects was by Mrozowski [9] in October 1931. He examined the spectrum of HgH using a Gehrcke–Lummer interferometer crossed with a quartz spectrograph—resolving power, $\sim 350\,000$. He was unable to explain the number and intensity of lines found in this spectrum, even allowing for the number of naturally occurring stable isotopes of mercury [196 (0.15), 198(10.02), 199(16.84), 200(23.13), 201(13.22), 202(29.80), and 204(6.85)], but the analysis was not completely convincing since the magnetic nuclei 199 and 201 have very small magnetic moments (~ 0.5 and ~ 0.6, respectively), so that the splittings are not sufficient to easily be distinguishable from the simple isotopic mass shift effects. With hindsight, and with information more recently gained from isotopically enriched samples it certainly would appear that Mrozowski did observe hyperfine effects even though no analysis was possible.

In fact, his ascription of the observation to a hyperfine origin was disputed early the following year (1932) by Hulthén [10]. Professor Hulthén had also been searching for evidence of hyperfine effects in diatomic metal hydrides, in particular, BiH. In his letter to *Nature*, Hulthén cited work in progress by himself and Heimer on the spectrum of BiH and particularly drew attention to the $^1\Pi \leftarrow {}^1\Sigma^*$ system (in the red) in which they had observed "a small but distinct broadening of the first few lines in the series" and which they "interpreted as an effect of the nuclear spin in bismuth." The analysis of this system was announced later in 1932 [11] and published [12] in detail in 1935, but the system shows only line broadening (at low J) and no resolved hyperfine structure.

Mrozowski continued his work on HgH, publishing work on nuclear isotope shift effects in 1935 [13] as well as a very much higher resolution study [14] in 1949 in which he used a Fabry–Perot interferometer. In the latter studies, he was able to establish the presence of two components for each line in the ^{199}HgH spectrum at low J values. This study was the first in which resolved nuclear hyperfine structure was actually observed, although Mrozowski was unable to analyze his results in detail.

The first clear analysis of hyperfine effects in an electronic transition of a diatomic molecule came in 1956 from Hulthén and Neuhaus [15]. They observed a clear splitting of the $J = 1, 2$, and 3 lines in the system at $16\,340\ \text{cm}^{-1}$ of BiH (and BiD) and were able to assign the hyperfine structure and to discuss the nuclear coupling case involved. They analyzed the transition as $B^1\Sigma \rightarrow A^1\Pi$, but there are reasons to doubt their assignment and these are discussed further in Section C. For historical interest, their Fortrat diagram is reproduced in Fig. 2.

Since that time, hyperfine structure has been resolved in a spectrum of one other hydride, indium hyride [16, 17] (as well as InD). The spectra of HgH [18, 19], HgD [19], and HgT [19], have also been completely resolved at low J and fully analyzed by Davis and his collaborators. The nonhydrides CN

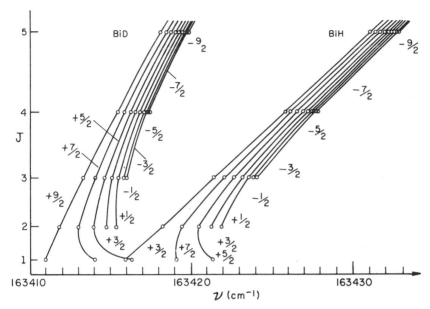

FIG. 2. Fortrat diagram of the hyperfine structure in the Q branches of the BiH and BiD spectra at $\lambda = 6118$ Å. The curves are drawn according to the magnetic quantum numbers M_I of the Bi nucleus.

[20, 21], LaO [22], ScO [23, 24], LuO [25], NbN [26], and NbO [27] have also been studied and hyperfine effects observed and analyzed. In addition, unresolved features which can be attributed to hyperfine origins have been observed and analyzed in VO [29, 28] and BiO [30]. Most of these hyperfine effects can be analyzed without recourse to the effects of nuclear quadrupole interactions, but in at least two cases, some quadrupolar interaction has been found necessary for an understanding of the spectra, and in one particular case, that of InH, it has been found to play a very important role.

B. Theoretical

1. MAGNETIC INTERACTIONS

The basic work on magnetic hyperfine interactions in diatomic molecules is that of Frosch and Foley [31] and their general treatment will be followed here. Discussion will be restricted to those diatomic molecules containing only one magnetic nucleus even though some of the molecules considered experimentally (e.g., metal hydrides) may have both nuclei with $I \neq 0$. Even so, in the cases which we shall examine, the magnetic moment of one of the nuclei usually dominates the situation even though this may not always be expected to be so, as in molecules such as In_2, etc.

In general, we may expect four sources of magnetic moment which must be appropriately coupled: (a) that due to electronic orbital angular momentum (vector $\mathbf{L}$); (b) moment due to electronic spin angular momentum (vector $\mathbf{S}$); (c) moment due to nuclear spin angular momentum (vector $\mathbf{I}$); (d) moment due to overall rotation of the diatomic molecule (vector $\mathbf{J}$); it is convenient to consider the coupling of $\mathbf{I}$ with $\mathbf{L}$ and $\mathbf{S}$ separately. Thus [32],

$$H_{IL} = 2g_I\mu_0\mu_n\Lambda(1/r^3)_{av}\mathbf{I} \cdot \mathbf{k}$$

where g_I is the nuclear "g" factor, μ_0 is the Bohr (electron) magneton, μ_n is the nuclear magneton, Λ is the average projection of the orbital angular momentum of the electron on the internuclear axis, $\mathbf{k}$ is the unit vector along this axis, and r is the distance of the nth electron from the magnetic nucleus.

The classical interaction between two magnetic dipoles $\boldsymbol{\mu}_1$ and $\boldsymbol{\mu}_2$ has the form

$$W = (\boldsymbol{\mu}_1 \cdot \boldsymbol{\mu}_2/r^3) - [3(\boldsymbol{\mu}_1 \cdot \mathbf{r})(\boldsymbol{\mu}_2 \cdot \mathbf{r})/r^5]$$

and if subscript 1 denotes the magnetic nucleus and 2 the spinning electron, $\boldsymbol{\mu}_1 = g_I\mu\mathbf{r}$ and $\boldsymbol{\mu}_2 = -2\mu_0\mathbf{S}$, whence

$$H'_{IS} = 2g_I\mu_0\mu_n\{(\mathbf{I} \cdot \mathbf{S}/r^3) - [3(\mathbf{I} \cdot \mathbf{r})(\mathbf{S} \cdot \mathbf{r})/r^5]\}$$

Such an expression is valid only for non-s electrons, i.e., those for which $\psi \to 0$ as $r \to 0$ and, for a single nucleus containing s-electron density, it has been shown that

$$H''_{IS} = (16\pi/3)g_I\mu_0\mu_n\psi^2(0)\mathbf{I} \cdot \mathbf{S}$$

The total interaction is the sum of these and, for the internal axis system, it has been shown [31] for the Hund electronic coupling cases (a) and (b) that

$$H^1 = a\Lambda\mathbf{I} \cdot \mathbf{k} + b\mathbf{I} \cdot \mathbf{S} + c(\mathbf{I} \cdot \mathbf{k})(\mathbf{S} \cdot \mathbf{k})$$

where

$$a = 2g_I\mu_0\mu_n(1/r^3)_{av}$$
$$b \sim 2g_I\mu_0\mu_n \{(8/3)\pi\psi^2(0) - [(3\cos^2\chi - 1)/2r^3]\}_{av}$$
$$c \sim 3g_I\mu_0\mu_n [(3\cos^2\chi - 1)/r^3]_{av}$$

In these expressions, the "averaging" is over the electronic space coordinates for the states in question and all matrix elements are assumed to be diagonal in Λ. The first term in b is referred to as the "Fermi contact term" and describes the contribution from any s-electron density. It should also be noted that the angle χ is the angle defined by $\mathbf{r}$ and $\mathbf{k}$ so that, if averaged over a completely spherical (s) electron distribution, $3\cos^2\chi - 1 = 0$ and, for such a case,

$$c = 0 \quad \text{and} \quad b = (16\pi/3)g_I\mu_0\mu_n\psi^2(0)$$

For $\psi^2(0) = 0$, i.e., no s-electron contribution at the magnetic nucleus,

$$3b + c = 0$$

Thus, if the magnitudes of b and c can be ascertained, the presence of unpaired s-electron density may be confirmed or denied.

It is now necessary to discuss the manner in which the various angular momenta are coupled in the molecule and the following are the most important extreme cases. Hund's electronic case (a)→(a_α, a_β), and Hund's electronic case (b)→(b_β) only (b_α being illogical), where the Greek subscripts denote the nuclear analogs of Hund's electronic coupling cases.

a. Case (a)

(i) Case (a_α)

Such a case is the nuclear analog of Hund's case (a) coupling and it implies that the magnetic interaction of the nuclear moment with the electronic orbital and spin moments will be sufficiently strong to force the nuclear spin to be quantized in the internal (molecular axis) coordinate frame (see Fig. 3a).

FIG. 3. The vector model of case (a) nuclear coupling: (a) case (a_α); (b) case (a_β).

(a)   (b)

This case is not expected to arise very often, if at all, since the coupling energies of nuclear magnetic moments are only $\sim 1/1000$th of those for electron moments, so that they are very small indeed. Evidence of such behavior will be exhibited by the appearance of equally spaced components in the nuclear hypermultiplet, although such a spacing will not be maintained once the molecule starts to rotate, because of spin uncoupling from the molecular axis. So far, no experimental example of this coupling case has been found.

(ii) Case (a_β)

For molecules with $\Lambda \neq 0$ (and $S \neq 0$), this is expected to be the most commonly occurring type of coupling. The subscript β implies quantization only in the external (laboratory) coordinate frame and, as such, the hyperfine components will be expected to exhibit a Landé-type spacing, i.e., proportional to the larger value of F. The vector diagram is given in Fig. (3b).

Since $\mathbf{I} \cdot \mathbf{k} = (\mathbf{I} \cdot \mathbf{J})(\mathbf{J} \cdot \mathbf{k})/J(J + 1)$ for good case (a) coupling, $(\mathbf{J} \cdot \mathbf{k}) = \Lambda + \Sigma = \Omega$ and $(\mathbf{S} \cdot \mathbf{k}) = \Sigma$, and the hyperfine operator H^1 simplifies to yield the hyperfine energy

$$W(a_\beta) = [a\Lambda + (b + c)\Sigma] \cdot \Omega \cdot \mathbf{I} \cdot \mathbf{J}/J(J + 1)$$

where $\mathbf{I} \cdot \mathbf{J} = 1/2[F(F + 1) - I(I + 1) - J(J + 1)]$. Strictly, this expression holds only for the part of the energy diagonal in J [since we assumed "ideal" case (a) coupling], but there are also nonvanishing terms which are off-diagonal in J and there, matrix elements have the form [31]

$$\pm 1/2[(J^2 - \Omega^2)^{1/2}/J(4J^2 - 1)^{1/2}]$$
$$[(F + J - I)(F + I - J + 1)(F + I + J + 1)(J + I - F)]^{1/2}$$

and may be important in those cases where the molecular reciprocal moment of inertia is small and the hyperfine energies are large—as is easily possible for molecules such as InO, etc., i.e., where case (a) is likely to still be a reasonable approximation, but where the reciprocal moment of inertia is ~ 0.35 cm^{-1} and where $\mu' \approx 5.5$ (see Table I).

Considering only the term diagonal in J, it is immediately clear that the hyperfine component separations decrease with increasing J, i.e., they might be expected to be observable only at low J values in the various rotational branches. Also, the separations should be Ω-dependent (and should vanish for $\Omega = 0$, e.g., $^3\Pi_0$). Finally, in optical hyperfine effects, we may anticipate that $a \ll b \gg c$, so that the main contributing term is simply $b\Sigma$ and the hyperfine effects should be vanishingly small for $\Sigma = 0$ (as, e.g., in $^3\Pi_1$, $^3\Delta_2$, $^3\Phi_3$, etc.). Any departure from this last condition (in the absence of electric quadrupole effects) will usually represent good evidence in favor of case (c) tendencies rather than case (a), so that such effects serve as a very sensitive indication as to the nature of the electronic coupling.

Since, in case (a), $\Lambda \neq 0$, we must enquire as to what effects might be expected in the almost degenerate $\pm \Omega$ components i.e., the c, d, lambda doublets.

Such effects have been considered in detail by both Frosch and Foley [31] and by Townes and Schawlow [32], who have calculated the terms off-diagonal in both Λ and J, and show that for the former, there are nonvanishing terms connecting states for which $\Delta\Lambda = \pm 1, \pm 2$, i.e., the only case (a) states involved should be Π states for which $\Delta\Lambda = \pm 2$ for each lambda doublet. For case (a) this leads to an additional term in the energy—the so-called "hyperfine doubling" term, i.e.,

$$W(a_\beta) = [a\Lambda + (b + c)\Sigma] \cdot \Omega \cdot [\mathbf{I} \cdot \mathbf{J}/J(J + 1)] \pm d(J + 1/2) \cdot [\mathbf{I} \cdot \mathbf{J}/2J(J + 1)]$$

where $d = 3\mu_0 g_I \mu_I [(\sin^2\chi)/r^3]_{av}$. This expression may be greatly simplified in special cases and some of these will be discussed in Section C.

b. *Case* (b)

When neither I nor S are internally quantized and if, as is more frequent, $\Lambda = 0$, the hyperfine operator reduces to

$$b(\mathbf{I} \cdot \mathbf{S}) + c(\mathbf{I} \cdot \mathbf{k})(\mathbf{S} \cdot \mathbf{k})$$

Figure 4 gives the possible ways in which the nuclear spin might be imagined to couple with the other Hund case (b) vectors. Thus, one may envisage: initial coupling of I and N ($= K$ if $\Lambda = 0$), case ($b_{\beta N}$) (Fig. 4a); coupling of I

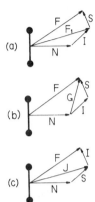

FIG. 4. The vector model of case (b) nuclear coupling: (a) case ($b_{\beta N}$); (b) case ($b_{\beta S}$); (c) case ($b_{\beta J}$).

directly to S, case ($b_{\beta S}$) (Fig. 4b); coupling of I to J, case ($b_{\beta J}$) (Fig. 4c), where the notation should be self-explanatory.

(i) *Case* ($b_{\beta N}$)

This is unlikely to be found in practice, since both **S** and **J** usually have much larger associated magnetic moments than does **N** (or **K**), so that **I** will couple to them rather than to **N**.

(ii) *Case* ($b_{\beta S}$)

This coupling scheme is not expected to be very important for molecules which are composed of elements of low atomic number, but it may well be very important for many of the diatomic molecules containing transition elements, particularly those molecules having $^2\Sigma$ electronic states.

In this scheme, **I** first couples to **S** to produce a resultant **G** which, in turn, couples to **N(K)** to yield **F**.

In the first place, it should be clear that case ($b_{\beta S}$) will be the rule for the nonrotating molecule, since there are no competing magnetic moments of rotational origin under such circumstances and the diagonal part of the energy reduces to

$$W(b_{\beta S}) = [(3b + c)/6][F(F + 1) - S(S + 1) - I(I + 1)]$$
$$= [(3b + c)/6][G(G + 1) - S(S + 1) - I(I + 1)]$$
$$\approx (b/2)[G(G + 1) - S(S + 1) - I(I + 1)]$$

The second line follows from the first since, for $N = 0$, $F = G$, and the final

approximation results from the assumption of $b \gg c$. Clearly, such a formulation is exactly what would be obtained for a free-space coupling of the two vectors $\mathbf{I}$ and $\mathbf{S}$, i.e.,

$$\mathbf{G} = \mathbf{I} + \mathbf{S}$$

The question remains as to the effect of rotation upon this coupling case, and this is not easy to answer in a closed form since, in general, rotation will imply a tendency towards the final coupling case $(b_{\beta J})$ as $\mathbf{S}$ becomes decoupled from $\mathbf{I}$ and couples to $\mathbf{N}$. It has been shown [20] that such an intermediate coupling case can be formulated in a closed, albeit much parametrized, form for $^2\Sigma$ states, but this is beyond the scope of this present review. There is, however, a relatively simple criterion for how rapidly the case $(b_{\beta S})$ coupling will convert to case $(b_{\beta J})$ under the influence of rotation. It should be clear that this depends primarily upon the magnitude of the spin uncoupling with $\mathbf{I}$ or, rather, on the magnitude of the $\mathbf{S} \cdot \mathbf{N}$ interaction. This interaction—for $^2\Sigma$ states at least—is usually expressed in terms of the spin doubling constant γ, i.e.,

$$W = \gamma \mathbf{S} \cdot \mathbf{N}$$

Now, the magnitude of γ depends upon a number of factors, but it may be viewed as made up of a part due to the coupling of the magnetic moment of $\mathbf{S}$ with the magnetic moment generated by the rotational motion of the positive and negative charges which make up the molecule and, more importantly, a part which can be described in terms of second-order spin–orbit coupling or terms which are off-diagonal in Λ. The operation of this latter effect is best seen in the case of " pure precession " discussed so elegantly by Van Vleck [33], in which he treated the relationship between the Λ doubling constant of a Π state and the spin doubling constant of the related Σ state for the particular situation where the two states are simply generated by different projections of the same $\mathbf{L}$ vector on the internuclear axis. In such an approximation, Van Vleck showed that the two constants are equal, and simply represent the extent to which electronic angular momentum is mixed into the Σ state under the influence of molecular rotation. In accord with the usual perturbation form of these constants, their magnitudes are inversely proportional to the energy separation of the Σ and Π states. Thus, their magnitude, i.e., $\gamma = \pm 4AB/\Delta v(\Pi\text{–}\Sigma)$ may be very large indeed (about 1 cm^{-1} or so) for small Π–Σ separations and for large spin–orbit coupling energies and reciprocal inertial constants, and such $^2\Sigma$ states will rapidly move from case $(b_{\beta S})$ to case $(b_{\beta J})$, even for very small values of N.

On the other hand, and most importantly, there exist situations where a $^2\Sigma$ state is not generated by the zero projection of a nonzero $\mathbf{L}$ vector, i.e., when the $^2\Sigma$ state arises from an atomic S term which, in turn, arises from a purely s-electron configuration. Since l (or $\mathbf{L}$) is not defined in the molecule, it is not

possible to find pure "s-origin" Σ states, except in such circumstances that other atomic orbital states capable of contributing to Σ states are well separated from the "s-origin" Σ state on *both* the magnetic nucleus *and* the nonmagnetic nucleus [34]. Such conditions are well satisfied in compounds between transition metal atoms and elements such as C, N, O, halogen, i.e., those elements with very large ionization potentials relative to the uncharged transition metal atom.

Thus, a transition metal (ion) possessing an unpaired ns electron and forming a diatomic molecule with a fully filled shell, first-row element (ion) should go a long way to fulfilling the above requirements since the lowest nonzero "l" state will be about 15–20 000 cm^{-1} above the ns state with a concomitantly near-vanishing contribution to the spin doubling constant of the (ground) $^2\Sigma$ state of predominantly s origin. Examples have now been found with precisely these characteristics (e.g., ScO) and will be discussed further in Section 3. For the present, all that need be observed is the fact that the hyperfine splitting levels should be unchanged by increasing N to a very high degree. In fact, the X $^2\Sigma$ (ground) state of ScO fulfills these expectations completely.

It might also be noted that case $(b_{\beta S})$ coupling is unlikely for those states with spin multiplicities exceeding 2—i.e., for more than a single unpaired "s" electron unless the configuration is $ns\ ms$, since the spin–spin and associated pseudoquadrupolar interactions are also sufficient to cause a departure from "pure" case $(b_{\beta S})$ coupling. A correlation diagram for case $(b_{\beta S}) \rightarrow$ case $(b_{\beta J})$ coupling is given in Fig. 5, and it should be noted that N remains well defined in both coupling cases and that no levels change in N value going from one extreme to the other.

(iii) *Case* $(b_{\beta J})$

The complete hyperfine Hamiltonian may be much simplified if one retains only those terms which yield energies diagonal in $N(K)$. Under such circumstances, $c(\mathbf{I} \cdot \mathbf{k})(\mathbf{S} \cdot \mathbf{k})$ can be ignored since $(\mathbf{S} \cdot \mathbf{k})$ has no such elements and if $\Lambda = 0$ is assumed, i.e., Σ states only, then the only term remaining is that in $b(\mathbf{I} \cdot \mathbf{S})$. Using Frosch and Foley's matrix elements, two terms are obtained, one diagonal and the other off-diagonal in J, i.e., for the diagonal term

$$W(b_{\beta J}) = \{[J(J + 1) - N(N + 1) + S(S + 1)]/2J(J + 1)\}\mathbf{I} \cdot \mathbf{J}$$
$$= (g_J - 1)\mathbf{I} \cdot \mathbf{J}$$

This formula has a very similar appearance to that obtained for normal atomic hyperfine coupling [35]. There is also a term off-diagonal in J ($\Delta J = \pm 1$) [29] which will be discussed in Section C. In fact, the energy problem can be solved in specified cases [31, 32] ($S = 1/2, 1, 3/2, \ldots$) for those levels having

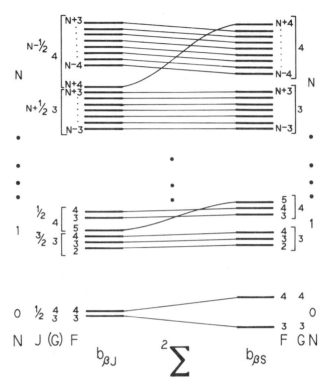

FIG. 5. Schematic correlation diagram for case $(b_{\beta J}) \leftrightarrow (b_{\beta S})$ nuclear coupling for $^2\Sigma$ states. In practice, one of the spin components in $(b_{\beta J})$ is a regular hypermultiplet, while the other component is inverted.

the same value of N, without the assumption that the term in c vanishes, and these energy values for $^2\Sigma$, $^3\Sigma$, and $^4\Sigma$ states are given in Table II.

Exactly what is to be expected in case $(b_{\beta J})$ coupling is not really apparent from the formulas presented in Table II, but if the c term is once again ignored, the expressions in Table III are obtained. From these expressions, the following observations can be made. First, the hypermultiplets have the expected Landé form. Second, there are significant differences in both the N dependence and the overall widths of the multiplets. Third, some of the hypermultiplets are inverted (those preceded by the negative sign).

For the $^2\Sigma$ state, the overall multiplet width should quickly become independent of N with *both* the F_1 and F_2 stack widths being identical and of absolute width $\frac{1}{2}Ib$.

Note the inverted form of the F_2 stack hypermultiplet. This inversion will not generally have spectroscopic consequences, but may cause different linewidths if the transition occurs from (or to) an upper state having a significant hypermultiplet width caused by coupling of a different type e.g., case $(b_{\beta S})$,

TABLE II

MAGNETIC HYPERFINE ENERGIES OF $^2\Sigma$, $^3\Sigma$, AND $^4\Sigma$ STATES FOR CONSTANT N IN CASE $(b_{\beta J})$ [a]

$^2\Sigma$

$$W(F_1) = [1/(2N+1)]\{b + [c/(2N+3)]\}\mathbf{I} \cdot \mathbf{J}$$
$$W(F_2) = [1/(2N+1)]\{-b + [c/(2N-1)]\}\mathbf{I} \cdot \mathbf{J}$$

$^3\Sigma$

$$W(F_1) = [1/(N+1)]\{b + [c/(2N+3)]\}\mathbf{I} \cdot \mathbf{J}$$
$$W(F_2) = [1/(N+1)][(b/N) + (c/N)]\mathbf{I} \cdot \mathbf{J}$$
$$W(F_3) = (1/N)\{-b + [c/(2N-1)]\}\mathbf{I} \cdot \mathbf{J}$$

$^4\Sigma$

$$W(F_1) = [1/(N+\tfrac{3}{2})]\{3b/2 + [3c/4(N+\tfrac{3}{2})]\}\mathbf{I} \cdot \mathbf{J}$$
$$W(F_2) = [1/(N+\tfrac{1}{2})]\{[b(N+\tfrac{9}{2})/2(N+\tfrac{3}{2})] + [3c/4(N+\tfrac{1}{2})]\}\mathbf{I} \cdot \mathbf{J}$$
$$W(F_3) = [1/(N+\tfrac{1}{2})(N-\tfrac{1}{2})]\{[-b(N-\tfrac{7}{2})/2] + 3c/4\}\mathbf{I} \cdot \mathbf{J}$$
$$W(F_4) = [1/(N-\tfrac{1}{2})]\{-\tfrac{3}{2}b + [3c/4(N-\tfrac{1}{2})]\}\mathbf{I} \cdot \mathbf{J}$$

[a] Here, $F_1 = N + S$, $F_2 = N + S - 1$, etc. In these expressions, it has been assumed that *all* the unpaired electrons are equivalent. This is clearly not usual and the energies should therefore be corrected by a numerical factor of $\frac{1}{2}$ if only one of the electrons in the $^3\Sigma$ state is of s type and by $\frac{1}{3}$ if only one of the three electrons in the $^4\Sigma$ state is of s type. Correction in this manner is necessary to obtain an absolute magnitude for b. This footnote also applies to Table III, where the widths must be corrected by the same factors.

TABLE III

OVERALL WIDTHS OF MAGNETIC HYPERFINE ENERGY MULTIPLETS OF $^2\Sigma$, $^3\Sigma$, AND $^4\Sigma$ STATES FOR CASE $(b_{\beta J})$ COUPLING AND CONSTANT N [a]

$^2\Sigma$

$$\Delta W(F_1) = I[(N+1)/2N+1] \cdot b$$
$$\Delta W(F_2) = -I[N/(2N+1)] \cdot b$$

$^3\Sigma$

$$\Delta W(F_1) = 2I[(N+\tfrac{3}{2})/(N+1)] \cdot b$$
$$\Delta W(F_2) = 2I[(N+\tfrac{1}{2})/N(N+1)] \cdot b$$
$$\Delta W(F_3) = -2I[(N-\tfrac{1}{2})/N] \cdot b$$

$^4\Sigma$

$$\Delta W(F_1) = 3I[(N+2)/(N+\tfrac{3}{2})] \cdot b$$
$$\Delta W(F_2) = I[(N+1)(N+\tfrac{9}{2})/(N+\tfrac{1}{2})(N+\tfrac{3}{2})] \cdot b$$
$$\Delta W(F_3) = -I[N(N-\tfrac{7}{2})/(N+\tfrac{1}{2})(N-\tfrac{1}{2})] \cdot b$$
$$\Delta W(F_4) = -3I[(N-1)/(N-\tfrac{1}{2})] \cdot b$$

[a] Here, $\Delta W(F_1) = W(F_1)_{max} - W(F_1)_{min}$, where $(F_1)_{max} = N + S + I$ and $(F_1)_{min} = N + S - I$. Also see the footnote to Table II.

or with a different coupling constant. It is more usual to find—as will appear in Section C—that the combining state has a nonobservable hyperfine width, and, in such a case, the only difference between the two "spin component" hypermultiplets might simply be a mirror image intensity effect if the multiplet components are not individually resolved and the spin splitting is resolved (Fig. 6). Quadrupolar effects may also obscure this pattern by upsetting the Landé level distribution (see Section B2).

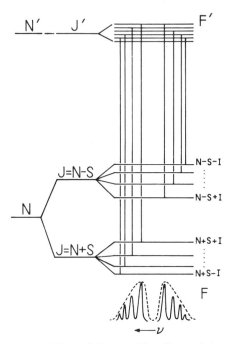

FIG. 6. Schematic representation of the possible effects of the spin splitting hypermultiplet inversion upon the spectrum of a case $(b_{\beta J})$ coupled $^2\Sigma$ state. The dashed contour represents the possible experimental envelope of the unresolved hyperfine structure.

For the $^3\Sigma$ state, the effects are somewhat more dramatic since the level width formulas show clearly that whereas $\Delta W(F_1)$ and $\Delta W(F_3)$ are independent of N (at moderate N), $\Delta W(F_2)$ is approximately inversely proportional to N. Thus, under most spectroscopic situations, the spectra—say, a $^3\Sigma \rightarrow {}^3\Sigma$ transition—will consist of two different types of lines, one with wide linewidths which quickly become constant with N, and one which will quickly become narrow and remain so for higher N. Such a case has not yet been observed, but it might be expected in a $^3\Sigma \rightarrow {}^3\Sigma$ transition of a molecule such as VC (which is, as yet, unknown).

The $^4\Sigma$ analog has already been well documented both for VO [28] and NbO [27]. In similar transitions observed in the visible region for both of

these molecules, $^4\Sigma^- \leftrightarrow {}^4\Sigma^-$, both wide and narrow branches are observed, the wide lines having widths ~ 0.4 cm^{-1} for VO and ~ 0.85 cm^{-1} for NbO. This will be discussed at greater length in Section C. It is important to realize that the actual linewidths also depend upon the nature of the excited-state hyperfine manifolds and, under certain conditions, it could happen that all lines are narrow because of compensating widths. The inverted nature of the F_3 and F_4 hypermultiplets should also be noted.

c. Case (c)

Theoretical studies of magnetic hyperfine effects in case (c) coupling have been made by Mustelin [36] Freed [37] and Atkins [38]. In particular, Freed applied his theoretical treatment to case (c) tendencies in InH and included the effects of quadrupolar interaction, leading to an F-dependent Λ doubling showing marked deviations from the interval rule in the splittings found for the $R(0)$, $Q(1)$, and $P(2)$ lines of the $(0, 0)$ band of the $^3\Pi_1 \leftrightarrow {}^1\Sigma$ system. In a pure case (a_β) coupling, there will be an extremely small magnetic hyperfine effect, since the only contributing term is that in $a\Lambda\Omega$ (since $\Sigma = 0$) and the value of A_F $(= \frac{1}{2}a)$ derived from the data is ~ 0.02 cm^{-1}, compared with the supposedly theoretically equivalent value for A_F in the $^1\Pi$ state of ~ 0.006 cm^{-1}. Both Mustelin's [36] work and Freed's [37] more general calculations (which allow correlation with Mustelin's more simple assumptions and formulas) show that in case (c) coupling the contribution of b is no longer zero $[A_F = \frac{1}{4}(a + b + c)]$ and will therefore contribute to the hyperfine splitting. In fact, Freed [37] did not rely upon this term to explain the observed splittings, since it does not produce an F-dependent Λ doubling, but explained them in terms of a combination of magnetic effects of unspecified origin together with the electric quadrupolar interaction, both diagonal and off-diagonal in Ω, the latter being necessary to explain the anomalous Λ doubling.

Atkins [38] derived explicit energy expressions for the $|\Omega| = \frac{1}{2}$ state of case (c) hyperfine interactions, particularly with the molecule BiO in mind. In this molecule, it is possible to show that quadrupolar terms are not involved since the ground term—the one being investigated—is X_1 $^2\Pi_{1/2}$ $(\Omega = \frac{1}{2})$, so that all matrix elements of the quadrupole tensor operator vanish. He was also able to show that even for states with $|\Omega| > \frac{1}{2}$, the widths observed by Barrow et al. are too large to be accounted for by the relatively small Q value for ^{209}Bi $(\sim 0.4 \times 10^{-24}$ cm$^2)$. For further details, the original papers should be consulted [30, 38].

2. Electric Quadrupole Interactions

As yet, there have been only a few cases where the presence of electric quadrupole effects have been shown to affect optical hyperfine structure. If the quadrupole "moment" is represented by Q, then for Σ states, it has been shown that [39]

$$\Delta W(Q) = \frac{e^2 qQ[(3/8)C(C + 1) - (1/2)I(I + 1)J(J + 1)]}{I(2I - 1)(2J - 1)(2J - 1)(2J + 3)}$$

where

$$C = 2\mathbf{I} \cdot \mathbf{J} \quad \text{and} \quad eq = (\partial^2 v/\partial z^2)_{av} \equiv \int [(3z^2 - r^2)/r^5] \, de$$

and where $\Delta W(Q)$ is the quadrupolar interaction energy of the nuclear electric quadrupole on the magnetic-cum-quadrupolar nucleus. There is no simple form unless $J \gg I$ (which is not, however, a good approximation for most of the cases so far studied in optical hyperfine effects), when

$$\Delta W(Q) = e^2 qQ[3(F - J)^2 - I(I + 1)]/4I(2I - 1)$$

This shows the asymptotic form of the pure quadrupole effect in that for $J \gg I$, $\Delta W(Q)$ is independent of the sign of $F - J$. The splitting is, therefore, non-Landé in type and such interactions, when combined with the magnetic effects, will cause deviations from the interval rule such as are observed in InH. Thus, high-J levels split into only $I + 1$ $(I + \frac{1}{2})$ hyperfine components rather than the $2I + 1$ expected for magnetic effects, and there will be a clustering into pairs of levels defined by $J \pm I$ which, in the high-J limit, will be degenerate. The theory of the quadrupolar effects has been worked out in details for use in rf and microwave spectroscopy and references in these fields will provide all the finer details [32, 40–43]. So far, the observations have been fragmentary in optical work, with the exception of new types of ultrahigh-resolution work [44, 45] described very briefly in Section D.

C. Experimental

It is convenient to classify the observed hyperfine effects under the various coupling cases to which they have been assigned, even though, as expected, they seldom can be totally described in such terms.

1. CASE (a_α)

None so far reported.

2. CASE (a_β)

Electronic states of the molecules BiH(D), InH(D), HgH(D and T), and NbN have been considered as examples of this type of coupling.

The initial observation of optically resolved hyperfine structure in the red system of BiH was originally analyzed as (a_β) coupling in the $^1\Pi$ state of the $^1\Sigma \rightarrow {}^1\Pi$ transition, but there are reasons to doubt the details of the assignment. Hulthén and Neuhaus [15] found a value of $A_F = 0.0540$ cm^{-1} for the coupling constant i.e., $\frac{1}{2}(a\Lambda + (b + c)\Sigma]\Omega = 0.0540$ cm^{-1} and for the $^1\Pi$ state

$\Sigma = 0$ and $\Omega = 1$, so that $a \approx 0.108$ cm^{-1}. Such a magnitude is almost certainly too large to be attributed to a purely orbital origin and it is far more likely that the transition is

$$0^+ \, (^1\Sigma) \to 1^\pm \, (^3\Pi_1)$$

Such an assignment allows a contribution from the b constant in the case (c) limit and this is clearly desirable if the value of a is not to be inflated and the intervention of electric quadrupole effects not invoked. The interval rule is well obeyed and this precludes a significant contribution from quadrupole effects. Indeed, if the deviations from case (a_β) can be treated in a manner similar to Mustelin's [36], then $b \approx 0.2$ cm^{-1}, a not unreasonable value in the light of the results known from the BiO molecule [30].

The InH molecule has also been discussed above from the standpoint of case (a_β) coupling—with the addition of electric quadrupole effects—and will not be considered further here.

Porter and Davis [18] and Eakin and Davis [19] have made a thorough examination of the $A_1 \, ^2\Pi_{1/2} \to X \, ^2\Sigma^+$ system of both ^{201}HgH and ^{199}HgH (D, T) and have been able to assign the nuclear coupling cases in both states, cases (a_β) and ($b_{\beta J}$), respectively. In the $^2\Pi_{1/2}$ states, the predominant hyperfine effect is from the " hyperfine doubling " term (no doubling was observable in the $A_2 \, ^2\Pi_{3/2}$ state) and, as can be seen from the previous section, for $I = \frac{1}{2}$, the energy difference between the $J + \frac{1}{2}$ and $J - \frac{1}{2}$ hyperfine components is given by

$$\Delta \dot{W}(F_{J+(1/2)} - F_{J-(1/2)}) = [(J + \tfrac{1}{2})/2J(J + 1)][a - \tfrac{1}{2}b - \tfrac{1}{2}c \pm d(J + \tfrac{1}{2})]$$

i.e., each of the components of the Λ doublet is split in equal and opposite directions, with the upper "hypermultiplet" a regular one, while the lower one is inverted. The scheme is shown in Fig. 7. The equation also shows that a constant splitting of $d/2$ is finally obtained for large J and it is in this way that the constant d was obtained by Eakin and Davis [19] ($d/2 = 0.0357$ cm^{-1}).

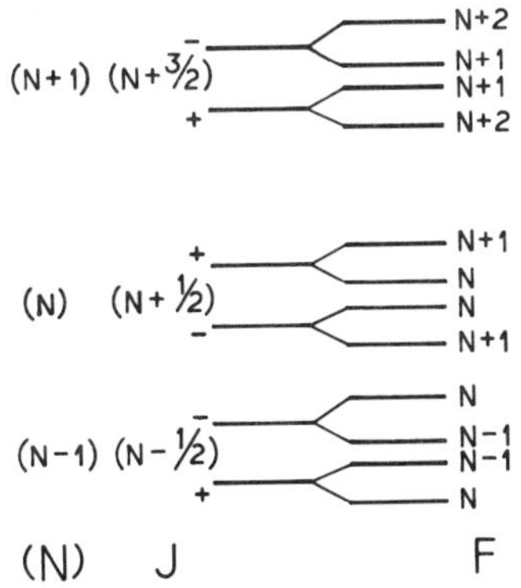

FIG. 7. The effects of Λ doubling upon the hyperfine doubling in a $^2\Pi_{1/2}$ state for a molecule such as HgH where $I(\text{Hg}) = \frac{1}{2}$.

The value of b in the $^2\Pi_{1/2}$ state can also be obtained by using the usual approximation $a \ll b \gg c$, but this was not done in the original paper and since the actual splittings were not given, no estimate could be made by the present author.

The only example of case (a_β) coupling for a nonhydride molecule so far known occurs in the $^3\Delta$ state of the $^3\Phi \to {}^3\Delta$ transition of NbN in the red region of the spectrum [26]. All three subbands $^3\Phi_4 \to {}^3\Delta_3$, $^3\Phi_3 \to {}^3\Delta_2$, and $^3\Phi_2 \to {}^3\Delta_1$ are present and the hyperfine effects are limited to the $^3\Delta_3$ and $^3\Delta_1$ components, the $^3\Delta_2$ showing neither splitting nor broadening (see Fig. 8a.) The $^3\Delta_3$ component has a splitting constant almost exactly three times that of the $^3\Delta_1$ and noticeable broadening in the R branches in particular (which are clearly visible) can be observed out to $\sim R(9)$–$R(10)$ in the Δ_1 component and to $\sim R(20)$ in the Δ_3. Complete splitting of the lowest two R lines occurs in the $^3\Delta_1$ component, the $R(1)$ line splitting into what appears to be either four or five lines, while $R(2)$ yields six, and possibly seven (see Fig. 8b). Since the electric quadrupole moment of ^{93}Nb is only ~ -0.16, it does not give a sufficiently large effect to explain all the effects observed [25], and further work is continuing on this spectrum.

3. CASE $(b_{\beta N})$

None so far reported.

4. CASE $(b_{\beta S})$

Some discussion has already been given above with regard to the requirements for this coupling case. The only completely documented example to this time is the ground $^2\Sigma$ state of ScO [24, 46]. This molecule has two intense emission systems in the visible—one in the green-blue, which has been shown [24] to be B $^2\Sigma \to X\,^2\Sigma$, and another in the orange [23, 47], A $^2\Pi_r \to X\,^2\Sigma$. The main feature of both systems is a doubling of all lines by 0.25 cm^{-1}, so that the source of the doubling is most obviously the ground state. The remarkable feature which emerges from the analysis is that the doubling remains constant, within experimental error, to $N \approx 130$ in the green-blue system—the lines themselves being unchanged, either in width or separation.

Such an independence from the magnetic effects of overall rotation strongly suggests the presence of an "s-origin" $^2\Sigma$ state and this has been confirmed by the details of the analysis. Scandium-45 has a natural abundance of 100% with a large magnetic moment (see Table I) and the nuclear spin therefore couples directly to the electron spin to give the vector $\mathbf{G}$. Such an effect might also occur for many very low N levels of a $^2\Sigma$ state, but in this case, the $\mathbf{N} \cdot \mathbf{G}$ interaction constant is very close to zero. Thus, the scandium atom behaves as if it simply has an unpaired $4s(\sigma)$ electron localized on it and the usual formulation yields the fact that the splitting interval $\Delta v = 4b$, i.e., $b = 0.067$ cm^{-1}. It also becomes clear that the excited Π and Σ states may be viewed as the

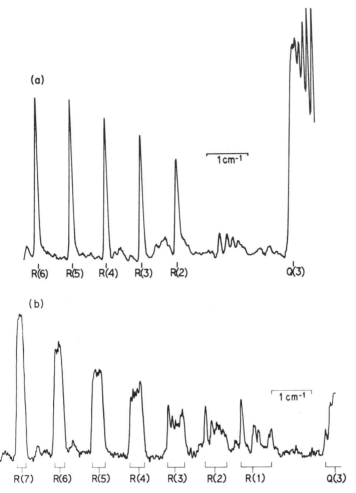

FIG. 8. (a) Microdensitometer record of the first few R and Q lines in the $^3\Phi_3 \to {}^3\Delta_2$ subband of the NbN red system. $R(2)$ has, perhaps, the faintest perceptible broadening. (b) Microdensitometer record of the first few R lines in the $^3\Phi_2 \to {}^3\Delta_1$ subband of the NbN red system showing extensive hyperfine splitting in $R(1) \to R(7)$.

Stark field split ^2P term arising from an odd "4p" electron outside closed shells [34] and because of the angular node in this "4p" wave function, the hyperfine coupling constant c $(b = 0)$ is very small, since it depends upon $\langle r^{-3} \rangle_{av}$, and is not resolved in either the $^2\Pi$ or $^2\Sigma$ excited states where, strictly, the coupling is case $(b_{\beta J})$. The correct analysis of this particular system confirmed the suspicions of Jorgensen [48] as well as of Berg *et al.* [49], who had arrived at a similar conclusion from molecular beam experiments

with the molecule LaO. There can be no doubt that the 0.48-cm^{-1} splitting observed in LaO by Akerlind [22] and the present author [25] and of a similar splitting in LuO [25] have a similar origin. The consequences of this particular analysis have been of some importance in an understanding of the nature of the bond between metals and nonmetals [34], but it is outside the scope of this report.

The other possible molecules which should behave in a very similar manner, namely the alkaline earth halides, have no hyperfine effects since the metal nuclei are of the even–even type. Isotopes ^{43}Ca, ^{87}Sr, and ^{137}Ba do exist, but have very small nuclear magnetic moments and their hyperfine structure may not be resolvable in the optical region. An ESR study of the matrix-isolated ScO molecule by Kasai and Weltner [46] has given the same result for the ground state as was obtained from the optical analysis and it will be interesting when the alkaline earth halides have been examined by the same methods in order to ascertain the nature of the ground state.

5. CASE ($b_{\beta J}$)

There have been quite a number of recent studies of molecular states showing this type of coupling. The best examples are HgH, CN, VO, and NbO. The radical CN was the first observed example of the hyperfine structure of an electronically excited $^2\Sigma$ state. The coupling is, in fact, an intermediate case and values of b, c, and eQq were obtained by Radford [20] from the data of Evenson et al. [21] and by Barger et al. [50]. The hyperfine structure was not detected in the usual way, but was detected from the change in the intensity of the 0, 0 band of the B $^2\Sigma \to$ X $^2\Sigma$ system of the CN molecule. Briefly, CN was prepared chemically in the $J = 3\frac{1}{2}$, $v = 10$ level of the A $^2\Pi$ state, which happens to lie only $\sim 10^4$ MHz lower than the $N = 4$, $J = 3\frac{1}{2}$, $4\frac{1}{2}$ of the $v = 0$ level of the B $^2\Sigma$ state. It is, therefore, possible to microwave "pump" molecules from the lower pair of levels to the higher, and population of the higher state leads to optical emission to the ground state, which may be monitored photoelectrically. Thus, scanning through a range of microwave frequencies (from $\sim 10^4$ MHz to ~ 8800 MHz) while monitoring the fluorescence in the 0–0 band of the B $^2\Sigma \to$ X $^2\Sigma$ system, allows the complete hyperfine structure to be mapped. [50]

The constants found by Radford [20] are

$$b = 467 \pm 10 \quad \text{MHz}, \qquad c = 60 \pm 15 \quad \text{MHz}, \qquad eQq = -5 \pm 5 \quad \text{MHz}.$$

It should be possible—and has been partly attempted—to obtain a much better idea of the nature of the excited B $^2\Sigma$ state CN from these values, but the conclusions are, as yet, somewhat unconvincing [20, 51].

The ground, X $^2\Sigma$ state of HgH has been found to be a case ($b_{\beta J}$) coupling from an analysis of the A $^2\Pi \to$ X $^2\Sigma$ transition using ^{201}Hg [18] and even more

completely with ^{199}HgH(D, T) [19]. The separation of the excited-state case
(a_β) coupling effects was greatly facilitated by the fact that both the A_2 $^2\Pi_{3/2} \to$
$^2\Sigma$ and A_1 $^2\Pi_{1/2} \to X$ $^2\Sigma$ subbands were observed, the former proving to have
no observable excited-state hyperfine effects, thereby allowing an easier
analysis of the hyperfine effects arising from the ground state. Unfortunately,
no precise frequencies are available in these two papers and, apart from some
comments to the effect that some "partial decoupling to case ($b_{\beta S}$) at low
values of J" occurs, no complete analysis has so far been given.

For the rest, the X $^2\Sigma$ state behaves as an almost ideal ($b_{\beta J}$) coupling case,
a value of $b = 0.2010$ cm^{-1} being obtained for the $v'' = 1$ level. By observing
several vibrational levels, Eakin and Davis [19] were able to observe the
changes in the hyperfine constants as a function of vibration, e.g., b decreases
with increasing vibrational quanta, more for HgH than for HgD, etc. These
changes, when sufficiently understood, may turn out to be one of the most
interesting contributions to a knowledge of the molecular wave function since
d, c, and a have $\langle r^{-3} \rangle_{av}$ behavior, while b gives a combination of $\psi^2(0)$ and
$\langle (3 \cos^2 \chi - 1)/2r^3 \rangle_{av}$ behavior. The evidence therefore favors a greater
change in the $\langle (3 \cos^2 \chi - 1)/2r^3 \rangle_{av}$ part of b than in the $\psi^2(0)$ part.

The VO molecule is also an extremely interesting example of case ($b_{\beta J}$)
coupling [28, 29]. This is quite certain, even though the individual hyperfine
components have never been resolved. Two systems are concerned, that in the
green having been analysed as $^4\Sigma^- \leftrightarrow ^4\Sigma^-$ and that in the red as $^4\Pi \leftarrow ^4\Sigma^-$.
Both of the systems contain lines of two types—one very broad, $\Delta v \approx 0.4$
cm^{-1}, and one rather narrow, $\Delta v \approx 0.1$ cm^{-1}. The broad lines are of constant
linewidth in the range $15 < N < 70$, and all of the hyperfine effects can be
shown to be confined to the ground, $^4\Sigma^-$ state. VO has also been examined in
matrix by ESR and the nature of the ground state is confirmed as $^4\Sigma^-$ [52].

The explanation of the structure is to be found in Tables II and III, particularly the latter, since it is clear from the entries in Table III that the total
hyperfine manifold widths of the F_1 and F_4 stacks (i.e., those for which $J =$
$N \pm \frac{3}{2}$) are about three times that for the F_2 and F_3 stacks, both of them
being independent of N for moderate N values. There is now good evidence
[28, 53] for the ground configuration of VO as $s\sigma^1 d\delta^2$, $^4\Sigma^-$ so that only one
of the electrons really contributes to the optically measurable hyperfine
width (whence the footnote to Tables II and III). The excited states of the
molecule are probably well described as $d\delta^2 p\sigma^1$, $^4\Sigma^-$ and $d\delta^2 p\pi^1$, $^4\Pi$ for the
green and red systems, respectively, and, following the same argument as for
the excited state of the ScO blue-green system, no hyperfine effects will be
observable for these case ($b_{\beta J}$) coupled excited states. Thus, transitions from
the F_1, F_4 stacks are broad, while those from F_2, F_2 are about one-third of
the width.

An estimate of b may be obtained from the linewidths, these being $\sim 3.5b$
and $\sim 1.2b$ for the broad, narrow lines respectively. Thus, $b \approx 0.1$ cm^{-1},

although, after allowing for Doppler broadening, a slightly lower value, ~ 0.08 cm^{-1}, is preferable. This should be compared with the b value found for ScO (0.067), due regard being paid to the fact that $\mu'(^{51}V) > \mu'(^{45}Sc)$, together with the addition of the accumulated nuclear charge quantum defect due to the presence of two extra d electrons on the vanadium atom. It seems clear that the comparison is well founded and that the analysis is correct. Further discussion is to be found in a recent review by Cheetham and Barrow [53].

It is also worthy of note that the green system of VO exhibits what might well turn out to be a unique type of perturbation [29]. Thus, extra lines are observed in the R_2, R_3, P_2, and P_3 branches in all of the vibrational bands studied (2–0, 1–0, 0–0, 0–1, 0–2) and a similar effect is also observed in the red system. Preliminary appearances suggested some type of perturbation between the F_2 and F_3 rotational stacks in the range $12 < N < 18$, whereas these two level stacks differ by $\Delta J = 1$ for the same N and should not perturb one another according to Kronig's rules. However, if due regard is paid to the fact that the total angular momentum quantum number is F rather than J and the F values are calculated for each J ($I = \frac{7}{2}$ for ^{51}V), seven of the eight hyperfine components of each of the F_3 and F_4 stacks have the same F value. The perturbation thus follows the selection rule $\Delta F = 0$. The part of the original hyperfine Hamiltonian responsible for the perturbation is the $\mathbf{I} \cdot \mathbf{S}$ part for those elements off-diagonal in J. The form of these matrix elements will not be given here since they have been given by both Frosch and Foley [31] and Richards and Barrow [29].

The identification of branches from the linewidths is quite a general feature of molecular hyperfine phenomena and has its almost direct counterpart in the differing energy widths of the "flag" patterns observed in atomic hyperfine structure for lines arising from the same components of a spin multiplet. Another molecular example, for which no optical spectra exist, is to be found in the microwave spectrum [54] of the oxygen molecule $^{16}O^{17}O$ with a $^3\Sigma_g^-$ ground state. Analysis of the hyperfine structure reported for this molecule (^{17}O has $I = \frac{5}{2}$) shows the F_1 and F_3 hypermultiplets to be ~ 6–7 times as wide as that arising from the F_2 stack. Once again, this effect is clearly evident from the information for $^3\Sigma$ states in Table III.

Finally, NbO also has two systems showing very large hyperfine effects [27], one in the red and the other in the blue. Analysis indicates that the blue system is $^4\Sigma^- \rightarrow {}^4\Sigma^-$ and the appearance of the red system suggests $^4\Pi \rightarrow {}^4\Sigma^-$, although there are some features of the latter analysis which are hard to reconcile with such an assignment. As with VO, both systems show narrow and broad lines, although in the case of NbO, it has proved possible, in many places on the spectrum, to completely resolve all ten hyperfine components in the broad branches. The appearance of part of these systems is shown in Figs. 9 and 10. A complete analysis has not yet been possible due to the very severe problems of the overlapping of the extraordinarily wide branches at low N, but some

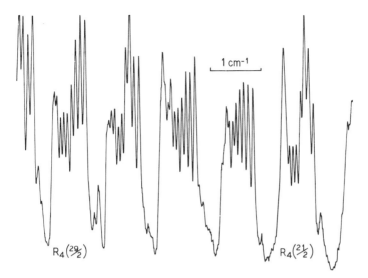

FIG. 9. Part of the R_4 branch in the red system of the NbO (probably $^4\Pi \rightarrow {}^4\Sigma^-$) showing completely resolved hyperfine structure. The irregularities are due to superposed lines from another branch which runs through the spectrum. The Landé spacing of the lines is quite obvious.

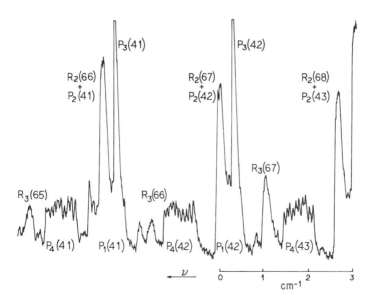

FIG. 10. Part of the system of NbO, $^4\Sigma^- \rightarrow {}^4\Sigma^-$ showing the narrow branch lines as well as the wide branch lines with all ten hyperfine component lines being quite clear. The Landé form is not apparent because of the very large N values.

idea of the constant b can be obtained from the overall hypermultiplet width of ~ 0.86 cm^{-1} (at the stage when this width is independent of N). This width gives $b \approx 0.19$ cm^{-1}, which is very large indeed, but it must be realized that, as shown in Table I, ^{93}Nb has the largest known nuclear magnetic moment (together with a very small $Q \approx -0.16$).

6. CASE (c$_\beta$)

An example of this is to be found in the well-studied spectra of the BiO molecule [30]. In particular, the ground state is X_1 $^2\Pi_{1/2}(\frac{1}{2})$ and the lowest excited state (apart from the companion X_2 level) is the A $^2\Pi_{1/2}(\frac{1}{2})$ state at $\sim 14,000$ cm^{-1}. The transition consists of a series of very wide lines ($\Delta\nu \approx 0.25$ cm^{-1}) in the region $25.5 < J < 90.5$. Two other transitions at higher energies also show lines of about the same width (B$\leftarrow$X$_1$ and C$\leftarrow$X$_1$), while the highest-energy transition (D$\leftarrow$X$_1$) has some quite sharp lines together with some very broad ones.

The analysis is somewhat complicated by the intermediate coupling involved but it seems clear that levels X_1 and D both have significant hyperfine widths, with A, B, and C very narrow. This results in the wide lines found for the first three systems and it appears that the hyperfine width cancels out for some lines of the D$\leftarrow$X$_1$ system due to a simple top$\rightarrow$top bottom$\rightarrow$bottom transition selection rule for the hypermultiplets, while it adds to the width in other lines by a top$\rightarrow$bottom, bottom$\rightarrow$top series of transitions. Atkins [38] has calculated the effects of case (c) upon the spectrum and concludes that the appearance of the lines is basically in agreement with theory, at least for the D$\leftarrow$X$_1$ system.

D. Summary

The past 15 years have seen a rapid growth in our knowledge of molecular hyperfine effects in optical spectroscopy. Needless to say, much of the theory has been calculated for the use of microwave and rf spectroscopists using molecular beams—both of which possess resolving powers far in excess of that available for direct optical hyperfine spectroscopy.

Recently, however, two new approaches have come to the subject—one of them being an essential outgrowth of the pioneering study of Evenson et al. [21] and Barger et al. [50], allied to certain aspects of level-crossing atomic spectroscopy. Thus, in 1968, van der Waals and collaborators [55] as well as Harris and co-workers [56, 57] were able to obtain excellent spectra of nuclear quadrupole and magnetic dipole hyperfine effects in the solid-state spectrum of the lowest electronic triplet transition in chloroquinoxaline and similar compounds. The principle simply involves excitation of the lowest spin-

allowed transition, whence intersystem crossing conveys the energy to the three zero-field levels of the lowest-lying molecular triplet state. Since nitrogen is one of the ring atoms and chlorine is a substituent, each of the zero-field levels really consists of a complex hypermultiplet of both quadrupolar and magnetic origin. Transitions between hypermultiplets belonging to different zero-field levels can be effected by microwave pumping, while the visible phosphorescence spectrum is monitored with a relatively low-resolution optical monochromator. In this way, even quadrupole coupling coefficients may be obtained, as well as a great deal of information regarding energy transfer. Even though these molecules are not diatomic and are not in the gas phase, nonetheless, these PMDR (ParaMagnetic Double Resonance) experiments are a direct offshoot of very similar ones in diatomic molecular spectroscopy and it is clear that the techniques employed here will find increasing use in the near future.

Recently, the development of laser technology has allowed the use of excitation of fluorescence and saturated absorption in a laser cavity to produce hyperfine structure [45]. In one particular case [44], the quadrupolar and magnetic hyperfine structure of the set of lines based upon $J'' = 127$ of the iodine molecule, Kroll was able to analyze the structure seen in the laser cavity experiment and resolving powers $\sim 10^8$ were achieved by this method. There is again no doubt that there will continue to be rapid progress in this aspect of hyperfine spectroscopy.

Finally, the ability to observe hyperfine effects in electronic spectroscopy provides a very sensitive probe for the molecular spectroscopist. Thus, the extreme sensitivity of such effects to relatively minor changes in electric field gradients and "central" field potentials enable a much more detailed study to be made of the precise nature of the chemical bond and the behavior of electrons in excited electronic states in general. Thus, e.g., case (c) tendencies in electronic coupling can be much more sensitively detected from the behavior of the hyperfine structure [58] than from a detailed analysis of the rotational energy levels of the molecule.

Already much information has been obtained regarding which electronic configurations give rise to the various molecular terms found in the spectra of transition metal compounds [34, 53] with oxygen, nitrogen, and the halogens and the information has enabled the role of the d and f electrons in the more complex coordination compounds to be better understood. Also, as theoretically constructed molecular wavefunctions improve for ground states, such information will be invaluable for a comparison of the theoretically calculated properties of excited states with those actually observed and it is with the realization that chemistry is mainly dependent upon the nature of the electronically excited states of the interacting species that the importance of hyperfine effects looms large to a chemical spectroscopist.

References

1. A. A. Michelson, *Phil. Mag.* **31**, 338 (1891).
2. C. Fabry and A. Perot, *Ann. Chim. Phys.* [7] **12**, 459 (1897).
3. O. Lummer and E. Gehrcke, *Ann. Phys.* **10**, 457 (1903).
4. L. Janicki, *Ann. Phys.* **29**, 833 (1909).
5. Ch. Wali-Mohammed, *Astrophys. J.* **39**, 185 (1914).
6. W. Pauli, *Naturwissenschaften* **12**, 741 (1924).
7. H. N. Russell, W. F. Meggers, and K. Burns, *J. Opt. Soc. Amer.* **14**, 449 (1927).
7a. H. E. White, *Phys. Rev.* **34**, 1397 (1929).
8. S. Goudsmit and E. Back, *Z. Phys.* **43**, 321 (1927); **47**, 174 (1928).
9. S. Mrozowski, *Z. Phys.* **72**, 776 (1931).
10. E. Hulthén, *Nature* **129**, 56 (1932).
11. E. Hulthén and A. Heimer, *Nature* **129**, 399 (1932).
12. A. Heimer, *Z. Phys.* **95**, 328 (1935).
13. S. Mrozowski, *Z. Phys.* **95**, 524 (1935).
14. S. Mrozowski, *Phys. Rev.* **76**, 1820 (1949).
15. E. Hulthén and H. Neuhaus, *Phys. Rev.* **102**, 1415 (1956).
16. H. Neuhaus, *Z. Phys.* **150**, 4 (1958).
17. H. Neuhaus, *Z. Phys.* **152**, 402 (1958).
18. T. L. Porter and S. P. Davis, *J. Opt. Soc. Amer.* **53**, 338 (1963).
19. D. M. Eakin and S. P. Davis, *J. Mol. Spectrosc.* **35**, 27 (1970).
20. H. E. Radford, *Phys. Rev. A* **136**, 1571 (1964).
21. K. M. Evenson, J. L. Dunn, and H. P. Broida, *Phys. Rev.* **136**, A1566 (1964).
22. L. Akerlind, *Ark. Fys.* **22**, 65 (1962).
23. L. Akerlind, *Ark. Fys.* **22**, 41 (1962).
24. A. Adams, W. Klemperer, and T. M. Dunn, *Can. J. Phys.* **46**, 2213 (1968).
25. T. M. Dunn, To be published.
26. T. M. Dunn and K. M. Rao, *Nature* **222**, 266 (1969).
27. T. M. Dunn and K. M. Rao, To be published.
28. D. Richards and R. F. Barrow, *Nature* **217**, 842 (1968).
29. D. Richards and R. F. Barrow, *Nature* **219**, 1244 (1968).
30. R. F. Barrow, W. J. M. Gissane, and R. Richards, *Proc. Roy. Soc. Ser. A* **300**, 469 (1967).
31. R. A. Frosch and H. M. Foley, *Phys. Rev.* **88**, 1337 (1952).
32. C. H. Townes and A. L. Schawlow, "Microwave Spectroscopy," p. 194. McGraw-Hill, New York, 1955.
33. J. H. Van Vleck, *Phys. Rev.* **33**, 467 (1929).
34. T. M. Dunn, Physical chemistry, an advanced treatise valency. *In* "Coordination Compounds" (H. Eyring, D. Henderson, and W. Yost, eds.), Vol. V, Chapter 5. Academic Press, New York, 1970.
35. H. E. White, "Introduction to Atomic Spectra," p. 366. McGraw-Hill, New York, 1934.
36. N. Mustelin, Thesis, Abo Akademi Abo, Finland.
37. K. F. Freed, *J. Chem. Phys.* **45**, 1714 (1966).
38. P. W. Atkins, *Proc. Roy. Soc. Ser. A.* **300**, 487 (1967).
39. H. B. Casimir, *Physica (Utrecht)* **2**, 719 (1935).
40. B. T. Feld, *Phys. Rev.* **72**, 111b (1947).
41. I. I. Rabi, S. Millman, P. Kusch, and J. R. Zacharias, *Phys. Rev.* **55**, 526 (1939).
42. P. Kusch, S. Millman, and I. I. Rabi, *Phys. Rev.* **57**, 765 (1940).
43. H. Kopfermann, "Nuclear Moments." Academic Press, New York, 1958.
44. M. Kroll, *Phys. Rev. Lett.* **23**, 631 (1969).
45. G. R. Hanes and C. E. Dahlstrom, *Appl. Phys. Lett.* **14**, 362 (1969).

46. P. H. Kasai and W. Weltner, Jr., *J. Chem. Phys.* **43**, 2553 (1965).
47. A. Adams and T. M. Dunn, To be published.
48. C. K. Jorgensen, *Mol. Phys.* **7**, 417 (1964).
49. R. A. Berg, L. Wharton, and W. Klemperer, *J. Chem. Phys.* **43**, 2416 (1965).
50. R. L. Barger, H. P. Broida, A. J. Estin, and H. E. Radford, *Phys. Rev. Lett.* **9**, 345 (1962).
51. K. F. Purcell, *J. Chem. Phys.* **47**, 1198 (1967); **48**, 5735 (1968).
52. P. H. Kasai, *J. Chem. Phys.* **49**, 4979 (1968).
53. C. F. Cheetham and R. F. Barrow. The spectroscopy of diatomic transition element molecules, *Adv. High Temp. Chem.* **1**, 7 (1967).
54. S. L. Miller and C. H. Townes, *Phys. Rev.* **90**, 537 (1953).
55. J. Schmidt and J. H. van der Waals, *Chem. Phys. Lett.* **2**, 640 (1968).
56. D. S. Tinti, M. A. El-Sayed, A. H. Maki, and C. B. Harris, *Chem. Phys. Lett.* **3**, 343 (1969).
57. C. B. Harris, D. S. Tinti, M. A. El-Sayed, and A. H. Maki, *Chem. Phys. Lett.* **4**, 409 (1969).
58. T. Larsson and H. Neuhaus, *Ark. Fys.* **27**, 275 (1964).

CHAPTER 5

MATRIX SPECTRA

5.1 Infrared and Ultraviolet Spectroscopic Studies of Free Radicals and Molecular Ions Isolated in Inert Solid Matrices

Dolphus E. Milligan and Marilyn E. Jacox

National Bureau of Standards
Washington, D.C.

General Discussion

In order to explain the detailed course of a large number of chemical reactions, for many years the chemist has found it necessary to postulate the existence of free radicals, or species possessing incompletely filled valence-shell electron octets in their ground states. Because of the great reactivity of such species, their concentrations in chemical reaction systems are characteristically small, and for a long time they eluded direct physicochemical observation. The first direct observations of free radicals were those of the physicist, who assigned prominent emission band systems observed in flames and other luminescent sources to such species as OH, CN, and C_2. However, studies of the emission band spectra of triatomic and polyatomic free radicals have been, with few exceptions, fraught with great difficulty. Processes giving rise to such emission band systems commonly are sufficiently energetic to reduce larger molecules to atomic and diatomic fragments, and, even when emission bands of more complicated molecules have been observed, the band structure has usually been too complex for a definitive analysis.

The flash photolysis technique, which involves the production of a high transient concentration of molecular fragments by an intense burst of ultraviolet radiation over a time interval of the order of 10^{-5} sec or less and their

subsequent detection by a variety of spectroscopic techniques, was first utilized by Porter [135, 137] for the spectroscopic study of free radicals. These pioneering studies, which were recently accorded the Nobel Prize in Chemistry, have provided the basis for studies in many laboratories. Especially detailed information on the high-resolution absorption spectra of free radicals in the gas phase has resulted from the utilization of apparatus similar to that of Callomon and Ramsay [20]. The detection and detailed spectroscopic analysis of electronic transitions of a large number of diatomic and simple polyatomic free radicals have resulted from flash photolysis studies in the laboratories of Herzberg, Ramsay, and Douglas of the National Research Council of Canada. These studies represent an outstanding contribution to the literature of chemical physics and spectroscopy.

Despite the great power of the flash photolysis technique, with few exceptions its use has been limited to studies of allowed electronic transitions. Although for a few systems it has been possible to assign " hot bands " and thus to obtain some data on the ground-state vibrational frequencies, the lack of a cumulative detector suitable for infrared observations has prevented the application of the technique to studies in this region of the spectrum. A few workers have attempted to circumvent this difficulty by coupling a rapid-scanning infrared spectrophotometer and a cooled, fast-response infrared detector with the flash photolysis apparatus, but these techniques have heretofore yielded only a limited amount of data on the most intense infrared absorption bands of a few free radicals [21, 57]. The matrix-isolation technique, first applied to infrared spectroscopic studies by Whittle et al. [173], has proved to be a powerful tool for the stabilization of free radicals in an inert solid environment in sufficient concentration for direct infrared and ultraviolet spectroscopic observation. In a typical matrix-isolation experiment, the molecule of interest is mixed with at least a hundredfold excess of an inert gaseous diluent, and the mixture is frozen onto the cold sample window of a cryostat at a temperature sufficiently low that molecular diffusion through the solid deposit is effectively inhibited. Very commonly, the matrix material is argon or nitrogen, which are transparent over an extremely wide spectral range and which very effectively inhibit molecular diffusion at temperatures between 4 and 20°K, readily accessible using liquid helium and hydrogen, respectively, as coolants.

Infrared absorptions observed for matrix-isolated molecules are generally very sharp, with half-widths of a few cm^{-1}; except for a few simple hydride molecules isolated in rare-gas matrices, the rotational structure is completely missing. Indeed, the absorptions in these matrices are frequently sufficiently sharp to permit resolution of the chlorine-isotopic splittings for stretching vibrations involving the motion of one or more chlorine atoms. In rare-gas matrices, absorption bands are generally observed within 5 or 10 cm^{-1} of the gas-phase band origins. Although the band origins of electronic transitions may be shifted by as much as a few hundred cm^{-1} from their positions for the gas-phase species, the upper-state vibrational spacings, like those of the

ground state, lie close to the gas-phase values. Frequently, an absorption observed in a matrix may show a simple splitting, or may be accompanied by weaker satellite peaks, presumably as a result of the trapping of the molecule in a number of different types of site in the solid lattice. Because of the sharpness of the absorptions and the elimination of difference bands, the technique has proved useful for elucidating the vibrational assignment of a number of stable molecules.

Although the absence of rotational structure may permit clarification of the vibrational band assignment, it is not an unmixed blessing. Information provided by the band contour concerning the symmetry of the vibration is lost, as is the possibility of deriving structural data from the rotational analysis. Thus, the observation of isotopically substituted species is even more crucial to the identification of free radicals in matrix-isolation studies than it is in gas-phase studies. With few exceptions, the identifications summarized in the following discussion have been supported by isotopic substitution studies. Structural data inferred from the isotopic substitution studies must, however, be regarded as semiquantitative.

A number of free radicals have been produced in the gas phase and, together with a large excess of an inert matrix material, have been rapidly frozen onto the cold cryostat sample window. Examples of this procedure are provided by the studies of the spectra of C_3, trapped in rare-gas matrices along with other products of the vaporization of graphite [12, 168, 171, 172], and of SiF_2 isolated in an argon matrix following the high-temperature reaction of silicon with SiF_4 [16, 55]. However, the great majority of the free radicals which have been stabilized in a matrix environment have been produced *in situ* from a suitable free-radical precursor trapped in the matrix.

The cage effect places important restrictions on the systems suitable for the *in situ* stabilization of free radicals. Although at least the lighter atoms can diffuse through the matrix [107], diatomic and polyatomic molecules cannot. Figure 1 illustrates the conditions under which it has been possible to stabilize

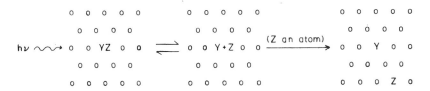

FIG. 1. Principles important in the *in situ* photoproduction of free radicals.

free radicals in a matrix. The first reaction shown is the photodecomposition of a molecule YZ which is completely isolated in the rigid matrix lattice. If both Y and Z are diatomic or polyatomic, they cannot diffuse through the matrix and may recombine. However, if there is an appreciable activation energy for such a recombination process, it will be inhibited, and the free

radical Y may be stabilized in sufficient concentration for spectroscopic study. Alternatively, if Z happens to be an atomic species, it will be able to undergo at least limited diffusion from the site of its photoproduction, as is illustrated in the second reaction of Fig. 1, leading to the stabilization of isolated Y free radicals in the matrix. Still another possibility results if the diffusing atom Z encounters another molecule and reacts with it to form a free radical.

The elucidation of the course of photochemical reactions by the study of the free radicals produced upon photolysis of matrix-isolated samples is subject to severe limitations. Processes which predominate in the gas phase may be completely inhibited in the matrix because of cage recombination of the photolysis products. Furthermore, an appreciable concentration of free radicals produced by secondary photodecomposition processes may also be stabilized in the matrix experiments.

An important special case of atom–molecule reactions in a matrix environment is that in which the atomic species is produced by codeposition of an atomic beam of an alkali metal with the sample of interest. Most commonly, lithium has been employed for these alkali-metal reaction studies, although sodium and the heavier alkali metals have been found to react to a lesser extent. The extent to which the reaction may occur in the gas phase, rather than in the matrix, is not known with certainty. However, in view of the very short time that the mixture is in the gas phase and of the ability of these atoms to diffuse to at least a limited extent in rare-gas matrices, it appears likely that a very significant fraction of the alkali-metal reaction occurs in the matrix. The most frequently encountered lithium-atom reaction involves the abstraction of a chlorine or a bromine atom from the molecule, exemplified by the stabilization of CCl_3 and CBr_3 upon reaction of a lithium atom with the matrix-isolated tetrahalide [1, 2, 5, 148].

The following discussion provides a review of the spectroscopic data obtained for diatomic and simple polyatomic free radicals stabilized in a matrix environment. It is useful and instructive to subdivide these species first according to the number of atoms which they contain, then according to the number of hydrogen atoms in the molecule, and finally according to the number of valence electrons.

Diatomic Free Radicals

MONOHYDRIDES

The simplest species which has been observed in a matrix is CH, found by Milligan and Jacox [109] to be stabilized in sufficient concentration for observation of the three lowest-lying electronic transitions [58] upon vacuum-ultraviolet photolysis of matrix-isolated methane. The infrared absorption of CH has not heretofore been detected.

Three electronic transitions involving the ground state have also been

observed at wavelengths longer than 2000 Å for the species SiH [36, 158], which possesses the same number of valence electrons as CH. The gas-phase data have permitted the determination of a value of 1971 cm^{-1} for $\Delta G(\frac{1}{2})$ of ground-state SiH and, recently, of 1433 cm^{-1} for $\Delta G(\frac{1}{2})$ of ground-state SiD [85]. In studies of the spectra of the products of the vacuum-ultraviolet photolysis of silane in an argon matrix, Milligan and Jacox [116] have observed infrared absorptions at 1967 and 1428 cm^{-1}, which it is reasonable to assign to SiH and SiD, respectively. None of the previously identified electronic transitions of SiH has been detected in the matrix experiments, possibly because they are overlapped by more prominent absorptions of Si$_2$.

Upon photolysis of HN$_3$ in an argon or a nitrogen matrix, an absorption appears at 3133 cm^{-1} which can be assigned to the vibrational fundamental of NH [102, 149], in good agreement with the $\Delta G''(\frac{1}{2})$ value of 3125.6 cm^{-1} obtained by Dixon [29] in a high-resolution study of the familiar 3360-Å A $^3\Pi_i$–X $^3\Sigma^-$ transition of NH. The very strong electronic transition of NH, first observed in matrix studies in the laboratory of Robinson [90, 144], was also observed in the studies of the photolysis of HN$_3$ in a matrix environment [102], as well as in studies of the vacuum-ultraviolet photolysis of ammonia in argon and nitrogen matrices [104].

The familiar 3100-Å transition of OH, first studied for matrix-isolated samples by Robinson and McCarty [144, 145], has often been observed in matrix experiments; traces of water impurity in the sample suffice to permit detection of at least the 0–0 band of OH in samples which are subjected to vacuum-ultraviolet photolysis. An especially detailed study of the absorption and fluorescence spectra of OH and OD trapped in solid neon is that of Tinti [153]. The corresponding electronic transition of SH has also been detected in studies in our laboratory of the photolysis of matrix-isolated H$_2$S with mercury-arc radiation.

Nonhydrides

A number of workers have attributed a band system with origin near 5200 Å which is prominent in the spectrum of the matrix-isolated products of a microwave discharge through various hydrocarbons [89], of graphite vapors trapped in various inert matrices [13, 14, 17, 168, 172], and of the products of the radiolysis of acetylene in various rare-gas matrices [45], to the Swan bands of triplet C$_2$. However, the upper-state vibrational spacing characteristic of the matrix-isolated species is some 200 cm^{-1} greater than that of the Swan bands, and the lower-state vibrational spacing, obtained in the studies of McCarty and Robinson [89] and of Frosch [45], is some 150 cm^{-1} too great. Such a large discrepancy between the vibrational spacings observed for the gas-phase molecule and for the molecule in a rare-gas matrix is unprecedented. Another problem has arisen as a result of the studies of Ballik and Ramsay [10, 11], who demonstrated that the lower state

of the Swan transition is not the ground state of C_2; the ground $x\ ^1\Sigma_g^+$ state of C_2 was found to lie 610 cm^{-1} below the $X'\ ^3\Pi_u$ lower state of the Swan transition. Weltner and McLeod [170] suggested that a band which appears at 2320 Å in the absorption spectrum of graphite vapors trapped in a neon matrix might correspond to the 0–0 Mulliken band of singlet C_2. Because considerable C_3 was also present in their experiments, and because an electronic transition of C_3 had been predicted to lie near this wavelength, it was not entirely certain whether this band did indeed arise from C_2. Milligan and co-workers [126] confirmed the contribution of this band by singlet C_2 in studies of the vacuum-ultraviolet photolysis of acetylene in various inert matrices in which no C_3 was present. The 2–0, 3–0, and 4–0 bands of the Phillips system of singlet C_2 were also observed. However, the 5200-Å band system previously attributed to the Swan transition of triplet C_2 was still prominent in the spectrum. Studies of deuterium- and ^{13}C-substituted acetylene demonstrated that these bands were contributed by a species of formula C_2, and it appeared necessary to conclude that C_2 could be trapped in an excited state in the matrix environment. Subsequent studies, to be discussed in a later section of this review, have demonstrated that the 5200-Å band system is contributed not by triplet C_2, but by the species C_2^- [115]. Further studies by Frosch [46] have led to the identification of the fluorescence spectrum of the Swan bands of triplet C_2, with vibrational spacings close to those of the gas-phase transition. The fluorescence bands previously attributed by Frosch [45] to the Swan transition have been reassigned to C_2^-.

In contrast, the species Si_2, which possesses the same number of valence electrons as does C_2, possesses a ground triplet state. A number of electronic transitions of Si_2 [35, 160] have been studied in the gas phase. In recent studies of the vacuum-ultraviolet photolysis of silane and of disilane in an argon matrix [116], two of these transitions, the H $^3\Sigma_u^-$–X $^3\Sigma_g^-$ transition, with origin near 4000 Å, and the K $^3\Sigma_u^-$–X $^3\Sigma_g^-$ transition, with origin near 3250 Å, were readily detected. In addition, a prominent band system between 2900 and 2700 Å behaved appropriately for assignment to Si_2. The upper-state vibrational band spacings observed for this transition were in close agreement with those reported in the emission studies of Douglas [35] for the D $^3\Pi_u$ state of Si_2. It was suggested that these bands may possibly be contributed by the heretofore undetected D $^3\Pi_u$–X $^3\Sigma_g^-$ transition of Si_2.

The violet bands of CN have frequently been observed in matrix-isolated samples. This transition has been studied in some detail by Milligan and Jacox [107], who have also observed the ground-state infrared absorption of CN isolated in an argon matrix.

The very prominent 2300-Å transition of SiO has also been observed in matrix-isolation experiments, and the vibrational fundamental of ground-state SiO has recently been detected at 1226 cm^{-1} in the silane photolysis experiments [116].

The 2050-Å B–X $^2\Pi$ transition of CF, studied in the gas phase by Andrews and Barrow [4], was detected by Jacox and Milligan [76] in studies of the vacuum-ultraviolet photolysis of methyl fluoride in argon and nitrogen matrices. The ground-state vibrational fundamental of CF was observed at 1279 cm^{-1} in an argon matrix. Similar studies of the vacuum-ultraviolet photolysis of matrix-isolated methyl chloride [77] have led to the detection of the vibrational fundamental of CCl at 870 cm^{-1} in an argon matrix, as well as of the familiar 2800-Å electronic transition of CCl [51, 159] and of another absorption near 2300 Å which may be related to an emission band system tentatively attributed to a second electronic transition of CCl by Barrow *et al.* [15].

The absorption and fluorescence spectra of the species S$_2$, which possesses one more valence electron, have received extensive study in the laboratory of Brewer [18, 19]. Like O$_2$, S$_2$ possesses a ground triplet state. Moreover, the isoelectronic species NF, NCl, and NBr have all been found to possess ground $^3\Sigma^-$ states. The first of these species to be observed in a matrix—and, indeed, the first diatomic free radical to yield an infrared absorption spectrum—was NCl [96], produced by the photolysis of ClN$_3$ in an argon matrix. The assignment of a pair of absorptions having 3:1 relative intensity at 824 and 818 cm^{-1} to the two chlorine-isotopic species of NCl was confirmed in the later study of Milligan and Jacox [101], in which the vibrational fundamental of NBr was observed at 691 cm^{-1} and that of NF at 1115 cm^{-1}. Subsequently, NF has also been identified in matrix-isolation studies of the mercury-arc photolysis of NF$_2$ [27], in unpublished studies in our laboratory of the vacuum-ultraviolet photolysis of NF$_3$, and in studies of the reaction of F atoms with NH [72]. Support for the infrared identification of NBr has been obtained from the studies of Milton *et al.* [129], who obtained a vibrational constant of 691.75 cm^{-1} for the lower state of the orange emission band system of NBr, produced by the reaction of bromine with active nitrogen. Moreover, Douglas and Jones [38] have obtained a value of 1123.4 cm^{-1} for $\Delta G''(\frac{1}{2})$ of NF in their gas-phase studies of the $b\,^1\Sigma^+$–X$\,^3\Sigma^-$ transition, in good agreement with the argon-matrix value, and Colin and Jones [26] have found $\Delta G''(\frac{1}{2}) = 816.8$ cm^{-1} for N^{35}Cl in their gas-phase studies of the $b\,^1\Sigma^+$–X$\,^3\Sigma^-$ transition, also in good agreement with the value obtained in the matrix experiments.

Triatomic Free Radicals

DIHYDRIDES

Simple molecular orbital theory leads to a correlation between the number of valence electrons in species of formula AH$_2$ and the geometry of the molecule [161]. Although the species BeH$_2$, with four valence electrons,

is predicted to possess a linear ground-state structure, the addition of a fifth valence electron, as for BH_2, is predicted to lead to bending of the molecule. The gas-phase studies of BH_2 by Herzberg and Johns [62] have yielded a ground-state valence angle of 131°, in accord with this prediction. On the other hand, CH_2, predicted to possess a somewhat more highly bent singlet ground state, was found to possess a slightly lower-lying triplet state [59]. It is presumed that electron repulsion, neglected in the theory of Walsh, leads to the relative stabilization of triplet CH_2. Nevertheless, the first singlet state of CH_2, with a valence angle of approximately 102° [61], may be separated from the ground triplet state by as little as 1800 cm^{-1} [42]. The spectroscopic observations of Herzberg [59] indicated that CH_2 in its ground triplet state is linear or nearly linear. Recent electron spin resonance observations of triplet CH_2 isolated in a xenon matrix [175–179] require that the molecule be bent, with a valence angle of approximately 136°. Herzberg and Johns [180] have noted that the spectroscopic data would be consistent with a bent molecule if the $^3A_2$ upper state of the observed transition is subjected to heterogeneous predissociation by a $^3B_2$ state.

The simplest triatomic dihydride free radical for which an infrared absorption spectrum has heretofore been detected is SiH_2 [116]. Previous gas-phase studies of this molecule [40, 41, 60] had led to the analysis of a $^1B_1-^1A_1$ transition observed in absorption between 5000 and 6000 Å and to an estimate of 1004 cm^{-1} for the lower-state bending frequency. Although the electronic spectrum of SiH_2 was not detected in the matrix experiments, an absorption was detected at 1008 cm^{-1} in samples of silane isolated in an argon matrix which had been subjected to vacuum-ultraviolet photolysis, and the displacement pattern of this absorption as deuterium was substituted in the molecule was consistent with its assignment to the bent SiH_2 structure determined by Dubois for the $^1A_1$ state. It was concluded that SiH_2, unlike the isoelectronic species CH_2, possesses a singlet ground state. The two stretching vibration fundamentals of SiH_2 were observed at 2022 and 2032 cm^{-1}, values which lead to a Si—H stretching force constant appreciably smaller than that characteristic of more stable silicon hydride molecules.

The addition of one more valence electron leads to the electronic structure of NH_2, for which a visible band system has been analyzed in some detail [39, 64]. Robinson and McCarty [143, 146] first detected this visible band system for matrix-isolated NH_2, and reported evidence for the rotation of NH_2 in rare-gas matrices. However, the detailed assignment of the rotational structure presented considerable difficulty. Milligan and Jacox [104] stabilized a sufficient concentration of NH_2 for detection of two vibrational fundamental absorptions in studies of the vacuum-ultraviolet photolysis of ammonia in argon and nitrogen matrices. In more recent, unpublished studies in this laboratory of the visible band system of NH_2 isolated in an argon matrix, a reversible temperature dependence of the intensities of certain of the peaks has

been noted, suggesting the depopulation of higher rotational levels and the population of the lowest accessible rotational levels as the temperature is lowered and providing further support for the occurrence of rotation of NH_2 in an argon matrix.

MONOHYDRIDES

The simplest triatomic monohydride heretofore observed is HCC, predicted by the theory of Walsh [163] to possess a linear ground state. Milligan and co-workers [126] have detected the C=C stretching fundamental of this species near 1850 cm^{-1} in studies of the vacuum-ultraviolet photolysis of acetylene in an argon matrix.

The next more complicated triatomic monohydride free radical is HCO. This species, in contrast to HCC, is predicted [163] to possess a bent structure in its ground state. This prediction has been confirmed by the high-resolution gas-phase study of the red band system of HCO [65, 82]. The infrared spectrum of HCO, produced by the reaction of H atoms with a CO matrix, was first reported by Ewing et al. [43]. Subsequently, Milligan and Jacox [103] completed the vibrational assignment for both HCO and DCO. The results of this study were in accord with earlier data indicating that the C—H bond of ground-state HCO is exceptionally weak; the C—H stretching fundamental of HCO appears at 2488 cm^{-1}. For many years, the hydrocarbon flame bands, a very complicated emission band system between about 2500 and 4100 Å which is common to hydrocarbon combustion systems, had been tentatively attributed to HCO [154–156]. However, attempts at a detailed assignment of the bands were less than completely successful. In a preliminary report on the rotational analysis of several of the bands, Dixon [32] noted that the lower-state moments of inertia of the emitting species were in satisfactory agreement with those of ground-state HCO and that the diffuseness of certain of the bands indicated a reassignment of the band origin. Milligan and Jacox [114] were able to analyze an absorption band system appearing between 2600 and 2100 Å in matrix-isolation systems in which a considerable concentration of HCO was known to be stabilized in terms of the excitation of two upper-state vibrations of HCO (or of DCO). Using these vibrational spacings and the vibrational frequencies determined from the infrared studies for ground-state HCO, it was possible to assign virtually all of the hydrocarbon flame bands. The proposed reassignment of the band origin was subsequently confirmed by the more detailed gas-phase band analysis of Dixon [33]. Furthermore, Dixon has reported evidence for the appearance of still another electronic transition of HCO in this spectral region, and the band origin proposed for this C–X transition lies very close to the position of the first member of an array of " unclassified bands " reported by Milligan and Jacox [114].

Theory predicts that the next more complicated free radical in the triatomic monohydride series, HCF, should be somewhat more highly bent than HCO and should possess a singlet ground state. Transitions characteristic of both singlet HCF [95] and singlet HCCl [94] have been obtained in gas-phase flash photolysis studies, and both species have been found to be bent, at least for the lowest vibrational levels of the lower electronic state. HCF has been stabilized in a matrix environment both by the vacuum-ultraviolet photolysis of methyl fluoride and by the reaction of carbon atoms (produced by the photolysis of cyanogen azide) with hydrogen fluoride [76]. Two vibrational fundamentals of HCF have been assigned. The appearance of the visible band system of singlet HCF in matrix-isolation experiments has confirmed the attribution of the lower singlet state of the gas-phase studies to the ground state of the molecule. Similar conclusions have resulted from matrix-isolation studies of HCCl, obtained by the reaction of photolytically produced carbon atoms with HCl [73] and by the vacuum-ultraviolet photolysis of methyl chloride [77]. The species HSiCl, with the same number of valence electrons, has also been stabilized in a matrix environment by the vacuum-ultraviolet photolysis of SiH_3Cl [119a]. Because of the great intensity with which the visible band system of HSiCl appears in the matrix experiments, it seems likely that the proposal of Hougen and Watson [69] that the $\Delta K = 2$ transitions observed in the gas-phase studies [67] result because of axis-switching is more satisfactory than the alternate explanation for this K-structure involving the occurrence of a $^3A'-^1A'$ transition.

The isoelectronic species HNO also possesses a bent singlet ground state. The familiar electronic transition of this species was first recognized for matrix-isolated HNO by Robinson and McCarty [144]. Subsequently, Milligan et al. [120] succeeded in stabilizing a sufficient concentration of HNO in a carbon dioxide matrix upon secondary photodecomposition of the product of the reaction of NH with CO_2 for the observation of two of the ground-state vibrational fundamentals of HNO.

A bent structure is both predicted and observed for triatomic mono-hydride species containing 13 valence electrons, as well. One such species is HO_2, first identified in experiments in which photolytically produced H atoms react with a small concentration of O_2 trapped in an argon matrix [99]. All three vibrational fundamentals of normal HO_2 and of its ^{18}O-substituted species were identified in this study, as were two of the fundamentals of DO_2. No discrete electronic transition of HO_2 has heretofore been identified. On the other hand, an electronic transition has been observed in absorption between 3800 and 5000 Å for the isoelectronic species HNF [50, 174] and involves an extended progression in the upper-state bending vibration. This transition has also been observed for HNF and for DNF by Jacox and Milligan [72], as were two of the vibrational fundamentals of each of these species, obtained by the reaction of F atoms with NH or ND in an argon matrix.

NONHYDRIDES

The theory of Walsh [162] has also received abundant support in spectroscopic studies of heavy-atom triatomic free radicals. In brief, this theory predicts that molecules of this type which possess fewer than 16 valence electrons (e.g., CO_2) should possess linear ground-state structures. As electrons are added to the π_g orbital which becomes filled for the CO_2 structure, the ground-state bending frequency of the molecule increases steadily. However, upon addition of a 17th valence electron, a bent molecular structure becomes relatively more stable, and increasingly more highly bent structures are predicted for molecules possessing up to 20 valence electrons.

The simplest such species heretofore observed is C_3. The high-resolution analysis of the familiar 4050-Å transition of gas-phase C_3 [47, 48], produced by the flash photolysis of diazomethane, has demonstrated that the bending frequency of ground-state C_3, which has no electrons in this π_g orbital, is only 63 cm^{-1}. Promotion of an electron to this orbital increases the bending frequency to 308 cm^{-1}. Strong Renner–Teller interaction occurs in the upper $^1\Pi_u$ state of the transition, leading to a very complex pattern of bands. This complexity has also been observed in the matrix experiments, in which C_3 has been stabilized by trapping the vapors of graphite in various inert solid matrices [12, 168, 171, 172]. Weltner et al. [172] have identified the antisymmetric stretching fundamental of ground-state C_3 at 2038 cm^{-1} in an argon matrix, an observation which has been confirmed in studies in which C_3 has been stabilized by the vacuum-ultraviolet photolysis of allene and of methyl acetylene in an argon matrix [119a]. Weltner and McLeod [168] have reported the observation of the fluorescence spectrum of C_3 and have estimated that the symmetric stretching fundamental of ground-state C_3 lies at approximately 1235 cm^{-1}. Weltner and McLeod [169] have also studied the electronic spectrum of matrix-isolated SiC_2, one of the numerous products of the vaporization of silicon carbide.

Addition of one more electron to the C_3 structure leads to the structures of the species CCN and CNC, which are predicted and observed to be linear in both their ground and their low-lying excited states and to have ground-state bending vibrations in the 300–400-cm^{-1} range [92, 93]. Neither of these species has heretofore been detected in matrix-isolation experiments.

Addition of still another electron to the C_3 structure would be expected to lead to linear triplet species with ground-state bending vibrations near 400 cm^{-1}. The first such species to be identified was NCN, to which Herzberg and Travis [66] assigned a very prominent $^3\Pi_u$–$^3\Sigma_g^-$ transition at 3290 Å which appeared in their gas-phase studies of species produced on flash photolysis of diazomethane. Subsequently, it was found that cyanogen azide isolated in an argon or a nitrogen matrix could be converted almost completely to NCN by irradiation of the sample with the 2288-Å cadmium line, which falls in the region of a strong cyanogen azide absorption [106, 123, 124]. A strong

absorption at 423 cm^{-1} and an extremely strong absorption at 1475 cm^{-1} were assigned to the bending and antisymmetric stretching fundamentals, respectively, of NCN, and an absorption at 2672 cm^{-1} was assigned to the combination $v_1 + v_3$. The magnitude of the carbon–nitrogen stretching force constant is consistent with a doubly bonded chain, but the stretching-interaction force constant is exceptionally large and positive, resulting in an atypically small value for v_3. The 3290-Å absorption band was extremely strong in the matrix studies. Furthermore, a second band system between 3000 and 2400 Å, involving a long progression in the upper-state symmetric stretching vibration, was also assigned to NCN.

Upon exposure of matrix-isolated NCN to 2537-Å mercury-arc radiation, photodecomposition occurs, and new absorptions assigned to the three vibrational fundamentals of the isoelectronic species CNN result [105]. The bending vibration appears at 393 cm^{-1}, again consistent with the predictions of theory. One electronic transition of CNN, with origin near 4200 Å, was assigned in the report of this work, and subsequent studies in this laboratory, as yet unpublished, are consistent with the assignment of a band system between 2550 and 2200 Å, as well as of bands between about 2050 and 1950 Å, to further electronic transitions of CNN.

Detailed isotopic studies indicate that CNN is formed by the detachment of a carbon atom from NCN and by its subsequent reaction with N_2 in the matrix, rather than by an intramolecular rearrangement of NCN. In experiments in which a small concentration of CO was also present in the matrix, the species CCO, also isoelectronic with NCN, was stabilized in sufficient concentration for assignment of all three vibrational fundamentals [80]. The bending fundamental of ground-state CCO was identified at 381 cm^{-1}, again consistent with predictions. Although no structured electronic transitions of CCO were observed in the matrix studies, the recent gas-phase flash photolysis studies of Devillers and Ramsay [28] have led to the assignment of a band system with origin near 8300 Å to a $^3\Pi-^3\Sigma^-$ transition of CCO. The bending frequency of CCO in the lower state of this transition was observed to be 379.4 cm^{-1}, in very good agreement with the matrix value.

Addition of one more electron to the molecule leads to the electron configuration characteristic of N_3 and of NCO. Both of these species possess linear ground states. The 2700-Å transition of N_3 has been analyzed by Douglas and Jones [37], who found all but the 0–0 band to be diffuse. Although this band has been observed in numerous matrix experiments involving the photolysis of azides, no further data on N_3 have resulted from matrix-isolation studies. Dixon [30, 31], has analyzed two transitions of NCO, produced by the gas-phase flash photolysis of HNCO. The ground-state bending vibration of NCO is strongly perturbed by Renner–Teller interaction. The unperturbed bending fundamental should lie near 535 cm^{-1}, in good agreement with the predicted value. Milligan and Jacox [110] have stabilized

a sufficient concentration of NCO in a matrix environment both by the vacuum-ultraviolet photolysis of HNCO and by the reaction of carbon atoms with NO for the observation of the two known electronic transitions and of all three vibrational fundamentals of the ground-state molecule. Only the lowest-frequency component of the perturbed bending fundamental was observed. The magnitude of the ^{13}C and ^{15}N isotopic shifts observed for this vibration strongly supports the presence of the carbon atom in the central position. Although this structure has commonly been presumed for NCO, the gas-phase data did not suffice for an unequivocal demonstration of the order of the atoms in the molecule.

With the addition of a 16th valence electron, the π_g orbital is filled, and addition of a 17th valence electron is predicted to lead to a bent molecular structure. Two such species have been observed in matrix-isolation experiments—FCO and ClCO, produced by the reaction of the corresponding halogen atom with CO in a matrix environment [71, 122]. All three ground-state vibrational fundamentals of both species and two electronic transitions of FCO have been observed. Although the matrix data do not suffice for the determination of detailed structures, they are consistent with a valence angle between 120° and 135° for both species.

Addition of an 18th valence electron is predicted to lead to a still more highly bent structure, and such molecules are expected to possess singlet ground states. Numerous examples of such 18-valence-electron molecules exist, including the relatively stable species O_3 and SO_2. Another example is the molecular fragment CF_2, which has a lifetime of the order of milliseconds. An extremely prominent electronic transition of CF_2, involving progressions in the upper- and lower-state bending vibrations, has its origin near 2700 Å [87, 88, 157]. Both the high-resolution band analysis of Mathews [91] and the microwave studies of Powell and Lide [138] have yielded a ground-state valence angle of 104.9° for CF_2. The first observation of the two ground-state stretching fundamentals of CF_2 was that of Milligan and co-workers [121], who found that CF_2 was stabilized in argon and nitrogen matrices upon mercury-arc photolysis of CF_2N_2. Subsequently, Herr and Pimentel [57] obtained a sufficient concentration of CF_2 in a rapid-scanning infrared study of the products of the gas-phase flash photolysis of CF_2N_2 to obtain the band contour of the 1102-cm^{-1} stretching absorption, fixing its assignment to v_3. CF_2 has also been stabilized in a matrix environment by the reaction of carbon atoms with F_2 [111], a process which has permitted study of the infrared spectrum of $^{13}CF_2$, and by the vacuum-ultraviolet photolysis of CH_2F_2.

The closely related species CCl_2, ClCF, and CBr_2 have been observed only in a matrix environment. CCl_2 was first obtained by the reaction of photolytically produced carbon atoms with Cl_2 [108]. The two stretching fundamentals and a rather weak absorption band system, probably the analog of the familiar CF_2 band system, between 5600 and 4400 Å were reported in this study. CCl_2

has also been stabilized in an argon matrix by Andrews [3], who studied the abstraction of chlorine atoms from CCl_4 by lithium atoms, and by Jacox and Milligan [77] in studies of the vacuum-ultraviolet photolysis of CH_2Cl_2. ClCF has been stabilized in sufficient concentration in argon and nitrogen matrices for observation of the two ground-state stretching fundamentals, and an electronic transition with origin near 3900 Å involving an extended progression in the bending vibration has been studied in both absorption and fluorescence, permitting an estimate of the ground-state bending frequency [150]. The two stretching fundamentals of CBr_2 were identified by Andrews and Carver [5] in their studies of the abstraction of bromine atoms from matrix-isolated CBr_4 by lithium atoms.

The isoelectronic species SiF_2 has been prepared by the high-temperature reaction between silicon and SiF_4 and has been found to have a lifetime of approximately 2 min [152]. A detailed structural determination, an accurate estimate of the ground-state vibrational frequency, and approximate values of the two ground-state stretching frequencies resulted from the microwave studies of Rao, Curl, and co-workers [140, 141]. The previously reported emission band system of SiF_2 [81, 139] was observed in absorption by Khanna and co-workers [83], who ascertained that the band structure of the transition, like that of CF_2, could be understood in terms of excitation of the upper- and ground-state bending vibrations only. The Si—F stretching absorption region has been studied for the trapped high-temperature reaction products by Bassler and co-workers [16] and Hastie and co-workers [55]. The absorptions attributed to the stretching vibrations of SiF_2 are consistent with those estimated by Rao and Curl from the microwave data and with the gas-phase observations of Khanna and co-workers [84]. Milligan and Jacox [113] have stabilized SiF_2 in a matrix environment by the vacuum-ultraviolet photolysis of SiH_2F_2. In this work, all three vibrational fundamentals have been detected, as has been the ultraviolet absorption band system of SiF_2. Milligan and Jacox [112] have also reported the identification of the two stretching fundamentals of $SiCl_2$, as well as of an unstructured absorption in the region of the band system tentatively ascribed to gas-phase $SiCl_2$ by Asundi et al. [9], in studies of the vacuum-ultraviolet photolysis of matrix-isolated SiH_2Cl_2. $SiCl_2$, like SiF_2 and the other 18-valence-electron molecules, apparently is quite highly bent.

Addition of a 19th valence electron is also predicted to result in a strongly bent molecule, as has been observed for NF_2, produced by the dissociation of N_2F_4 [54]. Infrared studies of the matrix-isolated dissociation products have permitted completion of the vibrational assignment of ground-state NF_2 [53]. The stretching fundamentals of $^{15}NF_2$ were also identified in matrix isolation studies of the reaction of F atoms with NH [72]. Goodfriend and Woods [49] and Kuznetsova and co-workers [86] have reported an absorption band system between about 2800 and 2350 Å for gas-phase NF_2, with

indistinct bands having approximately 380 cm^{-1} separation superposed on a continuous absorption. In unpublished studies of the vacuum-ultraviolet photolysis of matrix-isolated NF_3, Milligan and Jacox have identified not only the vibrational fundamentals of NF_2, but also this ultraviolet band system.

The 19-valence-electron molecules FOO [7, 151] and ClOO [8, 147] have been stabilized in matrix-isolation studies of the reaction of the corresponding halogen atom with O_2. Of special interest is the appearance of the oxygen–oxygen stretching vibration of these species near 1510 and 1430 cm^{-1}, respectively, indicating that the bond between the two oxygen atoms is exceptionally strong. The halogen–oxygen bonds are correspondingly weak.

Tetratomic Free Radicals

TRIHYDRIDES

The theory of Walsh [164] predicts that tetratomic trihydrides having up to six valence electrons should be planar, but that the introduction of a seventh valence electron should result in the stabilization of a pyramidal structure. The simplest trihydride heretofore observed is CH_3, with seven valence electrons. In contrast to the predictions of the theory, Herzberg [59] has found that CH_3 must be planar or nearly planar in its ground state. Theory predicts that NH_3, which possesses an eighth valence electron, should possess a pyramidal structure with an even smaller apex angle, as is observed. However, when one electron is promoted out of this highest occupied orbital, ammonia, too, is found to assume a planar structure [166]. Apparently, the presence of one electron in the $3a_1–1a_2''$ orbital, for which the pyramidal structure is relatively stable, is insufficient to counteract the stabilization of the planar structure resulting from the combined effect of the lower-lying filled orbitals. In matrix-isolation studies of the vacuum-ultraviolet photolysis of methane in argon and nitrogen matrices, Milligan and Jacox [109] assigned an infrared absorption band to v_2 of planar CH_3. The "negative anharmonicity" observed for this vibration as deuterium was substituted in the molecule can occur only if the vibration is nontotally symmetric, a condition fulfilled for a planar, but not a pyramidal, structure. A similar "negative anharmonicity" was also found by Walsh and Warsop [166] for v_2 of ammonia in certain of its planar excited states. Riveros [142] has fitted the matrix data for v_2 of CH_3 to an anharmonic potential function having the quartic term.

SiH_3, which possesses the same number of valence electrons as CH_3, was found in the electron spin resonance studies of Gordy and co-workers [70, 131] to be pyramidal in its ground state. These observations are consistent with the results of the studies of the vacuum-ultraviolet photolysis of silane in an argon matrix [116], in which five infrared absorptions, attributed to the four

vibrational fundamentals and to an overtone in Fermi resonance with one of the fundamentals, were assigned to SiH_3. The stretching frequencies and force constants of SiH_3, like those of SiH and SiH_2, were found to be somewhat smaller than those characteristic of more stable Si—H bonds.

DIHYDRIDES

Several of the vibrational fundamentals of H_2CF and H_2CCl have been identified in studies of the vacuum-ultraviolet photolysis of matrix-isolated CH_3F and CH_3Cl, respectively [76, 77]. H_2CCl has also been identified in the lithium-atom abstraction studies of Andrews and Smith [6]. Electron spin resonance studies [44] have indicated that H_2CF, like CH_3, is planar or nearly so, and the occurrence of "negative anharmonicity" for the lowest-frequency absorption of H_2CCl suggests that this molecule is planar. Although the C—F stretching frequency of H_2CF lies in the absorption region typical for such vibrations, the C—Cl stretching frequency of H_2CCl is somewhat higher than that for most such vibrations, and the C—Cl stretching force constant is exceptionally large. It has been suggested that the occurrence of (p–d)π bonding in H_2CCl may account for both the relatively strong C—Cl bond and the planar structure.

MONOHYDRIDES

When samples of water isolated in a carbon monoxide matrix are subjected to vacuum-ultraviolet photolysis, an elaborate pattern of infrared absorptions appears, including peaks characteristic of HCO, CO_2, formaldehyde, and formic acid. In addition, a number of absorptions attributable to a reactive molecule have been observed, and isotopic substitution studies are consistent with the assignment of these bands to a species of formula HCO_2 [118]. Since two peaks each are observed in the spectral regions characteristic of O—H and C=O stretching vibrations, it has been concluded that both *cis*- and *trans*-H—O—C=O are stabilized in this system.

The electron spin resonance observations of Fessenden and Schuler [44] have demonstrated that HCF_2 possesses a pyramidal structure. Three vibrational fundamentals of HCF_2 and three of DCF_2 have been observed by Carver and Andrews [24] in studies of the reaction of lithium atoms with the corresponding bromodifluoromethane in an argon matrix. Unpublished results of Milligan and Jacox [119a] on the infrared spectra of HCF_2 and DCF_2 produced by the reaction of H (or D) atoms with CF_2 and by the vacuum-ultraviolet photolysis of fluoroform in a matrix environment are consistent with the identification given by Carver and Andrews. Carver and Andrews [22, 23] have also reported the infrared identification of $HCCl_2$ and $HCBr_2$ in studies of the reaction of lithium atoms with matrix-isolated chloroform and

bromoform, respectively. Several of the absorptions attributed to these species have also been observed in studies of the vacuum-ultraviolet photolysis of matrix-isolated chloroform and bromoform, respectively [148]. Although the C—F stretching force constant appears to lie within the range typical of fluorocarbons, the C—Cl and C—Br stretching force constants are exceptionally large, possibly because of the occurrence of (p–d)π bonding.

NONHYDRIDES

The discussion by Walsh [165] of the characteristics of the molecular orbitals of nonhydride AB_3 species possessing threefold symmetry has indicated that species with as many as 24 valence electrons (e.g., BF_3, SO_3) should be planar in their ground states. Addition of further valence electrons should lead to stabilization of a pyramidal structure.

On the basis of these predictions, CO_3, with 22 valence electrons, would be expected to be planar. In infrared studies of the reaction of photolytically produced O atoms with solid CO_2, Moll et al. [130] assigned five infrared absorptions to vibrational fundamentals of CO_3, requiring that the molecule possess less than threefold symmetry. Product rule ratios obtained using data on isotopically substituted species of CO_3 were consistent with either a bent O—O—C=O structure or a planar O_2C=O structure. Similar structures had previously been proposed by Milligan and co-workers [98, 120] to explain the infrared spectra of the species produced by the reaction of CH_2 and NH, isoelectronic with the O atom, with a CO_2 matrix. The results of Moll and co-workers were supported by the independent identification of CO_3 in a matrix environment by Weissberger et al. [167]. In studies of the vacuum-ultraviolet photolysis of D_2O in a CO_2 matrix, Jacox and Milligan [78] obtained an extremely high yield of CO_3, definitively excluding the possible presence of hydrogen in the molecule. When the isotopic data for CO_3 were fitted to a seven-constant valence-force potential, it was found that the potential constants obtained for a cyclic O_2C=O structure having an O—C—O angle of 65°, close to the value recently found for the isoelectronic species cyclopropanone in the microwave studies of Pochan and co-workers [136], were more satisfactory than were those obtained for the structure favored by Moll, with an O—C—O angle of 80°.

Analysis of the 3600-Å band system of F_2CN [34] has shown that this molecule, with 23 valence electrons, is also planar in its ground state. This band system has also been observed in matrix isolation studies of the reaction of F atoms with FCN [74] as have been five of the vibrational fundamentals of ground-state F_2CN.

Theory predicts that CF_3, with 25 valence electrons, should be pyramidal, consistent with the electron spin resonance observations of Fessenden and Schuler [44], as well as with the detection of two C—F stretching fundamentals

of CF_3 both in the matrix-isolation studies of the reaction of F atoms with CF_2 [111, 125] and in the gas-phase flash-photolysis studies by Carlson and Pimentel [21]. Although two stretching fundamentals were also reported by Andrews [1, 2] for CCl_3 and two by Andrews and Carver [5] for CBr_3, the absorptions attributed to v_1 of these species were not detected in the experiments of Rogers and co-workers [148], who stabilized yields of these two species as great as those reported in the earlier studies with fewer complications due to the presence of other product species. The exceptionally high C—X stretching force constants obtained from the infrared data for these two species suggest that the C—X bonds may be strengthened by the occurrence of $(p–d)\pi$ bonding, which would tend to stabilize the planar configuration. Nevertheless, the absence of an absorption attributable to v_1 cannot be considered proof of a planar structure.

In matrix-isolation studies of the vacuum-ultraviolet photolysis of $HSiCl_3$ [75] and of $HSiF_3$ [127], absorptions assigned to the two stretching fundamentals of $SiCl_3$ and SiF_3, respectively, were observed, requiring that these species possess pyramidal ground-state structures. The two bending fundamentals and a combination band of SiF_3 were also observed.

Pentatomic Free Radicals

The photolysis of a wide variety of azides has been found to proceed by the elimination of molecular nitrogen and the formation of a nitrene intermediate. Thus, it was expected that the photolysis of matrix-isolated methyl azide might lead to the stabilization of the species CH_3N. Milligan [97] has found that CH_3N undergoes rapid intramolecular rearrangement even at temperatures near 4°K, leading to the stabilization of methylenimine, $H_2C=NH$, in concentration sufficient for detection of virtually all of its vibrational fundamental absorptions. Upon prolonged exposure of the sample to mercury-arc radiation, methylenimine decomposes by the elimination of molecular hydrogen, resulting in the stabilization of the previously unobserved species HNC in a matrix environment [100].

Molecular Ions

The anomalous behavior of the 5200-Å band system which has frequently been assigned to the Swan transition of triplet C_2 isolated in a rare-gas matrix has already been noted. Recently, Herzberg and Lagerqvist [63] reported a new band system with origin near 5400 Å which they demonstrated to be contributed by a species of formula C_2 produced in a flash discharge through methane gas. Since a consideration of the molecular orbitals of neutral C_2 indicates that no low-lying states of this species could account for the transition, Herzberg and Lagerqvist suggested that the band system could reason-

ably be attributed to the species C_2^-. Honig [68] has demonstrated that C_2 has an electron affinity of some 3 eV, consistent with the possible observation of C_2^- in this system. In supplementary mass-spectrometric observations, Herzberg and Lagerqvist demonstrated that C_2^- was indeed present. The principal difficulty with the assignment of the band system to C_2^- was the failure to observe a spin splitting. However, rotational lines with high J values were perceptibly broadened.

The correspondence between the upper- and lower-state vibrational spacings of this new gas-phase band system and those of the " Swan bands " of matrix-isolated C_2 is well within experimental error, strongly indicating the reassignment of the bands observed in the matrix experiments to this transition. Milligan and Jacox [115] found that, when a supplementary source of photoelectrons was added to a sample of acetylene in an argon matrix and the resulting deposit was subjected to vacuum-ultraviolet photolysis, the intensity of the 5200-Å band system was dramatically enhanced. Particularly suitable sources of photoelectrons were provided by atomic beams of the various alkali metals (excluding lithium), codeposited with the sample. Furthermore, although exposure of the sample to 2537-Å mercury radiation resulted in the disappearance of the 5200-Å band system in the absence of a photoelectron source, when alkali metal atoms were present the intensity of the 5200-Å band system was unchanged even on prolonged exposure of the sample to 2537-Å radiation; a steady state involving electron capture by C_2 and photodetachment of an electron from C_2^- resulted. It was concluded that the new band system of Herzberg and Lagerqvist is indeed contributed by the species C_2^- and that it is possible to stabilize a sufficient concentration of charged species in rare-gas matrices for their direct spectroscopic observation.

These results were followed by the identification of the antisymmetric stretching fundamental of NO_2^- isolated in an argon matrix [128, 182]. Although the spectrum of the nitrite ion in polar solvents and in ionic crystals has frequently been studied, this was the first identification of the ion in an inert, nonionic environment. The 1244-cm^{-1} absorption of NO_2^- appeared upon electron bombardment of NO_2 isolated in an argon matrix, upon photoionization of matrix-isolated NO_2 by 1236-, 1216-, or 1067-Å radiation, providing an electron source for capture by another NO_2 molecule, and upon introduction of a small concentration of alkali metal into the sample. When an alkali metal was present, NO_2^- was stabilized even in the absence of radiation effective for photoionizing the alkali metal. Evidence for the formation of a collision complex between alkali metal atoms and NO_2 was also obtained in the gas-phase molecular beam studies of Ham and Kinsey [52] and of Herm and Herschbach [56]. Moreover, Ham and Kinsey reported evidence for a collision complex between alkali metal atoms and SO_2, and Milligan and Jacox [119] observed three infrared absorptions, at 495, 985, and 1042 cm^{-1}, which can be assigned to the fundamentals of SO_2^- resulting

from this reaction in an argon matrix. The residual interaction of the alkali metal cation was sufficiently small that all of the isotopic data could be fitted within experimental error without considering the participation of the cation (Cs^+) in the fundamental vibrations of the complex. Studies by Milligan and Jacox [182] also have indicated that NO^- is formed by the interaction between an alkali metal and NO in an argon matrix. The stabilization of negative ions upon codeposition of an alkali metal and a molecule in an argon matrix may be considered to result from the formation of an "inner complex" in a charge-transfer interaction process. A detailed formulation of such interactions has been given by Mulliken [132, 133].

In argon-matrix studies of HCl codeposited with $Ar:Cl_2$ mixtures which had been passed through a glow discharge, Noble and Pimentel [134] observed absorptions at 696 and 956 cm^{-1} which they assigned to v_3 and $v_1 + v_3$, respectively, of an uncharged ClHCl radical. Isotopic studies were consistent with this composition and with a linear, symmetric structure. Milligan and Jacox [117] observed these same absorptions upon vacuum-ultraviolet photolysis of samples of approximately 1 % HCl isolated in an argon matrix, a concentration at which a significant fraction of HCl molecules are present as hydrogen-bonded pairs. Moreover, when a small concentration of alkali metal atoms was also present in the sample, exposure of the sample to 2537-Å radiation, ineffective in photolyzing HCl in an argon matrix, resulted in the appearance of prominent absorptions at 696 and 956 cm^{-1}, identical in position and contour with those reported in the study of Noble and Pimentel. It was concluded that these absorptions are more reasonably assigned to the same two vibrational modes of linear, symmetric $ClHCl^-$. In another recent study [181], absorptions at 728 and 892 cm^{-1} have been assigned to the corresponding vibrations of $BrHBr^-$. These two anions have frequently been studied in an ionic environment, but their infrared spectra are exceptionally sensitive to the nature of the cation. The spectroscopic behavior characteristic of argon-matrix experiments would be expected to approach that of the free ion. The mechanism by which $ClHCl^-$ and $BrHBr^-$ are formed in these studies is not entirely understood. In the experiments in which an alkali metal was present, unphotolyzed samples showed absorptions due to a complex within approximately 50 cm^{-1} of the positions in which absorptions attributed to the unperturbed anion appeared upon subsequent mercury-arc irradiation. The positions of the complex absorptions were dependent on the alkali metal used in the experiment, and their intensities diminished as the free anion absorptions appeared. It is inferred that an $M^+ \dots XHX^-$ complex is formed upon codeposition of the alkali metal and the $Ar:HX$ sample and that irradiation of the sample results in the destruction of the residual interaction between the cation and the bihalide anion. Photoelectrons may also be produced in both the vacuum-ultraviolet photolysis and the alkali metal experiments. The gas-phase studies of Christophorou and

co-workers [25] have provided evidence for the formation of negatively charged halogen atoms, as well as of small concentrations of XHX^- species, probably formed by reaction of X^- with HX, on interaction of very low-energy electrons with the hydrogen halide. In the matrix experiments, dissociative electron attachment to dimeric HX is likely to play a significant role.

As has already been noted, upon vacuum-ultraviolet photolysis of chloroform in an argon matrix using 1216-Å radiation, the 900-cm^{-1} absorption of CCl_3 became very prominent [148]. Another prominent absorption at 1037 cm^{-1} also possessed isotopic substitution behavior appropriate for assignment to a species of formula CCl_3, but did not appear in nitrogen-matrix experiments, in which the 900-cm^{-1} CCl_3 absorption remained extremely prominent. Jacox and Milligan [79] have noted that photoionization of CCl_3 can occur using 1216-Å radiation and have presented arguments for the assignment of the 1037-cm^{-1} absorption to $CCl_3{}^+$. When 1067-Å photolyzing radiation was used, very little CCl_3 was produced, and new absorptions at 1038 and 1290 cm^{-1} could be assigned to the two b_1 fundamentals of planar $HCCl_2{}^+$, produced by photoionization of the $HCCl_2$ primary photolysis product. Other absorptions near 840, 1270, 2500, and 2720 cm^{-1} were assigned to $HCCl_2{}^-$, produced upon dissociative electron capture by chloroform. The absorptions of $HCCl_2{}^-$ were even more prominent in experiments in which an $Ar:HCCl_3$ sample was codeposited with a small concentration of an alkali metal and the sample then subjected to mercury-arc irradiation. Evidence for both simple and dissociative electron attachment has been obtained in similar studies in which $HCCl_2F$ and $HCClF_2$ were substituted for chloroform.

Matrix-isolation studies of the infrared and ultraviolet spectra of free radicals, which are characterized by a deficiency of valence electrons, and of molecular ions, which may possess either a deficiency or an excess of valence electrons, have provided an important testing ground for the principles of molecular orbital theory. Already a great deal of information has been obtained on the structure and chemical bonding of such species. Table I summarizes the sources of spectroscopic data on free radicals and molecular ions heretofore observed in matrix-isolation experiments. The field remains an active one, and in the next few years it is anticipated that listings such as this one will undergo very considerable extension.

TABLE I

FREE RADICALS AND MOLECULAR IONS FOR WHICH VIBRATIONAL AND
ELECTRONIC SPECTRA HAVE BEEN OBSERVED IN MATRIX-ISOLATION
EXPERIMENTS

Species	Mode of production[a]	Spectral region	Ref.
CH	4	UV	[109]
SiH	4	IR, UV	[116]
NH	2	UV	[144]
	2	UV	[90]
	3	IR, UV	[102]
	3	IR	[149]
OH	2	UV	[144, 145]
	4	UV	[153]
SH	4	UV	[119a]
C_2	1	UV	[170]
	3, 4	UV	[126]
	3, 4	UV	[46]
Si_2	3, 4, 5a	UV	[116]
C_2^-	7	UV	[115]
	7	UV	[46]
CN	4	IR, UV	[107]
SiO	5a	IR, UV	[116, 119a]
CF	4	IR, UV	[76]
CCl	4	IR, UV	[77]
NO^-	5c	IR	[182]
S_2	1	UV	[19]
	1	UV	[18]
NF	3	IR	[101]
	4	IR	[27]
	4	IR	[72]
NCl	3	IR	[96]
	3	IR	[101]
NBr	3	IR	[101]
SiH_2	4	IR	[116]
NH_2	2	UV	[143, 146]
	4	IR, UV	[104]
HC_2	4	IR	[126]
HCO	5a	IR, UV	[43]
	5a	IR	[103]
	5a	IR, UV	[114]
HCF	4, 5a	IR, UV	[76]
HCCl	5a	IR, UV	[73]
	4	IR	[77]
HSiCl	4	UV	[119a]
HNO	2	UV	[144]
	3	IR	[120]
HO_2	5a	IR	[99, 100]

TABLE I (*continued*)

Species	Mode of production[a]	Spectral region	Ref.
HNF	5a	IR, UV	[72]
ClHCl$^-$	5c, 7	IR	[117]
BrHBr$^-$	5c, 7	IR	[181]
C$_3$	1	UV	[12]
	1	UV	[171]
	1	IR, UV	[172]
	1	UV	[168]
	3, 4	IR, UV	[119a]
SiC$_2$	1	UV	[169]
NCN	3	IR, UV	[123, 124]
	3	IR	[106]
CNN	5a	IR, UV	[105]
	5a	UV	[119a]
CCO	3, 5a	IR	[80]
N$_3$	4	UV	[119a]
NCO	4, 5a	IR, UV	[110]
FCO	4, 5a	IR, UV	[122]
ClCO	4, 5a	IR	[71]
NO$_2{}^-$	5c, 7	IR	[128, 182]
CF$_2$	3	IR	[121]
	5a	IR, UV	[111]
	4	IR, UV	[119a]
CFCl	4	IR, UV	[150]
CCl$_2$	5a	IR, UV	[108]
	5b	IR	[3]
	4	IR, UV	[77]
CBr$_2$	5b	IR	[5]
SiF$_2$	2	IR	[16]
	4	IR, UV	[113]
	2	IR	[55]
SiCl$_2$	4	IR	[112]
	2	IR	[119a]
NF$_2$	2	IR	[53]
	4	IR	[72]
	4	IR, UV	[119a]
SO$_2{}^-$	5c	IR	[119]
FOO	5a	IR	[7]
	5a	IR	[151]
ClOO	5a	IR	[147]
	5a	IR	[8]
CH$_3$	4	IR, UV	[109]
SiH$_3$	4	IR	[116]
H$_2$CF	4	IR	[76]
H$_2$CCl	4	IR	[77]
	5b	IR	[6]

TABLE I (*continued*)

Species	Mode of production[a]	Spectral region	Ref.
HOCO	5d	IR	[118]
$HCCl_2^+$	6	IR	[79]
HCF_2	5b	IR	[24]
	4, 5a	IR	[119a]
$HCCl_2$	5b	IR	[23]
	4	IR	[148]
	4	IR	[77]
	4, 6	IR	[79]
$HCBr_2$	5b	IR	[22]
	4	IR	[148]
HCF_2^-	5c, 7	IR	[119a]
$HCClF^-$	5c, 7	IR	[119a]
$HCCl_2^-$	5c, 7	IR	[79]
CO_3	5a	IR	[130]
	5a	IR	[167]
	5a	IR	[78]
$N_2O_2^-$	5c, 7	IR	[182]
F_2CN	5a	IR, UV	[74]
CCl_3^+	6	IR	[79]
CBr_3^+	6	IR	[119a]
$SiCl_3^+$	6	IR	[119a]
CF_3	4, 5a	IR	[125]
	5a	IR	[111]
CF_2Cl	4	IR	[119a]
$CFCl_2$	4, 5b	IR	[119a]
CCl_3	5b	IR	[1, 2]
	4	IR	[148]
CBr_3	5b	IR	[5]
	4	IR	[148]
SiF_3	4	IR	[127]
$SiCl_3$	4	IR	[75]
$H_2C{=}NH$	3	IR	[97]
$HCClF_2^-$	5c, 7	IR	[119a]
$HCCl_2F^-$	5c, 7	IR	[119a]

[a] (1) Vaporization. (2) Chemical reaction or electric discharge with subsequent trapping of products. (3) Molecule split off, high activation energy for reverse process. (4) Atom split off, diffuses away from site. (5a) Diffusing atom adds to another species. (5b) Diffusing atom abstracts one or more atoms from another species. (5c) Diffusing atom forms charge-transfer complex with another species. (5d) Radical reacts with matrix. (6) Photoionization of uncharged precursor or electron detachment from charged species. (7) Electron capture, including dissociative electron capture.

References

1. L. Andrews, *J. Phys. Chem.* **71**, 2761 (1967).
2. L. Andrews, *J. Chem. Phys.* **48**, 972 (1968).
3. L. Andrews, *J. Chem. Phys.* **48**, 979 (1968).
4. E. B. Andrews and R. F. Barrow, *Proc. Phys. Soc. London Sect. A* **64**, 481 (1951).
5. L. Andrews and T. G. Carver, *J. Chem. Phys.* **49**, 896 (1968).
6. L. Andrews and D. W. Smith, *J. Chem. Phys.* **53**, 2956 (1970).
7. A. Arkell, *J. Amer. Chem. Soc.* **87**, 4057 (1965).
8. A. Arkell and I. Schwager, *J. Amer. Chem. Soc.* **89**, 5999 (1967).
9. R. K. Asundi, M. Karim, and R. Samuel, *Proc. Phys. Soc. London* **50**, 581 (1938).
10. E. A. Ballik and D. A. Ramsay, *Astrophys. J.* **137**, 61 (1963).
11. E. A. Ballik and D. A. Ramsay, *Astrophys. J.* **137**, 84 (1963).
12. R. L. Barger and H. P. Broida, *J. Chem. Phys.* **37**, 1152 (1962).
13. R. L. Barger and H. P. Broida, *J. Chem. Phys.* **43**, 2364 (1965).
14. R. L. Barger and H. P. Broida, *J. Chem. Phys.* **43**, 2371 (1965).
15. R. F. Barrow, G. Drummond, and S. Walker, *Proc. Phys. Soc. London Sect. A* **67**, 186 (1954).
16. J. M. Bassler, P. L. Timms, and J. L. Margrave, *Inorg. Chem.* **5**, 729 (1966).
17. G. D. Brabson, Ph.D. Thesis, Univ. of California, Berkeley, California, 1965.
18. L. Brewer and G. D. Brabson, *J. Chem. Phys.* **44**, 3274 (1966).
19. L. Brewer, G. D. Brabson, and B. Meyer, *J. Chem. Phys.* **42**, 1385 (1965).
20. J. H. Callomon and D. A. Ramsay, *Can. J. Phys.* **35**, 129 (1957).
21. G. A. Carlson and G. C. Pimentel, *J. Chem. Phys.* **44**, 4053 (1966).
22. T. G. Carver and L. Andrews, *J. Chem. Phys.* **50**, 4223 (1969).
23. T. G. Carver and L. Andrews, *J. Chem. Phys.* **50**, 4235 (1969).
24. T. G. Carver and L. Andrews, *J. Chem. Phys.* **50**, 5100 (1969).
25. L. G. Christophorou, R. N. Compton, and H. W. Dickson, *J. Chem. Phys.* **48**, 1949 (1968).
26. R. Colin and W. E. Jones, *Can. J. Phys.* **45**, 301 (1967).
27. J. J. Comeford and D. E. Mann, *Spectrochim. Acta* **21**, 197 (1965).
28. C. Devillers and D. A. Ramsay, *Can. J. Phys.* **49**, 2839 (1971).
29. R. N. Dixon, *Can. J. Phys.* **37**, 1171 (1959).
30. R. N. Dixon, *Phil. Trans. Roy. Soc. London Ser. A* **252**, 165 (1960).
31. R. N. Dixon, *Can. J. Phys.* **38**, 10 (1960).
32. R. N. Dixon, *Proc. Int. Conf. Spectrosc., 1st, Bombay, 1967*, p. 176.
33. R. N. Dixon, *Trans. Faraday Soc.* **65**, 3141 (1969).
34. R. N. Dixon, G. Duxbury, R. C. Mitchell, and J. P. Simons, *Proc. Roy. Soc. Ser. A* **300**, 405 (1967).
35. A. E. Douglas, *Can. J. Phys.* **33**, 801 (1955).
36. A. E. Douglas, *Can. J. Phys.* **35**, 71 (1957).
37. A. E. Douglas and W. E. Jones, *Can. J. Phys.* **43**, 2216 (1965).
38. A. E. Douglas and W. E. Jones, *Can. J. Phys.* **44**, 2251 (1966).
39. K. Dressler and D. A. Ramsay, *Phil. Trans. Roy. Soc. London Ser. A* **251**, 553 (1959).
40. I. Dubois, *Can. J. Phys.* **46**, 2485 (1968).
41. I. Dubois, G. Herzberg, and R. D. Verma, *J. Chem. Phys.* **47**, 4262 (1967).
42. G. Duxbury, *J. Mol. Spectrosc.* **25**, 1 (1968).
43. G. E. Ewing, W. E. Thompson, and G. C. Pimentel, *J. Chem. Phys.* **32**, 927 (1960).
44. R. W. Fessenden and R. H. Schuler, *J. Chem. Phys.* **43**, 2704 (1965).
45. R. P. Frosch, Ph.D. Thesis, California Inst. of Technol., Pasadena, California, 1965.
46. R. P. Frosch, *J. Chem. Phys.* **54**, 2660 (1971).

47. L. Gausset, G. Herzberg, A. Lagerqvist, and B. Rosen, *Discuss. Faraday Soc.* **35**, 113 (1963).
48. L. Gausset, G. Herzberg, A. Lagerqvist, and B. Rosen, *Astrophys. J.* **142**, 45 (1965).
49. P. L. Goodfriend and H. P. Woods, *J. Mol. Spectrosc.* **13**, 63 (1964).
50. P. L. Goodfriend and H. P. Woods, *J. Mol. Spectrosc.* **20**, 258 (1966).
51. R. D. Gordon and G. W. King, *Can. J. Phys.* **39**, 252 (1961).
52. D. O. Ham and J. L. Kinsey, *J. Chem. Phys.* **48**, 939 (1968).
53. M. D. Harmony and R. J. Myers, *J. Chem. Phys.* **37**, 636 (1962).
54. M. D. Harmony, R. J. Myers, L. J. Schoen, D. R. Lide, Jr., and D. E. Mann, *J. Chem. Phys.* **35**, 1129 (1961).
55. J. W. Hastie, R. H. Hauge, and J. L. Margrave, *J. Amer. Chem. Soc.* **91**, 2536 (1969).
56. R. R. Herm and D. R. Herschbach, *J. Chem. Phys.* **52**, 5783 (1970).
57. K. C. Herr and G. C. Pimentel, *Appl. Opt.* **4**, 25 (1965).
58. G. Herzberg, "Molecular Spectra and Molecular Structure. I. Spectra of Diatomic Molecules," 2d ed. Van Nostrand-Reinhold, Princeton, New Jersey, 1950.
59. G. Herzberg, *Proc. Roy. Soc. Ser. A* **262**, 291 (1961).
60. G. Herzberg, "Molecular Spectra and Molecular Structure. III. Electronic Spectra and Electronic Structure of Polyatomic Molecules," pp. 493, 584. Van Nostrand-Reinhold, Princeton, New Jersey, 1966.
61. G. Herzberg and J. W. C. Johns, *Proc. Roy. Soc. Ser. A* **295**, 107 (1966).
62. G. Herzberg and J. W. C. Johns, *Proc. Roy. Soc. Ser. A* **298**, 142 (1967).
63. G. Herzberg and A. Lagerqvist, *Can. J. Phys.* **46**, 2363 (1968).
64. G. Herzberg and D. A. Ramsay, *J. Chem. Phys.* **20**, 347 (1952).
65. G. Herzberg and D. A. Ramsay, *Proc. Roy. Soc. Ser. A* **233**, 34 (1955).
66. G. Herzberg and D. N. Travis, *Can. J. Phys.* **42**, 1658 (1964).
67. G. Herzberg and R. D. Verma, *Can. J. Phys.* **42**, 395 (1964).
68. R. E. Honig, *J. Chem. Phys.* **22**, 126 (1954).
69. J. T. Hougen and J. K. G. Watson, *Can. J. Phys.* **43**, 298 (1965).
70. G. S. Jackel and W. Gordy, *Phys. Rev.* **176**, 443 (1968).
71. M. E. Jacox and D. E. Milligan, *J. Chem. Phys.* **43**, 866 (1965).
72. M. E. Jacox and D. E. Milligan, *J. Chem. Phys.* **46**, 184 (1967).
73. M. E. Jacox and D. E. Milligan, *J. Chem. Phys.* **47**, 1626 (1967).
74. M. E. Jacox and D. E. Milligan, *J. Chem. Phys.* **48**, 4040 (1968).
75. M. E. Jacox and D. E. Milligan, *J. Chem. Phys.* **49**, 3130 (1968).
76. M. E. Jacox and D. E. Milligan, *J. Chem. Phys.* **50**, 3252 (1969).
77. M. E. Jacox and D. E. Milligan, *J. Chem. Phys.* **53**, 2688 (1970).
78. M. E. Jacox and D. E. Milligan, *J. Chem. Phys.* **54**, 919 (1971).
79. M. E. Jacox and D. E. Milligan, *J. Chem. Phys.* **54**, 3935 (1971).
80. M. E. Jacox, D. E. Milligan, N. G. Moll, and W. E. Thompson, *J. Chem. Phys.* **43**, 3734 (1965).
81. J. W. C. Johns, G. W. Chantry, and R. F. Barrow, *Trans. Faraday Soc.* **54**, 1589 (1958).
82. J. W. C. Johns, S. H. Priddle, and D. A. Ramsay, *Discuss. Faraday Soc.* **35**, 90 (1963).
83. V. M. Khanna, G. Besenbruch, and J. L. Margrave, *J. Chem. Phys.* **46**, 2310 (1967).
84. V. M. Khanna, R. Hauge, R. F. Curl, Jr., and J. L. Margrave, *J. Chem. Phys.* **47**, 5031 (1967).
85. L. Klynning and B. Lindgren, *Ark. Fys.* **33**, 73 (1967).
86. L. A. Kuznetsova, Yu. Ya. Kuzyakov, and V. M. Tatevskii, *Opt. Spektrosk.* **16**, 542 (1964).
87. R. K. Laird, E. B. Andrews, and R. F. Barrow, *Trans. Faraday Soc.* **46**, 803 (1950).
88. D. E. Mann and B. A. Thrush, *J. Chem. Phys.* **33**, 1732 (1960).
89. M. McCarty, Jr. and G. W. Robinson, *J. Chim. Phys.* **56**, 723 (1959).
90. M. McCarty, Jr. and G. W. Robinson, *J. Amer. Chem. Soc.* **81**, 4472 (1959).

91. C. W. Mathews, *J. Chem. Phys.* **45**, 1068 (1966).
92. A. J. Merer and D. N. Travis, *Can. J. Phys.* **43**, 1795 (1965).
93. A. J. Merer and D. N. Travis, *Can. J. Phys.* **44**, 353 (1966).
94. A. J. Merer and D. N. Travis, *Can. J. Phys.* **44**, 525 (1966).
95. A. J. Merer and D. N. Travis, *Can. J. Phys.* **44**, 1541 (1966).
96. D. E. Milligan, *J. Chem. Phys.* **35**, 372 (1961).
97. D. E. Milligan, *J. Chem. Phys.* **35**, 1491 (1961).
98. D. E. Milligan and M. E. Jacox, *J. Chem. Phys.* **36**, 2911 (1962).
99. D. E. Milligan and M. E. Jacox, *J. Chem. Phys.* **38**, 2627 (1963).
100. D. E. Milligan and M. E. Jacox, *J. Chem. Phys.* **39**, 712 (1963).
101. D. E. Milligan and M. E. Jacox, *J. Chem. Phys.* **40**, 2461 (1964).
102. D. E. Milligan and M. E. Jacox, *J. Chem. Phys.* **41**, 2838 (1964).
103. D. E. Milligan and M. E. Jacox, *J. Chem. Phys.* **41**, 3032 (1964).
104. D. E. Milligan and M. E. Jacox, *J. Chem. Phys.* **43**, 4487 (1965).
105. D. E. Milligan and M. E. Jacox, *J. Chem. Phys.* **44**, 2850 (1966).
106. D. E. Milligan and M. E. Jacox, *J. Chem. Phys.* **45**, 1387 (1966).
107. D. E. Milligan and M. E. Jacox, *J. Chem. Phys.* **47**, 278 (1967).
108. D. E. Milligan and M. E. Jacox, *J. Chem. Phys.* **47**, 703 (1967).
109. D. E. Milligan and M. E. Jacox, *J. Chem. Phys.* **47**, 5146 (1967).
110. D. E. Milligan and M. E. Jacox, *J. Chem. Phys.* **47**, 5157 (1967).
111. D. E. Milligan and M. E. Jacox, *J. Chem. Phys.* **48**, 2265 (1968).
112. D. E. Milligan and M. E. Jacox, *J. Chem. Phys.* **49**, 1938 (1968).
113. D. E. Milligan and M. E. Jacox, *J. Chem. Phys.* **49**, 4269 (1968).
114. D. E. Milligan and M. E. Jacox, *J. Chem. Phys.* **51**, 277 (1969).
115. D. E. Milligan and M. E. Jacox, *J. Chem. Phys.* **51**, 1952 (1969).
116. D. E. Milligan and M. E. Jacox, *J. Chem. Phys.* **52**, 2594 (1970).
117. D. E. Milligan and M. E. Jacox, *J. Chem. Phys.* **53**, 2034 (1970).
118. D. E. Milligan and M. E. Jacox, *J. Chem. Phys.* **54**, 927 (1971).
119. D. E. Milligan and M. E. Jacox, *J. Chem. Phys.* **55**, 1003 (1971).
119a. D. E. Milligan and M. E. Jacox, Unpublished work (1971).
120. D. E. Milligan, M. E. Jacox, S. W. Charles, and G. C. Pimentel, *J. Chem. Phys.* **37**, 2302 (1962).
121. D. E. Milligan, D. E. Mann, M. E. Jacox, and R. A. Mitsch, *J. Chem. Phys.* **41**, 1199 (1964).
122. D. E. Milligan, M. E. Jacox, A. M. Bass, J. J. Comeford, and D. E. Mann, *J. Chem. Phys.* **42**, 3187 (1965).
123. D. E. Milligan, M. E. Jacox, J. J. Comeford, and D. E. Mann, *J. Chem. Phys.* **43**, 756 (1965).
124. D. E. Milligan, M. E. Jacox, and A. M. Bass, *J. Chem. Phys.* **43**, 3149 (1965).
125. D. E. Milligan, M. E. Jacox, and J. J. Comeford, *J. Chem. Phys.* **44**, 4058 (1966).
126. D. E. Milligan, M. E. Jacox, and L. Abouaf-Marguin, *J. Chem. Phys.* **46**, 4562 (1967).
127. D. E. Milligan, M. E. Jacox, and W. A. Guillory, *J. Chem. Phys.* **49**, 5330 (1968).
128. D. E. Milligan, M. E. Jacox, and W. A. Guillory, *J. Chem. Phys.* **52**, 3864 (1970).
129. E. R. V. Milton, H. B. Dunford, and A. E. Douglas, *J. Chem. Phys.* **35**, 1202 (1961).
130. N. G. Moll, D. R. Clutter, and W. E. Thompson. *J. Chem. Phys.* **45**, 4469 (1966).
131. R. L. Morehouse, J. J. Christiansen, and W. Gordy, *J. Chem. Phys.* **45**, 1751 (1966).
132. R. S. Mulliken, *J. Amer. Chem. Soc.* **74**, 811 (1952).
133. R. S. Mulliken, *J. Phys. Chem.* **56**, 801 (1952).
134. P. N. Noble and G. C. Pimentel, *J. Chem. Phys.* **49**, 3165 (1968).
135. R. G. W. Norrish and G. Porter, *Nature (London)* **164**, 658 (1949).
136. J. M. Pochan, J. E. Baldwin, and W. H. Flygare, *J. Amer. Chem. Soc.* **91**, 1896 (1969).
137. G. Porter, *Proc. Roy. Soc. Ser. A* **200**, 284 (1950).

138. F. X. Powell and D. R. Lide, Jr., *J. Chem. Phys.* **45**, 1067 (1966).
139. D. R. Rao and P. Venkateswarlu, *J. Mol. Spectrosc.* **7**, 287 (1961).
140. V. M. Rao and R. F. Curl, Jr., *J. Chem. Phys.* **45**, 2032 (1966).
141. V. M. Rao, R. F. Curl, Jr., P. L. Timms, and J. L. Margrave, *J. Chem. Phys.* **43**, 2557 (1965).
142. J. M. Riveros, *J. Chem. Phys.* **51**, 1269 (1969).
143. G. W. Robinson and M. McCarty, Jr., *J. Chem. Phys.* **28**, 349 (1958).
144. G. W. Robinson and M. McCarty, Jr., *J. Chem. Phys.* **28**, 350 (1958).
145. G. W. Robinson and M. McCarty, Jr., *Can. J. Phys.* **36**, 1590 (1958).
146. G. W. Robinson and M. McCarty, Jr., *J. Chem. Phys.* **30**, 999 (1959).
147. M. M. Rochkind and G. C. Pimentel, *J. Chem. Phys.* **46**, 4481 (1967).
148. E. E. Rogers, S. Abramowitz, M. E. Jacox, and D. E. Milligan, *J. Chem. Phys.* **52**, 2198 (1970).
149. K. Rosengren and G. C. Pimentel, *J. Chem. Phys.* **43**, 507 (1965).
150. C. E. Smith, D. E. Milligan, and M. E. Jacox, *J. Chem. Phys.* **54**, 2780 (1971).
151. R. D. Spratley, J. J. Turner, and G. C. Pimentel, *J. Chem. Phys.* **44**, 2063 (1966).
152. P. L. Timms, R. A. Kent, T. C. Ehlert, and J. L. Margrave, *J. Amer. Chem. Soc.* **87**, 2824 (1965).
153. D. S. Tinti, *J. Chem. Phys.* **48**, 1459 (1968).
154. W. M. Vaidya, *Proc. Roy. Soc. Ser. A* **147**, 513 (1934).
155. W. M. Vaidya, *Proc. Phys. Soc. London Sect. A* **64**, 428 (1951).
156. W. M. Vaidya, *Proc. Roy. Soc. Ser. A* **279**, 572 (1964).
157. P. Venkateswarlu, *Phys. Rev.* **77**, 676 (1950).
158. R. D. Verma, *Can. J. Phys.* **43**, 2136 (1965).
159. R. D. Verma and R. S. Mulliken, *J. Mol. Spectrosc.* **6**, 419 (1961).
160. R. D. Verma and P. A. Warsop, *Can. J. Phys.* **41**, 152 (1963).
161. A. D. Walsh, *J. Chem. Soc.* p. 2260 (1953).
162. A. D. Walsh, *J. Chem. Soc.* p. 2266 (1953).
163. A. D. Walsh, *J. Chem. Soc.* p. 2288 (1953).
164. A. D. Walsh, *J. Chem. Soc.* p. 2296 (1953).
165. A. D. Walsh, *J. Chem. Soc.* p. 2301 (1953).
166. A. D. Walsh and P. A. Warsop, *Trans. Faraday Soc.* **57**, 345 (1961).
167. E. Weissberger, W. H. Breckenridge, and H. Taube, *J. Chem. Phys.* **47**, 1764 (1967).
168. W. Weltner, Jr. and D. McLeod, Jr., *J. Chem. Phys.* **40**, 1305 (1964).
169. W. Weltner, Jr. and D. McLeod, Jr., *J. Chem. Phys.* **41**, 235 (1964).
170. W. Weltner, Jr. and D. McLeod, Jr., *J. Chem. Phys.* **45**, 3096 (1966).
171. W. Weltner, Jr. and P. N. Walsh, *J. Chem. Phys.* **37**, 1153 (1962).
172. W. Weltner, Jr., P. N. Walsh, and C. L. Angell, *J. Chem. Phys.* **40**, 1299 (1964).
173. E. Whittle, D. A. Dows, and G. C. Pimentel, *J. Chem. Phys.* **22**, 1943 (1954).
174. C. M. Woodman, *J. Mol. Spectrosc.* **33**, 311 (1970).
175. E. Wasserman, W. A. Yager, and V. J. Kuck, *Chem. Phys. Lett.* **7**, 409 (1970).
176. E. Wasserman, V. J. Kuck, R. S. Hutton, and W. A. Yager, *J. Amer. Chem. Soc.* **92**, 7491 (1970).
177. R. A. Bernheim, H. W. Bernard, P. S. Wang, L. S. Wood, and P. S. Skell, *J. Chem. Phys.* **53**, 1280 (1970).
178. R. A. Bernheim, H. W. Bernard, P. S. Wang, L. S. Wood, and P. S. Skell, *J. Chem. Phys.* **54**, 3223 (1971).
179. E. Wasserman, V. J. Kuck, R. S. Hutton, E. D. Anderson, and W. A. Yager, *J. Chem. Phys.* **54**, 4120 (1971).
180. G. Herzberg and J. W. C. Johns, *J. Chem. Phys.* **54**, 2276 (1971).
181. D. E. Milligan and M. E. Jacox, *J. Chem. Phys.* **55**, 2550 (1971).
182. D. E. Milligan and M. E. Jacox, *J. Chem. Phys.* **55**, 3404 (1971).

CHAPTER 6

BIOPHYSICS

6.1 The Competition among Biprotonic Phototautomerism, Excimer Formation, and Proton Tunneling in DNA Base-Pairs[†]

M. Kasha[‡]

Department of Chemistry
and Institute of Molecular Biophysics
Florida State University
Tallahassee, Florida

P. Horowitz[§]

Institute of Molecular Biophysics
Florida State University
Tallahassee, Florida

M. Ashraf El-Bayoumi

Department of Biophysics
Michigan State University
East Lansing, Michigan

Rapid Excitation Phenomena in H-Bonded Base-Pairs

In the study of the biological effects of radiation ultimately the mutagenic effects must be related to the specific effects of radiation on the nucleic acids. One essential step in this study is to learn the diverse molecular changes which take place in DNA and its component base-pairs under the influence of radiation. The study of the photochemistry of DNA base-pairs and the rapid

[†] This work was supported in part by a contract with the Division of Biology and Medicine, U.S. Atomic Energy Commission. Work of first two authors carried out while at the Division of Natural Sciences, University of California, Santa Cruz, California.

[‡] Work supported in part by a National Institute of Health Fellowship No. 1-FO3-GM44011-01 from the General Medical Sciences Division.

[§] Present address: Department of Chemistry, Dartmouth College, Hanover, New Hampshire.

excitation events preceding photochemical changes offers a controllable and simplified situation for the elucidation of the most detailed molecular basis underlying the radiation effects in the more complex situation.

In the very rapid time scale range from 10^{-10} to 10^{-14} sec molecular electronic events may occur which determine entirely the course of subsequent profound changes in molecular structure which are finally manifested as a biological effect of radiation. Among the phenomena which have been discussed in the recent literature relevant to photomutagenic changes in DNA base-pairs are (1) proton tunneling, (2) molecular excimer formation, and (3) biprotonic phototautomerism.

Our purpose here is to describe the competition between these rapid excitation phenomena in a model base-pair and to describe the experimental and theoretical bases for the consideration of the occurrence of these events in DNA base-pairs. We shall also attempt to indicate the limitations of biological relevance of the phenomena in radiation mutagenesis.

Proton Tunneling and Molecular Excimer Formation

Watson and Crick, in their earliest consideration of the DNA base-pairing problem, discussed the possibility of alteration of the genetic code through tautomerization of the DNA bases [1]. Löwdin [2] extended this discussion with the suggestion that *quantum mechanical tunneling* of the protons through a double-minimum potential barrier could lead to a facile tautomerization. Extensive theoretical computation on the electronic states and the N—H ... N potential function for the guanine–cytosine (G–C) base-pair [3–5] led to the tentative conclusion that proton tunneling could proceed with a tautomer equilibration estimated rate constant of the order of 10^6 sec^{-1} for excited states of the G–C pair. Such a rate constant would be many orders of magnitude too small to compete with spontaneous fluorescence rate constants ($\sim 10^8$–10^9 sec^{-1}). Experimental study of a base-pair analog (see below) shows the competitive nature of fluorescence in a similar circumstance. Recently more detailed calculations by Clementi *et al.* [6] (discussed in the last section) put the quantitative aspects of the previous work [3–5] in doubt.

Molecular excimer formation has been adduced by a number of authors to interpret the luminescence [7] and photochemistry [8] of polynucleotide and DNA base-pairs. The formation of a thymine dimer has been well established as one of the photoproducts of irradiation of DNA and analog systems. An excited state (weakly bound, or van der Waals) dimer formation would seem to be a natural fast excitation step which could lead to *covalent* dimer formation [8]. However, the excimerlike diffuse fluorescence observed [7] in the luminescence of some polynucleotide systems may arise from another phenomenon (biprotonic phototautomerism, see next sections) and may be unrelated to the thymine covalent dimer formation, which would require a

pyrimidine–pyrimidine excimer instead of the purine–pyrimidine interaction involved in the proton transfer phenomenon.

Biprotonic Phototautomerism

Recently a new excited-state phenomenon was discovered [9] in a doubly H-bonded N-heterocyclic base-pair, a *biprotonic phototautomerism*.† The base-pair studied was 7-azaindole H-bonded dimer (left), which in the excited state at room temperature was found to go over rapidly to the tautomerized dimer (right); we shall refer to this mode of H-bonding as 7-*azaindole pairing*:

The basis for adducing such a phenomenon is the luminescence behavior of the dimer. Figure 1 shows the luminescence curves for 7-azaindole at 298°K in three solvents. In ethyl ether (curve *B*) only normal fluorescence (F_1), complementary to the normal absorption band, is observed. In hydrocarbon solvent (curve *A*), in which the H-bonded dimer is in equilibrium with the monomer, *two* distinct fluorescences are observed. The ultraviolet fluorescence at shorter wavelengths is the normal fluorescence F_1 related to the lowest singlet–singlet absorption bond. The green fluorescence (F_2) occurs at a wavelength for which there are no electronic transitions in 7-azaindole. At higher concentrations, where the equilibrium favors the dimer, the green fluorescence becomes the dominant emission. In ethanol solution (curve *C*) some green fluorescence F_2 is also observed, but is independent of concentration.

It has been proposed [9] that a cooperative two-proton transfer in the H-bonded dimer (or a cyclically H-bonded monomer in ethanol) could explain the observed new luminescence. This interpretation as a *biprotonic phototautomerism* was nicely confirmed by the direct comparison of the green fluorescence (F_2) with the absorption [10, 11] and fluorescence [12] of the N-methyl (7-methyl) *tautomer* of 7-azaindole.

---

† It would be logical to distinguish the two different mechanisms for excited state 2-proton tautomerism, e.g., by their full names: (1) proton-tunneling-dependent biprotonic phototautomerism and (2) Boltzmann-activation-dependent biprotonic phototautomerism. For brevity we shall use the term proton tunneling for the through-the-barrier mechanism, and biprotonic phototautomerism for the over-the-barrier mechanism.

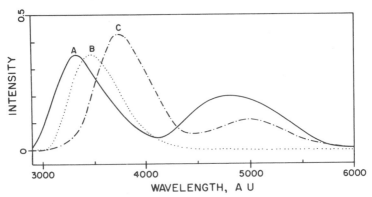

FIG. 1. Fluorescence spectra of 7-azaindole in fluid solution at 20°C. Normal fluorescence F_1 occurs in the UV and violet regions. The green emission F_2 centered on 5000 AU is due to a transient phototautomer. Curve A, in 3-methyl-pentane; curve B, in ethyl ether; curve C, in ethyl alcohol [9].

The molecule 7-azaindole was chosen as a restricted model for a DNA base-pair. Because of the facile solubility of 7-azaindole in various solvents from hydrocarbon to water, a full spectroscopic study was feasible. Cyclical H-bonding in the dimer and the presence of N—H ... N hydrogen bonds offers a formal structural analog to the N—H ... N bonds of the DNA base-pair. Of course, the actual molecular groupings involved in the H-bonding in DNA base-pairs are quite different, as are the sites involved on each base in H-bonding. We shall discuss the contrast between 7-azaindole pairing and Watson–Crick pairing in the latter part of this chapter. The consequence of this difference will be discussed in detailed form in the last section.

Temperature Dependence of Phototautomerism

In the first study of biprotonic phototautomerism [9] it was found that in dilute solutions at 77°K in rigid glass solvents only the normal fluorescence F_1 could be observed readily. It was not clear whether this inhibition of the biprotonic phototautomerism and the subsequent disappearance of the tautomer fluorescence F_2 was conditioned by the lowering of the temperature to 77°K or by the restrictive effect of the rigid glass solvent matrix environment.

An extension [12] of the study of 7-azaindole dimers as a function of temperature (preliminary curve given in Fig. 2) clearly indicates that biprotonic phototautomerism is temperature-dependent and not solvent-matrix-dependent. Over the range of temperatures depicted in Fig. 2 the hydrocarbon solvent is liquid. As the temperature is lowered from 50°C toward −50°C, the equilibrium shifts in favor of the H-bonded dimer of 7-azaindole, and the tautomer/normal molecule fluorescence ratio F_2/F_1 increases. Upon further

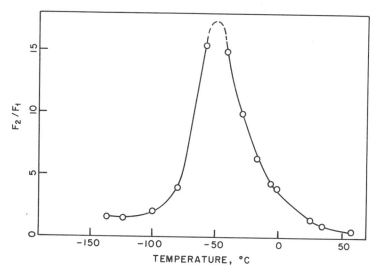

FIG. 2. Experimental temperature dependence of tautomer/normal molecule fluorescence F_2/F_1 for 7-azaindole in hydrocarbon solvent. (Peak height uncertain.) (After Ingham and El-Bayoumi [12], preliminary result.)

lowering of the temperature toward $-100°C$, the ratio F_2/F_1 rapidly diminishes.

Evidently, the potential barrier in the excited state of the dimer (Fig. 3) has a sufficient Boltzmann factor to prevent facile biprotonic phototautomerism below $-100°C$. At a temperature of about $-50°C$, where the equilibrium favors dimer formation, the tautomer fluorescence F_2 is at least 15 times the intensity of the normal 7-azaindole fluorescence. (There is some difficulty

FIG. 3. Schematic double-minimum potential for cooperative two-proton tautomerism in H-bonded N-heterocyclic base-pairs. Normal (left) and tautomerized (right) base-pairs labeled with exciton states indicated by asterisk for cooperative excitation [9].

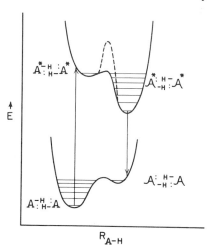

with nonequilibrium concentration effects as one approaches high viscosity and finally the glass matrix.)

However, at temperatures below $-100°C$ the tautomer F_2 emission is still dominant and appears to be temperature-independent. Evidently, proton tunneling is now the mechanism for tautomer formation in the excited state of the 7-azaindole dimer. These observations by Ingham and El-Bayoumi [12] indicate that for 7-azaindole dimer at $-50°C$ and higher temperatures biprotonic phototautomerism (over the barrier) is the dominant phenomenon, while at low temperatures (below $-100°C$) proton tunneling is the mechanism of excited-state tautomerization in the 7-azaindole dimer.

Tautomer Excitation Frequencies of Purines

Biprotonic phototautomerism has been established to be a highly probable phenomenon in 7-azaindole dimer, and shown to be associated with the appearance of a new, diffuse, long-wavelength fluorescence. Since molecular excimer fluorescence, shown to be absent from 7-azaindole dimer, has analogous characteristics, it became of direct interest to investigate the possibility that the fluorescence attributed [7] to "molecular excimers" in polynucleotides might arise also from biprotonic phototautomerism.

In 7-azaindole, the tautomer green fluorescence F_2 occurs some 10 000 cm^{-1} lower in energy than the normal ultraviolet fluorescence F_1. But in polynucleotides containing, e.g., adenine (e.g., poly-dA) the "excimer" fluorescence and the mononucleoside fluorescence are much closer together (~ 3000 cm^{-1}) and both lie in the ultraviolet region [7].

A calculation by the Pariser–Parr–Pople semiempirical SCF-MO method (with CI, including singly and doubly excited configurations) was recently carried out in this laboratory [13] to check the feasibility of assigning the DNA "excimer" luminescence of polynucleotides containing DNA purines to the tautomerized base. The calculation compares (Fig. 4, black circles) the lowest singlet–singlet π-electron excitation energy of N-perturbed indenes: the molecules from 0 to 5 nitrogens are successively indene, indole, 7-azaindole, 3,7-diazaindole (or 5,7-diazaindole), purine, adenine. The curve with open circles represents the corresponding excitation energy for the tautomerized molecule, with the pyrrole-H transferred to the 7-nitrogen. It is quite clear that the two curves converge as purine is approached, and this convergence is approximately preserved in adenine. We emphasize that in this calculation the base-pairs are taken as H-bonded with 7-azaindole pairing, all with identical ring-position H-bonding sites. This calculation is being extended to Watson–Crick pairing in DNA bases.

The present calculation suggests the clear possibility that if a tautomer of adenine were easily produced upon excitation by biprotonic phototautomerism, a broad luminescence with a maximum in the ultraviolet region

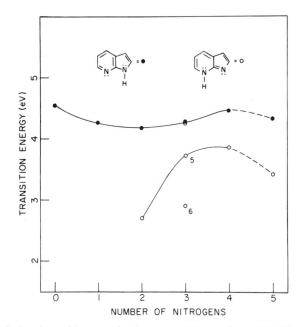

FIG. 4. Calculated transition energies (the normal H-pyrrole, and the H-pyridine tautomers) for N-perturbed indenes with 0–5 N atoms: left to right, indene, indole; 7-azaindole; 3,7-diazaindole(5), and 5,7-diazaindole (6) (5 and 6 normal tautomer points quasicoincident); purine; adenine (after Horowitz *et al.* [13]). All base interactions taken for 7-azaindole pairing.

would be produced. However, we must contrast the site of H-bonding in 7-azaindole pairing with that for Watson–Crick pairing before this possibility becomes realistic. Figure 5 explores the comparison of the formal ground-state bonding structure of the normal adenoside (left) (sugar bonding site indicated by S) and its proton-shifted tautomer (right). The arrows indicate

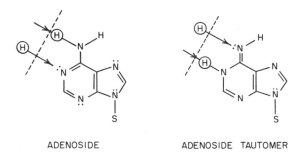

ADENOSIDE   ADENOSIDE TAUTOMER

FIG. 5. Formal molecular structures for the sugar derivatives of adenine, in Watson–Crick H-bonding, and its tautomer after a cooperative two-proton transfer (after Horowitz *et al.* [13]).

the H-bonding sites, with the diagonal dashed line as the molecular boundary for the integral base. After cooperative two-proton transfer (whether by biprotonic phototautomerism or by excited-state proton tunneling), a molecular tautomer of quite altered electronic structure results.

Qualitatively, we judge this type of structure for an adenine tautomer (Fig. 5, right) to be associated with possibilities of low-energy electronic transitions. For the present we conjecture that such an excited-state tautomer would exhibit fluorescence at longer wavelengths than the normal adenine molecule, and that such a fluorescence could be mistaken for an excimer emission. Thus, the luminescence observed for polynucleotides containing, e.g., adenine might be from the proton-displaced tautomer, and not from an excimer. It remains to investigate the quantitative details of biprotonic phototautomerism in its competition with molecular excimer formation and proton tunneling for the actual DNA base-pairs and analog polynucleotides.

Potential Energy Functions for Tautomerism of H-Bonded Base-Pairs

The double-minimum potential function (Fig. 3) for transfer of H-bonded protons with subsequent tautomerization of associated N-heterocyclic base-pairs will take widely varying forms according to the electronic properties of the system involved. The Herculean *ab initio* (all-atoms, all-electrons) calculations on the G–C base-pair (ground state) carried out by Clementi *et al.* [6] indicate that for single-proton movement in a hydrogen bond, only a single-minimum potential results. The extensive semiempirical theoretical work on the G–C base-pair (H-bonded skeletal model) by Rein, Harris, and associates [3–5] apparently yielded a double-minimum potential as the result of an inadvertent choice of an empirical parameter. Thus, the quantitative aspects of the latter work seem to be invalid.

However, for a simpler model case for which a complete calculation could be done [6] it was found that a double-minimum potential does result for a *cooperative* two-proton tautomerism. This case must correspond to the physically significant one, since intrabase electronic rearrangement would be expected to favor the cooperative two-proton transfer.

Now the fascinating question is opened concerning the detailed quantitative characteristics of the double-minimum potential for two-proton tautomerism in each of the DNA base-pairs and their analogs. Fortunately, most of the required information is accessible to experimental determination: the barrier height in the ground and excited states of the dimer, the transition energies in the precursor and tautomeric components, the rates of tautomerization.

The competition between biprotonic phototautomerism (over-the-barrier) excited-state two-proton tautomerism and excited-state proton tunneling

(through-the-barrier) is expected to be variable from case to case. It is possible that for a particular base-pair at low temperatures a residual excited-state proton tunneling occurs, and at higher or normal temperatures the two processes come into active competition near the top of the potential barrier.

In the polynucleotide structure of DNA, molecular exciton, charge transfer, and molecular excimer processes will provide further competitive events for the intra-base-pair phenomena.

Biological Implications

The biological relevance of these phenomena as described would be limited largely to radiation-induced phenomena. This could take two forms. First, the excited-state chemistry of DNA bases would very much depend on the fast excitation events described. Transfer of protons and electron redistribution will crucially determine which of a multiplicity of molecular species could be produced. Thus the detailed study of all aspects of rapid excitation phenomena would provide a mechanistic path to the elucidation of specific product formation, as has already been attempted in the correlation of molecular excimer formation in the thymine covalent dimer case.

The change of base-pairing with tautomerization of the DNA bases has long been recognised as of great genetic interest [1, 2]. As Fig. 6, modeled

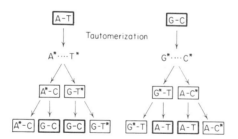

Fig. 6. Flow chart for changes in components of the DNA genetic code as a result of tautomerization of base-pairs.

after a diagram used by Löwdin [2] emphasizes, the formation of a single tautomerized base-pair acts catalytically to produce later "generations" of fully transformed base-pairs. Thus, e.g., adenine and thymine tautomers not only code falsely, but an A–T site leads to later G–C sites in its place after one A*–T* tautomerization step.

As far as DNA code changes directly or as a result of excitation processes [2–5] are concerned, this would seem to depend on facile excited-state tautomerization, with trapping of the tautomers in the ground state. Such a

circumstance would suggest radiation sensitivity of replicating systems, with a stabilization of the tautomer by the microenvironment. This type of effect could remove the very rapid time-scale restriction of the molecular electronic processes decribed here.

Summary

The competition between rapid excitation events in the 10^{-10}–10^{-14} sec time range in N-heterocyclic base-pairs has been discussed with particular reference to the DNA base-pairs. Experimental and theoretical results on the phenomena of proton tunneling, molecular-excimer formation, and biprotonic phototautomerism have been described. The application of quantitative studies of these phenomena in DNA and in component base-pairs and their analogs to radiation-induced mutagenesis has been projected.

References

1. J. D. Watson and F. H. C. Crick, *Nature* (*London*) **171**, 964 (1953); *Proc. Roy. Soc. Ser. A* **233**, 80 (1954).
2. P. O. Löwdin, *Rev. Mod. Phys.* **35**, 724 (1963); *Biopolym. Symp.* No. **1**, 161 (1964).
3. D. K. Rai and J. Ladik, *J. Mol. Spectrosc.* **27**, 79 (1968).
4. R. Rein and F. E. Harris, *Science* **146**, 149 (1964); *J. Chem. Phys.* **41**, 3393 (1964); **42**, 2177; **43**, 4415 (1965).
5. R. Rein and J. Ladik, *J. Chem. Phys.* **40**, 2466 (1964).
6. E. Clementi, J. M. André, M. Cl. André, D. Klint, and D. Hahn, *Acta Phys. Acad. Sci. Hung.* **27**, 493 (1969); E. Clementi, J. Mehl, and W. von Niessen, *J. Chem. Phys.* **54**, 508 (1971).
7. J. Eisinger, *Photochem. Photobiol.* **7**, 597 (1968).
8. A. Lamola, *Photochem. Photobiol.* **7**, 619 (1968).
9. C. A. Taylor, M. A. El-Bayoumi, and M. Kasha, *Proc. Nat. Acad. Sci. U. S.* **63**, 253 (1969).
10. A. G. Anderson, Jr. and H. L. Ammon, *Tetrahedron Lett.* **23**, 2579 (1966).
11. M. M. Robison and B. L. Robison, *J. Amer. Chem. Soc.* **77**, 6554 (1955).
12. K. Ingham, M. Abu-Elgheit, and M. A. El-Bayoumi, *J. Amer. Chem. Soc.*, **93**, 5023 (1971).
13. P. Horowitz, E. M. Evleth, and M. Kasha, Unpublished work, Florida State Univ., Tallahassee and Univ. California, Santa Cruz, 1971.

CHAPTER 7

INSTRUMENTAL TECHNIQUES

7.1 Fourier Spectroscopy

R. B. Sanderson

Department of Physics
The Ohio State University
Columbus, Ohio

I. Introduction

The purpose of any spectroscopic instrument is to determine the Fourier transform of a radiation field. This involves the measurement of the amplitude, and possibly the phase, of each frequency component of the field. Speaking generally, this is accomplished by mapping the Fourier components onto an observable set of orthogonal functions which can be separated to obtain the spectrum. In a grating spectrometer, the transform is performed by scattering the radiation from a periodic structure. Such a structure scatters each component in a different direction. The separation can be done either by using a slit to isolate the desired component or by using a detector with spatial resolution, such as a photographic film. In this case, the orthogonal functions are delta functions of the scattering angle. Since photographic film is not available for the infrared, the separation must be made by a slit which sequentially samples the frequency components. This is a simple method, but the necessity for sequential sampling makes it rather inefficient since only one component is observed at a time unless multiple detectors are used. The desire for a multiplexing technique, which would allow simultaneous observation of all frequency components with a single detector, led Fellgett [1] to propose the use of a two-beam interferometer. With the interferometer, the spectral components are mapped onto a set of sine functions of the

retardation, which can be separated by computing the Fourier transform of the detector signal. The interferometer also possesses the advantage of potentially greater throughput, as pointed out by Jacquinot [2]. Since the development of high-speed digital computers, the evaluation of the Fourier transform has become practical and both advantages have been realized in practice.

The basic principle is most easily understood by considering a Michelson interferometer (Fig. 1) aligned so that the detector sees the central fringe of

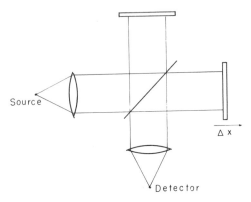

FIG. 1. Idealized Michelson interferometer for Fourier spectroscopy.

the interference pattern. One mirror is movable so that the retardation can be varied. Suppose that a monochromatic wave of the form

$$E(x, t) = \text{Re}\{\hat{E}_0 \exp i[2\pi\sigma(x - ct)]\} \qquad (1)$$

is incident on the interferometer. The caret indicates a complex number and σ stands for the wave number in cm^{-1}. If the beam splitter has amplitude reflectance $\hat{r}$ and amplitude transmittance $\hat{t}$, the detector signal is, as a function of the optical path difference Δx [3]

$$S(\Delta x) = \langle E^2(t) \rangle = |\hat{r}\hat{t}\hat{E}_0|^2[1 + \cos(2\pi\sigma \, \Delta x)] \qquad (2)$$

For an ideal beam splitter, $r = t = 2^{-1/2}$, so that $|rt|^2 = \frac{1}{4}$. The interference term thus imposes a cosine modulation on the detector signal. If other frequency components are added to the wave, the detector signal will be a superposition of terms like the right side of Eq. (2). For an incident wave of arbitrary spectral distribution, the detector signal can be written

$$S(\Delta x) = 2 \int_0^\infty p(\sigma)[1 + \cos(2\pi\sigma \, \Delta x)] \, d\sigma \qquad (3)$$

where $p(\sigma)$ is proportional to the spectral power density in the field. The first term is the total power in the field and is not usually of interest. Subtracting this term and rewriting the remainder in complex notation, we obtain the Fourier integral form

$$P(\Delta x) = \int_{-\infty}^{\infty} p(\sigma) \exp(-2\pi i\sigma \, \Delta x) \, d\sigma \tag{4}$$

$P(\Delta x)$ is called the interferogram and, by inverting the Fourier integral, the spectrum can be obtained. In Section II, the numerical evaluation of this transform is discussed and the influence of several kinds of error is considered. The multiplex and throughput advantages are also derived. In Section III, some recent instruments are described to show the performance achieved and to indicate the present state of the art.

A number of useful general references have appeared in recent years. Among these are the proceedings of three international conferences. The first of these was the "International Colloquium on the Recent Progress in Interferometric Spectroscopy" at Bellevue in 1957 [4]. The proceedings of this meeting are now chiefly of historical interest about the early development in this field. Meetings of greater current interest are the "Colloquium on New Methods of Interferometric Spectroscopy" held at Orsay in 1966 [5], and the "Conference on Fourier Transform Spectroscopy" at Aspen in 1970 [6]. The proceedings of the latter conference include a useful group of tutorial papers which provide a thorough discussion of Fourier transform techniques.

In a review article, Loewenstein [7] discusses some of the historical background, including the early contributions of Michelson [8] and of Rubens and Wood [9]. The earliest detailed analysis was given by Connes [10] in 1961. Other useful sources include the review article by Vanasse and Sakai [11], the book by Mertz [12], and a collection of articles in the March 1969 issue of Applied Optics [12a]. The latter includes an extensive bibliography.

II. Theory

A. GENERAL RELATIONS

Let us first rederive the interferogram from a slightly different viewpoint. Again, we consider a two-beam interferometer, such as a Michelson device, whose retardation τ can be varied. For the present, we assume that the detector is small compared with the central fringe of the interference pattern. The electric field at the detector can be written as

$$E(t) = E_1(t) + E_2(t - \tau) \tag{5}$$

where $E_1(t)$ is the field from the fixed arm and $E_2(t - \tau)$ is the field from the movable arm. The τ-dependent part of the detector signal is given by the correlation function $P_{12}(\tau)$ of E_1 and E_2 [13]

$$P_{12}(\tau) = \langle E_1(t)E_2(t - \tau) \rangle \equiv E_1(t) \star E_2(-t) \tag{6}$$

where $\star$ denotes the convolution operation [14]. The quantity $P_{12}(\tau)$ is known as the interferogram. For a symmetric interferometer, $E_1(t) = E_2(t)$, and the

interferogram is also symmetric. Fourier-transforming the symmetric interferogram, we obtain

$$P_{11}(\tau) \rightleftharpoons p_{11}(v) = |\hat{e}(v)|^2 \tag{7}$$

where

$$E(t) \rightleftharpoons \hat{e}(v) = \int_{-\infty}^{\infty} E(t) \exp(2\pi i v t)\, dt \tag{8}$$

defines the Fourier transform pair. In general, we shall use an upper-case
letter to denote a quantity in the time (or optical path) domain and the corresponding lower-case letter for the frequency (or wavenumber) domain. The
basic mathematical relations and a number of useful formulas are listed for
reference in Table I.

TABLE I

$$F(x) \rightleftharpoons f(\sigma) = \int_{-\infty}^{\infty} F(x) \exp(2\pi i \sigma x)\, dx$$

$$F(x) = \int_{-\infty}^{\infty} f(\sigma) \exp(-2\pi i \sigma x)\, d\sigma$$

Convolution: $A(x) \star B(x) = \int_{-\infty}^{\infty} A(x')B(x - x')\, dx'$

Convolution theorem: $A(x) \star B(x) \rightleftharpoons a(\sigma) \cdot b(\sigma)$

$$dF/dx \rightleftharpoons -2\pi i \sigma f(\sigma)$$

$$F(x - a) \rightleftharpoons \exp(2\pi i \sigma a) f(\sigma)$$

$$x \rightleftharpoons (2\pi i)^{-1}\, \delta'(\sigma)$$

$$\exp(2\pi i \sigma' x) \rightleftharpoons \delta(\sigma - \sigma')$$

$$\text{III}(x, \Delta x) = \Sigma_{j=-\infty}^{\infty}\, \delta(x - j\, \Delta x) \rightleftharpoons (1/\Delta x)\text{III}(\sigma, 1/\Delta x)$$

$$F(0) = \int_{-\infty}^{\infty} f(\sigma)\, d\sigma$$

Parseval's theorem $\int_{-\infty}^{\infty} |F(x)|^2\, dx = \int_{-\infty}^{\infty} |f(\sigma)|^2\, d\sigma$

We see from Eq. (7) that the Fourier transform of the symmetric interferogram is the spectral power density in the field. In practice, it is more convenient to replace the time variable by the optical path, $x = ct$, and the
frequency by the wave number, $\sigma = v/c$. With this substitution, the spectral
power density is related to the symmetric interferogram by the relation
obtained in Section I,

$$p_{11}(\sigma) = \int_{-\infty}^{\infty} P_{11}(x) \exp(2\pi i \sigma x)\, dx \tag{9}$$

It is instructive to consider the case where the interferogram is not symmetric. Suppose that a linear optical material is inserted into the fixed arm of
the interferometer. The effect of this sample on $E_1(t)$ can be expressed by the
response function $G(t)$, defined by

$$E_1\cdot(x) = G(x) \star E_1(x); \qquad \hat{e}_1\cdot(\sigma) = \hat{g}(\sigma) \cdot \hat{e}_1(\sigma) \tag{10}$$

$\hat{g}(\sigma)$ is a complex function which defines the *amplitude* transmittance of the sample. It is determined by the optical characteristics of the material and by the geometry of the sample. The interferogram becomes

$$P_{1'2}(x) = G(x) \star E_1(x) \star E_2(-x) = G(x) \star P_{12}(x) \tag{11}$$

and the transform,

$$\hat{p}_{1'2}(\sigma) = \hat{g}(\sigma) \cdot \hat{p}_{12}(\sigma) \tag{12}$$

Hence, the complete optical characteristics of the sample can be obtained by measuring two interferograms, transforming to obtain $\hat{p}_{1'2}(\sigma)$ and $\hat{p}_{12}(\sigma)$, and taking the ratio. Because of its sensitivity to the phase, this method is particularly useful in refractometry [13, 15]. We refer to this way of operating as the asymmetric mode.

In the more usual arrangement, the sample is placed outside the interferometer and the interferogram remains symmetric. This is equivalent to placing identical samples in both arms of the interferometer:

$$P_{1'2'}(x) = G(x) \star E_1(x) \star G(-x) \star E_2(-x)$$
$$= G(x) \star G(-x) \star P_{12}(x) \tag{13}$$
$$p_{1'2'}(\sigma) = |\hat{g}(\sigma)|^2 p_{12}(\sigma)$$

In this configuration, the phase information in $\hat{g}(\sigma)$ is lost and only the power transmittance is measured. If only the power transmittance is desired, this symmetric mode is normally preferable. In the asymmetric mode, the magnitude of the amplitude transmittance function is extremely sensitive to sample irregularities and there is a loss of linearity when the interferogram is truncated.

In the following discussion, we shall drop the subscripts and denote a general interferogram by $P(x)$ and its transform, which we shall call the spectrum, by $\hat{p}(\sigma)$. Since $P(x)$ is always real, $\hat{p}(\sigma) = \hat{p}^*(-\sigma)$. In the usual configuration, $P(x)$ is symmetric and $p(\sigma)$ is pure real. Although we do not assign a physical interpretation to the negative wave numbers, it is mathematically convenient to include them in the analysis.

In the remaining sections of Section II, we discuss the evaluation of the Fourier transform

$$P(x) \rightleftharpoons \hat{p}(\sigma) = \int_{-\infty}^{\infty} P(x) \exp(2\pi i\sigma x)\, dx \tag{14}$$

considering the effects on $\hat{p}(\sigma)$ of the approximations in the computation procedure and of errors in $P(x)$. It is our intention to develop these relations in a systematic and concise manner which emphasizes the symmetry between the interferogram space and the spectrum space. This formalism is particularly well suited for analysis of instrumental errors.

B. Truncation and Apodization

Since the interferogram cannot be measured to infinite path differences, it must be truncated. This is done by multiplying the interferogram by a function $A(x)$ which vanishes outside the range of the data. Such a function may, for the sake of generality, be called a filter in the interferogram space. Analogous filter functions in the spectrum space will be defined later.

Ordinarily, $A(x)$ is either a symmetric function nonzero over the range $-\frac{1}{2}L \le x \le +\frac{1}{2}L$ or a one-sided function nonzero over $0 \le x \le L$. We write the truncated interferogram

$$P'(x) = P(x) \cdot A(x) \rightleftharpoons \hat{p}(\sigma) \star \hat{a}(\sigma) \tag{15}$$

The calculated spectrum is the "true" spectrum convolved with the Fourier transform of the truncation function. The real part of $\hat{a}(\sigma)$ is called the apparatus function and is analogous to the slit function of a grating spectrometer. If the truncation function is picked so that $A(0) = 1$, then $\int_{-\infty}^{\infty} \hat{a}(\sigma)\, d\sigma = 1$, and the normalization of the spectrum is preserved. If the range of $A(x)$ is equal to L, the width of $\hat{a}(\sigma)$ is of the order of $1/L$. The resolution is thus limited by the maximum path difference on the interferogram.

The simplest truncation function is the window function $W(x, L)$, defined by

$$W(x, L) = \begin{cases} 0, & |x| > \frac{1}{2}L \\ 1, & |x| \le \frac{1}{2}L \end{cases} \tag{16}$$

$$W(x, L) \rightleftharpoons w(\sigma, 1/L) = L[\sin(\pi\sigma L)]/(\pi\sigma L) = L\,\mathrm{sinc}(\pi\sigma L)$$

The sinc function is inconvenient as an apparatus function because it possesses relatively large secondary maxima on either side of the principle maximum. In the neighborhood of sharp spectral features, these sidelobes give rise to oscillations which may lead to intensity errors or appear as spurious features. It is customary to suppress these lobes by modifying the truncation function to reduce the contribution to the spectrum at high spatial frequencies. This procedure, known as apodization, reduces the oscillations at the expense of a loss in resolution.

Several apodization functions and the corresponding apparatus functions are listed in Table II. The triangular apodization is the simplest, but is not used where high accuracy is required. The positive-definite apparatus function leads to systematic baseline errors away from the spectral features. The Happ–Genzel [16] apodization contains an adjustable parameter which can be chosen to make the sidelobes very small. When $a = 0.54$ and $b = 0.46$, the largest secondary maximum is only 0.008 times the central peak. The quartic apodization has a somewhat greater first sidelobe, but more remote sidelobes decrease very rapidly.

TABLE II

APODIZATION FUNCTIONS[a]

	$A(x)$	$a(\sigma)$	Width at half-maximum
Unapodized	1	$L \operatorname{sinc} y$	$1.22/L$
Triangular	$1 - (2|x|/L)$	$\tfrac{1}{2}L \operatorname{sinc}^2(y/2)$	$1.80/L$
Cosine	$\cos(\pi x/L)$	$\tfrac{1}{2}L [\operatorname{sinc}(y + \tfrac{1}{2}) + \operatorname{sinc}(y - \tfrac{1}{2})]$	$1.58/L$
Happ–Genzel [16]	$a + b \cos(2\pi x/L)$	$L(\operatorname{sinc} y)\{a - [by^2/(y^2 - \pi^2)]\}$	$1.82/L$
Quartic	$[1 - (2x/L)^2]^2$	$4(2\pi)^{1/2}LJ_{5/2}(y)/y^{5/2}$	$1.92/L$

[a] All $A(x) = 0$ for $|x| > \tfrac{1}{2}L$; $y = \pi\sigma L$.

Apodization can also be performed in the spectrum space after transformation by convolving the unapodized spectrum with the desired apparatus function [17]:

$$P(x) \cdot W(x, L) \cdot A(x) \rightleftharpoons \hat{p}(\sigma) \star w(\sigma, 1/L) \star \hat{a}(\sigma) = \hat{p}(\sigma) \star \hat{a}(\sigma) \qquad (17)$$

The last equality holds if $A(x)$ vanishes outside the window $W(x, L)$. This is a more convenient procedure if it is desired to use several different apodization functions on the same interferogram or if interpolation in the spectrum is required. In the latter case, interpolation and apodization can be performed in the same step. Formulas for performing these convolutions will be derived in Section II.C. If further data manipulation is not required, apodization in the interferogram is more efficient since it involves only multiplication, not convolution.

Filtering in Spectrum Space

The analog in the spectrum space of truncation in interferogram space is spectral filtering. This operation eliminates any wavenumber components which lie outside the desired spectral band. When working with long interferograms, it may be useful to perform this filtering before transforming, to optimize the efficiency of the Fourier transform calculation.

The expressions are slightly more complicated than the corresponding expressions for truncation in interferogram space. The filter $\hat{a}(\sigma)$ must satisfy $\hat{a}(\sigma) = \hat{a}^*(-\sigma)$ to assure that the interferogram remains real. Unlike an interferogram filter, $\hat{a}(\sigma)$ does not necessarily include the zero-wavenumber point. An ideal spectral filter is represented by [18]

$$\hat{p}(\sigma) \cdot [W(\sigma - \sigma_C, \sigma_R) + W(\sigma + \sigma_C, \sigma_R)]$$
$$\rightleftharpoons P(x) \star [2\sigma_R \operatorname{sinc}(\pi x \sigma_R) \cos(2\pi x \sigma_C)] \qquad (18)$$

where $\sigma_C = \frac{1}{2}(\sigma_1 + \sigma_2)$ and $\sigma_R = \sigma_2 - \sigma_1$, with σ_1 and σ_2 respectively the lower and upper limits of the filter. Thus, spectral filtering can be accomplished by a convolution in the interferogram space before the transformation is done.

In practice, the convolution integral in Eq. (18) is cut off after a few oscillations of the sinc function. This cutoff is equivalent to convolving the filter with $\mathrm{sinc}(2\pi\sigma x_c)$, where x_c is the cutoff point of the convolution integral. This introduces wavenumber components into the spectrum which may lie beyond the cutoff points of the filter. These extra components can cause serious errors when the sampled interferogram is transformed. (See Section II.C). These errors may be reduced by "apodizing" the filter function. A somewhat more convenient procedure, which has the same effect, is to multiply the transform of the filter function in Eq. [18] by the quartic apodization function $[1 - (x/x_c)^2]^2$ before evaluating the convolution integral [18].

C. Sampling of the Interferogram and Spectrum

The actual calculations are usually carried out using a digital computer. The interferogram is sampled and the spectrum computed at discrete, uniformally spaced points and the integrals replaced by sums. We may represent this in the following manner.

Define the Ш distribution, or Dirac comb [14], and its Fourier transform by

$$\text{Ш}(x, \Delta x) = \sum_{j=-\infty}^{\infty} \delta(x - j\,\Delta x) \rightleftharpoons (1/\Delta x)\text{Ш}(\sigma, 1/\Delta x) \qquad (19)$$

Sampling the interferogram at points $j\,\Delta x$ is represented by multiplication by $\text{Ш}(x, \Delta x)$:

$$P(x) \cdot \text{Ш}(x, \Delta x) \rightleftharpoons (1/\Delta x)\hat{p}(\sigma) \,\star\, \text{Ш}(\sigma, 1/\Delta x) \qquad (20)$$

Evaluating explicitly the transform of the left side, we obtain

$$\hat{p}(\sigma) \,\star\, \text{Ш}(\sigma, 1/\Delta x) = \sum_{j=-\infty}^{\infty} P(j\,\Delta x)\{\exp[2\pi i j(\Delta x)\sigma]\}\,\Delta x \qquad (21)$$

The convolution with the comb generates periodic replicas of $\hat{p}(\sigma)$ with period $1/\Delta x \equiv 2\sigma_R$. If the true spectrum is confined to one-half period of the comb, the periodic replicas do not overlap and no error is introduced by the sampling. Figure 2 shows the relation between sampling and replication. This replication is called aliasing and the periodic replicas are called aliases. To prevent overlapping of the aliases, the sampling interval must not be greater than $(2\sigma_R)^{-1}$. We may picture the effect of sampling as replacement of the single, sharply peaked apparatus function by a periodic sequence of such peaks at intervals $2\sigma_R$. Overlapping of the aliases occurs when more than one

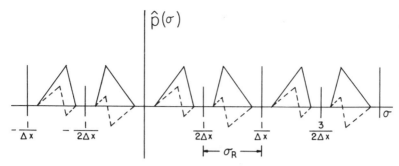

FIG. 2. Structure of the calculated periodic spectrum. The reconstruction is unambiguous if the entire occupied spectral range lies between $n/(2\,\Delta x)$ and $(n+1)/(2\,\Delta x)$, where n is any integer. (———) Real part; (— —) imaginary part.

peak scans the spectrum at a time. The sampling interval should be just fine enough to prevent this overlapping; more frequent sampling is a waste of time. This point will be discussed further in Section II.F.

The appropriate interval for calculating the spectrum can be determined from similar considerations. Assume the truncated interferogram of length L to be periodically extended:

$$P(x) \star \text{Ш}(x, L) \rightleftharpoons (1/L)\hat{p}(\sigma) \cdot \text{Ш}(\sigma, 1/L) \tag{22}$$

The periodically extended interferogram has Fourier components only at points separated by intervals $\Delta\sigma = 1/L$. The truncated interferogram is completely determined if $\hat{p}(\sigma)$ is known at these points. As might be expected, this interval is of the order of the resolution width.

The total number of sample points in the interferogram is $N = L/\Delta x = 2\sigma_R/\Delta\sigma$. This is equal to twice the number of points in the spectrum. Since the spectrum may be complex, the number of independent points is the same in both representations. If the interferogram is symmetric, only half of the input points are independent and the imaginary part of $\hat{p}(\sigma)$ vanishes.

The truncation and periodic extension of both interferogram and spectrum make it possible to represent each function by a finite set of discrete points, the so-called primary samples. The Fourier integral can then be replaced by a finite sum in a form suitable for numerical computation. It is useful to construct similar expressions for other integrals which arise in performing convolutions and in interpolating between primary samples.

The convolution integral in σ space, $\hat{c}(\sigma)$, may be expressed in the following manner. Consider a function $\hat{a}(\sigma)$ which is to be convolved with the sampled spectrum $\hat{p}(\sigma) \cdot \text{Ш}(\sigma, \Delta\sigma)$. The Fourier transform of $\hat{a}(\sigma)$, is cut off to lie within one period of the extended interferogram:

$$\hat{c}(\sigma) = [\hat{p}(\sigma) \cdot \text{Ш}(\sigma, \Delta\sigma)] \star [\hat{a}(\sigma) \star \text{sinc}(\pi\sigma L)]$$
$$\rightleftharpoons [P(x) \star \text{Ш}(x, L)]A(x) \cdot W(x, L) \tag{23}$$

Evaluating the convolution,

$$\hat{c}(\sigma) = \sum_k \hat{p}(k\,\Delta\sigma)\hat{f}(\sigma - k\,\Delta\sigma) \tag{24}$$

where $\hat{f}(\sigma) = \hat{a}(\sigma) \star \text{sinc}(\pi\sigma L)$.

Two limiting cases are of particular interest. If $\hat{a}(\sigma) = \delta(\sigma)$, the convolution reduces to

$$\hat{c}(\sigma) = \hat{p}(\sigma) = \sum_k \hat{p}(k\,\Delta\sigma)\,\text{sinc}\{[\pi(\sigma/\Delta\sigma) - k]\} \tag{25}$$

This is the interpolation formula which permits determination of $\hat{p}(\sigma)$ at an arbitrary wave number in terms of the primary samples [17]. A second special case arises when $A(x)$ is nonzero only within the range of the window function $W(x, L)$. In this case, the convolution again simplifies:

$$\hat{c}(\sigma) = \sum_k \hat{p}(k\,\Delta\sigma)\hat{a}(\sigma - k\,\Delta\sigma) \tag{26}$$

An apodization function satisfies this requirement, so that apodization and interpolation may be performed simultaneously in the σ domain using this relation.

In practice, these summations are cut off after a relatively small number of points. As discussed in the previous section, it is customary to apodize the interferogram space filter unless $\hat{a}(\sigma)$ is such as to automatically accomplish this.

Similar expressions are readily obtained for convolution in the interferogram space. They differ only because of the more complicated form of the filter function in spectrum space. The convolution $c(x)$ of $A(x)$ with the interferogram $P(x)$ is given by

$$c(x) = \sum_j P(j\,\Delta x)f(x - j\,\Delta x) \tag{27}$$

where

$$f(x) = A(x) \star \{\text{sinc}(\pi x\sigma_R)\cos[\pi(4r + q)x\sigma_R]\}$$

r and q are integers which index the desired alias. r is the number of complete periods of the spectrum between zero wave number and the period actually used. If the occupied spectrum lies in the lower half of the period, $q = 1$; if the spectrum is in the upper half of the period, $q = 3$. All considerations of limiting cases and apodization of the filter function apply here as in the case of convolution in the spectrum.

D. Asymmetry Considerations

In Section II.A, we saw that the Fourier transform of the symmetric interferogram is the spectral power density. In this case, the interferogram need be

measured on only one side of the center and only the cosine transform need be calculated. In the unapodized case, this may be expressed symbolically in the following manner:

$$P'(x) = P(x) \cdot W(x - \tfrac{1}{2}L, L) \rightleftharpoons p(\sigma) \; ☆ \; [Le^{i\pi\sigma L} \; \text{sinc}(\pi\sigma L)]$$

$$\hat{p}'(\sigma) = \tfrac{1}{2}\{p(\sigma)] \; ☆ \; 2L \; \text{sinc} \; (2\pi\sigma L) + ip(\sigma) \; ☆ \; L \; \sin^2(\pi\sigma L)/(\pi\sigma L)]\}$$

(28)

so that

$$p(\sigma) \; ☆ \; 2L \; \text{sinc}(2\pi\sigma L) = 2 \; \text{Re}\{\hat{p}'(\sigma)\} = 2 \int_0^L P(x) \cos(2\pi\sigma x) \, dx \qquad (29)$$

Our calculated spectrum has the desired form of the spectral power density convolved with a symmetric apparatus function which is the real part of the Fourier transform of the truncation function. This form assures the linearity of the instrumental response.

In practice, the interferogram is never perfectly symmetric. The asymmetry may be introduced deliberately, as when the asymmetric mode is used or when the interferogram is "chirped" [12] to reduce dynamic range requirements. Asymmetry may also arise when the interferometer is not perfectly achromatic or if the interferogram is not properly sampled. In this situation, we must decide what function provides the best representation of the spectrum and what corrections to the raw transform are necessary.

The Fourier transform of an asymmetric interferogram is complex:

$$P(x) \rightleftharpoons \hat{p}(\sigma) = |\hat{p}(\sigma)| e^{i\phi(\sigma)} \qquad (30)$$

In general, the magnitude $|\hat{p}(\sigma)|$ provides a suitable representation of the spectrum [19]. Ambiguity may arise in spectral regions where the noise may cause the signal to become negative or where the detector radiates to the source. If $\phi(\sigma)$ is reasonably well behaved, the latter type of ambiguity may be recognized by the 180° discontinuity in the phase.

The operation of taking the magnitude of a complex number is not, in general, linear, and when the interferogram is truncated, the concept of an apparatus function may no longer be valid. To see the limitations of this choice, consider an interferogram $P(x)$ and a truncation function $A(x)$ without assumptions about symmetry:

$$P(x) \cdot A(x) \rightleftharpoons \{|\hat{p}(\sigma)| e^{i\phi(\sigma)}\} \; ☆ \; \hat{a}(\sigma) \qquad (31)$$

If we restrict our attention to spectral regions where $\phi(\sigma)$ is constant, or at least $e^{i\phi(\sigma)}$ varies slowly compared with $\hat{a}(\sigma)$, the amplitude of the calculated spectrum can be written

$$|\hat{p}'(\sigma)|^2 = ||\hat{p}(\sigma)| \; ☆ \; a_r(\sigma)|^2 + ||\hat{p}(\sigma)| \; ☆ \; a_i(\sigma)|^2 \qquad (32)$$

where a_r and a_i are, respectively, the real and imaginary parts of $\hat{a}(\sigma)$. This expression was first given by Mertz [12]. The condition on ϕ is satisfied if the center of the interferogram is taken at what Mertz calls the point of stationary phase.

Looking at Eq. (32), we see that, in addition to the stationary phase condition, the interferogram must be truncated symmetrically so that $a_i(\sigma) = 0$. If both of these conditions are met, the magnitude response of the instrument can, apart from a sign, be represented by a convolution with a symmetric apparatus function.

An additional complication arises when the asymmetric mode is used with the sample in one arm of the interferometer. The interferogram is now a cross-correlation of two different fields and, consequently, its transform is not a power spectrum. Similarly, caution should be used in the interpretation of a spectrum obtained from a chirped interferogram. Normally, the asymmetric mode is used for measuring the amplitude response of a sample as discussed in Section II.A. It should be recognized that the apparatus function will not be meaningful in the neighborhood of strong spectral lines where the phase is changing rapidly. When the asymmetric mode is used, we are usually interested in phase measurements in relatively open regions of the spectrum and this limitation is not serious.

When using the symmetric mode, we prefer to truncate asymmetrically so that only one side of the interferogram need be measured. In this case, we would like a procedure to correct for the usually small asymmetry without loss of linearity [20, 21].

Assume that the asymmetry can be represented by subjecting the intrinsically real spectrum to an instrumental phase shift. The observed asymmetric interferogram is thus

$$P'(x) \rightleftharpoons p'(\sigma) = p(\sigma)e^{i\phi_I(\sigma)} \qquad (33)$$

$\phi_I(\sigma)$ is a smoothly varying function and can be measured by transforming a short, two-sided interferogram. Note that $p(\sigma)$, although real, is not the magnitude of $\hat{p}'(\sigma)$ since it may be negative to include the 180° phase shift mentioned earlier.

The phase correction may be performed in either domain. The simpler method, proposed by Mertz [12], involves a multiplicative process in the σ domain. Using a one-sided truncation function,

$$p''(x) = P'(x) \cdot A(x) \rightleftharpoons e^{i\phi_I(\sigma)}\{p(\sigma) \star \hat{a}(\sigma)\} \qquad (34)$$

if the stationary phase condition is met. Thus,

$$p(\sigma) \star a_r(\sigma) = \mathrm{Re}\{\hat{p}''(\sigma)e^{-i\phi_I}\} \qquad (35)$$

gives the desired correction. This method is simple to apply, but the necessity of satisfying the stationary phase condition restricts it to cases where the asymmetry is small. When this method is used, the interferogram should not be truncated with a step at $x = 0$. This multiplicative procedure corrects only one peak of the apparatus function. The error components of the peaks corresponding to other aliases are broad and introduce serious residual errors,

even for small phase errors. If the interferogram is truncated smoothly through $x = 0$, these peaks can be made much narrower and the residual error much smaller. This truncation is conveniently done by letting $A(x)$ cut off trapezoidally near the origin in such a way that $A(0) = \frac{1}{2}$.

The correction can also be performed by a convolution in the x domain. This method, described by Forman *et al.* [19], is more powerful, since the stationary phase condition need not be satisfied. For this reason, it is more widely used in spite of the relative computational inefficiency inherent in the convolution as compared with the multiplication. From Eq. (33),

$$p(\sigma) = \hat{p}'(\sigma) \cdot \hat{\theta}(\sigma), \qquad \text{where} \quad \hat{\theta}(\sigma) = e^{-i\phi_I}$$
$$P(x) = P'(x) \star \Theta(x) \tag{36}$$

If $\Theta(x)$ can be calculated, a symmetrized interferogram can be generated by carrying out the convolution. The formulas given in Section II.C can be applied directly to this calculation. The special case of a uniform sampling error will be discussed in Section II.H.

E. COMPUTATION

The Fourier transform is almost always performed using a digital computer programmed with the fast Fourier transform algorithm [22, 23]. The only important exception is where an on-line computer working in real time is available to calculate the spectrum as the interferogram is generated [24]. In the early days of Fourier spectroscopy, a number of analog computers were constructed to do the transform [25]. These have been superseded by modern digital computers with their great speed and capacity.

When the appropriate spectral intervals are specified, Eq. (21) becomes

$$p(\sigma_K) = \Delta x \sum_{j=0}^{N-1} P(j\,\Delta x) \exp(2\pi ijk/N) \tag{37}$$

where

$$\sigma_K \begin{cases} = 2r\sigma_R + k\,\Delta\sigma & \text{if} \quad q = 1 \\ = 2(r+1)\sigma_R - k\,\Delta\sigma & \text{if} \quad q = 3 \end{cases}$$

r and q are defined in Section II.C. The interferogram is taken as periodic with period $N\,\Delta x$. Any discontinuities due to truncation are removed by suitable apodization or by replacing the point on the discontinuity with the average of the function on either side of the discontinuity.

The computer time required for direct evaluation of this sum is proportional to N^2, and for N greater than a few hundred, rapidly becomes prohibitively long even for fast, modern computers. This obstacle has been surmounted by the development of the fast Fourier transform algorithm [22, 23] which, if $N = 2^M$ with M an integer, greatly reduces the computation time. With this

algorithm, the computation time is proportional to $N \ln_2 N$ and ceases to be the limiting factor. The length of the computation is now limited by the available core storage in the computer. With the IBM 360-75, 32K points can be transformed in about 1 min without use of external files [18]. Using external files, the Connes's have transformed up to 10^6 points in 22 min [26].

The fast Fourier transform procedure has been described in detail by Cochran *et al.* [23] and is available in the IBM Scientific Subroutine Package. The restriction $N = 2^M$ is not inconvenient in practice since the interferogram can always be extended by adding zeros at the end or, in the asymmetric case, at both ends. When this is done, the routine produces output points more closely spaced than required by the resolution and is equivalent to interpolation by Eq. (25). A further point is that the fast Fourier procedure is intrinsically complex and, hence, produces both sine and cosine transforms. This is necessary in the asymmetric case and often useful in the symmetric case when corrections are required.

F. SIGNAL–NOISE CONSIDERATIONS

The object of this section is to discuss the relation between random noise on the interferogram and noise on the spectrum and to demonstrate the Fellgett advantage. For generality, we assume that the noise on the interferogram is proportional to the nth power of the detector signal, where n may equal 0, $\frac{1}{2}$, or 1. These values correspond to three distinct and important sources of noise.

a. $n = 0$: This represents thermal detector noise which is independent of signal. This is normally the dominant source of noise in the infrared and is the only type for which the Fellgett advantage is obtained.

b. $n = \frac{1}{2}$: Photon noise in the radiation field ultimately limits the performance of any spectroscopic instrument. In the infrared, this limit is approached only at high frequencies.

c. $n = 1$: Noise proportional to the signal may arise from some types of source fluctuations or from "scintillation" in the intervening medium. This kind of noise is a severe handicap in Fourier spectroscopy and, if present, must be minimized by special averaging procedures or by compensation [12].

We represent the sampled noisy interferogram as the sum of the true, noiseless interferogram and a noise interferogram $B(x)$.

$$B(j\,\Delta x) = E_j[P_0 + P(j\,\Delta x)]^n \tag{38}$$

The statistically random parameter E_j is characterized by the correlation function.

$$\langle E_j E_{j'}^* \rangle = E^2 \delta_{jj'} \tag{39}$$

where $\langle\ \rangle$ denotes an ensemble average. Thus, $\langle E_j \rangle = 0$ and E^2 is the mean square deviation of the E_j. Here P_0 is that part of the detector signal which is independent of the optical path and does not contribute to the interferogram. It is related to the average value of the spectrum by $P_0 = \overline{p(\sigma_k)}N\,\Delta\sigma$. Using the Fourier transform expression given by Eq. (37) we may, following the analysis of Bell [13], determine the mean square deviation of the noise on the spectrum.

$$b^2 = \langle |b_k|^2 \rangle = E^2(\Delta x)^2 \sum_j [P_0 + P(j\,\Delta x)]^{2n} \tag{40}$$

If N is much greater than one,

$$b^2 \approx E^2(\Delta x)^2 NP_0^{2n} \tag{41}$$

Hence, the rms deviation is

$$b = E[\overline{p(\sigma_k)}]^n N^{n-1/2}(\Delta\sigma)^{n-1} \tag{42}$$

which is independent of wavenumber. The phases are distributed randomly over 0 to 2π. In the symmetric mode, or for high signal–noise ratio in the asymmetric mode, only the in-phase component of b contributes to the noise on the spectrum. This is given by $b_r = b/\sqrt{2}$. In the asymmetric mode, the quadrature component becomes significant in low signal regions, causing a further loss of signal–noise ratio. The noise on the phase arises principally from the quadrature component and, in regions with high signal–noise ratio, is given by $b/(|p|\sqrt{2})$ radians.

In the general case, the signal–noise ratio in the output of the interferometer is given by

$$\left(\frac{S}{N}\right)_i = \frac{p(\sigma_k)}{b} = \frac{p(\sigma_k)\,\Delta\sigma}{E[p(\sigma_k)\,\Delta\sigma]^n}\,N^{-n+(1/2)} \tag{43}$$

For a monochromator with resolution $\Delta\sigma$,

$$\left(\frac{S}{N}\right)_m = \frac{p(\sigma_k)\,\Delta\sigma}{E[p(\sigma_k)\,\Delta\sigma]^n} \tag{44}$$

The ratio of these two quantities is approximately

$$\frac{(S/N)_i}{(S/N)_m} \approx N^{-n+(1/2)} = \begin{cases} N^{1/2} & n = 0 \\ 1 & n = \frac{1}{2} \\ N^{-1/2} & n = 1 \end{cases} \tag{45}$$

For $n = 0$, this ratio is just the Fellgett advantage. We see that the multiplex procedure yields a gain only for the case on signal independent noise. In the other cases, the noise increases rapidly enough with N to cancel the multiplex advantage.

Let us consider the important $n = 0$ case more closely. In this case, E is proportional to $t^{-1/2}$, where t is the time required for the measurement of a single data point, whether on the interferogram with the interferometer or on the spectrum with a monochromator [27]. Putting $E = Kt^{-1/2}$, we rewrite Eq. (43) obtaining

$$\left(\frac{S}{N}\right)_i = \frac{p(\sigma_k)\,\Delta\sigma}{K[p(\sigma_k)\,\Delta\sigma]^n}\,T^{1/2} \tag{46}$$

where $T = Nt$ is the total time required for the run. This gives the important result that, for a given resolution, the signal–noise ratio depends only on the total time taken for the run. In particular, there is nothing to be gained by reducing the step size. Oversampling the interferogram improves the signal–noise ratio only to the extent that the oversampled run takes longer. If the duty cycle is less than 100%, it is more efficient to sample minimally and spend more time at each step.

If t_m is the time used for measuring one point of the spectrum with a monochromator, Eq. (45) becomes, in terms of the times,

$$(S/N)_i/(S/N)_m = (T/t_m)^{1/2} \tag{47}$$

We see the Fellgett advantage in another form. The signal–noise ratio from the interferometer is the same as we would get from the monochromator if the monochromator measured each spectral component for a time equal to the entire duration of the interferometer run.

G. Aperture and Throughput Considerations

In all our previous analysis, we have assumed an infinitesimally small detector, or equivalently, perfectly collimated radiation in the interferometer. Since a perfectly collimated beam is not consistent with finite throughput, we wish to consider departures from this ideal case.

This is conveniently treated by considering a circular monochromatic source, wave number σ', in the focal plane of the collimator, subtending a solid angle Ω as seen from the collimator. Passing through the interferometer, the radiation from an element of area dA on this source suffers a retardation

$$x = x_0 \cos \theta \tag{48}$$

where x_0 is the retardation of the axial ray and θ is the small angle between the axis and dA as seen from the collimator. The radiation from this element produces an interferogram

$$dP \sim \cos[2\pi\sigma' x(1 - \tfrac{1}{2}\theta^2)]\,dA \tag{49}$$

Integrating over the disk yields the interferogram,

$$P(x) \sim \text{sinc}(\tfrac{1}{2}\,\sigma'x\Omega)\cos\{2\pi\sigma'[1 - (\Omega/4\pi)]x\} \tag{50}$$

Two effects are immediately obvious. The calculated wave numbers are shifted to the red by the spread in optical path differences. Second, the interferogram is modulated by a slowly varying sinc function. This modulation arises from the contraction of the fringes in the plane of the detector as the displacement increases. Each oscillation of the sinc function corresponds to another fringe entering the detector. This imposes an upper limit on the resolving power of the interferometer. Transforming the interferogram in Eq. (50), we obtain

$$p(\sigma) \sim W\left[\sigma - \sigma'\left(1 - \frac{\Omega}{4\pi}\right), \frac{\sigma'\Omega}{2\pi}\right] + W\left[\sigma + \sigma'\left(1 - \frac{\Omega}{4\pi}\right), \frac{\sigma'\Omega}{2\pi}\right] \tag{51}$$

The output is a square peak of width $\sigma'\Omega/2\pi$. The resolving power is thus $2\pi/\Omega$. This represents the maximum resolving power attainable with the instrument. Higher resolution can be obtained only by stopping down the source and thus reducing the solid angle.

We can now derive the Jacquinot, or throughput, advantage of the interferometer. Consider an interferometer whose beam splitter is of area A and for which a resolving power R is desired. The maximum possible throughput is $E_i = A\Omega = 2\pi A/R$. We compare this with a grating spectrometer with the same area and resolving power [11]. The solid angle is limited by the slit,

$$\Omega = hw/f^2 \tag{52}$$

where h is the slit height and w its width, and f is the focal length of the monochromator. w is determined by the dispersion of the grating and the spectral slit width $\Delta\sigma$:

$$w = f(d\theta/d\sigma)\,\Delta\sigma \tag{53}$$

Hence, the throughput is, for a grating spectrometer,

$$E_g = (h/f)(\sigma\,d\theta/d\sigma)(A/R) \tag{54}$$

Since the quantity $\sigma\,d\theta/d\sigma$ is generally of the order of unity and h/f is much less than unity, the throughput of a grating spectrometer is usually much less than that of an interferometer of the same size and resolving power. This superiority of the interferometer is the Jacquinot advantage. It should be made clear that, in this discussion, only the intrinsic limitations of the monochromator or interferometer are considered. In practice, the throughput may be limited elsewhere in the system. In the far-infrared, the throughput is often limited by the size and acceptance angle of the detector. In this case, the Jacquinot advantage cannot be realized. Alternatively, it may be possible to increase $\sigma\,d\theta/d\sigma$, as by multipassing the grating, and overcome the Jacquinot advantage.

H. ERROR DISCUSSION

In this section, we discuss some of the errors which can arise in measuring the interferogram and their effect on the calculated spectrum. They may conveniently be divided into sampling errors and intensity errors.

Sampling Errors

These errors arise from a failure to adequately control the optical path difference in the interferometer. If the errors are small compared to the period of the interferogram fringes, the effect can be approximated by a Taylor expansion of the interferogram:

$$P'(x) = P(x) + E(x)\, dP/dx \rightleftharpoons \hat{p}(\sigma) - 2\pi i\hat{e}(\sigma) \star [\sigma\hat{p}(\sigma)] \qquad (55)$$

where $E(x)$ is the sampling error. For example, if $E(x) = A \sin(2\pi g x)$, such as might arise from periodic errors in a drive screw, the measured spectrum becomes

$$\hat{p}'(\sigma) = \hat{p}(\sigma) + \pi A[(\sigma - g)\hat{p}(\sigma - g) - (\sigma + g)\hat{p}(\sigma + g)] \qquad (56)$$

Each spectral feature is accompanied by side bands displaced by $\pm g$ from the real feature. These bands are equivalent to Rowland ghosts [3] in a grating spectrometer but are, in general, more intense. In a grating instrument, the Fourier transform of the grating profile is the amplitude spectrum, which must be squared to obtain the spectral power density. Any ghosts due to periodic ruling errors are thus reduced relative to the more intense real features. In the interferometer, the Fourier transform yields the power spectrum directly. For this reason, the permissible error in determining the path difference is less than the corresponding error allowed in ruling the grating [10].

This formalism may be used to estimate the spectral error associated with random sampling errors. Let the interferogram be represented by the expression in Eq. (55), where $E(x)$ is a random variable with average value zero. Applying the formalism of Section II.F to the error term, the mean-square noise amplitude becomes

$$b^2 = E^2(\Delta x)^2 \sum_j |dP_j/dx|^2 \qquad (57)$$

where E is the rms sampling error. The sum can be evaluated using Parseval's theorem:

$$\sum_j |dP_j/dx|^2 = (4\pi^2/N) \sum_k |\sigma_k p_k(\sigma)|^2 = (4\pi^2/\Delta x) \int_{2\sigma_R} d\sigma\, [\sigma p(\sigma)]^2 \qquad (58)$$

The noise may now be written

$$b = 2\pi E\, [\sigma p(\sigma)]_{rms} \qquad (59)$$

This relation permits an estimate of the errors caused by random sampling errors. The actual appearance of the noise on a spectrum from a single interferogram depends strongly on the spectral structure. On a broad band spectrum, where dP/dx is large only near the interferogram center, the noise will vary more slowly with wave number than on a highly structured spectrum.

For the special case of a monochromatic signal, where the interferogram is given by

$$P(x) = \cos(2\pi\sigma_0 x)W(x, X) \rightleftharpoons \tfrac{1}{2}X\{\text{sinc}[\pi(\sigma - \sigma_0)X] + \text{sinc}[\pi(\sigma + \sigma_0)X]\} \tag{60}$$

Eq. (59) can be evaluated to yield

$$b = 2^{1/2}\pi E\sigma_0 N^{1/2}\,\Delta x \tag{61}$$

This expression has been given by Sakai [28] from a somewhat different approach.

In a well-designed interferometer under laboratory conditions, the only important sampling error is a constant displacement of the sampled points away from the points specified by $\text{Ш}(x, \Delta x)$. This type of error may arise when a finite minimum step size is used which does not permit any point to coincide exactly with the white-light position. It may also occur in interferometrically controlled instruments when there is a shift between the path of the reference beam and the infrared beam. The analysis is most conveniently done using the formalism of Section II.D, setting the instrumental phase shift to $2\pi\sigma\varepsilon$, where ε is the constant step error. The calculated spectrum, using a one-sided cosine transform is, assuming stationary phase,

$$\text{Re}[\hat{p}'(\sigma)] = [\cos(2\pi\varepsilon\sigma)][p(\sigma) \star a_r(\sigma)] - [\sin(2\pi\varepsilon\sigma)][p(\sigma) \star a_i(\sigma)] \tag{62}$$

The effect of this error is to make an intrinsically symmetric line profile asymmetric. When $\varepsilon = \lambda/4$, the profile actually becomes antisymmetric. The correction is done by specializing the equations of Section II.D. If the error is small, so that the stationary phase condition is satisfied, the multiplicative method in spectrum space can be used:

$$p(\sigma) \star a_r(\sigma) = \text{Re}\{\hat{p}'(\sigma)\exp(-2\pi i\sigma\varepsilon)\} \tag{63}$$

More generally, the correction can be done by interpolating in the interferogram:

$$P(m\,\Delta x) = \sum_j P'(j\,\Delta x)\,\text{sinc}\{\tfrac{1}{2}\pi[(m - j - (\varepsilon/\Delta x)]\}$$
$$\times \cos\{\tfrac{1}{2}\pi(4r + q)[(m - j - (\varepsilon/\Delta x)]\} \tag{64}$$

ε is usually determined by calculating the phase of a short two-sided interferogram or by curve-fitting near the point of zero path difference. The sum in Eq. (64) should be weighted to reduce the truncation errors, as discussed in

Section II.C. This correction is very important, since the asymmetric apparatus function can lead to large systematic errors in a broad band spectrum, even for small values of ε [18].

Intensity Errors

These are errors in the value of a properly sampled interferogram. They may arise from a variety of causes, such as nonlinearity in the detector, vignetting in the interferometer, or fluctuations in the source intensity or detector sensitivity.

An isolated error, as from a noise spike, can be regarded as a delta function added to the interferogram. Its transform adds a sinusoid to the spectrum. A spurious sine wave of period $1/a$ and amplitude A on the spectrum can be traced to a localized error on the interferogram at $x = a$ with magnitude $A/\Delta x$.

Drift in the interferogram may result from vignetting in the interferometer which changes with path difference or from secular changes in the source or detector. It may be approximately represented by adding a linear term to the interferogram:

$$P'(x) = P(x)(1 + kx)A(x) \rightleftharpoons \hat{p}(\sigma) \star \hat{a}(\sigma) + (k/i)(d\hat{p}/d\sigma) \star \hat{a}(\sigma) \qquad (65)$$

where $k = k/2\pi$. In the symmetric case,

$$\mathrm{Re}\{\hat{p}'(\sigma)\} = p(\sigma) \star a_r(\sigma) + k[(dp/d\sigma) \star a_i] \qquad (66)$$

In this case, the error term qualitatively resembles a second derivative of the spectrum. A symmetric line is broadened, but remains symmetric. In the asymmetric case, this analysis leads to a phase error of the form

$$\tan \Delta\phi = -k[d(\ln|p|)/d\sigma]/(1 + k \, d\phi/d\sigma) \qquad (67)$$

This error raises the phase on one side of the line and lowers it on the other, leading to possible systematic errors in calculated line strengths.

Since the signal at the center of the interferogram is much greater than elsewhere, the detector must have a large dynamic range. This requirement is particularly severe when a wide spectral range is to be covered, that is, when the gains to be expected from Fourier spectroscopy are the greatest. If the detector becomes nonlinear at high signal levels, we expect behavior of the following sort:

$$P'(x) = P(x) - aP^2(x) \rightleftharpoons \hat{p}(\sigma) - a\{\hat{p}(\sigma) \star p(\sigma)\} \qquad (68)$$

The autoconvolution is a symmetric function with maximum at $\sigma = 0$. There is a loss of zero signal level in the spectrum and an introduction of extraneous wavenumber components through the nonlinear response. In many cases, the nonlinearity will significantly affect only the central peak of the interferogram.

When this happens, the only effect on the spectrum is the subtraction of a constant. Thus, the absence of a spectral signal in regions known to be black is a simple test for linearity.

I. SUMMARY

We have outlined the theory of Fourier spectroscopy and briefly discussed the effect of some common errors. We have indicated, as the principal advantages of the method, the Fellgett and Jacquinot advantages. We may briefly consider some other differences between grating spectrometers and interferometers. The freedom from stray radiation is a particularly valuable advantage, especially in the far-infrared. This radiation is not modulated by the scanning of the interferometer and does not contribute to the interferogram. So long as it does not overload the detector, it can be ignored. The separation of radiation which passes through the interferometer, but lies outside the desired spectral band, is easier than the separation of unwanted grating orders. Grating orders are harmonically related and always superpose in the same way, regardless of the grating spacing. With an interferometer, the aliases can be shifted at will by changing the step size and the presence of unwanted aliases more readily detected. If such unwanted aliases are present, the step size can be made small enough to fit the spectral band within one-half period of the computed spectrum.

Connes [29] has pointed out that, in the future, the development of powerful, tunable, monochromatic sources may make both the Fellgett and Jacquinot advantages irrelevant. When this time comes, the principal reason for using Fourier techniques may be the great accuracy possible in wavenumber measurement. Since the path difference may be controlled directly by a standard reference, the wave numbers can be determined relative to this standard with high accuracy. Only small and easily determined corrections are required.

The interferometer is not without disadvantages. Obviously, the interferometer cannot be used when it is desired to irradiate the sample with monochromatic radiation. It also appears unlikely that interferometers will come into wide use for routine low-performance applications in the near-infrared. Even if the need for a computer ceases to be an obstacle, the sophisticated control system required to translate the mirror with the requisite accuracy will probably remain more expensive than a diffraction grating, which need be ruled only once.

III. Instruments

In the final two sections, we shall discuss current practices in instrument design and describe a few actual interferometers. The emphasis will be on the

interferometer proper, that is, on the beam-dividing element and the mecha-nism for scanning the interferogram. We shall not discuss sources, detectors, or sampling handling since standard infrared techniques are used with little modification.

A. THE FAR-INFRARED

The most extensive use of Fourier methods has been in the far-infrared ($\sigma < 200$ cm^{-1}), in spite of the fact that neither the Fellgett nor the Jacquinot advantage is as great in this region as in the near-infrared. The lack of good sources and detectors makes it necessary to use wide slits in a grating spectro-meter and it is not difficult to provide all the throughput the detector can handle. The Fellgett advantage still exists, but cannot be made as large since the total bandwidth is narrower. However, the poor performance of existing grating spectrometers makes even small gains welcome and the long wave-lengths greatly ease the tolerances in the drive system. It is possible to scan the interferogram with sufficient accuracy using much simpler mechanisms than are necessary in the near-infrared. The freedom from stray radiation is also an important advantage in this region.

Most far-infrared interferometers have been constructed in one of two basic configurations, the Michelson or the lamellar grating. The lamellar grating is mounted in a Czerny–Turner or Littrow configuration at zero order and scanned by translating one set of facets with respect to the other. It was used by Strong and Vanasse [30] in their original instrument. Other lamellar grating interferometers have been built by Richards [31] and Dowling et al. [32]. The principal advantage of the lamellar grating is its high efficiency at very long wavelengths, where it is impossible to find good beam splitters for a Michelson. With his lamellar grating, Richards [31] was able to observe a resonance at 3 cm^{-1} with resolution approaching 0.1 cm^{-1}. At high wave numbers, the necessity of closing down the slits to prevent receiving counter modulated higher grating orders reduces the throughput [30, 31].

A lamellar grating interferometer is, in general, more difficult to con-struct and maintain than a Michelson. The sets of facets must be ground accurately plane and kept parallel during translation. Those who have used such instruments over a period of years have found that the surface figure tends to degrade and that the grating must be rebuilt. At high resolution, the space between facets can act like a waveguide and significantly change the phase velocity of the radiation at low wave numbers, thus causing an error in wavelength determination [32, 33].

The use of the Michelson in the far-infrared was introduced by Gebbie [34] and, with the exceptions noted above, has become the most widely used con-figuration. The beam splitter is usually a Mylar film [35, 36]. The index of refraction is high enough ($n = 1.7$) to make the efficiency reasonably good

without any coating. The spectral band is limited by the channel spectrum in the film, the minima lying at $m\lambda = 2nd$. Normally, the thickness d is chosen so that the first maximum lies in the region of interest and the first minimum at the cutoff determined by the sampling interval. Electroformed metal mesh [37] has a higher efficiency over a narrower spectral band. Mesh beam splitters are efficient at wave numbers below the inverse lattice spacing where the first-order difraction disappears. In spite of these limitations of spectral range, the simplicity of construction and operation and the freedom from shadowing effects rule in favor of the Michelson for most purposes. The physical separation of the beams, which permits refractometry [13, 15], is an added bonus. The principal exception to this rule is at wave numbers below 30 cm^{-1}, where the greater efficiency of the lamellar grating is very helpful.

In the far-infrared, sufficiently accurate control of the optical path difference is possible without elaborate interferometric servomechanisms. In most of the early instruments, the mirror was scanned continuously and the signal read off at intervals determined by some monitoring system, such as a pair of Moiré grids [30] or a visible fringe system [38]. This arrangement has the disadvantage of a rather poor duty cycle. The duty cycle can be improved by integrating over an appreciable fraction of the sampling interval with resulting attenuation of the high-wavenumber part of the spectrum [12].

To improve the duty cycle, most modern interferometers use a stepwise motion in which the mirror is held fixed at the sampling point, then advanced rapidly to the next sampling point. In the far-infrared, satisfactory operation has been obtained simply by driving an accurate micrometer screw with a stepping motor [39, 40]. A less accurate screw can be tolerated if a servo-mechanism is provided to lock the path difference to some reference. This refinement, essential in the near-infrared, is seldom used in the far-infrared.

The highest-resolution lamellar grating interferometer is the one constructed by Dowling [32]. His grating is constructed from Pyrex, with 24 fixed and 24 movable facets, each 0.63×30.5 cm. The maximum optical path difference is 16 cm, permitting a resolution of 0.063 cm^{-1}. The grating is driven by a stepping motor geared down to provide a minimum step size of less than 0.5 μm. The position of the grating is measured to 1.5 μm by the inductive coupling between a pair of linear pole patterns, one fixed to the base and the other to the movable part of the grating. The signal derived from this device drives the stepping motor to regulate the optical path.

The most unusual feature of this instrument is a difference mode of operation in which the interferogram is the difference between interferograms with sample in and sample out. The great virtue of this mode is the suppression of the large central peak and consequent reduction of the dynamic range requirements of the detector. This interferometer has been used in the range from 20 to 240 cm^{-1} at nearly theoretical resolution for analysis of the rotational bands of several molecules [41–43] and for linewidth studies [33].

Recently, a Michelson interferometer has been constructed at The Ohio State University having comparable resolution and capable of being used in the asymmetric mode [44]. The beam splitter, which may be either Mylar or metal mesh, is 10 cm in diameter. To accomodate the cell for asymmetric operation, the arms are 70 cm long. To make it possible to carry well-collimated radiation through such long arms without undue loss of throughput, the optical system is built entirely on axis and the arms are terminated with "cats-eye" retroreflectors [45] of length 25 cm. With this arrangement, alignment is very simple in spite of the long arms, and sensitivity to yaw and pitch is greatly reduced. The drive system is very simple, consisting of a 20-cm comparator screw driven by a stepping motor with minimum step size 0.63 μm. This instrument has been used over the range 30–200 cm^{-1} with resolution of 0.06 cm^{-1}. Its performance at high resolution is illustrated by the water vapor spectra in Fig. 3, which show essentially theoretical resolution. The asymmetric mode yields data of the type shown in Fig. 4. Here, HCl was introduced into a cell in the fixed arm. The resulting asymmetric interferogram

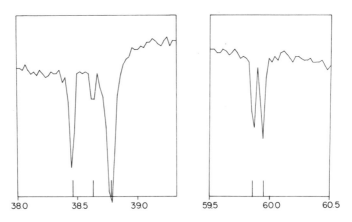

FIG. 3. Resolution achieved with the Ohio State far-infrared interferometer. Lines in the pure rotational spectrum of H_2O from an unapodized interferogram with maximum optical path difference 18 cm (from Sanderson and Scott [44]).

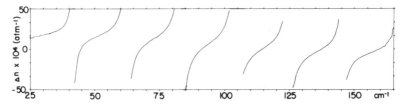

FIG. 4. Relative index of refraction of HCl measured with the Ohio State interferometer. The zero on the ordinate scale is arbitrary (from Sanderson and Scott [44]).

was transformed to give a phase spectrum from which the index of refraction was calculated. This type of information is particularly useful for measuring transition probabilities [15, 46, 47].

B. THE NEAR-INFRARED

The development of interferometers for the near-infrared occurred later than did that for the far-infrared. The obvious reason for this was that, while an accuracy of the order of 1 μm in setting the optical path difference was sufficient to give a significant improvement over existing far-infrared grating instruments, a precision 10^3–10^4 times better was required in the near-infrared. When the problem of obtaining this precision had been solved, the improvement over existing techniques was more spectacular than in the far-infrared. In the near-infrared, much greater gains are to be realized from the Fellgett and Jacquinot advantages.

The best performance in this region has been demonstrated by the series of interferometers constructed by the Connes's. The first [48], built primarily for astronomical purposes, had a maximum resolution of 0.1 cm^{-1}. The results obtained with this instrument on planetary atmospheres [49] conclusively demonstrated the potential of Fourier techniques in the near-infrared. A second instrument [50], designed for laboratory use with a resolution of 0.005 cm^{-1}, has been described by Pinard. A third instrument [26] is optically similar to the second, but is capable of scanning 50 points sec^{-1} to permit covering extended spectral ranges at very high resolution. We shall discuss some of the salient features of the latter two interferometers and show some spectra from the second.

The second interferometer [50] was constructed in the Michelson configuration with cats-eye end mirrors about 8 cm in diameter. The beam, having a diameter somewhat less than half this size, enters the cats-eye on one side and leaves on the other. This separation of entrance and exit beams gives access to both outputs and permits balanced operation. The beam splitter is a plate of quartz or CaF$_2$ with the two halves coated on opposite sides with silicon to give complete compensation. The other two quadrants of the cats-eye are used by reference beams. A monochromatic beam and a white-light beam pass through in opposite directions to define the path difference scale and the zero path difference point, respectively. The monochromatic source is either the 0.6328-μm He–Ne laser line or the superradiant Ne line at 3.39 μm. In addition, a fraction of the incident infrared beam is split off to monitor source fluctuations.

The carriage supporting the movable cats-eye is driven along two stainless steel rods by a linear motor controlled by the laser fringes. The servomechanism can hold the optical path difference to within one-thousandth of a fringe, that is, 6 Å. The infrared signal is internally modulated by oscillating

the cats-eye secondary with a piezoelectric crystal. This oscillation is in the form of a square wave with peak-to-peak amplitude equal to one wavelength of the reference signal. Since the time of the jump from one half-cycle to the other is short compared with the response time of the servo, regulation of the optical path is not affected. This type of modulation produces an antisymmetric interfergogram which is essentially the derivative of the usual interferogram.

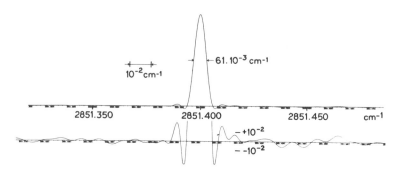

FIG. 5. Apparatus function of the Connes's interferometer, obtained by measuring the superradiant line in Xe at 2851 cm^{-1}. Maximum optical path 167 cm. The apodized theoretical resolution width is 0.0057 cm^{-1} (from Pinard [50]).

The performance of this instrument is illustrated in Figs. 5–7 [50] Figure 5 shows the apparatus function obtained by measuring the superradiant Xe line at 2851 cm^{-1}. The difference between the observed width, 0.0061 cm^{-1}, and the calculated resolution width, 0.0057 cm^{-1} can be attributed to the natural and Doppler widths of the line. Figure 6 shows the absorption spectrum of a portion of the P branch of the $(20^01–00^00)$ band of N_2O, overlaid by the l-type doubled hot band $(21^11–01^10)$. This band shows graphically the resolution achieved. The wavenumber precision is shown by the comparison

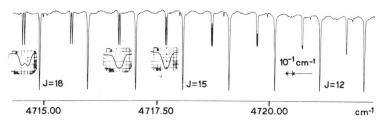

FIG. 6. Portion of the P branch of the $(20^01–00^00)$ band of N_2O, measured with the Connes's interferometer. It is overlaid by the hot band $(21^11–01^10)$ which shows l-type doubling. Maximum optical parth difference is 102.5 cm. The apodized theoretical resolution width is 0.0073 cm^{-1} (from Pinard [50]).

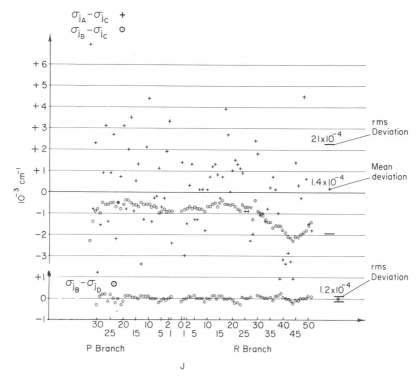

FIG. 7. Difference between measured and calculated wave numbers in the $(20^00 1-00^0 0)$ band of N_2O. The grating values are from Rao *et al.* [51]. The interferometer values are from Connes. σ_{j_A}: Obs. grating. σ_{j_B}: Obs. interferometer. σ_{j_C}: Calc. grating. σ_{j_D}: Calc. interferometer (from Pinard [50]).

with grating measurements in Fig. 7. The grating values are those quoted by Rao *et al.* [51]. Using the interferometer, the rms deviation between measured and calculated wave numbers is reduced by a factor of 20.

The third-generation instrument [26], is, apart from its larger optics, very similar. The principal difference is in a much more elaborate control system which can be programmed to give an optical path difference which varies with time in an arbitrary manner. The linear motor runs continuously with the fine control of path difference and internal modulation done by driving the cats-eye secondary. With this instrument, sampling as many as 50 points sec^{-1}, interferograms have been made with as many as 10^6 points.

Another type of near-infrared interferometer, widely used in low-resolution applications, is the rapid-scanning interferometer. Instruments of this type are built by Block Engineering [52]. The beam splitters and mirrors are built into a small cube to provide a very compact design. The resolution seldom exceeds 0.5 cm^{-1}. These interferometers are useful in situations where small size and

ruggedness are important, as in measurements from aircraft or from satellites. The mirror scans the interferogram in 1 sec, producing fringe frequencies in the kilohertz region which can provide suitable modulation without external chopping [12]. Normally, the interferogram is scanned repetitively and the scans averaged so that the total time can be made arbitrarily long. This mode is useful in averaging out certain types of fluctuations whose periods are long compared to 1 sec. Such fluctuations would seriously degrade the performance of a single slow scan interferometer.

References

1. P. Fellgett, Thesis, Univ. of Cambridge, Cambridge, England, 1951.
2. P. Jacquinot, *Rep. Progr. Phys.* **23**, 267 (1960).
3. M. Born and E. Wolf, " Principles of Optics." Pergamon, Oxford, 1964.
4. *J. Phys. Radium,* **19**, 185–240 (1958).
5. *J. Phys. (Paris)* **28**–C2 (1967).
6. *Aspen Int. Conf. Fourier Transform Spectrosc.,* 1970 (G. A. Vanasse, A. T. Stair, Jr., and D. J. Baker, eds.; AFCRL-71-0019, Special Rep. 114. Bedford, Massachusetts, 1971.
7. E. V. Loewenstein, *Appl. Opt.* **5**, 845 (1966).
8. A. A. Michelson, *Phil. Mag.* **34**, 280 (1892).
9. H. Rubens and R. W. Wood, *Phil. Mag.* **21**, 249 (1911).
10. J. Connes, *Rev. Opt. Theor. Instrum.* **40**, 45, 116, 171, 231 (1961).
11. G. A. Vanasse and H. Sakai, *Progr. Opt.* **6**, 261 (1967).
12. L. Mertz, " Transformations in Optics." Wiley, New York, 1965.
12a. *Appl. Opt.* **8**, 497–519 (1969).
13. E. E. Bell, *Infrared Phys.* **6**, 57 (1966).
14. A. Papoulis, "The Fourier Integral and its Applications." McGraw-Hill, New York, 1962.
15. J. E. Chamberlain, *J. Quant. Spectrosc. Radiat. Transfer* **7**, 151 (1967).
16. H. Happ and L. Genzel, *Infrared Phys.* **1**, 39 (1961).
17. A. S. Filler, *J. Opt. Soc. Amer.* **54**, 762 (1964).
18. J. Connes, *Aspen Int. Conf. Fourier Transform Spectrosc., 1970* (G. A. Vanasse, A. T. Stair, Jr., and D. J. Baker, eds.).
19. M. Forman, W. H. Steel, and G. A. Vanasse, *J. Opt. Soc. Amer.* **56**, 59 (1966).
20. L. Mertz, *Infrared Phys.* **7**, 17 (1967).
21. H. Sakai, G. A. Vanasse, and M. Forman, *J. Opt. Soc. Amer.* **58**, 84 (1968).
22. M. Forman, *J. Opt. Soc. Amer.* **56**, 978 (1966).
23. W. T. Cochran, J. W. Cooley, D. L. Favin, H. D. Helms, R. A. Kaenel, W. W. Lang, G. C. Maling, D. E. Nelson, C. M. Rader, and P. D. Welch, *Proc. IEEE* **55**, 1664 (1967).
24. P. Connes and G. Michel, *Aspen Int. Conf. Fourier Transform Spectrosc., 1970* (G. A. Vanasse, A. T. Stair, Jr., D. J. Baker, eds.).
25. J. D. Strong and G. A. Vanasse, *J. Phys. Radium* **19**, 192 (1958).
26. J. Connes, H. Delouis, P. Connes, G. Guelachvili, J.-P. Maillard, and G. Michel, *Nouv, Rev. Opt. Appl.* **1**, 3 (1970).
27. R. C. Jones, *J. Opt. Soc. Amer.* **39**, 327 (1949).
28. H. Sakai, *Aspen Int. Conf. Fourier Transform Spectrosc., 1970* (G. A. Vanasse, A. T. Stair, Jr., and D. J. Baker, eds.).
29. P. Connes, Footnote to J. Pinard, *J. Phys. (Paris)* **28**–C2, 136 (1967).
30. J. D. Strong and G. A. Vanasse, *J. Opt. Soc. Amer.* **50**, 113 (1960).

31. P. L. Richards, *J. Opt. Soc. Amer.* **54**, 1474 (1964).
32. R. T. Hall, D. Vrabec, and J. M. Dowling, *Appl. Opt.* **5**, 1174 (1966).
33. J. M. Dowling, *J. Quant. Spectrosc. Radiat. Transfer* **9**, 1613 (1969).
34. H. A. Gebbie, *In* "Advances in Quantum Electronics" (J. Singer, ed.) p. 155, Columbia Univ. Press, New York, 1961.
35. J. E. Chamberlain, G. W. Chantry, F. D. Findlay, H. A. Gebbie, J. E. Gibbs, N. W. B. Stone, and A. J. Wright, *Infrared Phys.* **6**, 195 (1966).
36. D. J. James and J. Ring, *J. Phys. (Paris)* **28**–C2, 150 (1967).
37. P. Vogel and L. Genzel, *Infrared Phys.* **4**, 257 (1964).
38. B. F. Hochheimer and C. F. Bradley, *Appl. Opt.* **8**, 557 (1969).
39. E. E. Russell and E. E. Bell, *Infrared Phys.* **6**, 75 (1966).
40. G. W. Chantry, H. N. Evans, J. E. Chamberlain, and H. A. Gebbie, *Infrared Phys.* **9**, 85 (1969).
41. R. T. Hall and J. M. Dowling, *J. Chem. Phys.* **47**, 2454 (1967).
42. R. T. Hall and J. M. Dowling, *J. Chem. Phys.* **52**, 1161 (1970).
43. J. M. Dowling, *J. Mol. Spectrosc.* **27**, 527 (1970).
44. R. B. Sanderson and H. E. Scott, *Appl. Opt.* **10**, 1097 (1971).
45. R. Beer and D. Marjaniemi, *Appl. Opt.* **5**, 1191 (1966).
46. R. B. Sanderson, *Appl. Opt.* **6**, 1527 (1967).
47. R. B. Sanderson, H. E. Scott and J. T. White, *J. Mol. Spectrosc.* **38**, 252 (1971).
48. J. Connes and P. Connes, *J. Opt. Soc. Amer.* **56**, 896 (1966).
49. J. Connes, P. Connes, and J.-P. Maillard, "Near Infrared Spectra of Venus, Mars, Jupiter, and Saturn." CNRS, Paris, 1969.
50. J. Pinard, *Ann. Phys. (Paris)* **4**, 147 (1969).
51. K. Narahari Rao, C. J. Humphreys, and D. H. Rank, "Wavelength Standards in the Infrared." Academic Press, New York, 1966.
52. T. Hirschfeld and P. Griffiths, *Symp. Mol. Struct. Spectrosc., Columbus*, 1969.

7.2 Grille Spectrometers

Jacques Moret-Bailly

Laboratoire de Spectroscopie Moleculaire
Faculté des Sciences de Dijon
Dijon, France

I. Introduction

The object of this article is to discuss some of the advantages of replacing slits by grilles in infrared spectrographs. Golay [1] was the first to conceive of this idea and also to construct the first grille spectrometer. Subsequently, Girard [2–5] developed an operating instrument by making one of the grilles vibrate.

II. Simplified Theory of a Grille Spectrometer

Any plane object with opaque and transparent parts can be used as a grille. If we replace the entrance and exit slits of a conventional spectrometer by two plane grilles G_0 and G located perpendicular to the beam, we arrive at the system shown in Fig. 1. When the entrance grille is illuminated by appropriate

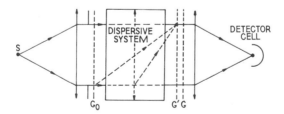

Fig. 1. Outline of a simple grille spectrometer.

monochromatic radiation, the dispersive system produces an exact image of the entrance grille on the exit grille. If we change the adjustment of the dispersive part of the instrument (e.g., by a rotation of the prism or the grating), the image G' of G_0 is translated in the dispersion direction; a change in the wavelength of the incident radiation produces the same effect. The results are equivalent if we put a real grille on the image G' and suppress G_0. We thus

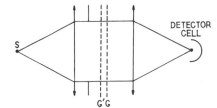

FIG. 2. System equivalent to Fig. 1 for monochromatic light.

obtain the simplified scheme shown in Fig. 2. Our interest is to evaluate the intensity ϕ transmitted through this system when the entrance and exit grilles consist of identical patterns of opaque and transparent parts.

The properties of the different types of grilles are very similar. Let us, therefore, consider a simple grille like the one shown in Fig. 3a consisting of opaque, randomly distributed but similarly oriented rectangles (see Fig. 3b for

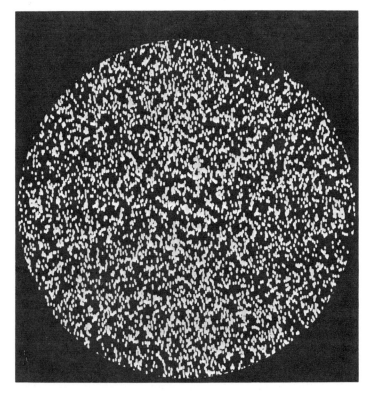

FIG. 3a. Random grille.

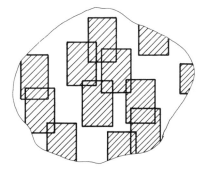

FIG. 3b. Sketch of a part of a random grille (larger scale).

clarification). If the intensity of the incident beam is ϕ_0, the intensity after passing through grille G' is $\phi_0/2$. If the image G' is exactly superimposed on G, no further loss of intensity occurs (since the grilles are similar); however, if the vector $O\Omega$ in Fig. 4 is not zero, and is not small compared to the element-

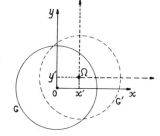

FIG. 4. Superposition of two grilles, where x refers to displacement parallel to the dispersion and y refers to displacement perpendicular to the dispersion.

ary rectangles of the grille, then due to the random distribution of the rectangles the grille G stops another half of the radiation incident on it. Thus, the light emerging from the system of two displaced grilles is $\phi_0/4$. This result is illustrated schematically in the plot displayed in Fig. 5. This figure supposes that G' extends to infinity. Actually, we should take account of the fact that

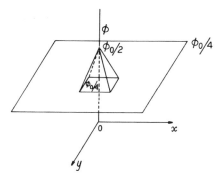

FIG. 5. Idealized intensity of the beam versus x and y.

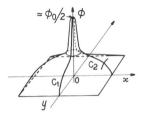

FIG. 6. Practical intensity of the beam.

there is an entrance aperture and also consider the effects of the imperfections of the grilles, etc. Figure 6 presents a more realistic representation. The general shape of this figure is the same for all types of grilles. At large values of x, the intensity ϕ is zero. In Fig. 6, curves C_1 and C_2 are, respectively, the intersections of the $\phi(x, y)$ surface with the plane $YO\phi$ and another plane parallel to $YO\phi$.

Following Girard [2–5], if we let y be a sine function of time with a frequency F, for a certain x (see Fig. 4), the point which gives the value of the intensity moves on a segment of curve C which is the intersection of the plane $\phi(x, y)$ and a plane parallel to $YO\phi$. Figure 7 considers two cases: for small values of x, we obtain the C_1 curve, and for large x, the C_2 curve.

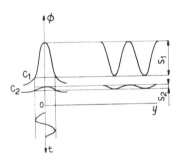

FIG. 7. C_1, C_2: Section of the surface shown in Fig. 6 by two planes parallel to $YO\phi$. The vibration produces a modulation near the coincidence.

Since y is a sine function with a frequency F, the intensity is a periodic function of time. If the plane $XO\phi$ is a symmetry plane for the $\phi = \phi(x, y)$ surface, the Fourier development of ϕ contains only terms with frequencies $0, 2F, 4F, \dots$. If we detect the $2F$ frequency signal, near the coincidence, we obtain a large amplitude S_1, and far from it, the small amplitude S_2 which corresponds to sidelobes. If these side lobes are small, we say that we have a good "far apodization." To obtain a small $2F$ component for the signal S_2, it is sufficient that for small values of y and large values of x, the surface $\phi = \phi(x, y)$ be approximately a cylindrical surface with the axis of the cylinder parallel to the OY axis. The shape of the surface for small values of both x and y will give the shape of the instrument function, in particular, the width of the slit equivalent to the grille, or "near apodization."

III. Problems Encountered in an Actual Grille Spectrometer

Replacing slits by grilles increases the signal significantly when we use monochromatic radiation. In cases where the photon noise is dominant, the signal-to-noise ratio is a little worse in the grille spectrometer than in a slit spectrometer. In an actual grille spectrometer, we should concern ourselves with the following problems: (a) the fundamental optical distortion of a spectrometer, (b) the practical aberrations of optical instruments, (c) the loss of uniformity of light beams, and (d) problems peculiar to this kind of instrumentation.

A. FUNDAMENTAL OPTICAL DISTORTION OF A SPECTROMETER

It is well known that the image of a straight slit through dispersive systems is generally curved; let us, for instance, consider a spectrometer using a reflection grating. In monochromatic light, for a certain position of the grating, there exists an "autocollimating point" O, which is imaged onto itself (see Fig. 8). The image A' of a point A is not the point a symmetric to A through

FIG. 8. Distortion in a spectrometer.

O; it is given in the third order of approximation by $\mathbf{aA'} = \vec{\alpha}(\mathbf{OA})^2$, where α depends not only on the characteristics of the instrument, but also on the angle of incidence on the grating. If we consider a transmission spectrometer (using a prism, for instance) the result is equivalent; the autocollimating point O is replaced by two points (one of these is O itself) corresponding to the minimum deviation of the beam. To minimize distortion, it is necessary that $|\mathbf{OA}|$ be as small as possible; all points of the grille must be near O.

Bouchareine uses both a prism and a grating. The prism is designed so that the distortion constant $|\alpha|$ is zero; since the dispersion of the grating is much larger than that of the prism, the system is almost equivalent to one having only the grating. But this method cannot be used for high resolution because the prism would be too large.

If the wavelength is greater than 20 μm, the distortion can usually be neglected. However, for high resolution at shorter wavelengths (5 and 10 μm), the distortion cannot be ignored. For this reason, Girard used an exit grille slightly different from the entrance grille; the exit grille is a photograph of the entrance grille seen through the spectrometer in an order of the grating which is convenient for visible light.

However, this method is not satisfactory at wavelengths shorter than 5 μm. For high resolution, we have to use grilles with much smaller elements (rectangular or otherwise).

At the University of Dijon, France, we have used another method: an image of a grille is formed on a curved screen (see Fig. 9). Taking an off-axis picture

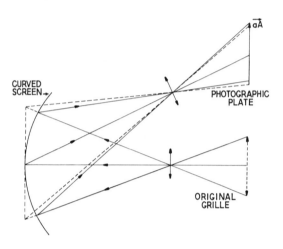

FIG. 9. Distortion of a grille.

gives a distortion which can be useful. The difficulty is not in introducing the right distortion, but in avoiding unwanted trapezoidal distortion. More recently, we started using a plotter connected to a computer to obtain the pictures of grilles.

There is another problem; $|\alpha|$ is not constant—it depends on the angle of incidence on the grating; the grille should be changed as the grating angle is changed. This would be very hard to do in the near-infrared, where great accuracy is necessary. In a Littrow spectrometer, the autocollimating point O is accessible and if OA is small, the same grille can be used for all angles of incidence. We obtained this by putting the autocollimating point in the center of a grille and using a single grille working by transmission for the entrance beam and by reflection for the exit beam. In this case, the grille is obtained from a drawing which possesses a center of symmetry. While photographing the grille, the symmetry is changed a little to take account of the distortion.

B. Practical Aberrations of Optical Instruments

For wavelengths shorter than about 4 μm, plane gratings must be considered to be a little spherical, and, except for the zeroth order, which is not useful, a point source does not give a point image, but instead we obtain two focal lines.

To obtain high resolution, one uses the focal plane which is perpendicular to the dispersion direction. Therefore, each point of the entrance grille produces a line on the exit grille. The grille system will perform poorly if the image obtained is of a poor quality; so it is necessary to make the useful spatial frequencies in the drawing of the grille, along the OY axis, large.

C. Loss of Uniformity of Light Beams

When studying the properties of a grille, we suppose that the intensity of light through a certain element is proportional to the surface area of this element. This can be true to a good approximation if the following conditions are satisfied:

(a) There must be only two systems of optically conjugated diaphragms (the source, the grating, and the detector being particular diaphragms). This condition excludes the use of certain types of instruments, for instance, a Littrow double-pass spectrometer.

(b) If the image of the source is focused on the entrance grille, the emissivity of the source must be constant. If the source is imaged on the grating, the emissivity of the source must be isotropic.

(c) The transparency of the spectrometer must be the same for all rays.

It is very difficult to fulfill all these conditions. A multiple-path cell, for instance, has an undesirable influence on the uniformity of a light beam. The effects of not fulfilling the above conditions depend very much on the type of grille. The final result can be in the appearance of large sidelobes.

D. Special Practical Problems

A large amount of unmodulated light often reaches the detector; if it happens that this light is modulated, even very slightly, it would result in noise. Thus, the spectrometer must be well protected against the vibrations produced by the mechanical system which vibrates the grille G'.

In the Girard spectrometers, the vibration of G' is produced by a rotation of the beam which is reflected by a vibrating mirror. If the spectrometer obstructs a part of the beam, the intensity of the light is decreased in a way which changes during the vibration, resulting in noise.

In the instrument at Dijon, we allow the grille to have a very precise translational movement. The plane of the grille is conjugate to the plane of the detector and as a result, the image on the detector does not vibrate and is confined to one spot.

IV. Special Properties of Some Types of Grilles

A. GOLAY AND NEILL GRILLES (FIG. 10)

These grilles are built from two families of parallel equidistant lines which define equal rectangles (or squares). An iterative procedure is used to determine which rectangles should be transparent and which opaque. Suppose that we have computed two grilles A and B which are of the same size. Let us give the names A_1 to a grille identical to A and $\bar{B}_1$ to a grille complementary to B. We put the four grilles side by side to obtain a new grille twice as large (see Fig. 11). We shall study now the grille function obtained with this composite grille and a similar one $A'\ B'\ A_1'\ \bar{B}_1'$ superimposed on it (Fig. 12). At coin-

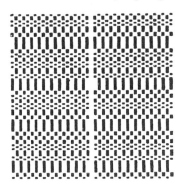

FIG. 10. Neill's grilles.

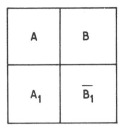

FIG. 11. Juxtaposition of elementary grilles.

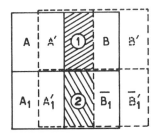

FIG. 12. Superposition of entrance and exit grilles. The modulation given by zone 1 is not, practically, equal to that given by zone 2.

cidence, each elementary grille gives its maximum signal. If x is not small, the signal given by the light going through one elementary grille and the corresponding elementary grille is zero. But, the part of the A' grille which is on the B grille gives a certain signal. A_1' and $\bar{B}_1$ give the same signal with the opposite phase and, so, the total signal is zero. We can now place the composite grilles side by side. We should consider the influence of the sides of the elementary grilles.

Golay published the first spectrum obtained in this way, and Neill [13], with the same grille, obtained the spectra as shown in Fig. 13. The quality

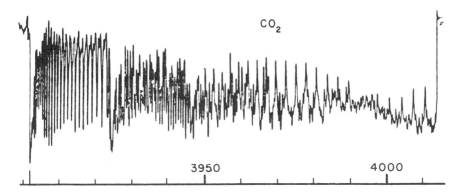

FIG. 13. A Neill spectrum.

of these spectra is perhaps not good; we would never obtain good spectra with such grilles, due to the following reason. The modulation given by A' and B is large. In practice, the modulation given by A_1' and $\bar{B}_1'$ is not exactly equal; so, some signal remains, which gives sidelobes.

B. HYPERBOLIC GIRARD GRILLES (FIG. 14)

These grilles are very well known; almost all grille spectrometers use them. They modulate 25 % of the incident light. They are not sensitive to a rotation in their plane. The sidelobes are not very small; they are tolerable for absorption spectroscopy, but for emission work, it is necessary to defocus the spectrometer slightly so that the sidelobes vanish. Girard's grille was the first to be much less sensitive to intensity defects of the light beam. It is somewhat disadvantageous in that the spatial frequencies that are lower than the frequency that corresponds to the dimension b of the grille are not transmitted. Figure 15 is a routine spectrum recorded in an industrial laboratory. It shows that high-resolution emission spectra can be recorded with high speed.

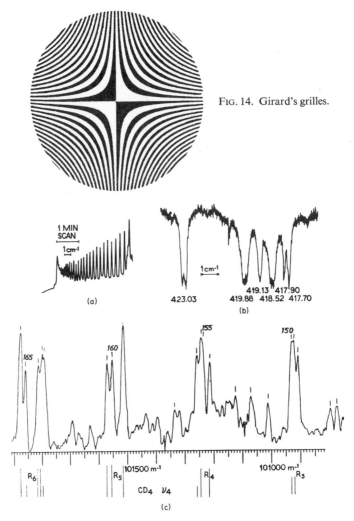

FIG. 14. Girard's grilles.

FIG. 15. Spectra obtained on Girard spectrometers: (a) Emission spectrum of methane near 3.3 μm (ν_3). Temperature, 300°C. Path length 15 cm. Pressure, 50 Torr. Scan time, 4 min. (b) Water vapor band near 24 μm. (c) CD_4 spectrum.

C. VERMANDE AND TINSLEY CIRCULAR GRILLES (FIGS. 16 AND 17)

These two types of grille are very similar [6–8]. To a good approximation, they can be considered as obtained from a photograph of Newton's rings recorded on a high-contrast plate. The rings are divided by radii defining equal sectors. As one goes across a radius, a transparent part becomes opaque. One rotates these grilles around the center. This rotation is continuous on

Fig. 16. Vermande's grilles.

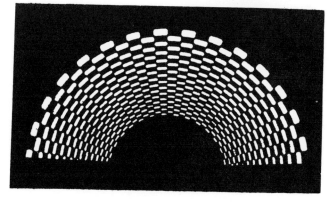

Fig. 17. Tinsley's grilles.

Vermande's spectrometer but is oscillating on Tinsley's. The properties of these grilles are almost those of hyperbolic ones. They modulate 50% of the light.

Tinsley's grilles can be used on an Ebert–Fastie spectrometer; the focal lines can be in the direction of the tangent to the cirlces which define the rings.

Vermande is able to change the modulation frequency very easily; he can detect the $4F$, $6F$, ... frequency signals. After detection, these can be mixed with the $2F$ signal so that the apodization and the linewidth change.

D. GRILLES USING A RANDOM DISTRIBUTION OF RECTANGLES

These grilles have been described earlier by Cadot [9]. They were the first to allow a resolution larger than 100 000. We use them on a Littrow double-pass, 6.5-m focal length spectrometer. On this instrument, Girard's grilles do not work well because there is too much astigmatism. Golay's grilles or Neill's grilles do not work at all because the transparency of a Littrow double-pass spectrometer is given by a triangular function (with a rectangular grating) as a function of the angle of the beam with the plane perpendicular to the lines of the grating. In other words, there is a large signal, but no spectrum at all.

The theory of random grilles shows quickly that they are not sensitive to

defects in the transparency of the spectrometer. There are sidelobes because the number of rectangles is not infinite; they have a very small random intensity if the number of rectangles is large. As in the near-infrared, the number of rectangles must be very large. This type of grille proved very convenient. The grille was prepared in the following way: we allowed small, round, white paper punches (from a paper punch) to fall slowly on a surface covered with wet, black paint. We made a photograph while moving the surface slightly in order to obtain elongated images. A center of symmetry was necessary when working with a single grille; therefore a second photograph was taken on the same plate after turning the painted surface by 180° around the axis normal to the surface. In order to take the distortion into account, the painted surface was made to be part of a sphere and the camera was kept away from the axis of the system.

Cadot [9] measured a resolution $\lambda/\Delta\lambda = 130\,000$; this resolution is an experimental one, $\Delta\lambda$ being the half-width of the line measured on the spectrum (so $\Delta\lambda$ includes the Doppler width, which is large for methane) (Fig. 18).

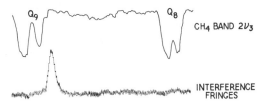

FIG. 18. Spectrum of $2\nu_3$ of methane obtained with random grilles. Neon emission, $\lambda = 5782.132$, $K = 43$.

E. COMPUTED GRILLES

As in the case of Golay's grilles, computer-generated grilles [10] are obtained from a regular distribution of similar rectangles. A computer was used to determine which rectangles should be opaque based on the following considerations: (a) The far apodization must be very good; (b) the useful modulation of the beam must be as large as possible; (c) the grilles must not be sensitive to uneven distribution of the light.

These conditions cannot be fulfilled simultaneously, but a good compromise is possible.

If G_n is a partly computed grille which gives a G_{n+1} grille by adding an elementary grille g, then to say that "G_n and G_{n+1} give well-apodized spectra" means that if we use g as entrance grille and G_{n+1} as output, the spectrum remains good (see Fig. 19).

The experimental resolving power of Fig. 20 is $200\,000$ near $2.5\ \mu m$; the speed with which the spectrum can be obtained is determined by the response of the recorder. The apodization is very satisfactory.

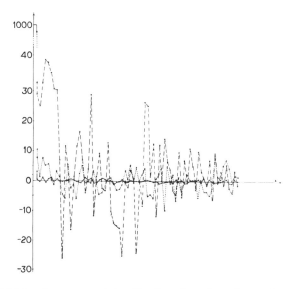

FIG. 19. Sidelobes for a computed grille; they depend on the number of rectangles. $(-\cdot-)G_1$: 1700 elements. $(---)G_1 + G_2 + \cdots G_5$: 8500 elements. ——$G_1 + G_2 + \cdots G_{62}$: 106 000 elements.

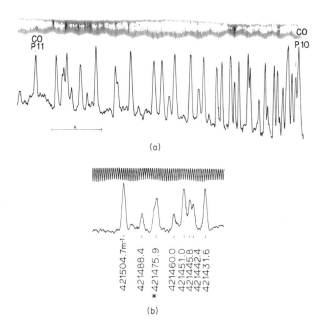

FIG. 20. (a) Spectrum obtained with computed grilles (methane $\nu_1 + \nu_4$). Resolving power, 200 000. (b) The A part of the spectrum displayed in Fig. 19(a).

F. A Grille Spectrograph

Bouchareine [11, 12] used a grille on the entrance slit and decoded the image G' by a photographic plate. Normally, for obtaining photographs of weak lines, preexposures are needed; but with the grille spectrograph, this was not the case. Figures 21a–c show comparisons of the spectra obtained with conventional slit spectrographs; the one obtained with the grille spectrograph shows that there is a linearization of the photographic plate.

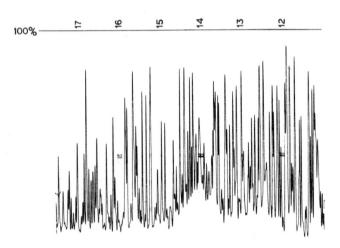

FIG. 21a. Conventional iron spectrum (plate exposed 1 hr).

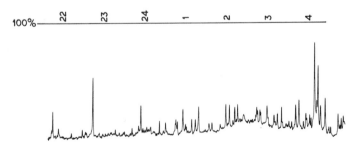

FIG. 21b. The same as in Fig. 21a, exposure time: 6 min.

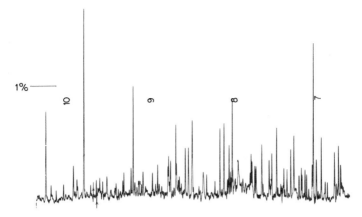

Fig. 21c. Obtained on the same spectrometer as Fig. 21a, with the slits replaced by grilles (plate exposed for 30 sec).

ACKNOWLEDGMENT

I thank Professor Narahari Rao very much for the great help he gave to me in my writing of this paper.

References

1. M. Golay, *J. Opt. Soc. Amer.* **41**, 468 (1951).
2. A. Girard, *Opt. Acta* **1**, 81 (1960).
3. A. Girard, *J. Phys. (Paris)* **24**, 139 (1963).
4. A. Girard, *Appl. Opt.* **2**, 79 (1963).
5. A. Girard, Thesis, Faculté des Sci. d'Orsay 1966; *Off. Nat. Etud. Rech. Aeronaut. Publ.* No. **117** (1966).
6. P. Vermande, *C.R. Acad. Sci. Ser. B* **264**, 1347 (1967).
7. P. Vermande, *J. Phys. (Paris)* **29**, 1041 (1968).
8. B. A. Tinsley, *Appl. Opt.* **5**, 1139 (1966).
9. J. Cadot, *Nouv. Rev. Opt. Appl.* **1**, No. 2, 79 (1970).
10. J. Moret-Bailly, C. Milan, and J. Cadot, *Nouv. Rev. Opt. Appl.* **1**, No. 3, 137 (1970).
11. P. Bouchareine and P. Jacquinot, *J. Phys. (Paris)*, **28–C2**, 183 (1967).
12. P. Bouchareine, *Nouv. Rev. Opt. Appl.* **2**, No. 1, 15 (1971).
13. H. W. Neill, "High Resolution Vacuum Spectrometer with Golay Coded Grilles." R360-FR. 104/211-1/R 011-01-01, Naval Ordnance Laboratory, Corona, California, 1965.

7.3 Large Plane Gratings for High-Resolution Infrared Spectrographs

K. Narahari Rao

Department of Physics
The Ohio State University
Columbus, Ohio

I. Introduction

The past decade has seen many notable advances in achieving high resolution in infrared spectroscopy. Progress has been made in three directions: Fourier transform spectroscopy has expanded the frontiers of technology to extents not conceived of before; for instance, the high resolution attained in the infrared spectra of cosmic sources by employing this technique has provided a new dimension to the type of information available to astrophysicists; procedures such as those discussed in Chapter 7.2 on grille spectrometers are being explored to increase the signal-to-noise ratio in grating spectrographs; and, finally, the ceaseless efforts of Professor George R. Harrison at M.I.T. and the replication processes developed by Bausch and Lomb, Inc. have produced large gratings, especially echelles of superior quality. The present article has the primary objective of focusing attention on this last development. First, the grating equation will be derived for a reflection grating installed in an infrared spectrograph, and then the advantages in using echelles will be discussed.

II. Grating Equation

Figure 1 shows a schematic of an infrared grating spectrograph in a Czerny–Turner mounting. The choice of this system of optics is incidental; the relations developed in this section are applicable to any other mounting in which the grating is rotated. The radiation to be studied enters the slit S_1 and is collimated by the spherical mirror M_1. This collimated beam illuminates the entire surface of the grating G. The dispersed beam is focused on the exit slit S_2 by the mirror M_2. Therefore, in such an arrangement, we can say that we have a plane wavefront incident on a plane reflection grating. This is sketched

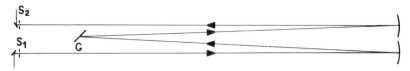

FIG. 1. Schematic of a Czerny–Turner spectrograph. S_1: Entrance slit. S_2: Exit slit. G: Grating.

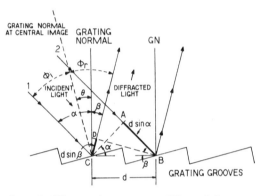

FIG. 2. Geometric path difference between rays diffracted from two adjacent grating grooves in a reflection grating.

in Fig. 2, where the wavefront is shown to be incident at an angle α measured with respect to the grating normal. In the infrared spectrograph of Fig. 1, the grating is rotated by an angle θ from the central image position (i.e., the position for which the grating acts as a mirror) in order to observe the appropriate diffracted beam. In Fig. 2, θ is shown in terms of the rotation of the grating normal. The geometric path difference between rays reflected from successive grooves separated by d (i.e., rays 1 and 2 of Fig. 2) is given by

$$d \sin \alpha - d \sin \beta$$

where β is the angle made by the diffracted beam with the grating normal. For constructive interference to take place, we have

$$n\lambda = d \sin \alpha - d \sin \beta \tag{1}$$

where n is an integer giving the spectral order and λ is the diffracted wave‑length. If β is on the same side of the normal as α (see Fig. 3), this formula becomes

$$n\lambda = d \sin \alpha + d \sin \beta \tag{2}$$

Therefore, we arrive at the standard grating formula

$$n\lambda = d(\sin \alpha \pm \sin \beta) \tag{3}$$

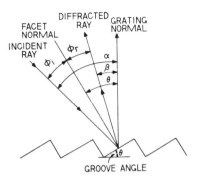

Fig. 3. Illustrating the situation when the incident and diffracted rays are on the same side of the grating normal in a reflection grating. $\phi_i = \phi_r = \phi$(in text).

From Fig. 2, for which Eq. (1) applies,

$$\alpha = (\phi + \theta) \qquad \text{and} \qquad \beta = (\phi - \theta) \tag{4}$$

Substituting these in Eq. (1), we find

$$n\lambda = d[\sin(\phi + \theta) - \sin(\phi - \theta)] \tag{5}$$

i.e.,

$$n\lambda = 2d \sin \theta \cos \phi \tag{6}$$

We now obtain the *grating equation:*

$$n\lambda = k \sin \theta \tag{7}$$

where

$$k = 2d \cos \phi \tag{8}$$

In expressing the grating equation in wave number units, we write

$$v = 1/\lambda = n/(k \sin \theta) \tag{9}$$

or

$$v = nK \csc \theta \tag{10}$$

where

$$K = 1/k \tag{11}$$

To avoid confusion, it may be reiterated that the lower case k has been used for the grating constant when the grating equation is expressed in terms of wavelengths [Eq. (7)] and capital K has been used for the grating constant when the grating equation is expressed in terms of wave numbers [Eq. (10)].

III. Echelles

An echelle is a precisely ruled reflection grating designed for use at a high angle of incidence; for example, many echelles operate at about 63° angle of incidence, as compared to a 15° angle for ordinary gratings. The groove spacing in an echelle is large relative to the wavelengths used. As may be

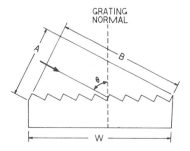

FIG. 4. Schematic of an echelle grating where the steep side of the groove becomes the optically active facet.

noticed from Fig. 4, the steep side of the groove becomes the optically active facet for an echelle. Some of the advantages in equipping spectrographs with echelles are discussed below.

RESOLVING POWER

The theoretical resolving power (RP) is given by

$$RP = \lambda/\Delta\lambda = v/\Delta v = nN \tag{12}$$

where N is the total number of grooves on the grating and n is the spectral order, as before. Substituting in Eq. (12) for n from Eq. (7),

$$RP = [(k \sin \theta)/\lambda]N$$

or

$$RP = (Nk/\lambda) \sin \theta \tag{13}$$

This formula shows that for a particular grating and at a given λ, the resolution is a function of the sine of the angle at whch λ is observed. As pointed out earlier, many echelles operate at about 63°, compared to a 15° angle for ordinary gratings; so the resolution obtained with them has the possibility of being about three times greater.

DISPERSION

From Eq. (7), we also notice that the angular dispersion

$$d\theta/d\lambda = (1/\lambda) \tan \theta \tag{14}$$

For the same typical angles mentioned above, the echelle dispersion is seven times as large as that of an ordinary grating.

SPECTRAL SLIT WIDTHS RELATED TO PHYSICAL SLIT WIDTHS

Next, it is of interest to note that an echelle facilitates the use of wider physical slits. To consider this, let us develop an expression relating the physical slit width S (let us assume for simplicity that in the spectrograph outlined

in Fig. 1, S_1 and S_2 have exactly the same widths, namely S) to the corresponding spectral width dv. Differentiating Eq. (10) with respect to θ, we obtain

$$dv = (nK \csc \theta) \cot \theta \, d\theta \qquad (15)$$

or

$$dv = v \cot \theta \, d\theta \qquad (16)$$

Now,

$$d\theta = S/2f \qquad (17)$$

where f is the focal length of the spectrograph. The factor two in the denominator occurs because of the well-known fact that for a beam of radiation incident on a reflecting surface, when the reflecting surface is rotated by an angle θ, the reflected ray is rotated by 2θ. By combining Eqs. (16) and (17), we obtain

$$dv = v(\cot \theta)S/2f \qquad (18)$$

If observations are made at an angle $\theta = 26°35'$ ($\cot \theta = 2$) with a spectrograph of focal length 5 m, a spectral slit width of 0.1 cm^{-1} at a wavelength of 10 μm corresponds to a physical slit width of 0.5 mm; however, if observations are made at an angle $\theta = 63°25'$ ($\cot \theta = \frac{1}{2}$), the same spectral slit width of 0.1 cm^{-1} can be attained by opening the slit to 2 mm.

RESOLVING POWER AT A GIVEN ANGLE AND WAVELENGTH

Sometimes it is convenient to express the resolving power in a slightly different way. Referring to Eqs. (13) and (8), we can write

$$RP = (Nk/\lambda) \sin \theta = N[(2d \cos \phi)/\lambda] \sin \theta \qquad (19)$$

When $\phi \to 0$, this becomes

$$RP = 2(Nd)(\sin \theta)/\lambda \qquad (20)$$

or

$$= 2W(\sin \theta)/\lambda \qquad (21)$$

where W, the width of the grating, is given by

$$W = Nd \qquad (22)$$

If B represents the projected width of the grating (see Fig 4), then

$$RP = 2B/\lambda \qquad (23)$$

This last equation shows that at a given angle and wavelength, the resolving power $\lambda/\Delta\lambda$ is independent of the number of grooves. Expressing in wave number units, we readily see that

$$v/\Delta v = 2Bv \qquad (24)$$

This leads to a simple and convenient formula

$$\Delta v = 1/2B \tag{25}$$

AVAILABILITY OF ECHELLES AND THEIR PERFORMANCE

In 1949, Harrison [1] first discussed the design of an echelle spectrograph and used it in the region 3500–7000 Å [2]. About ten years later, Rank and his co-workers [3] described an echelle-type spectrograph for the near-infrared region (1–5 μm) of the spectrum. In 1962, Rao *et al.* [4] discussed some of the spectroscopic advantages in using a 40 groove mm^{-1}, 8 in. × 4 in. Bausch and Lomb plane replica grating (with its primary blaze at 23°) "echelle fashion" by mounting it so that it is operated at its secondary blaze of 67°. In addition to demonstrating that reasonably good spectra could be recorded with this grating in a wide range of the infrared (4–37 μm), it was emphasized that the possibility of observing with this grating the 1–0 vibration–rotation band of the carbon monoxide molecule in many spectral orders would make the calibration procedures somewhat simpler. Nowadays, specially ruled echelles are becoming available in larger sizes [5] and contributing much to the success of high-resolution infrared spectroscopy. In infrared spectroscopy, it is customary to mean by spectral resolution the full-width in cm^{-1} at half the height of well-resolved lines. Figure 5 shows that working resolution of 0.015_5 cm^{-1} has been clearly reached at 2.6 μm with a 10-m focal length Czerny–Turner

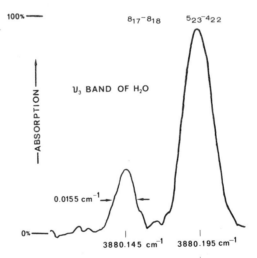

FIG. 5. Working spectral resolution achieved with a 10-m focal length Czerny–Turner spectrograph (vacuum prism-grating monochromator) equipped with a 406 mm × 203 mm (16 in. × 8 in.), 79 grooves mm^{-1} Harrison-ruled echelle. Detector: PbS cooled to 193°K. Source: Carbon furnace operating at 300 A. Path length: 124 m. Pressure: 80 μm Hg. Amplifier: PAR Model HR-8; time constant, 1 sec. (The Ohio State University.)

type vacuum-infrared spectrograph equipped with the new 79 groove mm^{-1}, 16 in. × 8 in. echelle [6].† These echelles have excellent blaze efficiencies‡ because of the highly sophisticated technology developed in obtaining smooth groove profiles. Several echelle references other than those indicated above are included in the bibliography at the end of this article [7–14].

IV. Wavelength Calibration Techniques

The problems involved in determining spectral positions in the infrared with grating spectrographs have been primarily related to the use of scanning systems in infrared spectrographs. Most often, the scanning is accomplished by a rotation of the grating. Therefore, it is imperative that adequate care be taken in the design of the mechanical drive employed for rotating the grating. Many of the techniques currently used have been described by Rao et al. [15]. In this same publication, several wavelength standards useful in the infrared are also included. At this time, it seems relevant to add a few comments concerning the absorption standards in the infrared. Since much of the work done in infrared spectroscopy pertains to a study of the absorption spectra of polyatomic molecules, absorption standards play a vital role in the infrared. In particular, the 1–0 and 2–0 band lines of carbon monoxide are being used more extensively. The reasons for this have been elaborated in earlier publications by Rao [16], Rao and co-workers [4], and Rao et al. [15]. In view of their usefulness, the wave numbers of these CO lines are reproduced in Table I. The spectral charts given in Figs. 6 and 7 are designed to complement the data given in Table I and help the experimenter in acquiring better familiarity with the spectra, which in turn should assist in the selection of proper standards required in investigations. The 2–0 band shown in Fig. 7 has been taken from the monograph by Rao et al. [15], while the 1–0 band displayed in Fig. 6 has been newly observed by Griggs and Rao [17]; several lines in this band have been identified as due to the various isotopic species of the carbon monoxide molecule. All this isotopic structure has been observed in the natural CO sample procured commercially. It has been mentioned before [15] that the absolute accuracy of the data appearing in Table I is at least within ±0.002 cm^{-1}. This contention has been verified by the Connes' data [18] obtained by

† The tests made at 5461 Å on the 16 in. × 8 in. echelles having 300 grooves mm^{-1} and 79 grooves mm^{-1} indicate resolving power ($\lambda/\Delta\lambda$ or $\nu/\Delta\nu$) capabilities in excess of one million.

‡ "For a reflection grating, efficiency is defined as the amount of monochromatic light diffracted into the order being measured relative to the specular reflection from a polished blank coated with the same material," Diffraction Grating Handbook, Bausch and Lomb, Inc. [6a]. Figures 2–4 in this chapter follow similar ones appearing in this handbook with modifications introduced where necessary.

TABLE I

Vacuum Wave Numbers (cm^{-1}) for the Rotational Structure of the
1–0 and 2–0 Bands of Carbon Monoxide (^{12}C^{16}O)

	1–0 Band		2–0 Band	
J	$R(J)$	$P(J)$	$R(J)$	$P(J)$
0	2147.0831	—	4263.8396	—
1	2150.8579	2139.4281	4267.5445	4256.2196
2	2154.5975	2135.5482	4271.1790	4252.3047
3	2158.3016	2131.6336	4274.7430	4248.3201
4	2161.9700	2127.6844	4278.2365	4244.2659
5	2165.6028	2123.7008	4281.6592	4240.1423
6	2169.1996	2119.6829	4285.0111	4235.9494
7	2172.7604	2115.6309	4288.2918	4231.6874
8	2176.2850	2111.5449	4291.5014	4227.3564
9	2179.7733	2107.4251	4294.6397	4222.9565
10	2183.2251	2103.2715	4297.7065	4218.4880
11	2186.6403	2099.0845	4300.7018	4213.9509
12	2190.0187	2094.8640	4303.6250	4209.3454
13	2193.3601	2090.6103	4306.4764	4204.6716
14	2196.6645	2086.3234	4309.2558	4199.9298
15	2199.9317	2082.0037	4311.9630	4195.1200
16	2203.1616	2077.6511	4314.5978	4190.2424
17	2206.3540	2073.2658	4317.1601	4185.2971
18	2209.5087	2068.8480	4319.6498	4180.2843
19	2212.6256	2064.3979	4322.0666	4175.2041
20	2215.7045	2059.9155	4324.4106	4170.0568
21	2218.7454	2055.4011	4326.6814	4164.8423
22	2221.7481	2050.8547	4328.8790	4159.5609
23	2224.7124	2046.2766	4331.0033	4154.2128
24	2227.6381	2041.6668	4333.0540	4148.7980
25	2230.5252	2037.0255	4335.0310	4143.3167
26	2233.3735	2032.3529	4336.9342	4137.7691
27	2236.1829	2027.6491	4338.7635	4132.1553
28	2238.9531	2022.9142	4340.5187	4126.4755
29	2241.6841	2018.1484	4342.1996	4120.7297
30	2244.3757	2013.3519	4343.8061	4114.9183

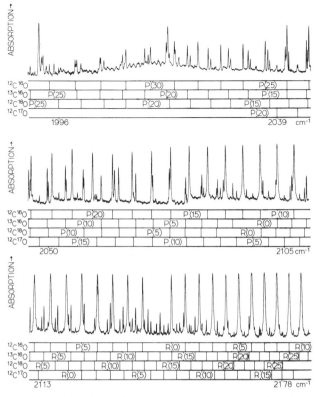

FIG. 6. Scan of the 1–0 band of carbon monoxide at 4.7 μm: Path length, 11 m; pressure ranged between 5 and 25 mm Hg.

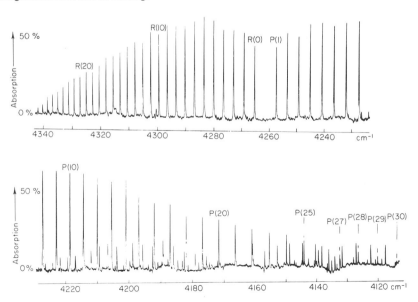

FIG. 7. Scan of the 2–0 band of $^{12}C^{16}O$. Path length: 35 m. Pressure: 0.2 mm Hg. (Reproduced from Rao *et al.* [15]).

employing Fourier transform spectroscopy. It is important to remember that in much of the research done presently with grating spectrographs, we are dependent on the validity of the integral relation between overlapping orders. Although the quality of the modern gratings seems to be so excellent that this criterion does appear to apply to a high degree of precision, it would be necessary to satisfy ourselves that this relation is valid in the case of each spectrograph before extensive data are collected with it.

ACKNOWLEDGMENTS

I would like to express my thanks to Dean George R. Harrison of M.I.T. and Dr. Erwin G. Loewen of Bausch and Lomb for reading the above paper and making valuable comments. I am also grateful to the National Science Foundation for its support.

References

1. G. R. Harrison, Design of echelle gratings and spectrographs, *J. Opt. Soc. Amer.* **37**, 522 (1949).
2. See, S. P. Davis, "Diffraction Grating Spectrographs," pp. 38–41. Holt, New York, 1970.
3. D. H. Rank, D. P. Eastman, W. B. Birtley, G. Skorinko, and T. A. Wiggins, Echelle-type spectrograph for the near infrared, *J. Opt. Soc. Amer.* **50**, 821 (1960).
4. K. Narahari Rao, W. W. Brim, V. L. Sinnett, and R. H. Wilson, Wavelength calibrations in the infrared: Part IV, Use of a 1000 lines per inch Bausch and Lomb plane replica grating, *J. Opt. Soc. Amer.* **52**, 862 (1962).
5. G. R. Harrison and S. W. Thompson, Large diffraction gratings ruled on a commercial measuring machine controlled interferometrically, *J. Opt. Soc. Amer.* **60**, 591 (1970).
6. K. Narahari Rao, A. W. Mantz, B. D. Alpert, and J. A. Vigil, To be published.
6a. "Diffraction Grating Handbook." Bausch and Lomb, Inc., 1970.
7. G. R. Harrison, S. P. Davis, and H. S. Robertson, Precision measurement of wavelengths with echelle spectrographs, *J. Opt. Soc. Amer.* **43**, 853 (1953).
8. R. B. Dunn, Sacramento peak new solar telescope, *Sky and Telescope* **38**, 368 (1969).
9. R. Tousey, The extreme ultraviolet-past and future, *Appl. Opt.* **1**, 679 (1962).
10. W. G. Elliot, New dimension in spectrometric analysis, *Amer. Lab.* pp. 67–72. (1970).
11. D. J. Schroeder, An echelle spectrometer-spectrograph for astronomical use, *Appl. Opt.* **6**, 1976 (1960).
12. P. M. Griffin, R. A. Loring, and J. R. McNally, Sr., The use of an echelle spectrograph in the investigation of Zeeman spectra, *J. Opt. Soc. Amer.* **42**, 880 (1952).
13. W. A. Rense, Techniques for rocket solar UV and far UV spectroscopy, *Space Sci. Rev.* **5**, 234 (1966).
14. G. W. Stroke and H. H. Stroke, Tandem use of gratings and echelles to increase resolution, luminosity and compactness of spectrometers and spectrographs, *J. Opt. Soc. Amer.* **53**, 333 (1963).
15. K. Narahari Rao, C. J. Humphreys, and D. H. Rank, "Wavelength Standards in the Infrared." Academic Press, New York, 1966.
16. K. Narahari Rao, Infrared CO bands as secondary standards in the infrared, *J. Chem. Phys.* **18**, 213 (1950).
17. J. L. Griggs, Jr. and K. Narahari Rao, To be published.
18. P. Connes, J. Connes, L. D. Kaplan, and W. S. Benedict, Carbon monoxide in the Venus atmosphere, *Astrophys. J.* **152**, 731 (1968).

CHAPTER 8

TABLES OF STANDARD DATA

C. Weldon Mathews

K. Narahari Rao

Department of Chemistry
The Ohio State University
Columbus, Ohio

Department of Physics
The Ohio State University
Columbus, Ohio

During the past two decades, much work has been done to determine improved values for the physical constants, wavelength standards, masses of elements, and other standards of data required in the normal investigations of a research laboratory. The International Commissions, such as Commission 14 of the International Astronomical Union, have been attempting to examine critically the available results and to make recommendations periodically. The major purpose of this chapter is to collect many of the previously recommended standards into a single convenient form useful to spectroscopists. Additional references are included where appropriate, or when additional data appear useful even though they have not yet been recommended as standards.

Table I. Fundamental Physical Constants

These constants were taken from the compilation by Taylor *et al.* [1]. They are tabulated both in SI units (see Table II) and in cgs units. Numbers in parentheses following the numerical values of the constants are estimates of error in the last digits based on three times the standard deviation. In addition it should be emphasized that the constants are correlated, so that when two or more constants are used in a calculation, the general law of propagation of errors must be used in order to determine the error of the final result. The necessary correlation coefficients and required procedures are given by Taylor *et al.* [1]. The unified atomic mass unit (amu) has been used throughout the tables, where one amu (sometimes abbreviated as u) is defined as 1/12 the mass of one atom of the ^{12}C nuclide. Additional abbreviations in the table include: C = coulomb, Hz = hertz (= cycles/second), J = joule, K = kelvin (= degrees kelvin), and T = tesla = 10^4 G (magnetic flux density).

Table II. Defined Quantities and Standard Prefixes

This table contains the definitions which form the basis for the International System of Units (SI units). No attempt will be made to summarize the extensive recommendations on nomenclature and units which are available in two recent publications of the International Union for Pure and Applied Physics (IUPAP) [2] and the International Union for Pure and Applied Chemistry (IUPAC) [3]. Additional spectroscopic notation should be based on the recommendations adopted by the Joint Commission on Spectroscopy for atoms [4], diatomic molecules [5], and polyatomic molecules [6].

Table III. Conversion Factors

These conversion factors were derived from the constants given in Table I.

Tables IV–X. Wavelength Standards

Wavelength standards recommended by Commission 14 of the International Astronomical Union [7–10] have been collected in these tables. The values originally recommended in terms of λ_{air} (Å), ν_{vac} (cm^{-1}), or λ_{vac} (Å) are indicated by an asterisk (∗), or, within a column, between the asterisks. The number of significant figures correctly indicates the precision for the original values only. The number of significant figures for the calculated values may exceed the number required in some instances.

The interconversion of λ_{air} and λ_{vac} was based on the recommended formula for the dispersion of standard air as given by Edlén [11]. More recently, Svensson [12] has suggested a slightly improved dispersion formula which fits the observed refractive indices more precisely, especially for wavelengths between 2000 and 2300 Å. Even in this range, however, the difference in the vacuum correction calculated with the two formulas is less than 2×10^{-5} Å. Svensson also discusses in some detail the corrections necessary when wavelength measurements are made in nonstandard air.

The bibliography at the end of this chapter includes a number of additional references, primarily from the Journal of the Optical Society of America, Applied Optics, and Arkiv för Fysik, concerned with wavelength standards. Most of these references report the precise measurement of wavelengths which may be useful, even though they have not yet been reviewed and recommended as secondary standards. This part of the bibliography is divided into three sections: (1) Measurements related to those tabulated in the present chapter [13–40], (2) thorium wavelength measurements [41–53], and (3) vacuum ultraviolet wavelength measurements [54–73]. Titles of the papers have been included for convenience, and a dagger (†) has been placed by the reference number of an article which appears particularly useful.

Table XI. Atomic Mass, Nuclear Spin, and Abundance (or Half-Life) of Each Element

These values of the atomic masses and estimated errors were taken from the "1964 Atomic Mass Table" reported by Mattauch et al. [74]. In addition, Wapstra et al. [75] have reported new or more precise measurements for a number of nuclides with mass numbers greater than 212.

An estimate of the relative abundances (per cent) of each of the isotopes is included as a qualitative guide only. The most recently published compilation appears to be by Fuller [76]. A number in parentheses under "abundance" refers to the half-life in years (y) of a radioisotope. Only those radioisotopes with a half-life greater than about one year have been included in the table. These values and the nuclear spins were taken from the compilation by Fuller and Cohen [77]. A nuclear spin within parentheses indicates that the reported spin is consistent with experimental results, but that it could not be derived directly from them.

Table XII. 1969 Table of Atomic Weights

The values tabulated have been recommended recently by the IUPAC [78]. They apply to elements as they exist in materials of terrestrial origin and to certain artificial elements. When used with due regard to the footnotes given with the table, they are considered reliable to ± 1 in the last digit or ± 3 if that digit is a subscript.

TABLE I

Fundamental Physical Constants[a]

Quantity	Symbol	Value	(3σ)[b]	Units	
				SI	cgs
Velocity of light	c	2.9979250	(30)	10^8 m sec^{-1}	10^{10} cm sec^{-1}
Fine structure constant	α	7.297351	(33)	10^{-3}	10^{-3}
	α^{-1}	137.0360	(6)		
Electron charge	e	1.602192	(21)	10^{-19} C	10^{-20} emu
		4.80325	(6)		10^{-10} esu
Planck's constant	h	6.62620	(15)	10^{-34} J sec	10^{-27} erg sec
	$\hbar = h/2\pi$	1.054592	(24)	10^{-34} J sec	10^{-27} erg sec
Avogadro's number	N	6.02217	(12)	10^{26} kmole^{-1}	10^{23} mole^{-1}
Atomic mass unit	amu	1.660531	(33)	10^{-27} kg	10^{-24} g
Electron rest mass	m_e	9.10956	(16)	10^{-31} kg	10^{-28} g
	$m_e{}^*$	5.48593	(10)	10^{-4} amu	10^{-4} amu
Proton rest mass	M_p	1.672614	(33)	10^{-27} kg	10^{-24} g
	$M_p{}^*$	1.00727661	(24)	amu	amu
Neutron rest mass	M_n	1.674920	(33)	10^{-27} kg	10^{-24} g
	$M_n{}^*$	1.00866520	(30)	amu	amu
Electron charge-to-mass ratio	e/m_e	1.758803	(16)	10^{11} C kg^{-1}	10^7 emu g^{-1}
		5.272759	(48)		10^{17} esu g^{-1}

Quantity	Symbol	Value		Units (SI)	Units (cgs)
Rydberg constant	R_∞	1.09737312	(33)	10^7 m^{-1}	10^5 cm^{-1}
Bohr radius	a_0	5.291771	(24)	10^{-11} m	10^{-9} cm
Electron magnetic moment in Bohr magnetons	μ_e/μ_B	1.0011596389	(9)		
Bohr magneton	μ_B	9.27410	(19)	10^{-24} J T^{-1}	10^{-21} erg G^{-1}
Electron magnetic moment	μ_e	9.28485	(19)	10^{-24} J T^{-1}	10^{-21} erg G^{-1}
Proton magnetic moment	μ_P	1.410620	(30)	10^{-26} J T^{-1}	10^{-23} erg G^{-1}
Nuclear magneton	μ_m	5.05095	(15)	10^{-27} J T^{-1}	10^{-24} erg G^{-1}
Gas constant	R_0	8.3143	(10)	10^3 J kmole^{-1} K^{-1}	10^7 erg mole^{-1} K^{-1}
Boltzmann's constant R_0/N	k	1.38062	(18)	10^{-23} J K^{-1}	10^{-16} erg K^{-1}
Stefan–Boltzmann constant	σ	5.6696	(29)	10^{-8} W m^{-2} K^{-4}	10^{-5} erg sec^{-1} cm^{-2} K^{-4}
First radiation constant $8\pi hc$	c_1	4.99258	(11)	10^{-24} J m	10^{-15} erg cm
Second radiation constant hc/k	c_2	1.43883	(18)	10^{-2} m K	cm K
Gravitational constant	G	6.673	(9)	10^{-11} N m^2 kg^{-2}	10^{-8} dyn cm^2 g^{-2}

[a] B. N. Taylor, W. H. Parker, and D. N. Langenberg, *Rev. Mod. Phys.* **41**, 375 (1969).

[b] Estimated error based on 3 standard deviations; applies to last digits in preceeding column.

TABLE II

DEFINED QUANTITIES AND STANDARD PREFIXES[a]

Definitions of the SI base units

Meter (m): The length equal to 1 650 763.73 wavelengths in vacuum of the radiation corresponding to the transition $2p_{10}-5d_5$ in ^{86}Kr.

Kilogram (kg): The mass of the international prototype of the kilogram.

Second (s): The duration of 9 192 631 770 periods of the radiation corresponding to the transition between the two hyperfine levels of the ground state of ^{133}Ce.

Ampere (A): That constant current which, if maintained in two straight parallel conductors of infinite length, and of negligible cross section, and placed 1 m apart in vacuum, would produce between these conductors a force equal to 2×10^{-7} newton per meter of length.

Kelvin (K): The unit of thermodynamic temperature is the fraction 1/273.16 of the thermodynamic temperature of the triple point of water.

Candela (cd): The luminous intensity, in the perpendicular direction, of a surface of 1/600 000 square meter of a black body at the temperature of freezing platinum under a pressure of 101 325 newtons per square meter.

Standard prefixes

Multiple	Prefix	Symbol
10^{12}	tera	T
10^9	giga	G
10^6	mega	M
10^3	kilo	k
10^2	hecto	h
10^1	deka	da
10^{-1}	deci	d
10^{-2}	centi	c
10^{-3}	milli	m
10^{-6}	micro	μ
10^{-9}	nano	n
10^{-12}	pico	p
10^{-15}	femto	f
10^{-18}	atto	a

[a] M. L. McGlashan, *Pure Appl. Chem.* **21**, 1 (1970).

TABLE III

CONVERSION FACTORS

Units		cm^{-1}	Hz	erg	cal mole^{-1}	eV
1 cm^{-1}	=	1	2.997925×10^{10}	1.986486×10^{-16}	2.85922	1.239855×10^{-4}
1 Hz	=	3.33564×10^{-11}	1	6.62620×10^{-27}	9.53731×10^{-11}	4.135707×10^{-15}
1 erg	=	5.034015×10^{15}	1.509161×10^{26}	1	1.439334×10^{16}	6.24145×10^{11}
1 cal mole^{-1}	=	0.349746	1.048513×10^{10}	6.94766×10^{-17}	1	4.33634×10^{-5}
1 eV	=	8065.46	2.417966×10^{14}	1.602192×10^{-12}	23 060.9	1

Numerical factors relating moments of inertia (I) and rotational constants (B).

$$h/(8\pi^2 c) = 27.9933 \times 10^{-40} \ (\text{g cm}^2)(\text{cm}^{-1}) = I(\text{g cm}^2) \times B(\text{cm}^{-1})$$
$$= 16.8580 \ (\text{amu Å}^2)(\text{cm}^{-1}) = I(\text{amu Å}^2) \times B(\text{cm}^{-1})$$
$$h/(8\pi^2 \times 10^6) = 8.39218 \times 10^{-35} \ (\text{g cm}^2)(\text{MHz}) = I(\text{g cm}^2) \times B(\text{MHz})$$
$$= 5.05391 \times 10^5 \ (\text{amu Å}^2)(\text{MHz}) = I(\text{amu Å}^2) \times B(\text{MHz})$$

TABLE IV

Wavelength Standards from the Emission Spectra of
Magnesium, Calcium, Mercury, and Cadmium[a]

$\nu_{vac}(cm^{-1})$	$\lambda_{vac}(\text{Å})$	$\nu_{vac}(cm^{-1})$	$\lambda_{vac}(\text{Å})$
Magnesium II		Mercury-198	
105 629.73	946.7032*	82 824.076	1207.3784*
105 622.34	946.7694	82 766.096	1208.2242
97 468.92	1025.9681	82 464.175	1212.6478
97 455.13	1026.1133	82 378.871	1213.9035
80 650.026	1239.9252	81 942.550	1220.3672
80 619.500	1240.3947	81 808.217	1222.3711
76 527.846	1306.7139	81 153.727	1232.2293
76 459.883	1307.8754	80 916.813	1235.8371
76 368.326	1309.4434	79 963.940	1250.5637
73 230.878	1365.5442	79 412.866	1259.2418
73 115.011	1367.7082	78 813.093	1268.8247
73 023.450	1369.4231	76 863.342	1301.0103
67 750.687	1475.9998	76 467.162	1307.7509
67 527.430	1480.8797	71 295.198	1402.6190
67 435.872	1482.8903	69 661.988	1435.5031
57 641.81	1734.852	54 068.907	1849.4918*
57 121.18	1750.664		
57 029.65	1753.474*		
Calcium II		Cadmium	
74 521.81	1341.889*	68 059.393	1469.3049*
74 486.51	1342.525	65 501.414	1526.6846*
60 835.76	1643.770		
60 810.94	1644.441		
60 611.28	1649.858		
		Cadmium 114	
60 533.02	1651.991		
59 742.15	1673.860	68 059.370	1469.3054*
59 109.38	1691.779	67 842.126	1474.0104*
58 886.47	1698.183		
55 330.02	1807.337		
55 111.75	1814.495		
54 256.77	1843.088		
54 033.87	1850.691*		

[a] B. Edlén, *Trans. Int. Astron. Union* **10**, 218 (1960).

TABLE V

WAVELENGTH STANDARDS FROM THE EMISSION SPECTRUM OF GERMANIUM[a]

$\nu_{vac}(cm^{-1})$	$\lambda_{vac}(\text{Å})$	$\nu_{vac}(cm^{-1})$	$\lambda_{vac}(\text{Å})$
61 343.18	1630.173*	56 683.404	1764.1848*
61 152.47	1635.257	56 648.099	1765.2843
60 857.12	1643.193	56 623.070	1766.0646
60 696.89	1647.531	56 020.975	1785.0457
60 595.34	1650.292	55 988.897	1786.0684
60 549.980	1651.5282	55 770.243	1793.0709
60 534.37	1651.954	55 474.673	1802.6244
60 299.99	1658.375	55 245.57	1810.100
60 050.149	1665.2748	54 308.647	1841.3274
59 959.181	1667.8013	54 217.88	1844.410
59 844.05	1671.010	54 174.929	1845.8723
59 742.51	1673.850	54 064.712	1849.6353
59 727.52	1674.270	53 760.98	1860.085
59 681.54	1675.560	53 731.81	1861.095
59 476.30	1681.342	53 617.794	1865.0525
59 170.41	1690.034	53 304.614	1876.0102
59 140.019	1690.9024	52 764.969	1895.1968
59 133.462	1691.0899	52 533.093	1903.5620
59 114.749	1691.6252	52 398.983	1908.4340
59 106.353	1691.8655	52 148.726	1917.5924
59 019.951	1694.3423	51 989.449	1923.4672
58 967.149	1695.8595	51 818.143	1929.8260
58 741.043	1702.3872	51 705.020	1934.0482
58 374.36	1713.081	51 591.593	1938.3003
58 280.635	1715.8358	51 437.255	1944.1162
58 248.432	1716.7844	51 147.886	1955.1150
58 190.526	1718.4928	50 968.064	1962.0129
58 183.910	1718.6882	50 932.762	1963.3728
58 114.319	1720.7463	50 880.668	1965.3830
57 994.279	1724.3080	50 738.767	1970.8796
57 533.483	1738.1183	50 305.637	1987.8488
57 521.55	1738.479	50 295.058	1988.2669
57 500.927	1739.1024	50 273.556	1989.1173
57 398.856	1742.1950	50 054.905	1997.8062
57 337.697	1744.0533	50 027.840	1998.8870*
57 331.083	1744.2545		
57 180.204	1748.8570		
57 141.453	1750.0430		
56 873.802	1758.2788		
56 841.723	1759.2711*		

[a] B. Edlén, *Trans. Int. Astron. Union* **10**, 231 (1960).

TABLE VI

WAVELENGTH STANDARDS FROM THE EMISSION SPECTRA OF KRYPTON-86[a, b] AND KRYPTON-84[a]

λ_{air}(Å)	ν_{vac}(cm⁻¹)	λ_{vac}(Å)	λ_{air}(Å)	ν_{vac}(cm⁻¹)	λ_{vac}(Å)
Krypton-86			Krypton-86 (Contd.)		
4263.2849	23 449.491	4264.4849*	13 622.4156*	7338.8353	13 626.1404
4273.9687	23 390.874	4275.1715	13 634.2209	7332.4809	13 637.9489
4282.9666	23 341.734	4284.1718	13 738.8500	7276.6400	13 742.6064
4286.4861	23 322.570	4287.6922	14 426.7935	6929.6530	14 430.7369
4300.4858	23 246.647	4301.6956	14 734.4360	6784.9680	14 738.4631
4351.3588	22 974.869	4352.5820	15 239.6159	6560.0526	15 243.7803
4362.6410	22 915.455	4363.8671	15 334.9587	6519.2665	15 339.1490
4376.1206	22 844.870	4377.3503	16 785.1275	5956.0282	16 789.7123
4399.9654	22 721.069	4401.2014	16 853.4885	5931.8694	16 858.0919
4410.3674	22 667.482	4411.6061	16 890.4409	5918.8919	16 895.0543
4425.1892	22 591.560	4426.4318	16 896.7530	5916.6808	16 901.3682
4453.9166	22 445.849	4455.1668	16 935.8057	5903.0374	16 940.4315
4463.6889	22 396.709	4464.9417	17 098.7696	5846.7771	17 103.4397
4502.3533	22 204.378	4503.6163	17 367.6050	5756.2742	17 372.3483
5228.1764	19 121.805	5229.6319	17 842.7376	5602.9911	17 847.6101
5490.9352	18 206.775	5492.4608	18 002.2291	5553.3512	18 007.1450
5500.7093	18 174.424	5502.2375	18 167.3153	5502.8880	18 172.2762
5520.5096	18 109.239	5522.0431	21 902.5111	4564.4408	21 908.4887
5562.2244	17 973.428	5563.7690	28 655.7172*	3488.7533	28 663.5341
5570.2886	17 947.407	5571.8354			
5580.3860	17 914.933	5581.9355			
5649.5606	17 695.580	5651.1286	Krypton-84		
5672.4497	17 624.177	5674.0238			
5707.5107	17 515.913	5709.0942	5562.2251	17 973.4251	5563.7698*
5832.8553	17 139.511	5834.4723	5570.2896	17 947.4042	5571.8364
			5580.3872	17 914.9291	5581.9367
5870.9140	17 028.403	5872.5412	5649.5616	17 695.5772	5651.1296
5879.8993	17 002.382	5881.5289	5832.8564	17 139.5074	5834.4734
5993.8487	16 679.151	5995.5089			
6012.1544	16 628.367	6013.8195	5993.8501	16 679.1474	5995.5103
6035.8327	16 563.136	6037.5041	6012.1555	16 628.3643	6013.8206
			6056.1263	16 507.6343	6057.8032
6056.1252	16 507.637	6057.8021	6082.8612	16 435.0821	6084.5452
6082.8601	16 435.085	6084.5441	6236.3516	16 030.5817	6238.0768
6151.4056	16 251.949	6153.1080			
6222.7324	16 065.666	6224.4539	6421.0267	15 569.5299	6422.8015
6236.3506	16 030.584	6238.0758	6456.2890	15 484.4944	6458.0733*
6373.5888	15 685.411	6375.3508			
6421.0257	15 569.532	6422.8005*			
6456.2875	15 484.498	6458.0718*			
11 819.3759*	8458.3685	11 822.6109			
13 177.4119*	7586.6687	13 181.0158			

[a] B. Edlén, *Trans. Int. Astron. Union* **10**, 227 (1960).
[b] C. Moore-Sitterly, *Trans. Int. Astron. Union* **12B**, 180 (1966).

TABLE VII

WAVELENGTH STANDARDS FROM THE EMISSION SPECTRA OF KRYPTON[a], MERCURY-198[b], CADMIUM[c], AND XENON-136[d]

λ_{air}(Å)	ν_{vac}(cm^{-1})	λ_{vac}(Å)	λ_{air}(Å)	ν_{vac}(cm^{-1})	λ_{vac}(Å)
Krypton			Mercury-198		
4273.9703*	23 390.8657	4275.1731	4046.5711	24 705.3010	4047.7143*
4282.9681	23 341.7263	4284.1735	4077.8377	24 515.8782	4078.9891
4286.4869	23 322.5654	4287.6930	4347.4954	22 995.2854	4348.7175
4300.4861	23 246.6457	4301.6959	4358.3375	22 938.0815	4359.5625
4318.5529	23 149.3944	4319.7674	5460.7532	18 307.4046	5462.2707
4319.5805	23 143.8874	4320.7953	5769.5984	17 327.4234	5771.1985*
4351.3623	22 974.8504	4352.5855	5790.6628	17 264.3930	5792.2685*
4362.6422	22 915.4485	4363.8683	10 139.789 *	9859.4356	10 142.568
4376.1227	22 844.8595	4377.3524	11 287.401	8857.0102	11 290.492
4399.9674	22 721.0587	4401.2034	13 570.564	7366.8761	13 574.275
4425.1905	22 591.5534	4426.4331	13 673.391	7311.4756	13 667.130
4453.9184	22 445.8397	4455.1686	15 295.966*	6535.8855	15 300.146
4463.6907	22 396.7002	4464.9435			
4502.3550	22 204.3701	4503.6180			
5562.2279	17 973.4163	5563.7725	Cadmium		
5570.2903	17 947.4019	5571.8371	10 394.6251	9617.7210	10 397.4736*
5580.3890	17 914.9233	5581.9385	13 978.4682	7151.9045	13 982.2897
5649.5628	17 695.5734	5651.1308	14 327.2608	6977.7938	14 331.1772
5672.4514	17 624.1717	5674.0255	14 473.2756	6907.3979	14 477.2317
5707.5128	17 515.9071	5709.0963	15 153.8200	6597.1933	15 157.9611*
5832.8600	17 139.4967	5834.4770			
5866.7514	17 040.4852	5868.3775			
5870.9169	17 028.3948	5872.5441	Xenon-136		
5879.9004	17 002.3785	5881.5300			
5993.8513	16 679.1442	5995.5115	20 262.2395*	4933.9418	20 267.7706
			23 193.3328	4310.4076	23 199.6619
6012.1570	16 628.3603	6013.8221	24 824.7157	4027.1447	24 831.4891
6056.1274	16 507.6315	6057.8043	26 269.0832	3805.7181	26 276.2500
6082.8630	16 435.0772	6084.5470	26 510.8645	3771.0096	26 518.0971
6236.3520	16 030.5807	6238.0772	30 475.4527	3280.4346	30 483.7653
6421.0285	15 569.5256	6422.8033	31 069.2302	3217.7409	31 077.7046
6456.2910*	15 484.4897	6458.0753	32 739.2788	3053.6022	32 748.2082
			33 666.6991	2969.4843	33 675.8812
			35 070.2520*	2850.6420	35 079.8165

[a] B. Edlén, *Trans. Int. Astron. Union* 9, 210 (1957).
[b] B. Edlén, *Trans. Int. Astron. Union* 9, 211 (1957); 10, 213, 228 (1960).
[c] G. Herzberg, *Trans. Int. Astron. Union* 11B, 214 (1961).
[d] C. Moore-Sitterly, *Trans. Int. Astron. Union* 12B, 179 (1966).

TABLE VIII

Wavelength Standards from the Emission Spectrum of Argon[a]

λ_{air}(Å)	ν_{vac}(cm⁻¹)	λ_{vac}(Å)	λ_{air}(Å)	ν_{vac}(cm⁻¹)	λ_{vac}(Å)
3947.5047*	25 325.2907	3948.6220	7723.7600*	12 943.4999	7725.8857
3948.9788	25 315.8374	3950.0965	7724.2067	12 942.7513	7726.3325
3957.1332	25 263.6706	3958.2530	7948.1759	12 578.0434	7950.3621
3979.7154	25 120.3194	3980.8411	8006.1563	12 486.9539	8008.3582
4044.4180	24 718.4531	4045.5606	8014.7854	12 473.5100	8016.9896
4045.9654	24 708.9996	4047.1084	8103.6921	12 336.6621	8105.9204
4054.5257	24 656.8327	4055.6710	8115.3109	12 318.9996	8117.5423
4158.5907	24 039.8299	4159.7632	8264.5215	12 096.5890	8266.7932
4164.1795	24 007.5664	4165.3535	8408.2086	11 889.8725	8410.5192
4181.8835	23 905.9324	4183.0621	8424.6474	11 866.6722	8426.9624
4190.7129	23 855.5660	4191.8938	8521.4412	11 731.8810	8523.7824
4191.0293	23 853.7651	4192.2103	8578.0611	11 654.4444	8580.4176
4198.3173	23 812.3573	4199.5002	8667.9430	11 533.5946	8670.3238
4200.6747	23 798.9942	4201.8582	8874.800	11 264.767	8877.237
4251.1849	23 516.2332	4252.3817	9122.9667	10 958.3389	9125.4706
4259.3617	23 471.0894	4260.5607	9194.638	10 872.920	9197.161
4266.2866	23 432.9925	4267.4874	9224.4980	10 837.7242	9227.0294
4272.1689	23 400.7285	4273.3712	9291.532	10 759.535	9294.081
4300.1009	23 248.7281	4301.3106	9340.581	10 703.035	9343.144
4333.5612	23 069.2232	4334.7797	9354.2180	10 687.4322	9356.7845
4335.3378	23 059.7698	4336.5567	9486.060	10 538.893	9488.662
4345.1678	23 007.6030	4346.3893	9657.7858	10 351.5012	9660.4345
4363.7949	22 909.3955	4365.0213	9784.502	10 217.442	9787.185
4423.9944	22 597.6613	4425.2367	9951.846	10 045.633	9954.574
4510.7334	22 163.1276	4511.9986	10 254.025	9749.5959	10 256.835
4522.3233	22 106.3284	4523.5915	10 470.053	9548.434	10 472.922
4589.2893	21 783.7624	4590.5752	10 478.034	9541.161	10 480.905
4596.0966	21 751.4989	4597.3843	10 673.566	9366.374	10 676.490
4628.4409	21 599.4982	4629.7372	10 681.771	9359.180	10 684.697
4702.3163	21 260.1660	4703.6321	10 683.404	9357.749	10 686.331
6677.2811	14 972.0216	6679.1248	10 700.984	9342.376	10 703.915
6965.4300	14 352.6567	6967.3512	10 722.229	9323.865	10 725.166
7067.2175	14 145.9400	7069.1661	10 773.368	9279.606	10 776.319
7147.0410	13 987.9486	7149.0111	10 861.077	9204.669	10 864.052
7272.9354	13 745.8189	7274.9395	10 880.941	9187.865	10 883.921
7383.9801	13 539.1023	7386.0141	10 892.361	9178.232	10 895.344
7471.1636	13 381.1109	7473.2211	10 950.726	9129.314	10 953.725
7503.8680	13 322.7918	7505.9343	11 078.868	9023.722	11 081.902
7514.6512	13 303.6742	7516.7204	11 248.350	8887.759	11 251.430
7635.1054*	13 093.7918	7637.2071	11 393.703*	8774.375	11 396.822

[a] B. Edlén, *Trans. Int. Astron. Union* **9**, 208, 209 (1957); C. Moore-Sitterly, *Ibid.* **12B**, 183 (1966).

TABLE VIII (*continued*)

$\lambda_{air}(\text{Å})$	$\nu_{vac}(\text{cm}^{-1})$	$\lambda_{vac}(\text{Å})$	$\lambda_{air}(\text{Å})$	$\nu_{vac}(\text{cm}^{-1})$	$\lambda_{vac}(\text{Å})$
11 441.832*	8737.4670	11 444.964	13 599.333*	7351.2917	13 603.051
11 467.545	8717.8755	11 470.684	13 622.659	7338.7042	13 626.384
11 488.108	8702.2711	11 491.253	13 678.549	7308.7186	13 682.289
11 645.867	8584.3874	11 649.055	13 718.576	7287.3938	13 722.327
11 668.709	8567.5831	11 671.903	13 825.717	7230.9210	13 829.497
11 687.604	8553.7322	11 690.803	13 907.476	7188.4120	13 911.278
11 719.487	8530.4617	11 722.695	13 992.808	7144.5752	13 996.633
11 896.632	8403.4404	11 899.888	14 093.640	7093.4599	14 097.493
12 026.648	8312.5939	12 029.939	14 174.712	7052.8890	14 178.587
12 112.324	8253.7953	12 115.639	14 249.193	7016.0234	14 253.088
12 139.737	8235.1572	12 143.059	14 577.458	6858.0321	14 581.442
12 343.392	8099.2847	12 346.769	14 719.546	6791.8315	14 723.569
12 377.194	8077.1657	12 380.580	14 739.139	6782.8030	14 743.167
12 402.828	8060.4720	12 406.221	14 833.480	6739.6644	14 837.534
12 439.321	8036.8251	12 442.724	14 974.568	6676.1645	14 978.660
12 456.114	8025.9901	12 459.522	15 030.513	6651.3152	15 034.621
12 487.663	8005.7132	12 491.079	15 031.174	6651.0227	15 035.282
12 554.324	7963.2045	12 557.759	15 046.503	6644.2468	15 050.615
12 621.619	7920.7470	12 625.072	15 052.568	6641.5697	15 056.682
12 638.480	7910.1799	12 641.937	15 171.737	6589.4024	15 175.883
12 702.280	7870.4494	12 705.755	15 172.691	6588.9881	15 176.837
12 733.418	7851.2032	12 736.901	15 329.345	6521.6539	15 333.534
12 746.232	7843.3103	12 749.719	15 353.128	6511.5514	15 357.323
12 802.737	7808.6938	12 806.239	15 555.460	6426.8549	15 559.710
12 933.196	7729.9266	12 936.733	15 734.909	6353.5598	15 739.208
12 956.658	7715.9292	12 960.202	15 776.614	6336.7644	15 780.924
13 008.264	7685.3188	13 011.822	15 793.157	6330.1268	15 797.472
13 028.425	7673.4261	13 031.988	15 816.777	6320.6737	15 821.098
13 213.991	7565.6673	13 217.605	15 883.163	6294.2555	15 887.502
13 228.104	7557.5955	13 231.722	15 948.407	6268.5061	15 952.764
13 230.897	7556.0001	13 234.515	15 989.491	6252.3996	15 993.859
13 272.635	7532.2391	13 276.265	16 122.656	6200.7580	16 127.061
13 302.312	7515.4349	13 305.950	16 180.023	6178.7730	16 184.443
13 313.209	7509.2835	13 316.850	16 264.070	6146.8433	16 268.513
13 367.110	7479.0034	13 370.765	16 292.110	6136.2641	16 296.561
13 367.827	7478.6023	13 371.483	16 519.867	6051.6644	16 524.380
13 499.406	7405.7083	13 503.097	16 740.078	5972.0566	16 744.650
13 504.190	7403.0847	13 507.883	16 860.088	5929.5475	16 864.693
13 544.205	7381.2131	13 547.908	16 940.584	5901.3723	16 945.211
13 573.618*	7365.2186	13 577.329	17 401.908*	5744.9273	17 406.661

TABLE VIII (*continued*)

$\lambda_{air}(\text{Å})$	$\nu_{vac}(\text{cm}^{-1})$	$\lambda_{vac}(\text{Å})$	$\lambda_{air}(\text{Å})$	$\nu_{vac}(\text{cm}^{-1})$	$\lambda_{vac}(\text{Å})$
17 444.903*	5730.7683	17 449.667	23 469.437*	4259.6982	23 475.841
17 445.248	5730.6550	17 450.012	23 845.035	4192.6011	23 851.542
17 914.629	5580.5063	17 919.521	23 966.518	4171.3494	23 973.058
17 914.726	5580.4761	17 919.618	24 013.230	4163.2351	24 019.782
18 231.349	5483.5603	18 236.327	25 125.271	3978.9709	25 132.126
18 348.006	5448.6957	18 353.016	25 487.646	3922.3993	25 494.600
18 427.765	5425.1127	18 432.797	25 505.228	3919.6954	25 512.187
18 632.289	5365.5621	18 637.376	25 661.022	3895.8980	25 668.023
18 745.005	5333.2983	18 750.123	26 115.776	3828.0588	26 122.901
19 123.807	5227.6571	19 129.028	26 180.428	3818.6055	26 187.571
19 294.916	5181.2978	19 300.184	26 543.041	3766.4383	26 550.282
19 817.508	5044.6660	19 822.918	26 605.288	3757.6261	26 612.546
19 823.714	5043.0867	19 829.126	26 835.705	3725.3624	26 843.026
19 860.943	5033.6335	19 866.365	26 909.711	3715.1171	26 917.052
19 945.068	5012.4025	19 950.513	27 145.454	3682.8534	27 152.859
19 965.730	5007.2153	19 971.180	27 285.760	3663.9158	27 293.204
19 992.232	5000.5777	19 997.690	27 356.342	3654.4625	27 363.805
20 025.672	4992.2274	20 031.139	27 411.479	3647.1117	27 418.957
20 030.097	4991.1246	20 035.565	27 752.508	3602.2952	27 760.079
20 068.932	4981.4663	20 074.410	27 785.928	3597.9625	27 793.508
20 241.663	4938.9573	20 247.188	27 977.219	3573.3619	27 984.851
20 317.011	4920.6407	20 322.557	28 194.726	3545.7953	28 202.417
20 568.816	4860.4018	20 574.430	28 238.250	3540.3302	28 245.953
20 616.229	4849.2239	20 621.856	28 314.045	3530.8529	28 321.769
20 647.135	4841.9653	20 652.771	28 427.265	3516.7903	28 435.020
20 716.338	4825.7907	20 721.993	28 497.958	3508.0664	28 505.732
20 756.999	4816.3375	20 762.665	28 530.615	3504.0510	28 538.398
20 811.042	4803.8302	20 816.722	28 612.427	3494.0318	28 620.232
20 984.286	4764.1703	20 990.014	28 690.049	3484.5785	28 697.875
20 986.111	4763.7560	20 991.839	28 775.083	3474.2812	28 782.932
21 035.834	4752.4958	21 041.576	28 835.223	3467.0351	28 843.089
21 166.377	4723.1849	21 172.154	29 126.092	3432.4114	29 134.037
21 332.885	4686.3194	21 338.707	29 272.677	3415.2233	29 280.662
21 534.207	4642.5074	21 540.084	29 788.667	3356.0659	29 796.792
22 039.561	4536.0575	22 045.576	30 453.764	3282.7709	30 462.071
22 077.181	4528.3280	22 083.206	30 912.746	3234.0295	30 921.178
22 112.626	4521.0694	22 118.661	30 987.774	3226.1992	30 996.226
23 133.204	4321.6114	23 139.517	31 324.485	3191.5204	31 333.029
23 134.770	4321.3189	23 141.083	32 226.556	3102.1848	32 235.346
23 185.491*	4311.8655	23 191.818	32 297.104*	3095.4086	32 305.913

TABLE VIII (*continued*)

λ_{air}(Å)	ν_{vac}(cm^{-1})	λ_{vac}(Å)
32 325.060*	3092.7315	32 333.876
32 879.664	3040.5643	32 888.632
32 930.634	3035.8581	32 939.615
33 139.400	3016.7334	33 148.438
33 284.366	3003.5944	33 293.444
35 058.546	2851.5939	35 068.107
38 630.293	2587.9363	38 640.828
39 319.127	2542.5981	39 329.849
39 793.924	2512.2614	39 804.776
39 824.470	2510.3344	39 835.330
42 032.637	2378.4551	42 044.099
42 331.714	2361.6511	42 343.257
42 391.257	2358.3339	42 402.816
42 610.649	2346.1914	42 622.268
43 433.131	2301.7622	43 444.974
43 662.102	2289.6914	43 674.008
45 265.801	2208.5711	45 278.144
45 523.076	2196.0893	45 535.489
45 562.462	2194.1909	45 574.886
45 914.091	2177.3869	45 926.610
45 936.865	2176.3074	45 949.391
46 768.265	2137.6192	46 781.017
47 138.827	2120.8152	47 151.680
49 386.158	2024.3069	49 399.624
49 515.934	2019.0014	49 529.435
53 897.78	1854.8583	53 912.475
55 029.13	1816.7240	55 044.134
55 591.11	1798.3585	55 606.267
56 024.07	1784.4605	56 039.345
59 331.91	1684.9743	59 348.086
61 240.55	1632.4599	61 257.247
77 310.82 *	1293.1275	77 331.897

TABLE IX

WAVELENGTH STANDARDS FROM THE EMISSION SPECTRUM OF NEON[a]

$\lambda_{air}(\text{Å})$	$\nu_{vac}(\text{cm}^{-1})$	$\lambda_{vac}(\text{Å})$	$\lambda_{air}(\text{Å})$	$\nu_{vac}(\text{cm}^{-1})$	$\lambda_{vac}(\text{Å})$
3351.7492*	29 826.5946	3352.7126	6163.5939*	16 219.8120	6165.2996
3369.8080	29 666.7591	3370.7760	6217.2812	16 079.7523	6219.0013
3369.9078	29 665.8805	3370.8758	6266.4950	15 953.4713	6268.2283
3375.6490	29 615.4273	3376.6185	6304.7890	15 856.5739	6306.5326
3417.9035	29 249.3122	3418.8838	6334.4278	15 782.3816	6336.1793
3418.0062	29 248.4334	3418.9865	6382.9917	15 662.3050	6384.7563
3423.9126	29 197.9801	3424.8945	6402.2460	15 615.2021	6404.0157
3447.7028	28 996.5112	3448.6907	6506.5281	15 364.9344	6508.3259
3450.7650	28 970.7806	3451.7537	6532.8822	15 302.9517	6534.6870
3454.1949	28 942.0144	3455.1845	6598.9529	15 149.7351	6600.7755
3460.5243	28 889.0802	3461.5155	6652.0927	15 028.7133	6653.9296
3464.3387	28 857.2729	3465.3309	6678.2762	14 969.7907	6680.1201
3466.5787	28 838.6268	3467.5715	6717.0430	14 883.3945	6718.8974
3472.5711	28 788.8632	3473.5654	6929.4673*	14 427.1439	6931.3788
3498.0640	28 579.0643	3499.0649	7024.0504*	14 232.8750	7025.9874
3501.2163	28 553.3341	3502.2180	7032.4131*	14 215.9498	7034.3523
3510.7212	28 476.0312	3511.7253	7051.2923	14 177.8882	7053.2366*
3515.1907	28 439.8255	3516.1960	7059.1074	14 162.1921	7061.0538*
3520.4717	28 397.1647	3521.4783	7064.7587	14 150.8632	7066.7067*
3545.8432	28 193.9808	3546.8564	7173.9381*	13 935.5042	7175.9155
3562.9541	28 058.5845	3563.9717	7245.1666*	13 798.5026	7247.1632
3593.5262	27 819.8813	3594.5516	7437.3919	13 441.8714	7439.4403*
3593.6396	27 819.0034	3594.6651	7438.8984*	13 439.1493	7440.9472
3600.1691	27 768.5505	3601.1963	7472.4386	13 378.8278	7474.4964*
3609.1790	27 699.2314	3610.2085	7488.8712	13 349.4711	7490.9335*
3633.6646	27 512.5840	3634.7004	7535.7741	13 266.3841	7537.8490
3682.2426	27 149.6336	3683.2910	7544.0443	13 251.8407	7546.1215
3685.7357	27 123.9036	3686.7850	7833.0302	12 762.9399	7835.1854
3701.2250	27 010.3954	3702.2783	7839.0546	12 753.1315	7841.2114
3754.2156	26 629.1543	3755.2826	7839.9893	12 751.6111	7842.1463
5400.5617	18 511.4458	5402.0632	7927.1177	12 611.4564	7929.2983
5852.4878	17 082.0156	5854.1101	7936.9961	12 595.7604	7939.1793
5881.8952	16 996.6124	5883.5254	7943.1814	12 585.9521	7945.3663
5944.8342	16 816.6679	5946.4812	7944.1412	12 584.4315	7946.3264
5975.5340	16 730.2717	5977.1893	8082.458	12 369.072	8084.681
6029.9969	16 579.1653	6031.6667	8118.5492	12 314.0858	8120.7815
6074.3377	16 458.1435	6076.0194	8128.9108	12 298.3896	8131.1459
6096.1631	16 399.2208	6097.8507	8136.4057	12 287.0609	8138.6428
6128.4499	16 312.8248	6130.1461	8248.6824	12 119.8168	8250.9498
6143.0626*	16 274.0213	6144.7628	8259.3790	12 104.1207	8261.6493*

[a] B. Edlén, *Trans. Int. Astron. Union* **9**, 205, 206 (1957); G. Herzberg, *Ibid.* **11B**, 215 (1961).

TABLE IX (*continued*)

$\lambda_{air}(\text{Å})$	$\nu_{vac}(\text{cm}^{-1})$	$\lambda_{vac}(\text{Å})$	$\lambda_{air}(\text{Å})$	$\nu_{vac}(\text{cm}^{-1})$	$\lambda_{vac}(\text{Å})$
8266.0772	12 094.3125	8268.3493*	9221.580	10 841.153	9224.111*
8267.1166	12 092.7919	8269.3890	9226.690	10 835.149	9229.222
8300.3263	12 044.4087	8302.6077	9275.5	10 778.1	9278.1
8301.5597	12 042.6192	8303.8414	9297.9	10 752.1	9300.51
8365.7486	11 950.2187	8368.0477	9300.85	10 748.75	9303.41
8376.3614	11 935.0780	8378.6633	9310.5843	10 737.518	9313.139
8377.6065	11 933.3041	8379.9088	9313.973	10 733.611	9316.529
8417.1591	11 877.2292	8419.4721	9326.507	10 719.187	9329.066
8418.4274	11 875.4399	8420.7407	9373.308	10 665.665	9375.880
8463.3575	11 812.3960	8465.6830	9377.227	10 661.208	9379.800
8484.4435	11 783.0393	8486.7747	9425.379	10 606.743	9427.965
8495.3598	11 767.8986	8497.6959	9433.008	10 598.165	9435.596
8544.6958	11 699.9524	8547.0433	9459.210	10 568.808	9461.805
8571.3524	11 663.5662	8573.7071	9486.6818	10 538.203	9489.2842
8582.9029	11 647.8699	8585.2607	9534.1627	10 485.722	9536.778
8591.2587	11 636.5414	8593.6187	9547.4052	10 471.178	9550.024
8634.6470	11 578.0690	8637.0188	9665.4198	10 343.3254	9668.0706
8635.3175	11 577.1700	8637.6895	10 295.417	9710.398	10 298.239
8647.0411	11 561.4739	8649.4162	10 562.408	9464.945	10 565.302
8654.3831	11 551.6657	8656.7602	10 620.665	9413.027	10 623.575
8655.5224	11 550.1452	8657.8998	10 798.043	9258.401	10 801.001
8679.4925	11 518.2474	8681.8764	10 844.477	9218.758	10 847.448
8681.9211	11 515.0253	8684.3057	11 143.020	8971.771	11 146.071
8704.1116	11 485.6687	8706.5022	11 177.525	8944.073	11 180.588
8767.5360	11 402.5818	8769.9437	11 390.434	8776.894	11 393.553
8771.6563	11 397.2257	8774.0651	11 409.134	8762.508	11 412.258
8778.7329	11 388.0382	8781.1437	11 522.746	8676.112	11 525.900
8780.6210	11 385.5895	8783.0323	11 525.019	8674.400	11 528.175
8782.0012	11 383.8002	8784.4128	11 536.345	8665.884	11 539.503
8783.7533	11 381.5294	8786.1654	11 601.537	8617.189	11 604.712
8792.5050	11 370.2007	8794.9195	11 614.081	8607.882	11 617.260
8830.9072	11 320.7563	8833.3321	11 688.002	8553.441	11 691.201
8853.8669	11 291.3996	8856.2980	11 766.792	8496.167	11 770.013
8865.3063	11 276.8298	8867.7405	11 789.044	8480.131	11 792.270
8865.7552	11 276.2588	8868.1895	11 789.889	8479.523	11 793.116
8919.5007	11 208.3127	8921.9495	11 984.912	8341.541	11 988.192
8988.5565	11 122.2037	8991.0240	12 066.334	8285.254	12 069.636
9148.672	10 927.549	9151.183	12 459.389	8023.881	12 462.798
9201.75	10 864.506	9204.284	12 595.004	7937.484	12 598.450
9220.05	10 842.943	9222.588 *	12 689.201	7878.562	12 692.672*

TABLE IX (continued)

λ_{air}(Å)	ν_{vac}(cm^{-1})	λ_{vac}(Å)	λ_{air}(Å)	ν_{vac}(cm^{-1})	λ_{vac}(Å)
12 769.525	7829.0034	12 773.018 *	23 100.514	4327.7272	23 106.817 *
12 887.159	7757.5400	12 890.684	23 260.302	4297.9975	23 266.649
12 912.014	7742.6073	12 915.546	23 372.999	4277.2739	23 379.377
13 219.241	7562.6628	13 222.856	23 565.362	4242.3587	23 571.793
15 230.714	6563.8868	15 234.876	23 636.515	4229.5878	23 642.966
17 161.930	5825.2596	17 166.617	23 701.636	4217.9670	23 708.104
18 210.330	5489.8896	18 215.302	23 707.617	4216.9030	23 714.086
18 898.832	5289.8880	18 903.992	23 709.160	4216.6286	23 715.629
18 937.552	5279.0721	18 942.723	23 911.993	4180.8610	23 918.518
18 944.648	5277.0950	18 949.820	23 951.417	4173.9791	23 957.954
19 573.769	5107.4837	19 579.1129	23 956.459	4173.1011	23 962.995
19 577.136	5106.6054	19 582.4802	23 971.819	4170.4270	23 978.360
19 772.488	5056.1523	19 777.8852	23 978.114	4169.3321	23 984.657
20 130.459	4966.2410	20 135.954	24 086.956	4150.4920	24 093.529
20 134.704	4965.1940	20 140.200	24 092.384	4149.5570	24 098.958
20 138.476	4964.2640	20 143.973	24 098.557	4148.4940	24 105.133
20 350.238	4912.6065	20 355.793	24 149.890	4139.6760	24 156.480
20 353.877	4911.7281	20 359.433	24 155.965	4138.6350	24 162.556
20 366.653	4908.6469	20 372.213	24 161.429	4137.6990	24 168.022
20 411.629	4897.8310	20 417.201	24 218.932	4127.8750	24 225.540
20 415.993	4896.7841	20 421.566	24 249.639	4122.6480	24 256.255
20 419.872	4895.8539	20 425.446	24 309.766	4112.4510	24 316.399
20 565.121	4861.2750	20 570.735	24 365.048	4103.1203	24 371.696
20 848.762	4795.1390	20 854.453	24 371.601	4102.0170	24 378.251
20 895.895	4784.3230	20 901.599	24 383.359	4100.0390	24 390.012
20 904.533	4782.3461	20 910.239	24 388.581	4099.1610	24 395.236
20 961.237	4769.4091	20 966.958	24 447.853	4089.2229	24 454.524
21 008.881	4758.5930	21 014.615	24 452.415	4088.4600	24 459.087
21 013.504	4757.5459	21 019.240	24 453.103	4088.3450	24 459.775
21 017.612	4756.6161	21 023.349	24 459.367	4087.2980	24 466.041
21 041.295	4751.2624	21 047.038	24 459.678	4087.2460	24 466.352
21 708.145	4605.3091	21 714.069	24 464.934	4086.3680	24 471.609
22 070.324	4529.7349	22 076.347	24 525.786	4076.2291	24 532.478
22 171.245	4509.1160	22 177.296	24 776.473	4034.9861	24 783.233
22 247.345	4493.6919	22 253.417	24 903.733	4014.3669	24 910.528
22 428.130	4457.4700	22 434.251	24 928.870	4010.3190	24 935.672
22 466.804	4449.7971	22 472.935	24 935.480	4009.2559	24 942.284
22 530.401	4437.2360	22 536.552	24 999.787	3998.9430	25 006.608
22 661.813	4411.5058	22 667.997	25 064.382	3988.6370	25 071.221
22 687.768	4406.4590	22 693.959 *	25 161.682	3973.2131	25 168.547 *

TABLE IX (*continued*)

$\lambda_{air}(\text{Å})$	$\nu_{vac}(\text{cm}^{-1})$	$\lambda_{vac}(\text{Å})$	$\lambda_{air}(\text{Å})$	$\nu_{vac}(\text{cm}^{-1})$	$\lambda_{vac}(\text{Å})$
25 227.933	3962.7790	25 234.816 *	33 352.350	2997.4720	33 361.446 *
25 228.303	3962.7209	25 235.186	33 511.327	2983.2520	33 520.467
25 277.246	3955.0480	25 284.143	33 899.818	2949.0640	33 909.064
25 393.181	3936.9910	25 400.109	33 903.014	2948.7860	33 912.261
25 524.366	3916.7564	25 531.330	33 913.112	2947.9080	33 922.361
25 854.914	3866.6818	25 861.968	34 131.313	2929.0620	34 140.622
26 606.932	3757.3939	26 614.191	34 471.455	2900.1600	34 480.856
26 860.820	3721.8792	26 868.148	34 489.877	2898.6110	34 499.283
27 435.745	3643.8859	27 443.230	34 780.021	2874.4300	34 789.506
27 520.777	3632.6274	27 528.284	35 507.305	2815.5540	35 516.989
27 573.458	3625.6870	27 580.980	35 834.782	2789.8240	35 844.555
27 630.850	3618.1560	27 638.388	36 471.679	2741.1060	36 481.625
27 818.800	3593.7110	27 826.380	37 172.048	2689.4600	37 182.185
27 971.903	3574.0409	27 979.534	39 806.305	2511.4800	39 817.160
28 386.198	3521.8780	28 393.942	42 171.470	2370.6250	42 182.969
28 533.205	3503.7310	28 541.004	44 323.726	2255.5130	44 335.812
28 744.305	3478.0013	28 752.146	45 337.878	2205.0600	45 350.240
29 447.838	3394.9089	29 455.871	45 355.937	2204.1820	45 368.304
29 487.532	3390.3389	29 495.576	46 051.139	2170.9070	46 063.696
29 667.963	3369.7200	29 676.056	47 146.857	2120.4540	47 159.712
29 714.054	3364.4931	29 722.159	47 166.386	2119.5760	47 179.247
29 804.385	3354.2960	29 812.515	61 449.877	1626.8990	61 466.631 *
29 931.319	3340.0710	29 939.483			
29 932.977	3339.8860	29 941.142			
29 940.848	3339.0080	29 949.015			
30 118.917	3319.2671	30 127.133			
30 126.887	3318.3890	30 135.105			
30 129.748	3318.0740	30 137.966			
30 199.583	3310.4010	30 207.821			
30 200.477	3310.3030	30 208.715			
30 259.528	3303.8430	30 267.782			
30 267.572	3302.9650	30 275.828			
30 363.490	3292.5310	30 371.772			
30 594.959	3267.6210	30 603.304			
30 603.183	3266.7430	30 611.530			
30 666.971	3259.9480	30 675.336			
30 711.645	3255.2060	30 720.022			
31 859.980	3137.8781	31 868.669			
33 173.107	3013.6680	33 182.155			
33 332.700	2999.2390	33 341.791 *			

TABLE X

Wavelength Standards from the Emission Spectrum of Iron[a]

λ_{air}(Å)	ν_{vac}(cm^{-1})	λ_{vac}(Å)	λ_{air}(Å)	ν_{vac}(cm^{-1})	λ_{vac}(Å)
2457.5975*	40 677.8348	2458.3413	3017.6271*	33 128.9703	3018.5061
2501.1326	39 969.8397	2501.8864	3018.9827	33 114.0952	3019.8621
2540.9719	39 343.2038	2541.7351	3020.4909	33 097.5612	3021.3706
2545.9789	39 265.8353	2546.7432	3021.0727	33 091.1876	3021.9526
2549.6140	39 209.8559	2550.3792	3024.0328	33 058.7973	3024.9134
2576.6907	38 797.8523	2577.4623	3025.8423	33 039.0285	3026.7234
2584.5364	38 680.0837	2585.3098	3026.4612	33 032.2724	3027.3424
2599.3966	38 458.9716	2600.1735	3037.3885	32 913.4405	3038.2725
2606.8270	38 349.3563	2607.6057	3040.4272	32 880.5471	3041.3119
2635.8096	37 927.7031	2636.5952	3041.7381	32 866.3771	3042.6232
2666.3982	37 492.6264	2667.1911	3042.6643	32 856.3729	3043.5496
2679.0622	37 315.4078	2679.8582	3047.6039	32 803.1209	3048.4904
2689.2131	37 174.5623	2690.0115	3057.4457	32 697.5332	3058.3347
2706.5829	36 936.0036	2707.3855	3059.0859	32 680.0024	3059.9753
2711.6555	36 866.9125	2712.4593	3067.2437	32 593.0885	3068.1351
2723.5776	36 705.5413	2724.3843	3075.7193	32 503.2770	3076.6129
2733.5810	36 571.2265	2734.3901	3083.7409	32 418.7310	3084.6365
2737.3099	36 521.4100	2738.1199	3099.9678	32 249.0405	3100.8674
2742.4060	36 453.5474	2743.2173	3100.3032	32 245.5519	3101.2029
2778.2205	35 983.6431	2779.0405	3100.6649	32 241.7905	3101.5647
2804.5207	35 646.2133	2805.3471	3134.1099	31 897.7421	3135.0181
2806.9845	35 614.9268	2807.8115	3193.2245	31 307.2566	3194.1476
2813.2867	35 535.1478	2814.1152	3205.3959	31 188.3822	3206.3221
2823.2763	35 409.4200	2824.1073	3236.2219	30 891.3139	3237.1559
2825.5559	35 380.8538	2826.3874	3257.5935	30 688.6570	3258.5330
2832.4357	35 294.9203	2833.2689	3440.9888	29 053.0870	3441.9750
2851.7973	35 055.3054	2852.6353	3443.8761	29 028.7300	3444.8631
2953.9400	33 843.2017	2954.8032	3465.8602	28 844.6051	3466.8528
2957.3646	33 804.0133	2958.2286	3475.4497	28 765.0191	3476.4448
2965.2545	33 714.0721	2966.1205	3476.7020	28 754.6583	3477.6974
2981.4450	33 530.9984	2982.3150	3490.5740	28 640.3869	3491.5729
2983.5699	33 507.1186	2984.4404	3497.8407	28 580.8887	3498.8415
2987.2904	33 465.3892	2988.1619	3513.8177	28 450.9379	3514.8226
2994.4274	33 385.6303	2995.3006	3521.2610	28 390.7996	3522.2678
2999.5118	33 329.0415	3000.3863	3526.0397	28 352.3237	3527.0478
3000.9481	33 313.0904	3001.8230	3554.9245	28 121.9594	3555.9400
3003.0304	33 289.9921	3003.9058	3558.5149	28 093.5862	3559.5313
3007.2824	33 242.9253	3008.1589	3565.3789	28 039.5025	3566.3971
3008.1390	33 233.4594	3009.0157	3570.0963	28 002.4531	3571.1157
3009.5693*	33 217.6659	3010.4463	3581.1925*	27 915.6909	3582.2148

[a] B. Edlén, *Trans. Int. Astron. Union* **10**, 216 (1960).

TABLE X (*continued*)

λ_{air}(Å)	ν_{vac}(cm^{-1})	λ_{vac}(Å)	λ_{air}(Å)	ν_{vac}(cm^{-1})	λ_{vac}(Å)
3586.9836*	27 870.6229	3588.0074	3841.0476*	26 027.1812	3842.1372
3608.8591	27 701.6866	3609.8885	3843.2567	26 012.2211	3844.3468
3618.7675	27 625.8398	3619.7995	3846.8003	25 988.2597	3847.8914
3631.4630	27 529.2632	3632.4982	3856.3713	25 923.7618	3857.4648
3647.8422	27 405.6572	3648.8817	3859.9121	25 899.9818	3861.0066
3679.9129	27 166.8212	3680.9607	3865.5228	25 862.3896	3866.6187
3683.0541	27 143.6518	3684.1027	3867.2156	25 851.0691	3868.3120
3687.4560	27 111.2499	3688.5057	3869.5583	25 835.4188	3870.6553
3705.5658	26 978.7555	3706.6202	3872.5007	25 815.7890	3873.5984
3709.2458	26 951.9901	3710.3012	3873.7607	25 807.3922	3874.8588
3719.9345	26 874.5494	3720.9926	3878.0179	25 779.0621	3879.1171
3722.5629	26 855.5745	3723.6217	3878.5731	25 775.3720	3879.6724
3727.6187	26 819.1510	3728.6788	3886.2820	25 724.2447	3887.3833
3733.3168	26 778.2184	3734.3784	3887.0474	25 719.1794	3888.1489
3734.8643	26 767.1234	3735.9263	3888.5134	25 709.4833	3889.6153
3737.1317	26 750.8836	3738.1943	3895.6562	25 662.3453	3896.7600
3743.3614	26 706.3659	3744.4256	3897.8898	25 647.6404	3898.9942
3745.8988	26 688.2760	3746.9637	3898.0105	25 646.8462	3899.1149
3748.2618	26 671.4514	3749.3273	3899.7076	25 635.6853	3900.8124
3749.4852	26 662.7492	3750.5510	3902.9452	25 614.4203	3904.0509
3758.2326	26 600.6923	3759.3006	3906.4792	25 591.2487	3907.5858
3760.0491	26 587.8417	3761.1176	3920.2577	25 501.3054	3921.3679
3763.7887	26 561.4254	3764.8582	3922.9113	25 484.0558	3924.0222
3765.5385	26 549.0829	3766.6084	3927.9197	25 451.5624	3929.0319
3767.1912	26 537.4359	3768.2616	3930.2963	25 436.1725	3931.4091
3787.8800	26 392.4962	3788.9557	3935.8123	25 400.5247	3936.9265
3790.0923	26 377.0911	3791.1686	3937.3281	25 390.7462	3938.4427
3795.0017	26 342.9692	3796.0793	3949.9524	25 309.5976	3951.0703
3798.5110	26 318.6325	3799.5895	3951.1634	25 301.8405	3952.2816
3799.5468	26 311.4580	3800.6256	3952.6013	25 292.6363	3953.7199
3805.3424	26 271.3861	3806.4227	3956.6769	25 266.5840	3957.7966
3812.9638	26 218.8758	3814.0461	3969.2567	25 186.5082	3970.3797
3813.0514	26 218.2735	3814.1337	3977.7411	25 132.7873	3978.8663
3815.8401	26 199.1131	3816.9231	3981.7710	25 107.3513	3982.8972
3820.4251	26 167.6715	3821.5093	3983.9568	25 093.5764	3985.0836
3824.4432	26 140.1794	3825.5284	3997.3921	25 009.2383	3998.5224
3825.8808	26 130.3573	3826.9664	4001.6613	24 982.5576	4002.7927
3827.8227	26 117.1014	3828.9088	4005.2415	24 960.2267	4006.3739
3834.2219	26 073.5138	3835.3097	4009.7128	24 932.3937	4010.8463
3840.4376*	26 031.3151	3841.5270	4014.5308*	24 902.4720	4015.6656

TABLE X (*continued*)

λ_{air}(Å)	ν_{vac}(cm^{-1})	λ_{vac}(Å)	λ_{air}(Å)	ν_{vac}(cm^{-1})	λ_{vac}(Å)
4021.8663*	24 857.0532	4023.0030	4258.3150*	23 476.8585	4259.5137
4024.7251	24 839.3974	4025.8626	4260.4733	23 464.9656	4261.6726
4045.8139	24 709.9248	4046.9569	4271.7601	23 402.9679	4272.9623
4062.4409	24 608.7927	4063.5882	4282.4026	23 344.8086	4283.6076
4063.5942	24 601.8085	4064.7418	4291.4627	23 295.5242	4292.6701
4071.7371	24 552.6094	4072.8869	4294.1240	23 281.0869	4295.3321
4074.7858	24 534.2398	4075.9364	4299.2338	23 253.4170	4300.4432
4076.6294	24 523.1448	4077.7804	4307.9014	23 206.6314	4309.1131
4098.1757	24 394.2161	4099.3324	4315.0837	23 168.0055	4316.2973
4100.7374	24 378.9776	4101.8947	4325.7615	23 110.8182	4326.9779
4107.4880	24 338.9119	4108.6471	4337.0459	23 050.6881	4338.2653
4109.8016	24 325.2106	4110.9613	4352.7337	22 967.6120	4353.9572
4118.5446	24 273.5732	4119.7066	4367.5774	22 889.5554	4368.8048
4120.2061	24 263.7849	4121.3685	4369.7711	22 878.0646	4370.9991
4127.6083	24 220.2726	4128.7727	4375.9290	22 845.8707	4377.1586
4132.0576	24 194.1933	4133.2232	4383.5449	22 806.1793	4384.7765
4134.6770	24 178.8661	4135.8432	4404.7503	22 696.3875	4405.9875
4136.9974	24 165.3047	4138.1642	4415.1222	22 643.0706	4416.3622
4143.8680	24 125.2391	4145.0366	4422.5675	22 604.9521	4423.8094
4147.6687	24 103.1324	4148.8383	4427.3093	22 580.7418	4428.5525
4149.3658	24 093.2744	4150.5359	4461.6523	22 406.9324	4462.9045
4152.1693	24 077.0072	4153.3401	4466.5501	22 382.3625	4467.8036
4177.5932	23 930.4828	4178.7707	4469.3742	22 368.2198	4470.6285
4181.7542	23 906.6715	4182.9328	4476.0168	22 335.0250	4477.2728
4184.8914	23 888.7502	4186.0708	4482.1684	22 304.3715	4483.4260
4191.4297	23 851.4864	4192.6108	4489.7391	22 266.7620	4490.9987
4198.3036	23 812.4350	4199.4865	4494.5627	22 242.8655	4495.8236
4199.0948	23 807.9483	4200.2779	4528.6132	22 075.6249	4529.8831
4202.0282	23 791.3285	4203.2121	4647.4333	21 511.2302	4648.7346
4206.6953	23 764.9338	4207.8804	4871.3170	20 522.5972	4872.6776
4216.1826	23 711.4588	4217.3702	4891.4911	20 437.9565	4892.8571
4219.3597	23 693.6048	4220.5482	4920.5016	20 317.4592	4921.8753
4222.2128	23·677.5945	4223.4020	4957.5952	20 165.4424	4958.9787
4225.9553	23 656.6261	4227.1455	4966.0933	20 130.9353	4967.4791
4227.4257	23 648.3979	4228.6163	5110.4123	19 562.4412	5111.8365
4233.6019	23 613.8990	4234.7941	5133.6889	19 473.7444	5135.1193
4235.9361	23 600.8869	4237.1289	5166.2812	19 350.8927	5167.7202
4238.8087	23 584.8931	4240.0023	5167.4878	19 346.3744	5168.9272
4245.2564	23 549.0730	4246.4517	5168.8976	19 341.0978	5170.3373
4247.4246*	23 537.0520	4248.6204	5171.5955*	19 331.0081	5173.0359

TABLE X (*continued*)

λ_{air}(Å)	ν_{vac}(cm^{-1})	λ_{vac}(Å)	λ_{air}(Å)	ν_{vac}(cm^{-1})	λ_{vac}(Å)
5191.4535*	19 257.0654	5192.8992	5424.0686	18 431.2216	5425.5764
5192.3428	19 253.7672	5193.7888	5429.6963	18 412.1184	5431.2056
5204.5818	19 208.4910	5206.0310	5434.5237	18 395.7634	5436.0342
5216.2733	19 165.4385	5217.7256	5445.0425	18 360.2267	5446.5559
5227.1876	19 125.4218	5228.6429	5446.9168	18 353.9089	5448.4307
5232.9400	19 104.3981	5234.3968	5455.6093	18 324.6657	5457.1255
5263.3047	18 994.1836	5264.7696	5497.5159	18 184.9815	5499.0433
5266.5549	18 982.4617	5268.0206	5501.4633	18 171.9336	5502.9917
5281.7895	18 927.7100	5283.2593	5506.7785	18 154.3940	5508.3083
5283.6204	18 921.1512	5285.0907	5569.6174	17 949.5702	5571.1640
5302.2991	18 854.4974	5303.7744	5572.8419	17 939.1846	5574.3894
5307.3604	18 836.5172	5308.8370	5576.0874	17 928.7434	5577.6358
5324.1784	18 777.0172	5325.6595	5586.7555	17 894.5082	5588.3067
5332.8987	18 746.3135	5334.3821	5602.9442	17 842.8057	5604.4997
5339.9286	18 721.6347	5341.4139	5615.6434*	17 802.4565	5617.2023
5341.0236	18 717.7965	5342.5092	5624.5417*	17 774.2924	5626.1030
5367.4671	18 625.5820	5368.9598	5658.8156*	17 666.6395	5660.3861
5369.9621	18 616.9282	5371.4554	5709.3778*	17 510.1854	5710.9618
5371.4892	18 611.6355	5372.9829			
5383.3689	18 570.5650	5384.8658			
5393.1668	18 536.8277	5394.6663			
5397.1272	18 523.2256	5398.6278			
5405.7744	18 493.5958	5407.2773			
5410.9101	18 476.0430	5412.4143			
5415.1997	18 461.4075	5416.7051			

TABLE XI

ATOMIC MASS, NUCLEAR SPIN, AND ABUNDANCE (OR HALF-LIFE) OF EACH ELEMENT

ATOMIC NUMBER	ELEMENT		MASS NUMBER	ATOMIC MASS (amu)	ERROR amux10^{+6}	NUCLEAR SPIN	ABUNDANCE PER CENT
1	H	Hydrogen	1	1.007 825 19	0.08	1/2	99.99
			2	2.014 102 22	0.12	1	0.01492
			3	3.016 049 71	0.21	1/2	(12 y)
2	He	Helium	3	3.016 029 73	0.21	1/2	1.37×10^{-4}
			4	4.002 603 12	0.42	0	99.9999
3	Li	Lithium	6	6.015 124 7	1.2	1	7.42
			7	7.016 003 9	1.2	3/2	92.58
4	Be	Beryllium	9	9.012 185 5	1.0	3/2	100
			10	10.013 534 4	2.4		(2.7 My)
5	B	Boron	10	10.012 938 8	0.5	3	19.61
			11	11.009 305 30	0.32	3/2	80.39
6	C	Carbon	12	12.000 000 0	0.0	0	98.893
			13	13.003 354 4	0.9	1/2	1.107
			14	14.003 241 97	0.32	0	(5.6 ky)
7	N	Nitrogen	14	14.003 074 39	0.17	1	99.6337
			15	15.000 107 7	0.9	1/2	0.3663
8	O	Oxygen	16	15.994 915 02	0.28	0	99.759
			17	16.999 132 9	1.0	5/2	0.0374
			18	17.999 160 02	0.36	0	0.2039
9	F	Fluorine	19	18.998 404 6	0.8	1/2	100
10	Ne	Neon	20	19.992 440 5	0.5	(0)	90.92
			21	20.993 848 6	1.6	3/2	0.257
			22	21.991 384 7	0.6	(0)	8.82
11	Na	Sodium	22	21.994 436 6	2.9	3	(2.6 y)
			23	22.989 770 7	2.0	3 2	100
12	Mg	Magnesium	24	23.985 041 7	1.9	(0)	78.70
			25	24.985 839 0	2.0	5/2	10.13
			26	25.982 593 0	2.0	(0)	11.17
13	Al	Aluminum	26	25.986 890 9	2.4		(7.4 My)
			27	26.981 538 9	1.9	5/2	100
14	Si	Silicon	28	27.976 929 2	3.0	(0)	92.21
			29	28.976 495 8	4.0	1/2	4.70
			30	29.973 762 8	4.0	(0)	3.09
			32	31.974 020	50		(700 y)
15	P	Phosphorus	31	30.973 764 7	1.5	1/2	100

TABLE XI (*continued*)

ATOMIC NUMBER	ELEMENT		MASS NUMBER	ATOMIC MASS (amu)	ERROR amux10⁺⁶	NUCLEAR SPIN	ABUNDANCE PER CENT
16	S	Sulfur	32	31.972 073 7	0.9	0	95.0
			33	32.971 461 9	3.0	3/2	0.760
			34	33.967 864 6	2.9	(0)	4.22
			36	35.967 090	9	(0)	0.0136
17	Cl	Chlorine	35	34.968 851 1	1.3	3/2	75.529
			36	35.968 308 9	4.4	2	(0.3 My)
			37	36.965 898 5	1.1	3/2	24.471
18	Ar	Argon	36	35.967 544 5	2.4	(0)	0.337
			38	37.962 727 8	2.7	(0)	0.063
			39	38.964 317	6	7/2	(265 y)
			40	39.962 384 2	0.8	(0)	99.600
			42	41.963 048	43		(3.5 y)
19	K	Potassium	39	38.963 710 1	2.8	3/2	93.10
			40	39.963 999 8	1.3	4	0.01181
			41	40.961 832 3	3.8	3/2	6.88
20	Ca	Calcium	40	39.962 588 9	3.5	(0)	96.97
			41	40.962 275	8	7/2	(110 ky)
			42	41.958 625 2	3.8		0.64
			43	42.958 779 6	4.2	7/2	0.145
			44	43.955 490 5	4.4		2.06
			46	45.953 689	10		0.0033
			48	47.952 531	10		0.185
21	Sc	Scandium	45	44.955 918 9	3.3	7/2	100
22	Ti	Titanium	44	43.959 572	13		(1 ky)
			46	45.952 631 6	2.4		7.93
			47	46.951 768 5	2.7	5/2	7.28
			48	47.947 950 3	2.1	0	73.94
			49	48.947 870 3	2.1	7/2	5.51
			50	49.944 785 9	3.5		5.34
23	V	Vanadium	50	49.947 163 8	3.5	6	0.24
			51	50.943 961 2	2.5	7/2	99.76
24	Cr	Chromium	50	49.946 054 5	3.7		4.31
			52	51.940 513 1	3.2		83.76
			53	52.940 652 7	3.2	3/2	9.55
			54	53.938 881 5	4.0		2.38
25	Mn	Manganese	53	52.941 295	7	7/2	(2 My)
			55	54.938 050 3	3.5	5/2	100
26	Fe	Iron	54	53.939 617	5		5.82
			55	54.938 298 6	3.7		(2.7 y)

TABLE XI (*continued*)

ATOMIC NUMBER	ELEMENT		MASS NUMBER	ATOMIC MASS (amu)	ERROR amux10^{+6}	NUCLEAR SPIN	ABUNDANCE PER CENT
26	Fe	Iron (Contd.)	56	55.934 936 3	4.3		91.66
			57	56.935 397 8	4.5	1/2	2.19
			58	57.933 282	5		0.33
			60	59.933 964	33		(0.3 My)
27	Co	Cobalt	59	58.933 189 3	3.8	7/2	100
			60	59.933 813 4	4.8	5	(5.3 y)
28	Ni	Nickel	58	57.935 342	5		67.88
			59	58.934 342 3	4.3		(80 ky)
			60	59.930 787	5		26.23
			61	60.931 056	7	3/2	1.19
			62	61.928 342	5		3.66
			63	62.929 664	5		(92 y)
			64	63.927 958	6		1.08
29	Cu	Copper	63	62.929 592	5	3/2	69.09
			65	64.927 786	6	3/2	30.91
30	Zn	Zinc	64	63.929 145	5	(0)	48.89
			66	65.926 052	6	(0)	27.81
			67	66.927 145	10	5/2	4.11
			68	67.924 857	6	(0)	18.57
			70	69.925 334	6		0.62
31	Ga	Gallium	69	68.925 574 0	3.7	3/2	60.4
			71	70.924 706 0	4.6	3/2	39.6
32	Ge	Germanium	70	69.924 251 5	1.8	(0)	20.52
			72	71.922 081 8	1.7	(0)	27.43
			73	72.923 462 5	1.8	9/2	7.76
			74	73.921 180 6	1.7	(0)	36.54
			76	75.921 405 2	2.0	(0)	7.76
33	As	Arsenic	75	74.921 596 4	3.9	3/2	100
34	Se	Selenium	74	73.922 476	5	(0)	0.87
			76	75.919 207	7	(0)	9.02
			77	76.919 911	5	1/2	7.58
			78	77.917 313 7	2.6	0	23.52
			79	78.918 494 3	4.7	7/2	(60 ky)
			80	79.916 527 3	2.9	0	49.82
			82	81.916 707	7	(0)	9.19
35	Br	Bromine	79	78.918 329 1	3.3	3/2	50.537
			81	80.916 292	5	3/2	49.463

TABLE XI (*continued*)

ATOMIC NUMBER	ELEMENT		MASS NUMBER	ATOMIC MASS (amu)	ERROR amux10^{+6}	NUCLEAR SPIN	ABUNDANCE PER CENT
36	Kr	Krypton	78	77.920 403	5		0.354
			80	79.916 380	6		2.27
			81	80.916 610	110		(0.2 My)
			82	81.913 482	5	(0)	11.56
			83	82.914 131 4	4.8	9/2	11.55
			84	83.911 503 4	3.5	(0)	56.90
			85	84.912 523	7	9/2	(11 y)
			86	85.910 615 9	4.2	(0)	17.37
37	Rb	Rubidium	85	84.911 800	5	5/2	72.15
			87	86.909 186 5	3.3	3/2	27.85
38	Sr	Strontium	84	83.913 430 1	3.9		0.56
			86	85.909 285	5	(0)	9.86
			87	86.908 892 2	3.5	9/2	7.02
			88	87.905 641	6	(0)	82.56
			90	89.907 747	9		(28 y)
39	Y	Yttrium	89	88.905 871 9	4.8	1/2	100
40	Zr	Zirconium	90	89.904 699 6	4.1		51.46
			91	90.905 642	5	5/2	11.23
			92	91.905 030 9	3.5		17.11
			93	92.906 450	5		(0.95 My)
			94	93.906 313 4	3.7		17.40
			96	95.908 286	5		2.80
41	Nb	Niobium	93	92.906 382	5	9/2	100
			94	93.907 303	15		(20 ky)
42	Mo	Molybdenum	92	91.906 810 1	3.4	(0)	15.84
			93	92.906 830	14		(10 ky)
			94	93.905 090 1	2.9	(0)	9.04
			95	94.905 839 0	3.2	5/2	15.72
			96	95.904 673 8	2.6	(0)	16.53
			97	96.906 021 5	2.9	5/2	9.46
			98	97.905 408 8	2.8	(0)	23.78
			100	99.907 474 7	3.7	(0)	9.63
43	Tc	Technetium	97	96.906 340	1070		(2.6 My)
			98	97.907 110	210		(1.5 My)
			99	98.906 249	6	9/2	(210 ky)
44	Ru	Ruthenium	96	95.907 598	6		5.51
			98	97.905 288 7	4.4		1.87
			99	98.905 935 5	4.3	5/2	12.72
			100	99.904 218	5		12.62
			101	100.905 576 8	3.3	5/2	17.07

TABLE XI (*continued*)

ATOMIC NUMBER		ELEMENT	MASS NUMBER	ATOMIC MASS (amu)	ERROR amux10^{+6}	NUCLEAR SPIN	ABUNDANCE PER CENT
44	Ru	Ruthenium (Contd.)	102	101.904 347 8	4.7		31.61
			103	102.906 306	21		18.58
45	Rh	Rhodium	103	102.905 511 0	4.8	1/2	100
46	Pd	Palladium	102	101.905 609	11		0.96
			104	103.904 011	11		10.97
			105	104.905 064	12	5/2	22.23
			106	105.903 479	6		27.33
			107	106.905 131 6	4.6		(7 My)
			108	107.903 891	8		26.71
			110	109.905 164	14		11.81
47	Ag	Silver	107	106.905 094 0	4.5	1/2	51.35
			109	108.904 756	5	1/2	48.65
48	Cd	Cadmium	106	105.906 462 6	4.1		1.215
			108	107.904 186 6	4.4		0.875
			109	108.904 928	7		(1.3 y)
			110	109.903 011 8	3.8	(0)	12.39
			111	110.904 188 4	3.8	1/2	12.75
			112	111.902 762 5	3.2	(0)	24.07
			113	112.904 408 5	3.6	1/2	12.26
			114	113.903 360 3	3.0	(0)	28.86
			116	115.904 761 8	3.3	(0)	7.58
49	In	Indium	113	112.904 089	9	9/2	4.28
			115	114.903 871	8	9/2	95.72
50	Sn	Tin	112	111.904 835	10		0.96
			114	114.902 773	9		0.66
			115	114.903 346	7	1/2	0.35
			116	115.901 744 6	4.7	(0)	14.30
			117	116.902 958 1	3.4	1/2	7.61
			118	117.901 605 8	4.1	(0)	24.03
			119	118.903 313 3	3.3	1/2	8.58
			120	119.902 198 2	3.6	(0)	32.85
			122	121.903 441 1	4.4		4.72
			124	123.905 272	5		5.94
			126	125.907 640	1090		(0.1 My)
51	Sb	Antimony	121	120.903 816 1	2.8	5/2	57.25
			123	122.904 212 7	3.3	7/2	42.75
			125	124.905 232	9	7/2	(2.0 y)
52	Te	Tellurium	120	119.904 023	14		0.089
			122	121.903 066	6		2.46

TABLE XI (*continued*)

ATOMIC NUMBER	ELEMENT		MASS NUMBER	ATOMIC MASS (amu)	ERROR amux10^{+8}	NUCLEAR SPIN	ABUNDANCE PER CENT
52	Te	Tellurium (Contd.)	123	122.904 277	6	1/2	0.87
			124	123.902 842	6		4.61
			125	124.904 418	6	1/2	6.99
			126	125.903 322	5	(0)	18.71
			128	127.904 476	6	(0)	31.79
			130	129.906 238	6	(0)	34.48
53	I	Iodine	127	126.904 469 8	4.3	5/2	100
			129	128.904 987	7	7/2	(16 My)
54	Xe	Xenon	124	123.906 120	150		0.096
			126	125.904 288	9		0.090
			128	127.903 540	6		1.919
			129	128.904 784	5	1/2	26.44
			130	129.903 509	6		4.08
			131	130.905 085 3	4.2	3/2	21.18
			132	131.904 161 0	4.7	(0)	26.89
			134	133.905 397 1	4.9	(0)	10.44
			136	135.907 221	6	(0)	8.87
55	Cs	Cesium	133	132.905 355	38	7/2	100
			134	133.906 823	41	4	(2.2 y)
			135	134.905 770	110	7/2	(2 My)
			137	136.906 770	80	7/2	(30 y)
56	Ba	Barium	130	129.906 245	23		0.101
			132	131.905 120	300		0.097
			133	132.905 879	39		(7.5 y)
			134	133.904 612	41	(0)	2.42
			135	134.905 550	110	3/2	6.59
			136	135.904 300	80	(0)	7.81
			137	136.905 500	80	3/2	11.32
			138	137.905 000	60	(0)	71.66
57	La	Lanthanum	137	136.906 040	1080		(60 ky)
			138	137.906 910	60	5	0.089
			139	138.906 140	50	7/2	99.911
58	Ce	Cerium	136	135.907 100	500		0.193
			138	137.905 830	60		0.250
			140	139.905 392	19		88.48
			142	141.909 140	50		11.07
59	Pr	Praseodymium	141	140.907 596	18	5/2	100
60	Nd	Neodymium	142	141.907 663	16		27.11
			143	142.909 779	15	7/2	12.17
			144	143.910 039	15		23.85

TABLE XI (*continued*)

ATOMIC NUMBER	ELEMENT		MASS NUMBER	ATOMIC MASS (amu)	ERROR amux10^{+6}	NUCLEAR SPIN	ABUNDANCE PER CENT
60	Nd	Neodymium (Contd.)	145	144.912 538	15	7/2	8.30
			146	145.913 086	15		17.22
			148	147.916 869	15		5.73
			150	149.920 915	15		5.62
61	Pm	Promethium	145	144.912 691	18		(18 y)
			147	146.915 108	15	7/2	(2.6 y)
62	Sm	Samarium	144	143.911 989	15		3.09
			146	145.912 992	23		(50 My)
			147	146.914 867	15	7/2	14.97
			148	147.914 791	15		11.24
			149	148.917 180	14	7/2	13.83
			150	149.917 276	14		7.44
			152	151.919 756	15		26.72
			154	153.922 282	15		22.71
63	Eu	Europium	150	149.919 689	24		(5 y)
			151	150.919 838	21	5/2	47.82
			152	151.921 749	15	3	(13 y)
			153	152.921 242	18	5/2	52.18
			154	153.923 053	20	3	(16 y)
			155	154.922 930	19		(1.7 y)
64	Gd	Gadolinium	148	147.918 101	19		(130 y)
			150	149.918 605	24		(0.3 My)
			152	151.919 794	16		0.200
			154	153.920 929	20		2.15
			155	154.922 664	18	3/2	14.73
			156	155.922 175	19		20.47
			157	156.924 025	19	3/2	15.68
			158	157.924 178	19		24.87
			160	159.927 115	20		21.90
65	Tb	Terbium	157	156.924 090	22	(3/2)	(30 y)
			158	157.925 464	29	3	(150 y)
			159	158.925 351	26	3/2	100
66	Dy	Dysprosium	154	153.924 350	60		(1 My)
			156	155.923 930	180		0.0524
			158	157.924 449	30		0.0902
			160	159.925 202	21		2.294
			161	160.926 945	20	5/2	18.88
			162	161.926 803	19		25.53
			163	162.928 755	19	5/2	24.97
			164	163.929 200	19		28.18

TABLE XI (*continued*)

ATOMIC NUMBER		ELEMENT	MASS NUMBER	ATOMIC MASS (amu)	ERROR amux10^{+6}	NUCLEAR SPIN	ABUNDANCE PER CENT
67	Ho	Holmium	163	162.928 766	22		(1 ky)
			165	164.930 421	21	7/2	100
68	Er	Erbium	162	161.928 740	90		0.136
			164	163.929 287	43		1.56
			166	165.930 307	29		33.41
			167	166.932 060	29	7/2	22.94
			168	167.932 383	32		27.07
			170	169.935 560	70		14.88
69	Tm	Thulium	169	168.934 245	34	1/2	100
			171	170.936 530	70	1/2	(1.9 y)
70	Yb	Ytterbium	168	167.934 160	160		0.135
			170	169.935 020	60		3.03
			171	170.936 430	70	1/2	14.31
			172	171.936 360	70		21.82
			173	172.938 060	70	5/2	16.13
			174	173.938 740	60		31.84
			176	175.942 680	70		12.73
71	Lu	Lutetium	173	172.938 800	80		(1.3 y)
			175	174.940 640	60	7/2	97.41
			176	175.942 660	60	7	2.59
72	Hf	Hafnium	174	173.940 360	70		0.18
			176	175.941 570	60		5.20
			177	176.943 400	80	7/2	18.50
			178	177.943 880	80	(0)	27.14
			179	178.946 030	90	9,2	13.75
			180	179.946 820	100	(0)	35.24
			182	181.950 700	220		(9 My)
73	Ta	Tantalum	179	178.946 160	90		(1.6 y)
			181	180.948 007	42	7/2	99.9877
74	W	Tungsten	180	179.947 000	50		0.135
			182	181.948 301	41	(0)	26.41
			183	182.950 324	41	1/2	14.40
			184	183.951 025	43	(0)	30.64
			186	185.954 440	45	(0)	28.41
75	Re	Rhenium	185	184.953 059	43	5/2	37.07
			187	186.955 833	44	5/2	62.93
76	Os	Osmium	184	183.952 750	70		0.018
			186	185.953 870	70		1.59
			187	186.955 832	44	1/2	1.64

TABLE XI (*continued*)

ATOMIC NUMBER	ELEMENT		MASS NUMBER	ATOMIC MASS (amu)	ERROR amux10⁺⁶	NUCLEAR SPIN	ABUNDANCE PER CENT
76	Os	Osmium (Contd.)	188	187.956 081	47		13.3
			189	188.958 300	90	3/2	16.1
			190	189.958 630	80		26.4
			192	191.961 450	60		41.0
			194	193.965 229	25		(2 y)
77	Ir	Iridium	191	190.960 640	60	3/2	37.3
			193	192.963 012	35	3/2	62.7
78	Pt	Platinum	190	189.959 950	70		0.0127
			192	191.961 150	60		0.78
			193	192.963 060	31		(500 y)
			194	193.962 725	23	(0)	32.9
			195	194.964 813	18	1/2	33.8
			196	195.964 967	15	(0)	25.3
			198	197.967 895	23		7.21
79	Au	Gold	197	196.966 541	10	3/2	100
80	Hg	Mercury	196	195.965 820	14		0.146
			198	197.966 756	7	(0)	10.02
			199	198.968 279	7	1/2	16.84
			200	199.968 327	6	(0)	23.13
			201	200.970 308	7	3/2	13.22
			202	201.970 642	7	(0)	29.80
			204	203.973 495	7	(0)	6.85
81	Tl	Thallium	203	202.972 353	8	1/2	29.50
			204	203.973 865	8	2	(3.9 y)
			205	204.974 442	8	1/2	70.50
82	Pb	Lead	202	201.972 003	40		(0.3 My)
			204	203.973 044	8		1.48
			205	204.974 480	9		(30 My)
			206	205.974 468	7	(0)	23.6
			207	206.975 903	7	1/2	22.6
			208	207.976 650	7	(0)	52.3
83	Bi	Bismuth	208	207.979 731	9		(750 ky)
			209	208.980 394	8	9/2	100
84	Po	Polonium	208	207.981 243	12		(2.9 y)
			209	208.982 426	13	1/2	(103 y)
88	Ra	Radium	226	226.025 360	26		(1622 y)
			228	228.031 139	21		(6.7 y)
89	Ac	Actinium	227	227.027 753	22	3/2	(22 y)

TABLE XI *(continued)*

ATOMIC NUMBER	ELEMENT		MASS NUMBER	ATOMIC MASS (amu)	ERROR amux10⁺⁶	NUCLEAR SPIN	ABUNDANCE PER CENT
90	Th	Thorium	228	228.028 750	14		(1.91 y)
			229	229.031 652	23	5/2	(7.3 ky)
			230	230.033 087	25		(80 y)
			232	232.038 124	21		100
91	Pa	Protactinium	231	231.035 877	22	3/2	(34 ky)
92	U	Uranium	232	232.037 168	14		(73.6 y)
			233	233.039 522	23	5/2	(0.2 My)
			234	234.040 904	25		0.0056
			235	235.043 915	22	7/2	0.7205
			236	236.045 637	21		(23.9 My)
			238	238.050 770	23	0	99.2739
93	Np	Neptunium	236	236.046 624	17		(5 ky)
			237	237.048 056	23	5/2	(2.2 My)
94	Pu	Plutonium	238	238.049 511	25		(89 y)
			239	239.052 146	22	1/2	(24 ky)
			240	240.053 882	21		(6.58 ky)
			241	241.056 737	22	5/2	(13 y)
			242	242.058 725	24		(379 ky)
			244	244.064 100	1070		(76 My)
95	Am	Americium	241	241.056 714	22	5/2	(460 y)
			243	243.061 367	23	5/2	(8 ky)
96	Cm	Curium	243	243.061 370	22		(35 y)
			244	244.062 821	21		(17.6 y)
			245	245.065 371	23		(8 My)
			246	246.067 202	25		(5.48 My)
			247	247.070 280	1070		(40 My)
			248	248.072 220	1070		(470 ky)
98	Cf	Californium	249	249.074 749	24		(360 y)
			251	251.079 260	1070		(800 y)
			252	252.081 500	1070		(2.55 y)

TABLE XII

TABLE OF ATOMIC WEIGHTS, 1969[a]

Atomic No.	Name	Symbol	Atomic weight	Atomic No.	Name	Symbol	Atomic weight
1	Hydrogen[c, e]	H	1.008_0	44	Ruthenium	Ru	101.0_7
2	Helium[c, d]	He	4.00260	45	Rhodium[b]	Rh	102.9055
3	Lithium[d, e, f]	Li	6.94_4	46	Palladium	Pd	106.4
4	Beryllium[b]	Be	9.01218	47	Silver[d]	Ag	107.868
5	Boron[d, e, f]	B	10.81	48	Cadmium	Cd	112.40
6	Carbon[c, e]	C	12.011	49	Indium	In	114.82
7	Nitrogen[c, d]	N	14.0067	50	Tin	Sn	118.6_9
8	Oxygen[c, d, e]	O	15.999_4	51	Antimony	Sb	121.7_5
9	Fluorine[b]	F	18.9984	52	Tellurium	Te	127.6_0
10	Neon[d]	Ne	20.17_9	53	Iodine[b]	I	126.9045
11	Sodium[b]	Na	22.9898	54	Xenon	Xe	131.30
12	Magnesium[d]	Mg	24.305	55	Cesium[b]	Cs	132.9055
13	Aluminum[b]	Al	26.9815	56	Barium	Ba	137.3_4
14	Silicon[e]	Si	28.08_6	57	Lanthanum[c]	La	138.905_5
15	Phosphorus[b]	P	30.9738	58	Cerium	Ce	140.12
16	Sulfur[e]	S	32.06	59	Praseodymium[b]	Pr	140.9077
17	Chlorine[d]	Cl	35.453	60	Neodymium	Nd	144.2_4
18	Argon[c, d, e, h]	Ar	39.94_8	61	Promethium	Pm	—
19	Potassium	K	39.10_2	62	Samarium	Sm	150.4
20	Calcium	Ca	40.08	63	Europium	Eu	151.96
21	Scandium[b]	Sc	44.9559	64	Gadolinium	Gd	157.2_5
22	Titanium	Ti	47.9_0	65	Terbium[b]	Tb	158.9254
23	Vanadium[c, d]	V	50.941_4	66	Dysprosium	Dy	162.5_0
24	Chromium[d]	Cr	51.996	67	Holmium[b]	Ho	164.9303
25	Manganese[b]	Mn	54.9380	68	Erbium	Er	167.2_6
26	Iron	Fe	55.84_7	69	Thulium[b]	Tm	168.9342
27	Cobalt[b]	Co	58.9332	70	Ytterbium	Yb	173.0_4
28	Nickel	Ni	58.7_1	71	Lutetium	Lu	174.97
29	Copper[d, e]	Cu	63.54_6	72	Hafnium	Hf	178.4_9
30	Zinc	Zn	65.3_7	73	Tantalum[c]	Ta	180.947_9
31	Gallium	Ga	69.72	74	Tungsten	W	183.8_5
32	Germanium	Ge	72.5_9	75	Rhenium	Re	186.2
33	Arsenic[b]	As	74.9216	76	Osmium	Os	190.2
34	Selenium	Se	78.9_6	77	Iridium	Ir	192.2_2
35	Bromine[d]	Br	79.904	78	Platinum	Pt	195.0_9
36	Krypton	Kr	83.80	79	Gold[b]	Au	196.9665
37	Rubidium[d]	Rb	85.467_8	80	Mercury	Hg	200.5_9
38	Strontium[h]	Sr	87.62	81	Thallium	Tl	204.3_7
39	Yttrium[b]	Y	88.9059	82	Lead[e, h]	Pb	207.2
40	Zirconium	Zr	91.22	83	Bismuth[b]	Bi	208.9806
41	Niobium[b]	Nb	92.9064	84	Polonium	Po	—
42	Molybdenum	Mo	95.9_4	85	Astatine	At	—
43	Technetium[g]	Tc	98.9062	86	Radon	Rn	—

TABLE XII (*continued*)

Atomic No.	Name	Symbol	Atomic weight	Atomic No.	Name	Symbol	Atomic weight
87	Francium	Fr	—	96	Curium	Cm	—
88	Radium[b, g, h]	Ra	226.0254	97	Berkelium	Bk	—
89	Actinium	Ac	—	98	Californium	Cf	—
90	Thorium[b, g]	Th	232.0381	99	Einsteinium	Es	—
91	Protactinium[b, g]	Pa	231.0359	100	Fermium	Fm	—
92	Uranium[c, d, f]	U	238.029	101	Mendelevium	Md	—
93	Neptunium[c, g]	Np	237.0482	102	Nobelium	No	—
94	Plutonium	Pu	—	103	Lawrencium	Lr	—
95	Americium	Am	—				

[a] *Pure Appl. Chem.* **21**, 91 (1970).

[b] Mononuclidic element.

[c] Element with one predominant isotope (about 99–100% abundance).

[d] Element for which the atomic weight is based on calibrated measurements.

[e] Element for which variation in isotopic abundance in terrestrial samples limits the precision of the atomic weight given.

[f] Element for which users are cautioned against the possibility of large variations in atomic weight due to inadvertent or undisclosed artificial isotopic separation in commercially available materials.

[g] Most common long-lived isotope.

[h] In some geological specimens, this element has a highly anomalous isotopic composition, corresponding to an atomic weight significantly different from that given.

References

1. B. N. Taylor, W. H. Parker, and D. N. Langenberg, *Rev. Mod. Phys.* **41**, 375 (1969).
2. Symbols, units, and nomenclature in physics, Doc. UIP 11 (SUN 65–3). Int. Union of Pure and Appl. Phys. (IUPAP), 1965.
3. Manual of symbols and terminology for physiochemical quantities and units, Prepared for publ. by M. L. McGlashan, *Pure Appl. Chem.* **21**, 1 (1970).
4. W. F. Meggers and C. E. Moore, *J. Opt. Soc. Amer.* **43**, 422 (1953).
5. F. A. Jenkins, *J. Opt. Soc. Amer.* **43**, 425 (1953).
6. R. S. Mulliken, *J. Chem. Phys.* **23**, 1997 (1955).
7. B. Edlén, *Trans. Int. Astron. Union* **9**, 201 (1957).
8. B. Edlén, *Trans. Int. Astron. Union* **10**, 211 (1960).
9. G. Herzberg, *Trans. Int. Astron. Union* **11B**, 208 (1962).
10. C. Moore-Sitterly, *Trans. Int. Astron. Union* **12B**, 173 (1966); *J. Opt. Soc. Amer.* **56**, 987 (1966).
11. B. Edlén, *J. Opt. Soc. Amer.* **43**, 399 (1953).
12. K.-F. Svensson, *Ark. Fys.* **16**, 361 (1960).
†13. K. Narahari Rao, C. J. Humphreys, and D. H. Rank, "Wavelength Standards in the Infrared." Academic Press, New York, 1966.
†14. C. J. Humphreys and E. Paul, Jr., Interferometric wavelength determinations in the second spectrum of ^{136}Xe. *J. Opt. Soc. Amer.* **60**, 1454 (1970).

†15. C. J. Humphreys and E. Paul, Jr., Interferometric wavelength determinations in the first spectrum of ^{136}Xe. *J. Opt. Soc. Amer.* **60**, 1302 (1970).

†16. C. J. Humphreys and E. Paul, Jr., Interferometric observations in the spectra of ^{86}Kr. *J. Opt. Soc. Amer.* **60**, 200 (1970).

†17. V. Kaufman and C. J. Humphreys, Accurate energy levels and calculated wavelengths of ^{86}Kr I. *J. Opt. Soc. Amer.* **59**, 1614 (1969).

18. R. Mehlhorn, Transition probabilities and g values for neon I. *J. Opt. Soc. Amer.* **59**, 1453 (1969).

19. L. Radziemski, Jr. and V. Kaufman, Wavelengths, energy levels, and analysis of neutral atomic chlorine (Cl I). *J. Opt. Soc. Amer.* **59**, 424 (1969).

20. W. Persson, Extended analysis and new identifications in the spectrum of Ne II. *J. Opt. Soc. Amer.* **59**, 285 (1969).

21. L. Minnhagen, H. Strihed, and B. Petersson, Revised and extended analysis of singly ionized krypton, Kr II. *Ark. Fys.* **39**, 471 (1969).

22. P. W. Murphy, Transition probabilities in the spectra of Ne, I, Ar I, and Kr I. *J. Opt. Soc. Amer.* **58**, 1200 (1968).

†23. G. Norlen, Interferometric measurements of Ar I and Ar II wavelengths in the region 5000–7000 Å. *Ark. Fys.* **35**, 119 (1968).

24. W. Persson and L. Minnhagen, The nf and ng configurations of Ne II. *Ark. Fys.* **37**, 273 (1968).

25. B. Hernang, The spectrum of krypton, Kr I, in the extraphotographic infrared. *Ark. Fys.* **33**, 471 (1967).

26. U. Litzén, Improvements of Si I level values. *Ark. Fys.* **31**, 453 (1966).

27. U. Litzén, The Si I spectrum in the lead-sulphide region. *Ark. Fys.* **28**, 239 (1965).

28. K. B. Eriksson, I. Johansson, and G. Norlen, Precision wavelength measurements connecting the Cs 6s, 6p, and 6d levels, with a study of the correction for phase change in infrared interferometry. *Ark. Fys.* **28**, 233 (1965).

29. A. H. Cook, Wavelengths in the spectrum of ^{86}Kr I between 6701 and 4185 Å. *J. Opt. Soc. Amer.* **55**, 780 (1965).

30. I. Johansson, A study of the transition 3d–4f and the configuration 4f in Ne I. *Ark. Fys.* **25**, 381 (1964).

31. L. Minnhagen, The spectrum of singly ionized argon, Ar II. *Ark. Fys.* **25**, 285 (1964).

32. C. J. Humphreys and K. L. Andrew, Extension of observations and analysis of Ge I. *J. Opt. Soc. Amer.* **54**, 1134 (1964).

33. F. M. Phelps, III, ^{86}Kr vacuum wavelengths. *J. Opt. Soc. Amer.* **54**, 864 (1964).

34. J. F. Giuliani and M. P. Thekaekara, Interferometric measurements of faint titanium lines in the region 3341–4186 Å. *J. Opt. Soc. Amer.* **54**, 460 (1964).

35. L. Minnhagen, Correlation between observed wavelength shifts produced in electrode-less discharge tubes and predicted Stark-effect shifts in the spectrum of neutral germanium (Ge I). *J. Opt. Soc. Amer.* **54**, 320 (1964).

36. K. M. Baird, D. S. Smith, and K. H. Hart, Vacuum wavelengths of Kr^{86}, Hg^{198}, and Cd^{114}. *J. Opt. Soc. Amer.* **53**, 717 (1963).

37. L. Minnhagen, *Ark. Phys.* **14**, 483 (1958).

38. R. D. VanVeld and K. W. Meissner, Interferometric wavelength measurements of germanium lines of a hollow cathode discharge. *J. Opt. Soc. Amer.* **46**, 598 (1956).

39. K. W. Meissner and R. D. VanVeld, Interoferometric wavelength measurements of germanium lines emitted by a hollow cathode discharge. *J. Opt. Soc. Amer.* **45**, 903A (1955).

40. R. W. Stanley and G. H. Dieke, Interferometric wavelengths of iron lines from a hollow cathode discharge. *J. Opt. Soc. Amer.* **45**, 280 (1955).

†41. J. Junkes and E. W. Salpeter, "Spectrum of Thorium from 9400 Å to 2000 Å." Specola Vaticana, Citta del Vaticano, Rome, 1964; reviewed by R. Zalubas, *Appl. Opt.* **5**, 147 (1966).

†42. F. P. J. Valero, Analysis of interferometrically measured wavelengths and their application as secondary standards of length. *J. Opt. Soc. Amer.* **60**, 1675 (1970).

†43. A. Giacchetti, R. W. Stanley, and R. Zalubas, Proposed secondary-standard wavelengths in the spectum of thorium. *J. Opt. Soc. Amer.* **60**, 474 (1970).

44. D. Goorvitch, F. P. J. Valero, and A. L. Clúa, Interferometrically measured thorium lines between 2747 and 4572 Å. *J. Opt. Soc. Amer.* **59**, 971 (1969).

45. R. Zalubas, Present state of analysis of the first spectrum of thorium (Th I). *J. Opt. Soc. Amer.* **58**, 1195 (1968).

46. F. P. J. Valero, Improved values for energy levels, Ritz standards, and interferometrically measured wavelengths in Th I. *J. Opt. Soc. Amer.* **58**, 1048 (1968).

47. F. P. J. Valero, Thorium lamps and interferometrically measured thorium wavelengths. *J. Opt. Soc. Amer.* **58**, 484 (1968).

48. A. Giacchetti, "Averages of Interferometric Measurements of Thorium Lines." ANL-7209. Argonne Nat. Lab., Argonne, Illinois, 1966.

49. T. A. Littlefield and A. Wood, Interferometric wavelengths of thorium lines between 9050 and 2566 Å, *J. Opt. Soc. Amer.* **55**, 1509 (1965).

50. A. Giacchetti, M. Gallardo, M. J. Garavaglia, Z. Gonzalez, F. P. J. Valero, and E. Zakowicz, Interferometrically measured thorium wavelengths. *. Opt. Soc. Amer.* **54**, 957 (1964).

51. A. Davison, A. Giacchetti, and R. W. Stanley, Interferometric wavelengths of thorium lines between 2650 Å and 3400 Å. *J. Opt. Soc. Amer.* **52**, 447 (1962).

†52. R. Zalubas, "New Description of Thorium Spectra." Nat. Bur. Stand. U.S. Monogr. **17**, U.S. Govt. Printing Office, Washington, 1960.

53. W. F. Meggers and R. W. Stanley, Wavelengths from thorium–halide lamps. *J. Res. Nat. Bur. Stand.* **61**, 95 (1958).

†54. J. Junkes, E. W. Salpeter, and G. Milazzo, "Atomic Spectra in the Vacuum Ultraviolet from 2250 Å to 1100 Å. Part One: Al, C, Cu, Fe, Ge, Hg, Si, (H$_2$)." Specola Vaticana, Citta del Vaticano, Rome, 1965; reviewed by C. M. Sitterly, *Appl. Opt.* **5**, 147 (1966).

†55. J. A. R. Samson, "Techniques of Vacuum Ultraviolet Spectroscopy," Chapter 10. Wiley, New York, 1967.

†56. B. Edlén, Wavelength measurements in the vacuum ultraviolet. *Rep. Progr. Phys.* **26**, 181 (1963).

57. D. Goorvitch, G. Mehlman-Balloffet, and F. P. J. Valero, Vacuum-ultraviolet series of Mg I and Mg II. *J. Opt. Soc. Amer.* **60**, 1458 (1970).

58. G. Risberg, The spectrum of atomic calcium, Ca I, and extensions to the analysis of Ca II. *Ark. Fys.* **37**, 231 (1968).

59. V. Kaufman and J. F. Ward, Newly measured and calculated wavelengths in the vacuum ultraviolet spectrum of neutral nitrogen. *Appl. Opt.* **6**, 43 (1967).

60. L. J. Radziemski, Jr., K. L. Andrew, V. Kaufman, and U. Litzén, Vacuum ultraviolet wavelength standards and improved energy levels in the first spectrum of silicon. *J. Opt. Soc. Amer.* **57**, 336 (1967).

61. V. Kaufman and J. F. Ward, Measurement and calculation of Cu II, Ge II, Si II, and C I vacuum-ultraviolet lines. *J. Opt. Soc. Amer.* **56**, 1591 (1966).

62. V. Kaufman, L. J. Radziemski, Jr., and K. L. Andrew, Vacuum ultraviolet spectrum of neutral silicon. *J. Opt. Soc. Amer.* **56**, 911 (1966).

63. I. Johansson, Spectrum and term symbols of the neutral carbon atom. *Ark. Fys.* **31**, 201 (1966).

64. G. Risberg, The spectrum of atomic magnesium, Mg I. *Ark. Phys.* **28**, 381 (1965).

65. B. Petersson, Remeasured Ne I, Ar I, Kr I, and Xe I lines in the vacuum ultraviolet. *Ark. Fys.* **27**, 317 (1965).

66. L. Iglesias, New auxiliary wavelength standards for the region 1100–2000 Å. *An. Real Soc. Espan. Fis. Quim. Ser. A* **60**, 147 (1964); Article reviewed and wavelengths listed in *Chem. Abstr.* **63**, 6484b (1963).

67. P. G. Wilkinson and K. L. Andrew, Proposed standard wavelengths in the vacuum ultraviolet. Spectra of Ge, Ne, C, Hg, and N. *J. Opt. Soc. Amer.* **53**, 710 (1963).

68. V. Kaufman and K. L. Andrew, Germanium vacuum ultraviolet Ritz standards. *J. Opt. Soc. Amer.* **52**, 1223 (1962).

69. J. Reader, K. W. Meissner, and K. L. Andrew, Improved Cu II standard wavelengths in the vacuum ultraviolet. *J. Opt. Soc. Amer.* **50**, 221 (1960).

70. K. W. Meissner, R. D. VanVeld, and P. G. Wilkinson, Germanium standard wavelengths in the vacuum ultraviolet. *J. Opt. Soc. Amer.* **48**, 1001 (1958).

71. K. L. Andrew and K. W. Meissner, New germanium standard wavelengths in the region from 1998 Å to 1630 Å. *J. Opt. Soc. Amer.* **48**, 31 (1958).

72. P. G. Wilkinson, Provisional wavelength standards in the vacuum ultraviolet. II. Spectra of Cu II and Fe II. *J. Opt. Soc. Amer.* **47**, 182 (1957).

73. P. G. Wilkinson, Provisional wavelength standards in the vacuum ultraviolet. *J. Opt. Soc. Amer.* **45**, 862 (1955).

74. J. H. E. Mattauch, W. Thiele, and A. H. Wapstra, *Nucl. Phys.* **67**, 1 (1965).

75. A. H. Wapstra, C. Kurzeck, and A. Anisimoff, *Proc. Third Int. Conf. At. Masses*, (R. C. Barber, ed.). Univ. of Manitoba Press, Winnipeg, 1968.

76. G. H. Fuller, *Nucl. Data Tables U.S. At. Energy Comm.* p. 66 (1959).

77. G. H. Fuller and V. W. Cohen, *Nucl. Data Tables* **5**, Nos. 5 and 6 (1969).

78. "Atomic Weights of the Elements 1969." *Pure Appl. Chem.* **21**, 91 (1970).

AUTHOR INDEX

Numbers in parentheses are reference numbers and indicate that an author's work is referred to, although his name is not cited in the text. Numbers in italics show the page on which the complete reference is listed.

A

Abouaf, R., *177*
Abouaf-Marguin, L., 264(126), 267(126), 280(126), *285*
Abramowitz, S., 262(148), 275(148), 276(148), 279(148), 282(148), *286*
Abrams, R. L., *171, 172, 173*
Abu-Elgheit, M., *296*
Adams, A., 235(24), 248(24, 47), *256, 257*
Adams, W. S., 81(84), 95, 96, 101, *111*
Adel, A., 95, 96(88), *111*
Airey, J. R., 147(40), *166, 167*
Akerlind, L., 235(22, 23), 248(23), 250, *256*
Akitt, D. P., 146(61), 149(61), *167, 175, 176*
Albrecht, A. C., 196(135), 197, *203*
Albritton, D. L., 162(12), *164*, 216, *221*
Alekseevskii, N. E., *172*
Alexander, J. A. F., *171*
Alimpiev, S. S., *172*
Al-Joboury, M. I., 183(38), *200*
Allen, C. W., 81(195), *114*
Allison, A. C., 85(20), 93(20), 94(20), 105(20), *109*
Alpert, B. D., 145(30), *166*, 349(6), *352*
Amano, T., 22, *27, 28*, 37(14, 15, 16), 38(14, 15, 16), 41(21), *48*
Amat, G., 19, 20(118), 20, 21, *27*, 115, 119, 130, 132(7), 135, 136(7), *140*
Ammon, H. L., 289(10), *296*
Anderson, A. G., Jr., 289(10), *296*

Anderson, E. D., 266(179), *286*
Anderson, J. B., *167*
Anderson, P. W., 50, 52, *58*
André, J. M., *296*
André, M. Cl., *296*
Andresen, U., 70(34), *72*
Andrew, K. L., 354(32, 60, 62, 67, 68, 69, 71), *388, 389, 390*
Andrews, E. B., 265, 271(87), *283, 284*
Andrews, L., 262(1, 2, 5), 272, 274, 276, 281(3, 5, 6), 282(1, 2, 5, 22, 23, 24), *283*
Andrick, D., *204*
Angell, C. L., 261(172), 263(172), 269(172), 281(172), *286*
Angus, J. G., 194(123), 197(143), *202, 203, 205*
Anisimoff, A., 355(75), *390*
Anlauf, K. G., *167*
Antropov, E. T., *171*
Aoki, T., 97(114), *112*
Arakelyan, V. S., *172*
Arkell, A., 273(7, 8), 281(7, 8), *283*
Armstrong, D. R., 185(51), *200*
Asbrink, L., 194(121), *202, 205*
Asundi, R. K., 272, *283*
Atkins, P. W., 245, 254, *256*
Atkinson, G. H., *205*
Austin, J. W., *169*
Avduevsky, V. S., 101(138, 138a, 138b), *112*
Avizonis, P. V., *173*
Azumi, T., 179(2), 190(2), 194(2), 195(2), 197(2), 198(2), *199*

391

Wilkinson, P. G., 183(42), 190(89), *200*, *201*, 354(67, 70, 72, 73), *390*
Williams, A. J., III, 189(74), *201*
Williams, D., 104(171), *113*
Williams, D. R., 74(5), *77*
Williams, N. H., 9, *23*
Williams, Q., 15(60), *25*
Williams, W., *204*
Wills, M. S., 156(228), 160(228, 288), *173*, *174*, *177*
Wilson, D. T., *168*
Wilson, E. B., Jr., 10(9), 11, 12(37), 17, 18(100, 101), 19(117), *23*, *24*, *26*, *27*, 61(9), 62(18), 63(18), 66(27, 31), 68(9), *71*, *72*, 115, 116, 122(13), 131, *140*, 198(161), *203*
Wilson, R. H., 348(4), 349(4), *352*
Wilson, R. W., 77(15, 16, 22, 24, 25, 27, 28), *78*
Windsor, M. W., 197(154), *203*
Wing, R. F., 79, *108*
Winnewisser, G., 18(109), *26*
Winnewisser, M., 18(109), 20, 22(157), *26*, *27*, *28*, 37(14), 38(14), *48*
Winton, R. S., 11, 12, *24*, *175*
Wiswall, C. E., *166*
Witteman, W. J., *168*, *169*, *175*, *177*
Wittig, C., *166*
Wofsy, S. C., 14, *25*
Wolf, A. A., 15, *25*
Wolf, E., 298(3), 314(3), *324*
Wolga, G. J., *170*, *172*, *175*
Wollrab, J. E., 10(13), *24*, 198(160), *203*
Wood, A., 354(49), *389*
Wood, J. I., *170*
Wood, L. S., 266(177, 178), *286*
Wood, O. R., *169*, *173*
Wood, R. W., 223, *229*, 299, *324*
Woodman, C. M., 268(174), *286*
Woodman, J. H., 87, *109*
Woods, H. P., 268(50), 272, *284*
Woods, R. C., 12(38), *24*
Woszczyk, A., 81(152), 103(152), *113*

Wright, A. J., 318(35), *325*
Wright, F. J., 197(153), *203*
Wright, W. H., 197(147), *203*
Wu, A. A., *204*

Y

Yager, W. A., 266(175, 176, 179), *286*
Yajima, T., 12(34a), *24*
Yamaka, E., *171*, *173*
Yamamoto, G., 97(114), *112*
Yamamoto, J., *174*
Yamamoto, S., 134(25), *140*
Yamanaka, M., *174*
Yardley, J. T., 145(29), 146(61), 149(61), *166*, *167*
Yaroshetskiy, I. D., *172*
Yoshinaga, H., *174*
Young, A. T., 106(187), *114*
Yurkov, G. N., 207(3), 211(3), 216(3), 218(3), *221*

Z

Zabriskie, F., 84(17), *109*
Zacharias, J. R., 246(41), *256*
Zakowicz, E., 354(50), *389*
Zalubas, R., 354(43, 45, 52), *389*
Zamir, E., 106(182), *113*
Zanon, I., 182(34), *200*
Zare, R. N., 38(25), 44, *48*, 162(11,12), *164*, 182(35), 199, *200*, 212, 216(19), *221*, 223(2), *229*
Zeleznik, F. J., 162, *164*
Ziegler, X., 153(88), 155(88), *169*, *177*
Zimakov, V. P., *173*
Zimmerer, R. W., 11(21), *24*
Zinn, J., 19(110), *26*
Zuckerman, B., 74(6), 76(11, 12), 77(20), *77*, *78*

INDEX OF
MOLECULAR SPECIES

The chemical formulae of the molecules have been considered as "words"; for example: $CHBr_2$ appears under chbr, CNS appears under cns. If there are several molecules giving the same "word" they are listed in order of increasing numbers of the first, second, etc., atom; for example, CH_2F, CH_3F, C_3H_5F are arranged in this order, but C_3H_8 is ahead of all of these chf molecular species because the "word" for C_3H_8 is ch (see, for example, ref. [1], p. 199).

A

Acrylic acid, see $C_3H_4O_2$
AlH_2, 180
Allyl chloride, see C_3H_5Cl
Allyl cyanide, see C_3H_5CN
Allyl fluoride, see C_3H_5F
AsH_2, 180, 181
7-Azaindole, 289, 290, 291, 292, 293

B

BCl_3, 143, 160
BeH_2, 265
BF_3, 185, 204
BF_3^+, 185
BH_2, 180, 181, 266
BiD, 234
BiH, 234, 246
BiO, 235, 245, 247, 254
BO_2, 181
BOF_2, 185
$BrHBr^-$, 278, 280
BrO, 22, 35, 37, 38
n-Butane, see C_4H_{10}
Butene-1, see C_4H_8

C

C_2, 263, 264, 276, 277, 280
C_2^-, 264, 277, 280
C_3, 261, 264, 269, 280
CBr_2, 271, 272, 281
CBr_3, 276, 282
CBr_3^+, 282
CBr_4, 272
CCl, 265, 280
CCl_2, 271, 281
CCl_3, 276, 279, 282
CCl_3^+, 279, 282
CClF (ClCF), 271, 281
CClN (ClCN), 13
CClO (ClCO), 271, 281
CD_4, see CH_4
C_2D_4, see C_2H_4
C_2D_6, see C_2H_6
CDF_2, see CHF_2
$C_4D_4N_2$, see $C_4H_4N_2$
CF, 38, 265, 280
CF_2, 23, 271, 272, 281
CF_3, 275, 276, 282
CF_2Cl, 282
$CFCl_2$, 282

412

SUBJECT INDEX

417